INTERNATIONAL TEXTBOOKS IN CIVIL ENGINEERING

Consulting Editor

Russell C. Brinker

Professor of Civil Engineering
New Mexico State University

Water Supply and
Pollution Control

Water Supply and Pollution Control

JOHN W. CLARK

Professor of Civil Engineering
New Mexico State University

WARREN VIESSMAN, JR.

Director, Water Resources Center
and Professor of Civil Engineering
University of Maine

INTERNATIONAL TEXTBOOK COMPANY
Scranton, Pennsylvania

Fourth Printing, August 1970

To

Jacqueline and Gloria

Preface

Environmental Engineering is of such tremendous scope that it is impossible to write a textbook that will comprehensively cover all of its aspects. It is necessary, therefore, to separate the subject into specific fields, to subdivide these, and to examine the parts individually from various points of view. In doing so, an attempt has been made to examine each of the parts without losing sight of its relation to the whole. This book emphasizes those aspects of Environmental Engineering concerned with the development, transportation, processing, and treatment of water and liquid wastes.

The book is designed as a textbook suitable for either a one- or two-semester course in Sanitary Engineering and Water Resources. For one-semester programs the teacher will not be able to place equal emphasis on all the material covered but will have to select certain topics for accentuation. The book will also serve as a useful reference for graduate students and practicing engineers.

No attempt has been made to treat any aspect of the field exhaustively. Advanced students will find it necessary to consult other books and, particularly, to acquaint themselves with current articles in the technical journals. The book emphasizes an understanding and application of scientific principles. It differs from other introductory books on the same subject in the selection and sequence of topics and in the choice of problems at the end of each chapter. A list of references accompanies each topic presented.

The philosophy of the textbook has been to develop each area of discussion in the most general way, consistent with the capabilities of the upper-division engineering student. The many illustrative problems show in detail how the principles are applied.

Chapter 2, "Legal Considerations," is new to textbooks on water and wastes. It was introduced because water rights play an exceedingly important role in determining the availability and use of water in many parts of the country. The purpose of this chapter is to acquaint the reader with some of the legal problems that may be encountered in water resources engineering. Much of the material in Chapter 3, "Water Requirements and Waste Volumes," is the result of research completed in the past two years. A constantly increasing rate of water use, coupled with the influence of lawn irrigation on peak demands, has resulted in a need for change in past design practices.

Chapters 4, 5, and 6 are presented with the assumption that the student is properly prepared in the areas of fluid mechanics and mathematics. Material of a highly specific nature, such as the design of dams, is completely omitted. It is felt by the authors that the proper treatment of such material is beyond the scope of the text and does not add to an understanding of the overall water problem. Changes in standards brought about by the 1962 U.S. Public Health Service, Drinking Water Standards, and the eleventh edition of *Standard Methods* have necessitated the addition of new information in Chapter 7. A unit operations approach to water and waste problems has been used in Chapters 8 through 12. It is believed that this method will be more useful to the student than a succession of studies of specific systems. This involves an integrating of topic material in fewer lectures, a separation of analysis from design, and a rational approach to design. The objective is to develop creative engineers capable of performing in a changing technology and environment. Chapter 14, "Water Reuse," is considered to be highly important because of the increasing value waste flows are assuming as a potential source for municipal, industrial, agricultural, and recreational water supplies. Chapter 15, "Water Resources Engineering," is included to introduce the student to the broader aspects of water-resources planning and development.

The authors have drawn on many sources for information contained in the book. To these they are deeply indebted. It is hoped that suitable acknowledgment is made in the form of references to these works. In particular the authors would like to thank Professor Russell C. Brinker for his help and editorial assistance, Dr. Nelson L. Nemerow for his constructive reviews, and Mmes. Ralph H. Flowers, James C. Young, and Elton Endebrock for their help in preparing the manuscript.

JOHN W. CLARK
WARREN VIESSMAN, JR.

University Park, New Mexico
September, 1965

Contents

Reverse Osmosis. The Osmionic Process. Electrodialysis. Mineral By-products from the Sea. RADIOACTIVITY IN WATER AND WASTE TREATMENT. Radioactivity. Radioactive Pollutants. Removal of Radioactivity from Water. References. Problems.

ordination Between Economic and Technologic Concepts. Formulation of the Project. Analysis of the Project. Multipurpose Projects. ENGINEERING ASPECTS OF RIVER-BASIN DEVELOPMENT. Natural Control of Rivers. Engineering Control Methods. Municipal Water Supplies. Stream Pollution. Navigation. Flood Control. Power Development. Irrigation. Land Management. ECONOMIC ASPECTS OF WATER-RESOURCES PLANNING. Engineering Economy. Economic Decision-Making. An Economic Model for Water Use. Product Demand Functions. Production Function. Resource-Supply Functions. Benefit-Cost Analyses. References. Problems.

*Water Supply and
Pollution Control*

chapter 1

Introduction

Air, water, food, heat, and light constitute the five essentials for human existence. Environmental Engineering concerns itself, to some degree, with all of these. This book is primarily concerned with the development, transportation, processing, and disposal of water and waste.

Water and liquid wastes must be considered simultaneously as there is but a fine line of distinction between them. One community's waste may constitute part of another's water supply. The ultimate goal in water management is the maximum economic use of the total water resource.

1-1. HISTORY

Man's search for pure water began in prehistoric times. Much of his earliest activity is subject to speculation. Some individuals might have led water where they wanted it through trenches dug in the earth. Later, a hollow log was perhaps used as the first water pipe.

Thousands of years must have passed before our more recent ancestors learned to build cities and enjoy the convenience of water piped to the home and drains for water-carried wastes. Our earliest archeological records of central water supply and waste-water disposal date back about five thousand years to Nippur of Sumeria. In the ruins of Nippur there is an arched drain with the stones set in full "voussoir" position, each stone being a wedge tapering downward into place.[1]* Water was drawn from wells and cisterns. An extensive system of drainage conveyed the wastes from the palaces and residential districts of the city.

The earliest recorded knowledge of water treatment is in the Sanskrit medical lore and Egyptian Wall inscriptions.[2] Sanskrit writings dating about 2000 B.C. tell how to purify foul water by boiling in copper vessels, exposing to sunlight, filtering through charcoal, and cooling in an earthen vessel.

There is nothing on water treatment in the sanitary and hygienic code of the early Hebrews in the Old Testament, although three incidents may be cited as examples of the importance of fresh water. At Morah, Moses is said to have sweetened bitter waters by casting into them a tree shown

*Superscript numbers refer to references at the end of the chapter.

1

him by God.[3] During the wandering in the wilderness, the Lord commanded Moses to bring forth water by smiting a rock.[4] At a much later date, Elisha is said to have "healed unto this day" the spring water of Jericho by casting "salt" into it.[5]

The earliest known apparatus for clarifying liquids was pictured on Egyptian walls in the fifteenth and thirteenth centuries B.C. The first picture, in a tomb of the reign of Amenhotep II (1447–1420 B.C.), represents the siphoning of either water or settled wine. A second picture in the tomb of Rameses II (1300–1223 B.C.), shows the use of wick siphons in an Egyptian kitchen.

The first engineering report on water supply and treatment was made in A.D. 98 by Sextus Julius Frontinus, water commissioner of Rome. He produced two books on the water supply of Rome. In these he described a settling reservoir at the head of one of the aqueducts and pebble catchers built into most of the aqueducts. His writings were first translated into English by the noted hydraulic engineer Clemens Herschel in 1899.[2]

An Arabian alchemist, Geber, of the eighth century A.D. wrote a rather specialized treatise on distillation that included various stills for water and other liquids.

The English philosopher Sir Francis Bacon wrote of his experiments on the purification of water by filtration, boiling, distillation, and clarification by coagulation. This was published in 1627, one year after his death. Bacon also noted that clarifying water tends to improve health and increase the "pleasure of the eye."

The first known illustrated description of sand filters was published in 1685 by Luc Antonio Porzio, an Italian physician. He wrote a book on conserving the health of soldiers in camps, based on his experience in the Austro-Turkish War. This was probably the earliest published work on mass sanitation. He described and illustrated the use of sand filters and sedimentation. Porzio also stated that his filtration was the same as "by those who built the Wells in the Palace of the Doges in Venice and in the Palace of Cardinal Sachett, at Rome."[2]

The oldest known archeological examples of water filtration are in Venice and the colonies she occupied. The ornate heads on the cisterns bear dates, but it is not known when the filters were placed. Venice, built on a series of islands, depended on catching and storing rain water for its principal fresh water supply for over thirteen hundred years. Cisterns were built and many were connected with sand filters. The rainwater ran off the house tops to the streets where it was collected in stone-grated catch basins and then filtered through sand into cisterns (see Fig. 1-1).

A comprehensive article on the water supply of Venice appeared in the *Practical Mechanics Journal* in 1863.[6] The land area of Venice was 12.85 acres and the average yearly rainfall was 32 in. Nearly all of this rainfall was collected in 177 public and 1,900 private cisterns. These

FIG. 1-1. Venetian cistern head located at Dubrovnik, Yugoslavia, showing a stone grating.

cisterns provided a daily average supply of about 4.2 gpcd (gallons per
capita per day). This low consumption was due in part to the absence of
sewers, the practice of washing clothes in the lagoon, and the universal
drinking of wine. The article explained in detail the construction of the
cisterns. The cisterns were usually 10 to 12 ft deep. The earth was first
excavated to the shape of a truncated inverted pyramid. Well-puddled
clay was placed against the sides of the pit. A flat stone was placed in the
bottom and a cylindrical wall was built from brick laid with open joints.
The space between the clay walls and the central brick cylinder was filled
with sand. The stone surfaces of the court yards were sloped toward the
cistern, where perforated stone blocks collected the water at the lowest
point and discharged it to the filter sand. This water was always fresh
and cool with a temperature of about 52° F. These cisterns continued to
be the principal water supply of Venice until about the sixteenth century.

Many experiments were conducted in the eighteenth and nineteenth
centuries in England, France, Germany, and Russia.

Henry Darcy patented filters in France and England in 1856 and
anticipated all aspects of the American rapid sand filter except coagulation. He appears to be the first to apply the laws of hydraulics to filter
design.[7]

The first filter to supply water to a whole town was completed at
Paisley, Scotland, in 1804 but this water was carted to consumers.[2] In
Glasgow, Scotland, in 1807 filtered water was piped to consumers.[8]

In the United States little attention was given to water treatment until after the Civil War. Turbidity was not as urgent a problem as in Europe. The first filters were of the slow sand type similar to British design. About 1890 rapid sand filters were developed in the United States and coagulants were introduced to increase their efficiency. These filters soon evolved to our present rapid sand filters with slight modification.

The drains and sewers of Nippur and Rome are among the great structures of antiquity. These drains were intended primarily to carry away runoff from storms and the flushing of streets. There are specific instances where direct connections were made to private homes and palaces, but these were the exceptions, for most of the houses did not have such connections. The need for regular cleansing of the city and flushing of the sewers was well recognized by commissioner Frontinus of Rome, as indicated in his statement, "I desire that nobody shall conduct away any excess water without having received my permission or that of my representatives, for it is necessary that a part of the supply flowing from the water-castles shall be utilized not only for cleaning our city but also for flushing the sewers."

It is astonishing to note that from the days of Frontinus to the middle of the nineteenth century there was no marked progress in sewerage. In 1842, after a fire destroyed the old section of the city of Hamburg, Germany, it was decided to rebuild this section of the city according to modern ideas of convenience. The work was entrusted to an English engineer, W. Lindley, who was far ahead of his time. He designed an excellent collection system that included many of the ideas presently used. Unfortunately, the ideas of Lindley and their influence on public health were not recognized.

The history of the progress of sanitation in London probably affords a more typical picture of what took place in the middle of the nineteenth century. In 1847 a royal commission was appointed to look into the sanitary conditions of London following an outbreak of cholera in India which had begun to work westward. This royal commission found that one of the major obstacles was the political structure, due to the lack of central authority. The city of London was only a small part of the metropolitan area, comprising approximately 9½ percent of the land area and less than 6 percent of the total population of approximately 2½ million. This lack of central authority made the execution of sewerage works all but impossible. The existing sewers were at different elevations, and in some instances the sewage would have had to flow uphill. Parliament, in 1848, followed the advice of this commission and created the Metropolitan Commission of Sewers. That body and its successors produced reports that clearly showed the need for extensive sewerage works and other sanitary conditions.[9] Cholera appeared in London during the summer of 1848 and 14,600 deaths were recorded during 1849. In 1854 cholera claimed a mortality of 10,675 people in London. The connection was established between a contaminated water supply and spread of the disease, and it was determined that the absence of effective sewerage was a major hindrance in combatting the problem.

In 1855 Parliament passed an act "for the better local management of the metropolis," thereby providing the basis for the Metropolitan Commission of Sewers, which soon after undertook an adequate sewerage system. It will be noted that the sewerage system of London came as a result of the cholera epidemic, as was true of Paris.

The natural remedy for these foul conditions led to the suggestion that human excrement be discharged into the existing storm sewers and that additional collection systems be added. This created the combined sewers of many older metropolitan areas. These storm drains had been constructed to discharge into the nearest watercourse. The addition of sewage to the small streams overtaxed the receiving capacities of the waters and many of them were covered and converted into sewers. Much of the material was carried away from the point of entry into the drains, which in turn overtaxed the receiving waters. First the smaller and then the larger bodies of water began to ferment and create a general health problem, especially during dry, hot weather. The solution has been the varying degrees of treatment as presently practiced, dependent upon the capabilities of the receiving stream or lake to take the load.

The work on sewerage in the United States closely paralleled that of Europe, especially England. Some difficulty was experienced because of the variation in rainfall patterns in America as compared with those of England. The English rains are more frequent but less intense. Our storm drains must be larger for like topographical conditions. The more intense rains tend to have a better cleansing action and in general the receiving streams carry a larger volume of water. This, together with the lower population densities, tends to produce less nuisance than is being experienced in Europe. The density of population in England and the small amount of land suited for sewage farming led to interest in methods of treating sewage before it is discharged into fresh water.

More recent developments in water supply and waste-water disposal are discussed in later chapters under the appropriate headings.

1-2. CURRENT STATUS

Increased demands currently being placed on water supply and waste disposal have necessitated far broader concepts in the application of environmental engineering principles than those originally envisioned.

The average rate of water use for the urban population of the United States is approximately 150 gpcd; peak demands have developed considerably beyond past design practices. The standards for water quality have significantly increased with a marked decrease in raw-water quality available. Considerable research is being directed toward the ultimate use of brackish or sea water for domestic supplies.

Sewage-treatment-plant effluents normally discharge into a stream, lake, ocean, or other body of water. The degree of treatment required is determined by the ability of the receiving waters to assimilate the wastes, and the uses to which the receiving waters are put.

In general practice, large bodies of water or rivers in good condition receive wastes with very limited or no treatment. Expensive treatment is necessary where receiving waters are unable to assimilate additional pollution, or where the body of water is immediately used as a raw-water source for domestic purposes or satisfies extensive recreational demands. Effluent chlorination is usually required where receiving waters are to be used for water supply or bathing.

Land disposal of sewage effluents is practiced in the United States, especially in the semiarid Southwest. Removal of settleable and floating solids is usually required prior to the effluent being distributed over the land. Many state health departments regulate the use of effluents on crops, especially vegetables that might be eaten raw. Some sewage effluents are being used to recharge groundwater reservoirs and to check saltwater intrusion. Sewage-plant effluents are being utilized by industry with varying degrees of treatment.

Surface waters used as a raw-water supply are normally treated by coagulation, filtration, and disinfection. The degree of treatment is determined by the health hazards involved and by the quality of the raw water. Well waters are normally not treated, except for disinfection. Groundwaters are becoming polluted with increasing frequency however, and require additional surveillance.

Water supply and waste-water disposal are interrelated activities of the community. Although they are closely associated, the primary accent has been on providing a safe water supply. The reasons for this are threefold: (1) the effects of an unsatisfactory water supply are usually detectable immediately, (2) the unsafe water supply affects the community served, and (3) water systems are income-producing, while sewage systems normally derive most of their revenue from taxation. Upon the informal recommendations of the state and Federal health services, water systems have been constructed and willingly improved by the community served. The construction and improvement of sewage-treatment facilities have, in many instances, come about because of and after formal complaints and court action.

Public water must be palatable and wholesome. It must be attractive to the senses of sight, taste, and smell and must be hygienically safe.

Liquid waste-disposal systems must collect the wastes from homes and industry and convey those wastes without nuisance to hygienic disposal.

1-3. PROJECTED PROBLEMS

Today, as populations throughout the world multiply at an alarming rate, it is evident that environmental control is a critical factor. Land and water become increasingly important as the population increases. Most European and Asian nations have reached the maximum population that their land areas can bear comfortably. They are faced with the problem of providing for more people than the land will conveniently support.

There are important lessons to be learned from the countries of Europe and Asia—populations increase, but water resources do not. The use and control of our water resources must be nearly perfect to maintain our way of life.

Environmental-engineering needs are far greater than the available supply of trained personnel, and future needs are certain to be even greater. The future potential of any profession is usually determined by the basic factors of demand and/or need. Demand is the less reliable guide because it is subject to change, due both to technological advances and to the instability of social trends. A need is a more dependable guide. It is born of a requirement and thrives when the requirement determines the welfare of a nation.

Environmental engineering will continue to grow in importance because it fills a definite need. The services provided by water-resources engineers are growing in importance in a world staggering under the weight of the greatest population it has even known.

REFERENCES

1. Will Durant, *Our Oriental Heritage* (New York: Simon and Schuster, Inc., 1954), p. 132.

2. M. N. Baker, *The Quest for Pure Water* (New York: American Water Works Association, 1949), pp. 1-3, 6, 11.

3. *Old Testament* (King James Version), Exodus, 15:22-27.

4. *Ibid.*, Exodus, 17: 1-7.

5. *Ibid.*, II Kings, 2: 19-22.

6. Anonymous, "The Water Cisterns in Venice," *J. Franklin Inst.*, Third Series, vol. 70 (1860), pp. 372-373.

7. Henry Darcy, *Les fontaines publiques de la ville de Dijon; Distribution d'eau et filtrage des eaux.* (Paris: Victor Dalmont, 1856.)

8. D. Mackain, "On the Supply of Water to the City of Glasgow," *Proc. Inst. Civil Engrs. (London)*, vol. 2 (1842-43), pp. 134-136.

9. First Report of the Metropolitan Sanitary Commission. (London: 1848.)

chapter 2

Legal Considerations

The interrelated and competing uses of water often give rise to varied and complex problems in regions where water supply is inadequate to meet the needs of potential users. The combined development of the water resources of an area is necessary for maximum beneficial use in most drainage basins. Some states in their water laws have recognized an integrated action of all interests, while other states have framed their laws with reference to individual action. Large-scale multiple-purpose projects have created novel problems of reshuffling rights between users and uses, between watersheds, between states, and between countries.

In many areas the virgin opportunities for water development have been largely exhausted. It is becoming increasingly necessary for cities to acquire rights to additional waters needed for their growth through legal action. These additional waters may be available in the local areas, or the water may be conveyed for considerable distance to the places of use. The Feather River project in California proposes to take water from the northern Sierra Nevada and convey it almost to the Mexican Border. This project will cover a distance of several hundred miles down the Sacramento Valley, up the San Joaquin Valley, over a mountain range, and then into Southern California. This is an extreme example but the expansion of water supply and waste-treatment facilities today requires that the engineer have some knowledge of the legal problems involved.

Water rights play an important role in determining the availability and use of water in many parts of the country. Because water law is a complex subject, the purpose of this chapter is to acquaint the reader with some of the legal problems which may be encountered in water-resources engineering.

2-1. LEGAL CLASSIFICATION OF WATER[1]

Legal differences between waters on the surface of the earth and between various classes of groundwaters have been drawn since early times. Some Western states have abolished the distinctions between these waters but in many states they still exist. It is necessary, therefore, to investigate these legal distinctions before discussing water-rights doctrines.

(a) *Surface Watercourses.* A surface watercourse consists essentially of a definite stream, formed by nature, flowing in a definite natural channel; it includes the underflow.

(b) *Diffused Surface Waters.* Diffused surface waters are those waters originating from rain and melting snow and flowing vagrantly over the surface before becoming concentrated in watercourses or percolating into the ground.

(c) *Underground Streams.* A definite underground stream has the essential characteristics of a surface watercourse, with the exception that it is buried in the ground. Necessarily, the proof of physical aspects with reasonable certainty is difficult.

(d) *Underflow of Surface Streams.* Beneath a surface stream there is usually an underflow through the sands, gravel, and other subsoil over which the stream flows. This water is moving in the same direction as and in intimate contact with the surface stream. The lateral boundaries may extend for considerable distances beyond the banks of the surface channel. From a legal point of view, the surface stream and the underflow are a single watercourse.

(e) *Percolating Groundwater.* Percolating groundwater is water below the surface of the ground that is not part of an underground stream or the underflow of a surface stream. This water is free to move by gravity, and hence to enter wells.

2-2. THE BASIC WATER DOCTRINES

Ownership is the right of one or more persons to possess and use property to the exclusion of others. Before rules can be prescribed governing the use or the rights to the use of water, its ownership must be determined.

Riparian Rights. This doctrine came to America from the Roman law by several lines of descent via Spain, France, and England. The riparian philosophy was introduced into Texas by the Spanish and Mexican governments and was upheld by the succeeding governments of the Republic and State of Texas.

The riparian principles of the French civil law, which were also based on the Roman law, were brought to the Atlantic seaboard by two eminent American jurists, Joseph Story and James Kent, in the early part of the nineteenth century. After Story and Kent had taken the riparian doctrine from French sources it was adopted in England as a part of its common law and chief reliance was placed on these American authorities.[2] The doctrine became part of the law of numerous states when they adopted the English common law.

Under the philosophy of riparian rights the owner of land containing a natural stream or abutting a stream is entitled to receive the full natural flow of the stream without change in quality or quantity. Physical contact of land and water is an essential factor. The riparian owner is protected against the diversion of water except for domestic purposes upstream from his property, and from the diversion of excess flood waters towards his property.

The riparian concept has been modified to provide for actual use of the water for beneficial purposes such as irrigation, industry, and for the dilution of sewage effluent.

The riparian doctrine is generally followed in all states east of the Mississippi River. It is recognized to some degree in the six Western states that extend from North Dakota to Texas on the 100th meridian, and in the three states that border on the Pacific Ocean. In all other Western states it has been completely repudiated or has never been recognized. The supreme courts of New Mexico and Arizona have declared that in those states the riparian doctrine has never existed.

Where the riparian doctrine is in effect, the owner of a tract of land contiguous to the channel of a surface stream, called riparian land, has certain rights to the water flowing in the stream. The owner of the land may divert what water he needs for domestic use. Water for irrigation and other commercial purposes must be reasonable with respect to the requirements of all others. This same principle applies to the ownership of land that overlies an underground stream or the underflow of a surface stream. In each case the water right arises out of the physical contact of land and water source. A limited use of the water on nonriparian land may be permitted in some states. This nonriparian use is considered as a use without formal right rather than an exercise of the riparian right.

The Appropriation Doctrine.   The idea of the appropriation doctrine has various antecedents, both ancient and modern. One view as to the origin of this principle in the Southwest is that it had its roots in Roman civil law; another is that it developed from local customs in that area. The idea that it was brought to the New World by the Spaniards, who adopted it from Roman civil law, is supported by the fact that this doctrine has materially influenced the early development of water law in several states in which the Spaniards and Mexicans settled.

The Mormons, settling on public lands in Utah during the middle of the nineteenth century, developed their own system of appropriation. They diverted water from streams for irrigation and applied the principle of priority based on first in time.

During this same period, gold was discovered in California on what were then Mexican public lands. The miners improvised local rules and regulations for taking and holding mining claims and claims for the use of water. Water was essential to hydraulic and placer mining widely practiced in the area.

The principal feature of these doctrines of appropriation is the concept of "first in time, first in line." The first to appropriate the water for beneficial use has the first right to the water and his right must be completely supplied prior to any other water use. Each appropriator is entitled to use all the water he needs up to the limit of his appropriation prior to any one lower in line receiving any water. This is true regardless of his geographic position on the waterway. In periods of short water supply, water might be flowing in the stream crossing a person's property, but because of his appropriation in point of time he might not be allowed to divert any of the water for any purpose.

The appropriation doctrine gives no preference to the use of the water on land solely because of the contact of the land and the water supply. This right may be acquired and utilized in connection with land whether or not the land is contiguous to the water supply. In most Western states water may be appropriated for use outside the watershed in which it naturally flows. In some instances the watersheds of origin have preferential rights even though they have not been exercised. Generally the appropriator does not need to be the owner of the land in connection with which he proposes to appropriate water. He must be in lawful possession such as an entryman on public land or as a lessee on private land to establish water rights.

The appropriative right is to a specific amount of water. The element of priority negates any obligation on the part of the appropriator to share the water with others. However, the appropriator is not entitled to divert and use more water than he can put to beneficial use, even though the quantity he needs may be much less than that to which his right relates.

The appropriation doctrine in the United States was first based on custom, which, in the absence of legislation, the courts recognized as controlling. Generally throughout the West the early statutes codified prevailing local rules and regulations. Later, as development progressed and complications ensued, the appropriation doctrine became both statutory and judicial, with many high-court decisions and constitutional provisions.

2-3. DIFFUSED SURFACE WATER

Basically, custom has established that the capture, by the occupant of the land, of surface water resulting from precipitation prior to this water's reaching a definite natural stream constitutes ownership of the water. Generally, the owner of land on which such water occurs is entitled to the capture and use of such water while it is on his land, without reservation. The right to this water has not been very seriously contested. Most of the law referring to diffused surface water has to do with the avoidance or riddance of such waters. The changing of natural drainage to prevent such waters from entering upon one's property, or changing the manner in which the natural drainage leaves one's property to the detriment of others, is normally prevented.

This is an exception to most water law. The common-law doctrine of percolating groundwater and diffused surface water gives the exclusive ownership of the water while it is on one's land. This doctrine affords no right of protection against depletion by one's neighbor.

2-4. GROUNDWATER

Groundwater poses an extremely difficult legal problem. It is more complex than that for surface water in that it is in many cases difficult to determine the source and rates of recharge, the extent and variation of quality in storage, and the water movements. Three basic rules cover the use of groundwater.

The first, or English, rule is of absolute ownership and allows the overlying land owner to take groundwater from his land at any time and in any quantity, regardless of the effect on the water table of his neighbor's land. Under the rule it would be possible for a landowner to exhaust the total groundwater supply of an area by heavy pumping. This rule has been qualified in some areas to limit the malicious and wasteful use of the water.

The American rule, or rule of reasonable use, recognizes that the landowner has rights to the water under his land but that these rights may be limited. His rights to the water are limited to its reasonable use in relationship to the overlying land.

The third rule covering groundwater is the appropriative principle whereby the water is specifically allocated.

The English doctrine is followed in some states, both Eastern and Western. The American principle of reasonable use is followed by many states. In several of the Western states the appropriative principle has been applied by statute, court decision, or both, to the use of ground-water.

2-5. COMPARISON OF DOCTRINES

Each of the doctrines has certain advantages and disadvantages dependent upon the point of view. The problem is further complicated by a marked trend in point of view away from the individual water user to water use by large groups encompassing whole river basins. In many instances the present doctrines and projected uses are in direct conflict and are irreconcilable.

The appropriation doctrine provides for acquiring rights to water by putting it to beneficial use in accordance with procedures set forth in state statutes and judicial decisions. This assures the holder of the water right of his full appropriative supply, in order of priority, whenever the water is available. Early priority holders thus have reasonable assurance of a water supply each year. This enables development to be predicted on a reasonably assured annual supply and allows major investments in water-dependent operations.

Water can be appropriated and stored for beneficial use on either a temporary or a seasonal basis.

The operation of the doctrine allows a considerable measure of flexibility for changes in the exercise of water rights.

The appropriative right is gained by use and lost by disuse. Therefore, theoretically, all water is available for beneficial use.

It is probable that the appropriative doctrine has allowed the multiple appropriation of the same water in some instances and it is possible for a late priority to gain in time because of this condition. The problem arises where groundwaters and surface waters are appropriated and the excess has come about from groundwater storage. Late appropriators could use the percolating groundwater and materially diminish stream flow. An earlier in point of time water user is displaced therefore by a later appropriation. This problem is further complicated by state boundaries and the later developments of groundwater across a state line in areas where the groundwater is not subject to appropriation.

Holders of later priorities have little assurance of water supply in most seasons and the very late ones have no assurance except in very wet years.

Under the riparian doctrine, all landowners are assured of some water when it is available. This doctrine tends to freeze a large proportion of the water to lands whether it is being used or not. This unused right can be held indefinitely without forfeiture and thus can materially affect water-related development of an area. The riparian doctrine does not allow provision for storage of water that is essential for the full development of many water uses.

The unrestricted use of groundwater in many states is in direct conflict with both doctrines, as it is impossible to separate these waters under some conditions. There appears to be a need for modification of all existing doctrines in the future to meet the changing economic conditions in both the Eastern and Western portions of the United States.

EXAMPLE 2-1.   Under Oklahoma Law, priorities are determined under three separate divisions: First, those claiming beneficial use of water prior to statehood, November 15, 1907; second, those claiming right to beneficial use of water because they have made application to the Water Resources Board; and third, those making beneficial use commencing after November 15, 1907 but without application to the Board.

Assume that six users "A," "B," "C," "D," "E," and "F" are beneficial users of water from "Green River." "A" can prove that he began to use water for irrigation on March 15, 1904, and has used water from "Green River" for irrigation continuously since that date. "B" can prove that he began to use water for cooling purposes on January 1, 1900. "C" produces a copy of an application approved by the Board, dated October 1, 1910. "D" shows an affidavit and proves that he began to make beneficial use of water on July 1, 1910. "E" has an application approved by the Board, dated December 1, 1926. "F" brings forth an affidavit and demonstrates that he was making beneficial use of water commencing April 15, 1930.

Solution: In this example, the first priority would go to "B" and the second priority to "A." The first in time showing beneficial use will have the better right. Both of these claims were instituted prior to statehood, November 15, 1907, and since "B" began use prior in time to "A," his is a prior right.

"C" and "E" both are making beneficial use of water and submitted applications to the Board. "C" began using water on December 1, 1926, and therefore has a higher priority right than "E."

"D" and "F" are both making beneficial use of water, but have not made an application to the Board. "D" began using water on July 1, 1910, "F" on April 15, 1930. "D" therefore has a higher priority right than "F." "D" began using water before both "C" and "E," however, he did not make application to the Board. "C" and "E" by virtue of their applications, then, have a higher priority than "D." The priorities would accordingly be as follows: "B" first, "A" second, "C" third, "E" fourth, "D" fifth, and "F" sixth.

If "B" and "A" are taking more water now than they did on November 15, 1907, their right would be to the amount of water they were using on that date. If either, presently consuming more water, had made application for the additional water to the Board, the priority to the additional water would be dated from the date of application.

Had any of the six parties failed to beneficially utilize all or any part of the water claimed by him for which a right of use was vested for a period of two consecutive years, such unused water would revert to the public and become unappropriated water.

2-6.   THE FEDERAL GOVERNMENT

The authority of the Federal government over waters has been based on several sections of the U.S. Constitution. Article I, section 8, number 3, gives Congress authority over navigable waters which cross state boundaries or connect with the ocean. The term "navigation" has been rather loosely defined and could include most all waters in the broadest sense. Article IV, section 3, number 2, authorizes Congress to "dispose of and make all needful rules and regulations respecting the territory or other property belonging to the United States...." The treaty powers of the President and Senate under Article VI, number 2, have been used to designate and regulate water rights. Waters originating in the Rio Grande River in the United States are appropriated to Mexico according to a formula based on stream flow, as set up in a treaty between the United States and Mexico. Article I, section 8, number 1, "The Congress shall have power to lay and collect taxes, duties, imports and excises, to pay the debts and provide for the common defense and general welfare of the United States...." Basin development has contributed to the general welfare in the Tennessee Valley Authority and resulted in construction of the Wilson Dam on the Tennessee River during World War I to produce nitrate for ammunition.

A liberal interpretation of the Constitution allows for considerable Federal regulation over the nation's waters. The Supreme Court of the United States has ruled that every state has the power, within its dominion, to change the rule of the common law referring to the rights of the riparian owner to the continual natural flow of the stream, and to permit appropriation of the water for such purposes as it deems wise.[2] Thus we have fifty states, fifty water laws, and many interrelated problems.

2-7. INTERSTATE PROBLEMS

The natural flow of water does not respect state lines. A number of cases have arisen with respect to waters of interstate streams. Some of these suits have involved private parties only, others have involved interstate suits and have been decided by the U.S. Supreme Court which has original jurisdiction of litigated controversies between states.

The Supreme Court has laid down broad principles to govern its decisions in such cases. In addition to litigation in the Supreme Court, apportionment of waters between states has been made by compact, with the consent of Congress. The Supreme Court has recommended that this procedure, rather than court action, be the medium of settlement for such cases. These compacts or court actions are binding on the citizens of each state and on all water claimants.

Some states have statutes with respect to the transportation of water from one state for use in another. A few states make it very difficult or impossible to divert water from within their boundaries for conveyance across state lines. Other states have reciprocal statutes that permit water use across state lines.

The states of New York, Pennsylvania, New Jersey, and Delaware have been involved in the courts for years over the Delaware River. The futility of litigation has been recognized and the states have formed the Delaware River Basin Compact. This compact provides for the representatives of each state and the representatives of the cities of New York and Philadelphia to regulate the use of the waters of the Delaware River. This compact as approved by Congress is to assure a water supply for the 22 million people living in the river basin.

The states and their political subdivisions have waived appropriative water rights based upon use pursuant to the compact. However, they have expressly agreed to recognize riparian rights on the river.

The bold Federal claims to water in many of the Western states and the spread of water shortages to the East has made it necessary to clarify the relationship of the states to each other and with the Federal government. The U.S. Senate's Select Committee on National Water Resources found that the broadening pattern of these conflicts over water rights is conclusive proof of the urgent need of definitive action on the part of Congress to work out with the states, a redefining of Federal-state powers and responsibilities for control, use, and development of water resources.[3] This conclusion has been the result of extensive congressional hearings on the subject over the past decade. As a result of this action, the problem has been brought into clear focus and numerous legislative remedies have been proposed. The issue has emerged as a major jurisdictional conflict between state governments and between states and the Federal government.

The American Bar Association, at its 1963 meeting, urged Congress to consider favorably legislation designed to preserve the states' historic role in water-resource development. They proposed Federal legislation to clarify the issue and protect states' rights, meeting with stiff opposition from the Department of Justice.

In California, the Federal government lost on a historic case but has appealed the decision. This case covered more than 250 days of proceedings before a judge and special master. The litigation started in 1951 when several thousand water users in Southern California were accused by the Federal government of unlawfully reducing water supplies to the U.S. Marine base at Camp Pendleton.[5] This decision means that the Federal government may not compel upstream users to release water so that the government might export some to an area outside the river's watershed. This is one of the few cases that breaks the line of recent cases upholding Federal supremacy over water rights.

It seems inevitable that the interest of individual water users will come to be represented less and less by individual water rights acquired from the state and more and more by contracts with basin-management districts which will hold mass water rights in trust for the users.

2-8. ACQUIRING WATER RIGHTS

The riparian right to water accrues when the land title passes. There is no formality in acquiring the water right other than acquiring the land. Rights to the use of percolating groundwater and to vagrant surface water are secured in the same way.

Each of the seventeen Western states has a statutory procedure under which surface water may be appropriated, and most of the Western states have some formal procedure for groundwater appropriation. Nearly all of the procedures contemplate applications to state officials for water, and permits or licenses are issued when the request is approved.

In some Eastern states, legislation requires a permit from a state agency to take water for irrigation or other purposes from a watercourse or groundwater supply. It is doubtful whether, in most states, these permits establish any substantial water right. They have little effect on riparian rights but they do provide some administrative restraint upon the exercise of water rights. They do provide a record of use that should be extremely useful in considering water rights legislation in the future.

The following application to the state of Oklahoma for underground water is typical of the information necessary to complete an application.

UNDERGROUND WATER APPLICATION[4]
FILING INSTRUCTIONS
FOR WATER RIGHT APPLICATION FORMS

Applicant Must Own Land. In the case of individuals, no application will be accepted and no permit will be issued to construct works to an applicant to irrigate land not owned by him; the applicant must be prepared to offer proof of ownership. In the event that the applicant seeks to include land which the applicant does not own, it will be necessary for such landowner to join in the application, or furnish a statement showing his approval that such lands may be included.

Distribution System. The distribution system shall be set forth on the application blank in general terms, but it must be set forth with particularity on the maps and drawings that accompany the application.

Irrigation Information. Where it is proposed to irrigate land by direct diversion from a watercourse, reservoir, or well, a map shall be prepared on the enclosed tracing paper form, from aerial photographs showing the following:

1. Section lines
2. Section number
3. Township and range
4. Stream or reservoir
5. Point of diversion
6. Exact location of well or wells
7. *Boundary lines of each tract of land proposed to be irrigated, showing exact number of acres in each tract*

(Aerial photographs from which to make your map on the tracing paper are available at the local Agricultural Stabilization and Conservation service or local Soil Conservation Service Office.)

If Your Diversion Is from a Well, please fill in the attached well information forms with the assistance of your driller when your well is completed and return one copy of the completed form to this office.

Fill out all three copies of the attached application forms as fully as possible. Sign all three copies of the application before a Notary Public. Mail all copies of the completed application to:

Oklahoma Water Resources Board
535 State Capitol
Oklahoma City, Oklahoma 73105

UNDERGROUND WATER APPLICATION

State of Oklahoma
Oklahoma Water Resources Board

No. _____
Application for Permit to
Appropriate Ground Water
for Beneficial Use in
_____ County

Ground Water Basin _____ (To be determined by the Oklahoma Water Resources Board).

Comes now _____ whose address is _____ and makes application to the State of Oklahoma, acting by and through the Oklahoma Water Resources Board, for a permit to appropriate and apply to beneficial use water from the above underground basin, and for a permit to construct works for the appropriation of said waters as hereinafter set forth:

1. Purpose of Appropriation:
    (a) Irrigation: It is the purpose of the applicant to irrigate _____ acres, located in _____ of _____ Sec. _____ , Twp. _____ , Range _____ .

    (b) Municipal use _____ (c) Industrial use _____
    (d) other purposes _____ (If industrial or other use give the place of use and a full description of the use)
2. Well or wells located in _____ of _____ Sec. _____ , Twp. _____ Range _____ , and to consist of _____ wells.
3. Amount of water applied for: _____ gallon per minute.

If the water was placed to beneficial use prior to August 25, 1949, give date and amount of such prior use.

Applicant asks for a period of time not to exceed five (5) years to put the water herein applied for to beneficial use, as provided by Title 82, Sections 1005 and 1006, Oklahoma Statutes, 1961.

Subscribed and sworn to before me this _____ day of _____ 19 _____ .

_____
Notary Public
My commission expires:

_____

_____
Applicant

_____
Address

Application received in this office this _____ day of _____ 19 _____ .

OKLAHOMA WATER RESOURCES BOARD
By _____
Executive Director

(Application to be filed in triplicate and mailed to the Oklahoma Water Resources Board, Room 535, State Capitol, Oklahoma City, Oklahoma 73105).

WELL INFORMATION

Owner _____

Address _____

Well no. _____ in _____ ¼ of Section _____ Township

_____ Range _____ _____ County

Distance from nearest town or highway junction: _____

_____

Intended use (underline); Irrigation, Municipal, Industrial, Other

GENERAL DRILLING INFORMATION
(File one for each well)

Contractor _____ Address _____

Driller _____ Address _____

Dates: Started _____ Completed _____ Type

of rig: Cable tool _____ Rotary _____ Other _____

Size of hole _____ Total depth _____

Example: 8 in. by 55 ft

Water encountered at: _____ ft below the surface.

TESTS

Bailer test _____ bailer per hour. Size of bailer _____

gal. Pump test _____ gallons per minute for _____ hrs

Drawdown: _____ feet after pumping or bailing _____ hrs at

_____ gpm

Quality of Water: Taste _____ Odor _____ Color _____

Hard _____ Soft _____ Temperature _____

MATERIAL AND EQUIPMENT

Casing record _____

Example: 8 in. to 55 ft; 6 in. from 55 ft to 227 ft

Screen or perforation record _____

Gravel packed _____ Diameter _____ amount

of gravel used _____ Pump type _____ Rated

capacity _____ gpm against _____ ft of head.

Depth to bowls or cylinder _____ ft

Power: Electric _____ hp Gasoline motor _____ hp

_____

Signature of Owner

_____

Date

INDICATE ON THE MAP BELOW THE LOCATION OF THE WATER SOURCE (AND THE LANDS TO BE IRRIGATED)

SECTION _____ TOWNSHIP _____ RANGE _____

To be filed in duplicate and mailed to Room 535 State Capitol Oklahoma City, Oklahoma, within sixty (60) days after completion of the wells.

Several of the complications of water use and development do not result from engineering considerations. Water can be transported to any place if one has the ability to pay for it. Many of the vital considerations arise from priorities of allocation. New regulations to meet new problems are the result of a process that takes place over a period of time. The one best or ideal water law cannot be passed once and for all. Water legislation should not be discussed only as an academic ideal but also as a practical solution to a given problem at a specific time.

2-9. WASTE TREATMENT

The law has always made a distinction in the liability of a government when it is acting as a government and its liability when it is acting in a business enterprise. A city or political subdivision is liable for its torts committed in its proprietary capacity. It is generally recognized that if the function is for the benefit of the public at large it is governmental and if solely for the people of the community, it is proprietary. It seems to be generally recognized that a municipality is liable to the same extent as a private corporation for injuries resulting from the creation or maintenance of a nuisance.

The authorities are in conflict as to whether the operation of a waste-treatment plant is a governmental or proprietary function. The prevailing view seems to be that a municipality may be held liable for death or injury resulting from negligence or other tort in the operation of such a plant.

The owner of land taken for the construction of a waste-disposal plant is entitled to an award of the value of the land taken and damages to his business. The municipality has no more right to create a nuisance to the injury of another than has an individual. Authority to install a sewer system or treatment works carries no implication of authority to create or maintain a nuisance. It does not matter whether the nuisance results from negligence or from the design adopted.

Engineers and utility operating personnel frequently act in the capacity of an agent for the city or political subdivision. An agent is subject to liability if, by his acts, he creates an unreasonable risk of harm to the interests of others. This includes situations where an agent causes harm to a third person by his activities, and also those in which the agent's performance of his duties to his principal results in harm to third persons.

Lest an impression be left that waste-treatment plants are per se a nuisance, the courts seem to uniformly hold they are not. Most courts have taken the view that injunctive relief against proposed construction and operation of a waste-treatment plant does not appear warranted on the grounds of anticipatory nuisance.

It appears that an agent should be held personally liable for trespass committed by him or under his direction even though he is acting in his official capacity. Accordingly, when an engineer has mistakenly constructed a drain across land without first obtaining a right-of-way agreement, he personally can be held liable for the resulting damages. Utility employees cannot, in the course of necessary duties, go upon or interfere with land belonging to others, no matter how innocently this is done, without becoming personally liable for damages.

REFERENCES

1. Wells A. Hutchins and Harry A. Steele, "Basic Water Rights Doctrines and Their Implications for River Basin Development," *Law and Contemporary Problems,* vol. XXII, no. 2 (Spring 1957), Duke University School of Law.

2. *United States* v. *Rio Grande Dam and Irrigation Co.,* 174 U.S. 690, 43 L., ed. 1136, 19 Supp. 770.

3. United States Congress, Senate, *Select Committee on National Water Resources,* Committee Print 29, vol. 87, no. 1 (1961), p. 66.

4. State of Oklahoma, "Summary Water Laws of Oklahoma," *Oklahoma Planning and Resources Board, Div. Water Resources* (August 1960).

5. *United States* v. *Fallbrook Utility District,* 165 F. Supp. 806.

PROBLEMS

2-1. Prepare a summary of the procedure for appropriating surface water in your state. How are these water rights to be administered?

2-2. Prepare a summary of the procedure for appropriating groundwater in some state. Outline the most important rules for governing the use of this groundwater.

2-3. Investigate a particular state's laws concerning stream pollution and outline those provisions which should be considered in the design of a municipal sewerage system.

2-4. Prepare an outline of some interstate pollution-control compact. Is your state a party to any interstate pollution-control compact?

2-5. Investigate the local ordinances concerning the disposal of industrial waste into the municipal system for a large city in your state. Prepare a summary of those provisions which should be considered in the design of an industrial waste treatment plant to be located in that city.

chapter 3

Water Requirements and Waste Volumes

Under normal conditions, man uses about five pints of water daily for drinking purposes. His other community water uses bring the total demand to approximately 150 gpcd. Residential, commercial, and industrial requirements each account for about a third of the demand. Where lawn sprinkling is widespread and prolonged, requirements may be considerably in excess of 150 gpcd. Other local conditions may also have a pronounced effect, and thus caution should be exercised in using this or any other representative figure.

In the humid East, municipal water demands are generally met with little difficulty. Important exceptions are in evidence where cities have exceedingly large demands combined with complex collection and transportation systems. Most important Eastern and Midwestern cities however, are located on the Great Lakes or on major rivers and are adequately supplied at present.

The arid lands in the West face a considerably different situation. Municipalities must often transport water for considerable distances and groundwater in many instances becomes the primary source of supply. An illustration of the magnitude of the transportation problem is the Feather River Project in California. The outcome of this activity will be the transportation of water over four hundred miles from the northern to the southern part of the state.

Demands imposed on our water resources by industry and agriculture are often considerable. The manufacture of a single automobile requires about 100,000 gallons of water; some 70,000 gallons are used to produce a ton of wood pulp for use in the paper industry, and the national average water consumption per ton of steel produced is approximately 65,000 gallons. The production of 32 bushels of wheat under optimum conditions may require as much as 650,000 gallons of water. Part of this water will be lost to the region through evaporation or transpiration while the remainder will be available for various forms of reuse. The student should be made aware that figures such as those given above are not necessarily meaningful as reported, since they do not always distinguish between new water added per unit product and recirculated water, etc.

POPULATION ESTIMATES

The basis for the design of a water system is the estimated water requirement of the area under consideration. Usually the total demand estimate is based on an average figure such as 150 gpcd. In the following sections, considerable discussion related to estimating design flows will be given. For the present it will be sufficient to assume that this information is available and that the problem is to determine the total water needs of an area. An estimate of the future population of the area will permit this computation.

3-1. TYPES OF POPULATION ESTIMATES

Basically, there are two types of estimates which the designer is called upon to make in the operation and design of water-supply and waste-treatment works: (1) short-term population estimates for current periods and the recent past, usually 1 to 10 years, and (2) long-term population estimates of 10 to 50 years or more which represent the design period of the proposed project (often the economic life of the structure). The methods of solution used for these two kinds of forecasts differ appreciably.[19]

The prediction of future population is at best complex. It should be emphasized that there is no exact solution even though seemingly sophisticated mathematical equations are often used. War, technological developments, new scientific discoveries, government operations, and a whole host of other factors can drastically disrupt population trends. There is no present way to predict many of these occurrences and thus their impact can not be estimated. Nevertheless, population forecasts are exceedingly important and must be made.

3-2. METHODS OF FORECASTING

Both mathematical and graphical methods are used in estimating future populations. Usually the computations or analyses are based on past census records for the area, or on the records of what are considered to be similar communities. These estimates are based primarily on an extension of existing trends. They do not take into consideration factors such as the influx of workers when new industries settle in the area, the loss of residents due to curtailment of military activities, or changes in business or transportation facilities. To optimize the estimate, all possible information regarding anticipated industrial growth, local birth and death rates, government activities, and other related factors should be obtained and used. The local census bureau, the planning commission, the bureau of vital statistics, local utility companies, movers, and the chamber of commerce all are sources of information.

An example of the application of utilities information in estimating current populations is the count of residential light meters in Cuyahoga Falls, Ohio. A factor of 3.42 persons per meter was found to give reliable estimates for that area in 1963.[22]

The most widely employed mathematical or graphical methods for extending past municipal population data are: (1) arithmetical progression or uniform growth rate, (2) constant percentage growth rate, (3) decreasing rate of increase, (4) graphical extension, (5) graphical comparison with the growth rates of similar and larger cities, and (6) the ratio method based on a comparison of the local and national population figures for past census years.[9]

3-3. SHORT-TERM ESTIMATING

Short-term estimates are generally made to obtain population figures for the years between two censuses (a census is usually taken every ten years), or for the postcensal period. These estimates normally are made by arithmetic progression, geometric progression, decreasing rate of increase, or graphical extension.

Arithmetical Progression.   This method of estimation is based on a constant increment of increase and may be stated as follows:

$$\frac{dY}{dt} = K_u \qquad (3\text{-}1)$$

where Y = population

t = a period of time (usually years)

K_u = uniform growth-rate constant

If Y_1 represents the population at the census preceding the last census (time t_1), Y_2 represents the population at the last census (time t_2), and Y_m represents the midyear population (time t_m), then

$$\int_{Y_1}^{Y_2} dY = K_u \int_{t_1}^{t_2} dt$$

Integrating and inserting the limits, we obtain

$$Y_2 - Y_1 = K_u(t_2 - t_1)$$

Therefore

$$K_u = \frac{Y_2 - Y_1}{t_2 - t_1} \qquad (3\text{-}2)$$

An intercensal estimate of Y_m is thus given by

$$Y_{ml} = Y_1 + K_u \Delta t$$

or

$$Y_{ml} = Y_1 + \frac{Y_2 - Y_1}{t_2 - t_1} (t_{ml} - t_1) \qquad (3\text{-}3)$$

Correspondingly, a postcensal estimate of Y_m is given by

$$Y_{mp} = Y_2 + \frac{Y_2 - Y_1}{t_2 - t_1} (t_{mp} - t_2) \qquad (3\text{-}4)$$

Constant-Percentage Growth Rate. For equal periods of time this procedure assumes constant growth percentages. If the population increased from 90,000 to 100,000 in the past ten years, it would be estimated that the growth in the ensuing decade would be to 100,000 + 0.11 × 100,000 or 111,000. Mathematically this may be formulated as

$$\frac{dY}{dt} = K_p Y \qquad (3\text{-}5)$$

where the variables are defined as before, except that K_p represents a constant percentage increase per unit time. Integrating this expression and setting the limits yields

$$K_p = \frac{\log_e Y_2 - \log_e Y_1}{t_2 - t_1} \qquad (3\text{-}6)$$

An intercensal estimate of Y_m is thus given by

$$\log Y_{ml} = \log Y_1 + K_p(t_{ml} - t_1) \qquad (3\text{-}7)$$

and a postcensal estimate of Y_m is given by

$$\log Y_{mp} = \log Y_2 + K_p(t_{mp} - t_2) \qquad (3\text{-}8)$$

Decreasing Rate of Increase. If populations were not subject to all the unpredictable factors mentioned previously, they would be characterized by a growth curve which is applicable to all forms of life within limited boundaries. The curve has an S-shape (Fig. 3-1) and shows that initial growth takes place at increasing rates, midspan growth at approxi-

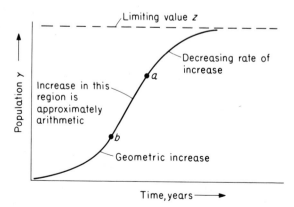

FIG. 3-1. Population growth curve.

mately uniform rates, and final growth at a decreasing rate as a limiting value is approached.

Estimates made on the basis of a decreasing rate of increase assume a variable rate of change. Mathematically, the decreasing rate of increase may be formulated as follows:

$$\frac{dY}{dt} = K_D(Z - Y) \tag{3-9}$$

where Z is the saturation or limiting value which must be estimated, and the other variables are as defined before. Then

$$\int_{Y_1}^{Y_2} \frac{dY}{Z - Y} = K_D \int_{t_1}^{t_2} dt$$

and upon integration,

$$-\log_e \frac{Z - Y_2}{Z - Y_1} = K_D(t_2 - t_1)$$

Rearranging,

$$Z - Y_2 = (Z - Y_1)e^{-K_D \Delta t}$$

Then, subtracting both sides of the equation from $(Z - Y_1)$,

$$(Z - Y_1) - (Z - Y_2) = (Z - Y_1) - (Z - Y_1)e^{-K_D \Delta t}$$

and

$$Y_2 - Y_1 = (Z - Y_1)(1 - e^{-K_D \Delta t})$$

Letting Y_2 equal the postcensal estimate Y_{mp}, and Y_1 equal the last census Y_2, the following expression for a postcensal estimate is obtained:

$$Y_{mp} = Y_2 + (Z - Y_2)(1 - e^{-K_D \Delta t}) \tag{3-10}$$

3-4. LONG-TERM POPULATION PREDICTIONS

Long-term predictions are usually made by graphical comparison with growth rates of similar and larger cities, or by selecting a mathematical trend such as the Gompertz or logistic curve and fitting this to the observed data.[1] These predictions are usually less reliable than short-term estimates since there is considerable opportunity for unpredictable factors to affect the anticipated trend.

Graphical Comparison with Other Cities. The population-time curve of a given community can be extrapolated on the basis of trends experienced by similar and larger communities. Population trends are plotted in such a manner that all of the curves are coincident at the present population value of the city being studied (see Fig. 3-2). The cities selected for comparison should not have reached the reference population value too far in the past since the historical periods involved may be considerably different. It should be understood that the future growth of a city may digress significantly from the observed development of communities of

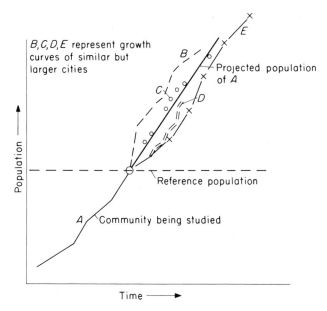

FIG. 3-2. Graphical prediction of population by comparison.

similar size. In making the final projection, consideration should be given to conditions which are anticipated for the growth of the community in question. With the exercise of due caution, this method should give reasonable results.

Mathematical Curve-Fitting. Generally, mathematical curve-fitting has its greatest utility in the study of large population centers, or nations. The Gompertz curve and the logistic curve are both used in establishing long-term population trends. Both of these curves are S-shaped and have upper and lower asymptotes, with the lower asymptotes being equal to zero.

The logistic curve in its simplest form is

$$Y_c = \frac{K}{1 + 10^{a + bX}} \qquad (3\text{-}11)$$

where Y_c = ordinate of the curve

X = time period in years (10-year intervals are frequently chosen)

K,a,b = constants

To fit this curve, three years, represented by X_0, X_1, and X_2, each equidistant from the other in succession, must be selected. These years are chosen so that one will be near the earliest recorded population for the area, one near the middle, and one near the end of the available record. The fitted curve will pass through the values of Y_0, Y_1, and Y_2 which are associated with X_0, X_1, and X_2. The origin on the x-axis is at the year indicated by X_0. The number of years from X_0, to X_1 or from X_1 to X_2 is designated as n. The constants are then obtained by using the following equations:

$$K = \frac{2Y_0 Y_1 Y_2 - Y_1^2(Y_0 + Y_2)}{Y_0 Y_2 - Y_1^2} \tag{3-12}$$

$$a = \log \frac{K - Y_0}{Y_0} \tag{3-13}$$

$$b = \frac{1}{n}\left[\log \frac{Y_0(K - Y_1)}{Y_1(K - Y_0)}\right] \tag{3-14}$$

Substitution of these values in eq. 3-11 permits determination of Y_c for any desired value of X.

3-5. POPULATION DENSITIES

A knowledge of the total population of a region will allow estimates of the total volume of water or waste water to be considered. In order to design conveyance systems for these flows, additional information regarding the physical distribution of the population to be served must be used. A knowledge of the population density as well as of the total population is important. Population densities may be estimated from data collected on existing areas and from zoning master plans for undeveloped areas. Table 3-1 may be used as a guide if more reliable local data are not available.

TABLE 3-1
A GUIDE TO POPULATION DENSITY

Area Type	Number of Persons per Acre
Residential—Single-family units	5–35
Residential—Multiple-family units	30–100
Apartments	100–1,000
Commercial areas	15–30
Industrial areas	5–15

WATER REQUIREMENTS

A reliable estimate of the quantity of water required for municipal, industrial, and agricultural uses in a region must be made before systems can be designed to transport, process, or distribute these flows. It has been estimated that by 1980 the demands on the national water resources will nearly double those of 1954, and that by the year 2000 demands will be triple those experienced in 1954. Figure 3-3 indicates projections made by the Senate Select Committee on National Water Resources.[2] Values shown are representative of total water withdrawn and do not reflect re-use. Even so, it is apparent that positive action must be taken to preserve

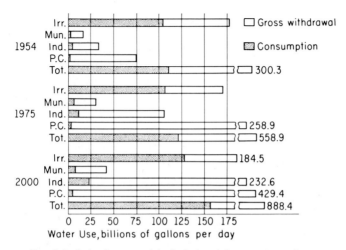

FIG. 3-3. Irrigation, municipal, industrial, power cooling, and total water use. (Courtesy of *Power*, January 1963, p. 49; copyright 1963 by McGraw-Hill, Inc.)

or improve water quality and to assure that demands are kept within the finite limits.

3-6. FACTORS AFFECTING THE USE OF WATER

Past records and estimated future average water consumption rates indicate a wide range in values across the United States. Some of the factors which are responsible for the nonuniformity are as listed.

Climatic Conditions. Lawn-sprinkling, gardening, bathing, and air-conditioning demands are usually greater in warm, dry regions than in humid areas. Regions subject to extreme cold often report significant drafts to prevent freezing of water lines. Definite correlations between climatic factors such as temperature and rainfall have been reported.[4,8] Brock has shown that correlation of the number of days prior to the last rainfall with days of high temperature offers a potential means for forecasting high water demands.[10] Future studies may provide data which will permit estimating the frequency of peak water demands in much the same way as flood and drought frequencies are now determined.

Data published by a task group of the American Water Works Association indicate that precipitation is the climatic factor having the greatest influence on per capita residential consumption.[15] Where summer precipitation exceeds 1.2 in., the area is termed the (f) climatic classification, where summer precipitation is less than 1.2 in., the area is classified as (s). The (f) area is located generally east of the 100th meridian in the United States and has an average domestic consumption of about 50 gpcd.

The average domestic consumption in the (s) area, west of the 100th meridian, is approximately 100 gpcd.

Economic Conditions.   Yarbrough, Linaweaver, and others have demonstrated that water use is a function of the economic status or living standard of the consumer.[3,4]   High-priced residential dwelling units, for example, will normally show rates which are significantly greater than those for medium and low-priced units.

Composition of the Community or Region.   The type and magnitude of residential, commercial, and industrial development in an area will have a pronounced effect on local water-use rates.   Industrial requirements often are exceedingly large.   The per capita requirements of a region endowed with large-scale industrial development might therefore be strikingly affected, providing industrial water is supplied by the municipality.

Water Pressure.   Rates of water use increase with increases in pressure.   This result is due partly to leakage and partly to the increased volumes of flow through fixture units per unit of time.   For example, the water-use rate has been known to increase by as much as 30 percent for a 20-psi change in line pressure.   Pressures in excess of those required for satisfactory service should be avoided whenever possible.

Cost of Water.   There is a tendency towards conservatism when costs are high.   Babbitt, Doland, and Cleasby have indicated the following relationship based on data by Seidel and Baumann:[5,6]

$$C = 21 - 10 \log Q \qquad (3\text{-}15)$$

where C = cost in dollars per 1,000 cu ft

Q = rate of water used in thousands of gallons per year

Other factors affecting water use rates are metering, water quality, presence or absence of sewerage, air conditioning, and management.

3-7.   RESIDENTIAL WATER USE

The growth and water-use patterns of communities should be reviewed annually for trends if water-supply systems are to keep abreast of continually increasing demands.   Evidence in recent years indicates that the average per capita consumption, the peak daily consumption, and the peak hourly consumption are all on the increase.[11]   Each of these demands is of special interest to the designer.   The first, average consumption, is used in estimating total water requirements and in designing storage works.   Peak daily and peak hourly rates are the basis for designing distribution works.

Residential water-use rates are continually fluctuating.   There are variations from hour to hour, day to day, and season to season.   Average daily winter consumption is only about 80 percent of the annual daily average, while summer consumption averages are about 25 percent greater

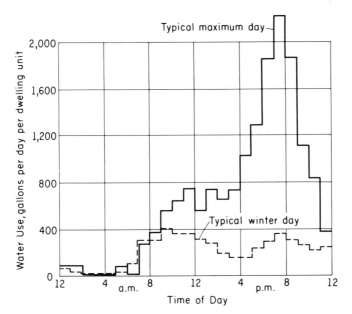

FIG. 3-4. Daily water-use patterns, maximum day and winter day. (Courtesy of the Residential Water-Use Research Project of The Johns Hopkins University and The Office of Technical Studies of the Architectural Standards Division of The Federal Housing Administration.)

than the annual daily average. Figure 3-4 compares a typical winter day with a typical maximum summer day in Baltimore, Maryland. Note the hourly fluctuation and the tendency toward two peaks. Studies by Wolff indicate that hydrographs of systems serving predominantly residential communities generally show two peak rates, the first, between the hours of 7 a.m. and 1 p.m., the second in the evening between 5 and 9 p.m.[7] During the summer when sprinkling demands are high, the second peak is usually the greatest while during the colder months or during periods of high rainfall, the morning peak is commonly the larger of the two.

In Fig. 3-5 the effects of lawn-sprinkling demands are strikingly demonstrated. This figure shows the effects of rainfall on two different days— one a hot, dry day with no antecedent rainfall for four days, and the other a day during which rainfall in excess of one inch was recorded. Lawn sprinkling has been found to represent as much as 75 percent of total daily volumes and as high as 95 percent of peak hourly demands where large residential lots are involved.[4]

A 1963 report on the residential Water Use Research Project carried on at the Johns Hopkins University has produced some interesting results obtained from gaging programs on four strata of residential areas in

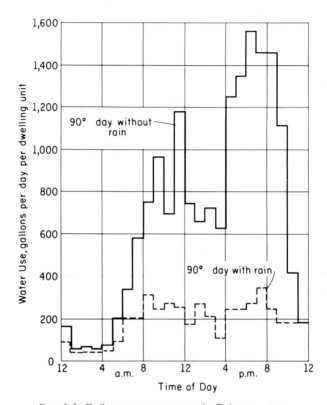

FIG. 3-5. Daily water-use patterns in R-6 area—maximum day and minimum day. (Courtesy of the Residential Water-Use Research Project of The Johns Hopkins University and the Office of Technical Studies of the Architectural Standards Division of the Federal Housing Administration.)

Towson, Maryland.[4] This study indicates that an inverse relationship exists between the number of persons per dwelling unit and the average daily per capita use. Values ranging from 85 gpcd for two persons per dwelling to 47 gpcd for five persons per dwelling are reported. The relationship is reported to hold regardless of the type of housing or season of the year. The overall average annual domestic use for the study areas was reported as 56 gpcd. This figure does not include sprinkling demands. The generally reported range in domestic requirements is 20 to 90 gpcd.

Table 3-2 indicates the measured water-use rates for the Towson, Maryland areas. The data clearly illustrate the tremendous impact of lawn sprinkling on total usage. For the Hampton area, the annual sprinkling load was found to be 39 percent of the total annual load, but during the peak hour this increased to 95 percent of the total usage. The high

TABLE 3-2
WATER-USE DATA

Area Studied	Net Lot Size, sq ft	Consumption for Given Period, Gallons per Day per Dwelling Unit			Ratios	
		Average Annual	Maximum Day	Peak Hour	Maximum Day to Average Annual	Peak Hour to Average Annual
Donnybrook Apartments	1,100	156	211	532	1.35	3.42
Country Club Park	7,000	227	657	1,380	2.90	6.07
Pine Valley	7,600	263	1,090	2,380	4.14	9.05
Hampton	28,000	332	1,380	4,100	4.16	12.1

DOMESTIC WATER-USE DATA
(Sprinkling Use Not Included)

Donnybrook Apartments	1,100	144	183	490	1.27	3.40
Country Club Park	7,000	187	213	414	1.14	2.21
Pine Valley	7,600	214	250	565	1.17	2.64
Hampton	28,000	202	290	860	1.44	4.26

SPRINKLING-USE DATA
(Domestic Use Not Included)

Donnybrook Apartments	1,100	12	67	303	5.58	25.2
Country Club Park	7,000	40	470	1,120	11.8	28.0
Pine Valley	7,600	49	880	2,080	18.0	42.5
Hampton	28,000	130	1,180	3,900	9.08	30.0

Courtesy of the Residential Water Use Research Project of The Johns Hopkins University and the Office of Technical Studies of the Architectural Standards Division of The Federal Housing Administration.

12.1 to 1 ratio of peak hourly rate to average annual rate for this area is due primarily to the sprinkling load. Figures such as these point to the conclusion that where heavy peak-hour consumption is imposed on a distribution system, this flow and not the fire flow plus maximum daily consumption may govern the design.[13] An illustration of this is given in Sec. 3-8.

Figure 3-6 relates the number of dwelling units to peak hourly demands. This relation, derived from the Towson data, permits the designer to determine total residential peak hourly demands based on a knowledge of the proposed housing density of the area. Figure 3-7 indicates the manner in which lot size and water use are related.

While representative of only one region of the United States, the Towson data do clearly illustrate the trends in residential water use and the extreme significance of the lawn-sprinkling demand.

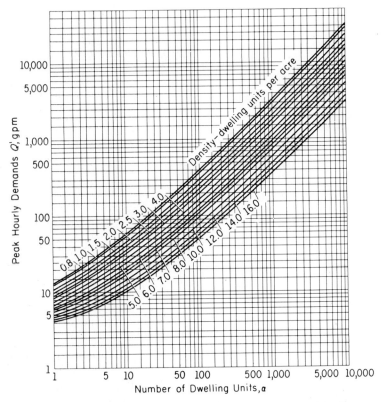

Fig. 3-6. Relation of total peak hourly demands to number of dwelling units in terms of housing density. (Courtesy of the Residential Water-Use Research Project of The Johns Hopkins University and the Office of Technical Studies of the Architectural Standards Division of the Federal Housing Administration.

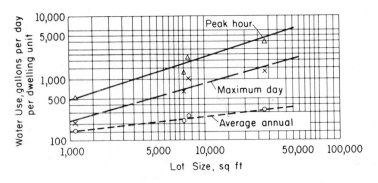

Fig. 3-7. Relationship of lot size to water use. (Courtesy of the Residential Water-Use Research Project of The Johns Hopkins University and the Office of Technical Studies of the Architectural Standards Division of the Federal Housing Administration.)

In general, maximum daily use can be considered to be about 180 percent of the average daily use with values ranging from about 120 percent to over 400 percent. Maximum hourly figures have been found to range from about 1.5 to over 12 times the average daily flow. A 1954 study of hourly demands in Baltimore County, Maryland, resulted in the following tabulation of peak-demand ratios shown in Table 3-3.[14]

TABLE 3-3
PEAK-DEMAND RATIOS

Neighborhood	Percent Peak Hour over Average Day
Older neighborhoods, well-settled, small lots	500–600
Newer neighborhoods average-size lots ($\frac{1}{4}$ to $\frac{1}{2}$ acre)	900
New and old neighborhoods, large lots ($\frac{1}{2}$ to 3 acres)	1,500

(From Jerome B. Wolff and John F. Loos, "Analysis of Peak Water Demands," *Public Works,* September 1956.)

The many factors affecting the use of water preclude any general statement regarding fluctuations in water use rates on a nationwide basis. General trends and average figures reported here are useful tools but it should be understood that values from many individual areas vary considerably from the stated mean values. The application of the data presented here must be done with the exercise of qualified judgment and experience by the designer. A careful study must be made of past records of the type and pattern of community water use, the physical and climatic characteristics of the area, expected trends in development, projected population values, and other factors related to water use.

EXAMPLE 3-1.   Consider that an urban area of 400 acres is to be developed with a housing density of 6 houses per acre. Find the peak hourly demand for this area.

Solution: The number of dwelling units a is equal to $400 \times 6 = 2,400$. Follow the curve marked 6.0 Density-dwelling units per acre, (Fig. 3-6) and read up from $a = 2,400$. Project this intersection over to the ordinate and read a value of 2,200 gpm for the peak hourly demand.

3-8.   FIRE DEMANDS

Fire-fighting demands must be considered in any municipal water-system design. Annual volumes required for fire purposes are small but during periods of need the demand may be exceedingly large and in many cases may govern the design of distribution systems, distribution storage, and pumping equipment. Quantities of water required for fire-fighting in high-value community districts, as recommended by the National Board of Fire Underwriters, are given in Table 3-4.[12] For communities of 200,000 people or less, the National Board of Fire Underwriters state that

$$Q = 1,020\sqrt{P}(1 - 0.01\sqrt{P}) \qquad (3\text{-}16)$$

where Q = demand in gallons per minute
P = population in thousands

TABLE 3-4

NATIONAL BOARD OF FIRE UNDERWRITERS RECOMMENDED
FIRE-FLOW CAPACITIES FOR HIGH-VALUE DISTRICTS

Population	Fire Flow, gpm	Duration, hr
1,000	1,000	4
2,000	1,500	6
3,000	1,750	7
4,000	2,000	8
5,000	2,250	9
6,000	2,500	10
10,000	3,000	10
20,000	4,350	10
40,000	6,000	10
60,000	7,000	10
80,000	8,000	10
100,000	9,000	10
150,000	11,000	10
200,000	12,000	10

From *Standard Schedule for Grading Cities and Towns of the United States with Reference to Their Fire Defenses and Physical Conditions* (New York: National Board of Fire Underwriters, 1956).

Where the population exceeds 200,000, from 2,000 to 5,000 gpm additional are added for a second fire, which brings the maximum to 20,000 gpm. Requirements for residential areas vary from 500 to 3,000 gpm, the required rate being a function of population density. Hydrant pressures should generally exceed 20 psi where modern motor pumpers are used, otherwise pressures in excess of 100 psi might be required. If recommended fire flows cannot be maintained for the indicated time periods, community fire-insurance rates may be adjusted upward.

The coincident draft during fire-fighting is usually considered to be equal to the maximum daily demand since the probability of the maximum rate of water usage for community purposes occurring simultaneously with a major conflagration is slight.

EXAMPLE 3-2. Consider a residential area consisting of 500 acres with a housing density of 6 houses per acre. Assume high-value residence with a fire requirement of 1,000 gpm. Find (a) the required combined flow and (b) the peak hourly demand.

Solution: (a) Assume a maximum daily requirement of 600 gallons per day per dwelling unit. The total residential requirement exclusive of fire draft equals 600 × 6 × 500 = 1,800,000 gpd or 1,250 gpm. The combined draft is thus 1,250 + 1,000 = 2,250 gpm.

(b) From Fig. 3-6 for a = 3,000 and D = 6, Q = 2,700 gpm. The peak hourly requirement would be the controlling design factor in this case.

3-9. COMMERCIAL WATER USE

The modern community generally is required to serve a variety of commercial water users along with residential and industrial water demands. In considering commercial requirements it is important that both the magnitude and the time of occurrence of the peak flow be known. Table 3-5 indicates typical requirements and periods of maximum demand for apartments, motels, hotels, office buildings, shopping centers, laundries, washmobiles and service stations.[4] Generally, it can be stated that commercial water users do not materially affect peak municipal demands. In fact, peak hours for many commercial establishments tend to coincide with the secondary residential peak period. The cessation of numerous commercial activities at about 6 p.m. precludes the imposition of large demands in the early evening when sprinkling demands are often high.

The commercial peak-hour demands given in Table 3-5 are compared to peak-hour demands for a typical individual residence on a one-acre lot. The data show that maximum commercial needs are considerably less important than peak sprinkling demands in determining peak loads on a distribution system subject to heavy sprinkling loads. An average figure of 20 gpcd is normally considered representative of commercial water consumption. The range is normally reported as 10 to 130 gpcd.

3-10. INDUSTRIAL WATER USE

As indicated in Fig. 3-3, industrial water use is rapidly increasing. An interesting attribute of this use is the relatively small quantity of water consumed compared to the amount used in the plant operation.[17] Also of interest is the fact that approximately 80 percent of the industrial water demand is imposed by only about 5 percent of the industries, whereas nearly 70 percent of the industrial plants use less than 2 percent of the total requirement. Major water users are the steel, petroleum products, wood pulp and paper, coke, and beverage industries. Table 3-6 presents some typical industrial water requirements.

As can be seen from the following tabulation, the quantities of water used by industry vary widely. They are also affected by many factors such as cost and availability of water, waste-disposal problems, management, and the type of process employed. Individual studies of the water requirements of a specific industry should therefore be made for each location.

TABLE 3-5
COMMERCIAL WATER USE

Unit	Unit	Average Annual Demand, gpd	Maximum Hourly Demand Rate, gpd	Hour of Peak Occurrence	Ratio Maximum Hourly to Average Annual	Average Annual Demand Per Unit	Ratio Maximum Hourly Demand to R-40 Demand*
Miscellaneous Residential							
Apartment building	22 units	3,430	11,700	5–6 p.m.	3.41	156 gpd/unit	2.2:1
Motel	166 units	11,400	21,600	7–8 a.m.	1.89	69 gpd/unit	4.0:1
Hotels:							
Belvedere	275 rooms	112,000	156,000	9–10 a.m.	1.39	407 gpd/room	29 :1
Emerson	410 rooms	126,000				307 gpd/room	
Office buildings							
Commercial Credit	490,000 sq ft	41,400	206,000	10–11 a.m.	4.89	0.084 gpd/sq ft	38 :1
Internal Revenue	182,000 sq ft	14,900	74,700	11–12 a.m.	5.01	0.082 gpd/sq ft	14 :1
State Office Building	389,000 sq ft	27,000	71,800	10–11 a.m.	2.58	0.070 gpd/sq ft†	13 :1
Shopping Centers							
Towson Plaza	240,000 sq ft	35,500	89,900	2–3 p.m.	2.50	0.15 gpd/sq ft	17 :1
Hillendale	145,000 sq ft	26,000				0.18 gpd/sq ft	
Miscellaneous Commercial							
Laundries							
Laundromat	10 8-lb washers	1,840	12,600	11–12 a.m.	6.85	184 gpd/washer	2.3:1
Commercial	Equivalent to 10 8-lb washers	2,510	16,200	10–11 a.m.	6.45	251 gpd/washer equivalent	3.0:1
Washmobile	Capacity of 24 cars per hour	7,930	75,000	11–12 a.m.	9.46	330 gpd per car per hr of capacity	14 :1
Service station	1 lift	472	12,500	6–7 p.m.	26.5	472 gpd/lift	2.3:1

*Lot type R-40 (one acre) peak hourly demand for single service is 5,400 gpd.

†Exclusive of air conditioning.

(Courtesy of the Residential Water Use Research Project of The Johns Hopkins University and the Office of Technical Studies of the Architectural Standards Division of The Federal Housing Administration.)

TABLE 3-6

INDUSTRIAL WATER REQUIREMENTS

Product	Water Requirement
Milk, dairy	340 gal/1,000 lb raw milk
Woolens	140,000 gal/ton
Thermoelectricity	80 gal/kwh
Coke	3,600 gal/ton
Steel	65,000 gal/ton
Oil refining	770 gal/bbl

The values in Table 3-6 should serve only as an approximate indicator of order of magnitude.

Industrial loads in a particular area may impose a draft on the distribution system in excess of that which a domestic population occupying the same area would impose. Accurate information relative to industrial location and requirements is therefore of considerable importance. The time distribution of the load is a further requirement. Future industrial demands for a region may be estimated on the basis of proposed industrial zoning and by considering the type of industries most likely to develop in the area. Accurate projected requirements are not easily secured, however, as there is often little reliable information on land-area requirements for various industries; nor are there consistent data on water requirements per unit of product.

In many instances industries develop their own water-supply systems and under these circumstances impose no demand on the local municipal system except possibly for the source.

3-11. AGRICULTURAL WATER USE

Total annual water requirements for agricultural use are exceedingly large. In many areas of the country, particularly in the arid regions, irrigation-water requirements comprise the bulk of the total developed water supply. This is clearly shown by Fig. 3-3.

Quantities of water required for agriculture vary widely based on the type of crop being irrigated, the distribution of precipitation in the region, and other related factors. In general, irrigation waters are supplied separately from municipal requirements and are therefore of no importance in designing municipal water works. They are mentioned here because they may be an important factor in multipurpose water-development projects and cannot be neglected when considering the appropriation of water in an area. For example, in designing combined storage works which will serve municipal, power, and irrigation requirements, reliable estimates of total agricultural requirements and periods of need are a prime requirement. Detailed information on irrigation requirements and practices is readily available in the literature. Table 3-7 indicates the

TABLE 3-7
IRRIGATION WITHDRAWALS FOR SEVENTEEN WESTERN STATES, 1955

State	Withdrawals for Irrigation, 1,000 acre-ft
Arizona	7,745
California	25,809
Colorado	7,065
Idaho	16,926
Montana	10,936
Nevada	2,149
New Mexico	2,818
Oregon	7,615
Utah	4,674
Washington	5,638
Wyoming	12,366
Kansas	829
Nebraska	2,858
North Dakota	136
Oklahoma	252
South Dakota	31
Texas	11,466

Source: K. A. MacKichan, "Estimated Use of Water in the United States–1955" (U.S. Geological Survey, Circular No. 398, 1957).

general order of magnitude of quantities of water used for irrigation in seventeen Western states.

QUANTITIES OF WASTES

The design of municipal sewerage systems must be based on a knowledge of the expected sewage flows. The time variation of these flows is also important, since sewers, which normally are gravity-flow systems, must be capable of handling the peak loads and must also be able to transport the minimum loads at velocities sufficient to assure cleansing action. The flow in a sewer consists principally of the wastes of the community and groundwater seepage or infiltration, although in the case of combined sewers or where illicit connections are made, stormwater runoff must also be considered.

3-12. RESIDENTIAL SEWAGE FLOWS

Figure 3-8 gives a comparison of water use and sewage flow on days when little lawn sprinkling occurred. The data are from the Pine Valley Subdivision in Baltimore County, Maryland.[4] Domestic sewage flows are highly variable throughout the day and as in the case of the hydrograph of water use, two distinct peaks have been observed. The primary peak takes place in the morning hours and the secondary peak occurs about

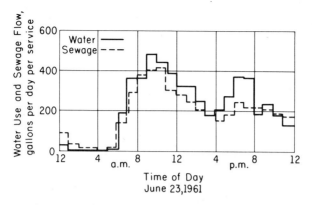

FIG. 3-8. Comparison of water-use and sewage flow on days when little sprinkling occurred. (Courtesy of the Residential Water-Use Research Project of The Johns Hopkins University and the Office of Technical Studies of the Architectural Standards Division of The Federal Housing Administration.)

dinner time and maintains itself during the evening hours. Extraneous flows resulting from infiltration or storm runoff tend to distort the basic hydrograph shape. Infiltration rates generally tend to gradually increase the total daily volume but do not ordinarily alter the twin-peaked character of the hydrograph. Storm runoff which enters the system may impose almost instantaneous changes; if the quantity is large, the entire characteristic of the hydrograph may be changed. Estimation of the various components of the flow is essential for design purposes. A 1963 study by Lentz of sewage flows in communities in California, Florida, Missouri, and Maryland provides considerable useful information regarding residential sewage flows, and the components of these flows.[16]

Average Rates of Flow. Lentz and Linaweaver have shown that when residential water is not being used for consumptive purposes (principally lawn sprinkling) and when infiltration and exfiltration do not produce large flow components, the sewage flow is essentially equal to the water use.[4,16] Thus, average daily water use rates which do not reflect sprinkling demands can be used to estimate annual average domestic sewage flows. It is generally reported that about 60 to 70 percent of the total water supplied becomes waste water. Figure 3-9 shows a derived relationship between average per capita sewage flow and average assessed valuation of property. This relationship was developed by Lentz, from data on the areas mentioned previously.[16]

Maximum and Minimum Rates of Flow. The peak daily flow from a residential area is normally considered to be about 225 percent of the average daily flow. Several mathematical expressions relating maximum

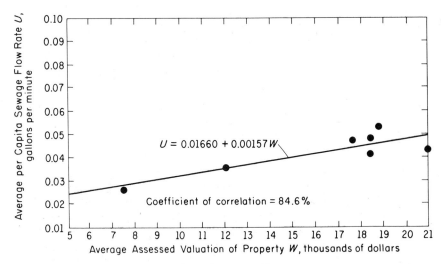

FIG. 3-9. Average per capita domestic sewage flow rate vs. average assessed valuation of property. (Courtesy of the Residential Water-Use Research Project of The Johns Hopkins University and the Office of Technical Studies of the Architectural Standards Division of The Federal Housing Administration.)

flow to average flow have been derived. One of these proposed by Harmon for use in the United States is as follows:[18]

$$\frac{Q_m}{Q_A} = \frac{18 + \sqrt{P}}{4 + \sqrt{P}} \tag{3-17}$$

where Q_m = maximum rate of flow of domestic sewage

Q_A = the average rate of flow

P = population in thousands

In 1963, Lentz showed that maximum per capita rates of sewage flow could be successfully estimated by using an extreme value frequency distribution.[16] A detailed discussion of the procedure is beyond the scope of this text and the reader is referred to the original source. As a guide, the ratios to the average shown in Table 3-8 may be used in estimating maximum and minimum flows.

Infiltration and Exfiltration. Infiltration and exfiltration are both functions of the height of the groundwater table in the vicinity of the

TABLE 3-8
RESIDENTIAL SEWAGE FLOWS
AS RATIOS TO THE AVERAGE

Description of Flow	Ratio to the Average
Maximum daily	2.25 to 1
Maximum hourly	3 to 1
Minimum daily	0.67 to 1
Minimum hourly	0.33 to 1

sewer, the type and tightness of sewer joints, and soil type. Exfiltration is undesirable since it may tend to pollute local ground waters, while infiltration has the effect of reducing the capacity of the sewer for conveying the waste flows for which it was designed. If the sewer is well above the groundwater table, infiltration will occur only during or after periods of precipitation when water is percolating downward through the soil. Where groundwater tables are high and sewers are not tight, infiltration rates in excess of 60,000 gpd per mile of sewer might be experienced. Rates of 3,500 to 5,000 gpd per mile per 24 hr for 8-in. pipe, 4,500 to 6,000 for 12-in. pipe, and 10,000 to 12,000 for 24-in. pipe represent the range in which the greater number of specifications fall.[21] Common practice is to design for the peak-design rate of sanitary sewage flow plus 30,000 gpd infiltration per mile of sewer and house connections.[20] This allowance represents average conditions and should be revised by the designer as required on the basis of the physical characteristics of the area and the type of pipe joint to be used.

Storm Runoff. Except for large combined sewers, storm runoff should be excluded from the sewerage system. Storm runoff may enter at manholes or through illicit roof drains connected to the sanitary system. Quantities of flow that enter in this manner vary with the degree of enforcement of regulations and the types of preventive measures that are taken. The American Society of Civil Engineers reports that test on leakage through manhole covers show that 20 to 70 gpm may enter a manhole cover submerged by 1 in. of water.[20] Rates of this magnitude may be considerably in excess of average sewage flows. Small sewers can be surcharged easily by a very few illicit roof-drain connections. For example, a rainfall of 1 in. per hr on a 1,000-sq-ft roof area will contribute flows in excess of 10 gpm. The average domestic sewage flow from a dwelling having this approximate roof area (consider 4 persons) would equal only about 1.5 percent of this.

EXAMPLE 3-3. Estimate the maximum hourly, average daily, and minimum hourly residential sewage flows from an area occupied by 750 people and having an average assessed valuation of $15,000. Consider the length of sewer and house drains equal to 1.3 miles.

Solution: From Fig. 3-9 for $W = 15,000$, find $U = 0.041$ gpm per capita, or $0.041 \times 1440 = 59$ gpcd average flow. Total average daily flow $= 59 \times 750 = 44,200$ gpd.

$$\text{Infiltration} = 30,000 \times 1.3 = 39,000 \text{ gpd}$$

Using Table 3-8,

$$\text{Maximum hourly flow} = 39,000 + 44,200 \times 3 \quad = 172,000 \text{ gpd}$$
$$\text{Average daily flow} \quad = 39,000 + 44,200 \qquad = 83,200 \text{ gpd}$$
$$\text{Minimum hourly flow} = 39,000 + 44,200 \times 1/3 = 53,600 \text{ gpd}$$

3-13. INDUSTRIAL-WASTE VOLUMES

Industrial-waste volumes are highly variable in both quantity and quality, depending principally on the product produced. Since very little water is consumed in industrial processing, large volumes are often returned as waste. These wastes may include toxic metals, chemicals, organic materials, biological contaminants, and radioactive materials. The design of treatment processes for these wastes is a highly specialized operation. Where industrial wastes must be processed in municipal sewage-treatment works, accurate estimates of the time distribution and total volume of the load are necessary along with a complete analysis of the characteristics of the waste. Under these circumstances, metering and analyzing the industrial waste is normally required and carried out by the engineer when the required information cannot be obtained from the industry or industries involved. For more complete information on volumes as well as characteristics of all types of industrial wastes the reader is directed to N. L. Nemerow *Theories and Practices of Industrial Waste Treatment*, Reading, Mass: Addison Wesley Publishing Company, Inc., 1963.

REFERENCES

1. F. E. Croxton and D. J. Cowden, *Applied General Statistics* (Englewood Cliffs, N.J.: Prentice-Hall, Inc., 1960).

2. R. H. Marks, "Water: How Industry Can Curb Growing Demands," *Power* (January 1963).

3. K. A. Yarbrough, *J. Am. Water Works Assoc.* (April 1956).

4. F. P. Linaweaver, Jr., "Report on Phase One, Residential Water Use Research Project." The Johns Hopkins University, Dept. of Sanitary Engineering, Baltimore, October 1963.

5. H. F. Seidel and E. R. Baumann, *J. Am. Water Works Assoc.* (December 1955), p. 150.

6. Harold E. Babbitt, James J. Doland, and John L. Cleasby, *Water Supply Engineering*, 6th ed. (New York: McGraw-Hill Book Co., Inc., 1962).

7. Jerome B. Wolff, "Peak Demands in Residential Areas," *J. Am. Water Works Assoc.* (October 1961).

8. Anonymous, *Water Sewage Works* (September 1958), p. R116.

9. Roger C. Schmitt, "Forecasting Population by the Ratio Method," *J. Am. Water Works Assoc.*, vol. 46 (1954), p. 960.

10. O. A. Brock, "Multiple Regression Analysis of Maximum Day Water Consumption of Dallas, Texas," *J. Am. Water Works Assoc.*, vol. 50 (October 1958), p. 1391.

11. Jerome B. Wolff, "Forecasting Residential Requirements," Presented at the Chesapeake Section, American Water Works Association, Baltimore, October 1956, mimeograph.

12. "Standard Schedule for Grading Cities and Towns of the United States

with Reference to Their Fire Defenses and Physical Conditions," National Board Fire Underwriters, New York, 1956.

13. Kenneth Carl, Jr., "Extension of Public Service to Suburban Areas— Fire Protection," *J. Am. Water Works Assoc.*, vol. 47, no. 10 (October 1955).

14. Jerome B. Wolff and John F. Loos, "Analysis of Peak Water Demands," *Public Works* (September 1956).

15. Task Group Report, "Study of Domestic Water Use," *J. Am. Water Works Assoc.*, vol. 50 (November 1958), p. 1408.

16. John J. Lentz, "Special Report No. 4 of the Residential Sewerage Research Project to the Federal Housing Administration," The Johns Hopkins University, Dept. of Sanitary Engineering, Baltimore, May 1963.

17. Joseph M. Willis, "Forecasting Industrial Requirements," Presented at the Chesapeake Section, American Water Works Association, Baltimore, October 1956 (mimeograph).

18. W. G. Harmon, "Forecasting Sewage Discharge at Toledo," *Eng. News-Record*, vol. 80 (1918), p. 1235.

19. G. M. Fair and J. C. Geyer, *Elements of Water Supply and Waste-Water Disposal* (New York: John Wiley and Sons, Inc., 1958).

20. "Design and Construction of Sanitary and Storm Sewers," *Am. Soc. Civil Engrs. Manual of Engineering Practice*, No. 37 (New York: American Society of Civil Engineers, 1960).

21. Charles R. Velzy and Joshua M. Sprague, *Sewage Ind. Wastes*, vol. 27, no. 3 (March 1955).

22. W. D. Moulton, "Estimating Population," *Public Works* (March 1964), p. 22.

PROBLEMS

3-1. Using the 1940 and 1950 census figures for Bakersfield, California, estimate the 1945 and 1955 populations by assuming arithmetic, geometric, and decreasing rates of increase.

Year	Population, Thousands
1900	4.8
1910	12.7
1920	18.6
1930	26.0
1940	29.2
1950	34.8

3-2. Obtain census data for your community through 1950. Estimate the 1955 and 1960 population by the methods outlined in Chap. 3. Compare the estimated 1960 value with the actual value. Explain any difference.

3-3. The Elephant Butte reservoir has a capacity of 2.64 million acre-ft. How many years would this supply the city of Las Cruces (pop. 40,000) if the evaporation losses are neglected? Assume a consumption rate of 130 gpcd.

3-4. If the minimum flow of a stream having a 150-sq-mile watershed is 0.07 cfs per sq mile, what population can be supplied continuously from the stream? Assume only distribution storage is provided. Consider a maximum average daily consumption rate of 180 gpcd.

3-5. Estimate the 1960, 1970, and 1980 population of Bakersfield, California by plotting the data for 1910 onward on arithmetic coordinate paper and extending the curve by eye. See Prob. 3-1 for data.

3-6. Of the 8-mgd average consumption in a town of 45,000 population, 1.2 mgd is estimated to be lost through leaks in water mains. Consider these leaks to behave as orifices and determine the amount of water that can be saved by reducing street-main pressure from 50 to 30 psi.

3-7. Estimate the size of water main needed to carry water from a municipal distribution system to a community of 8,000 population if the fire-fighting requirement is estimated to be 2,800 gpm and the coincident draft is 150 gpcd.

3-8. Write a short discussion of some of the factors that you feel might markedly affect population estimates for your community.

3-9. By visiting the university library, make a list of ten to twenty reference books or periodicals which provide information on water requirements of various kinds.

3-10. Write a paper describing procedures for determining the water requirements of an area. Use at least two of the reference listed in Prob. 3-9. Do not use material more than five years old.

3-11. Using the data given below, estimate the 1980 population by means of the logistic curve.

1900–5,600	1920– 7,200	1940–20,300
1910–6,100	1930–11,200	1950–28,000
		1960–34,700

3-12. Consider a residential area with a proposed housing density of 6 dwellings per acre. Total area involved is 530 acres. Find (a) the peak-hour requirement and (b) the required fire flow and coincident draft.

3-13. Estimate the maximum hourly, average daily, and minimum hourly residential sewage flows from an area serving 1,500 persons and having an average assessed property valuation of $17,000. Assume that the length of sewer and house drains equals 2.3 miles and that infiltration occurs.

3-14. Compare the maximum hourly domestic sewage flow from 10 houses (4 persons per house) with the roof drainage from these houses if the roof dimensions are 60 × 35 ft and the rainfall intensity is 3.2 in. per hr. Approximately what size sewer would be required to handle (a) the domestic flow alone, and (b) the combined flow if the pipe is laid on a 1.2 percent grade.

3-15. What would be the average dilution of a sewage effluent from a community of 55,000 persons if the flow enters a stream having a watershed of 110 sq miles and a mean annual flow of 0.72 cfs per sq mile?

3-16. A community having 2,000 houses experiences a thundershower which in one hour precipitates 1 in. of rain uniformly over the town. What percentage of the normal design size of the sewer conduit would the actual conduit need to be to handle the shower runoff if 1 percent of the houses have illicit plumbing? Assume that the roof area per house is 2,500 sq ft and that the maximum sewage flow per dwelling is 400 gpd.

3-17. Using the fire flow-rate-requirement equation

$$Q = 1020 \sqrt{P}(1.0 - 0.01 \sqrt{P})$$

plot a curve of Q vs. P for populations of 1,000 to 200,000 people.

3-18. Make a comparison between the annual water requirements of a 1,000-acre cotton farm fully irrigated by ditch and a city of 30,000 population. Assume an irrigation requirement of 3 acre-ft per year.

3-19. If 15 acres of farm land were developed for urban housing (4 houses per acre), what would be the difference in average annual water requirement after the changeover? Assume 3 acre-ft of water represents the annual agricultural requirement.

chapter 4

Development of Surface and Ground Water Supplies

Water is located in all of the regions of the earth. The problem is that the distribution, quality, quantity, and mode of occurrence are highly variable from one locale to another.

The most voluminous water source is the oceans. It is estimated that they contain about 1,060 trillion acre-ft of water.[1] Although this water serves many purposes, it is at present only indirectly thought of in respect to human consumption. There is no doubt that the challenge of broadening the utility of sea water exists. The energetic program being carried on by the Office of Saline Water is directed toward this goal.

The most valuable water supply (in terms of quality or freshness) is contained within the atmosphere, on the earth's surface, or underground. This supply however, amounts to only about 3 percent of that contained in the oceans.

THE DISTRIBUTION OF WATER IN THE UNITED STATES

Water resources vary widely in regional and local patterns of availability. The supply is dependent upon topographic and meteorological conditions as they influence precipitation and evapotranspiration. Quantities of water stored are dependent to a large extent on the physical features of the earth and on the earth's geological structure. Table 4-1 shows the major components of the water resources of the continental United States.

4-1. SOIL MOISTURE

Soil moisture is the most broadly used water source on the earth's surface. Except in irrigated areas, agriculture and natural plant life are dependent upon it for sustenance. Nevertheless, the quantity of water stored as soil moisture at any specified time is small. Estimates indicate an equivalent layer about 4.6 in. in thickness distributed over 57 million sq miles of land surface. This in itself would be insufficient to support ade-

TABLE 4-1
SUMMARY DATA CONCERNING WATER RESOURCES OF THE
CONTINENTAL UNITED STATES*

	Square Miles	Acre-ft
Gross area of continental U.S.	3,080,809	× 10⁶
Land area, excluding inland water	2,974,726	
Volume of average annual precipitation		4,750
Volume of average annual runoff (discharge to sea)		1,372
Estimated total usable groundwater.		47,500
Average amount of soil moisture		635
Estimated total lake storage		13,000
Total reservoir storage (capacity of 5,000 acre-ft or more)		365

*From E. A. Ackerman and G. O. Löf, *Technology in American Water Development* (Baltimore, 1959).

quate plant growth without renewal. It is therefore important that the frequency with which this supply is renewed and the length of time it remains available for use be known. The supply of soil moisture is dependent upon geographical location, climatic conditions, geologic structure, and soil type. Variations may be experienced on a seasonal, weekly, or even daily basis.

It is considered that the natural supply of soil moisture in most of the agricultural areas of this country is less than optimum for crop growth during an average year. It is evident then that a greater understanding of optimum water requirements for crops is essential if we are to economically and efficiently supply water artificially to overcome natural soil moisture deficiencies.

4-2. SURFACE WATERS AND GROUNDWATER

Surface waters are found nonuniformly distributed over the earth's surface. It is estimated that only about 4 percent of the United States land surface is occupied by fresh surface waters. These waters vary widely in quantity, seasonal distribution, quality, and frequency of occurrence.

Groundwater supplies are much more widely distributed than surface supplies. Nevertheless, strong local concentrations are found due to the variety of soils, rocks, and geologic structures located underground.

4-3. RUNOFF DISTRIBUTION

Approximately 30 percent of the average annual rainfall in the United States is estimated to appear as surface runoff. The allocation of this water is directly related to precipitation patterns and thus meteorologic, geographic, topographic, and geologic conditions. In the West, large regions are devoid of permanent runoff and some localities such as Death Valley, California, receive no runoff for years at a time. In contrast, some areas in the Pacific Northwest average about 6 ft of runoff annually. Mountain regions are usually the most productive of runoff, whereas flat areas, especially those experiencing lower precipitation rates, are generally poor runoff producers.

Runoff is distributed in a far from uniform pattern over the continental United States. In addition, it is subject to seasonal variations and definite annual periods during which the concentration is significantly greater. For example, about 75 percent of the runoff in the semiarid and arid regions of the country occurs during a period of a few weeks following the snow melt on the upper watershed. Even in the well-watered East an uneven distribution prevails which has been one of the factors in the recent expansion of supplemental irrigation to be found there. Figure 4-1 indicates the four major runoff regions in the United States.

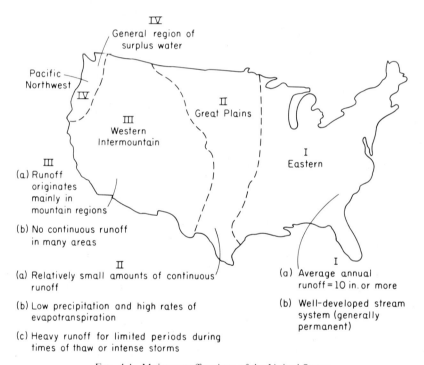

FIG. 4-1. Major runoff regions of the United States.

4-4. GROUNDWATER DISTRIBUTION

The usable groundwater storage in the United States is estimated to be about 48 billion acre-ft. This vast reservoir is distributed across the nation in quantities determined primarily by precipitation, evapotranspiration, and geologic structure.

There actually are two components to this supply. One may be considered a part of the hydrologic cycle, while the other, a part which has been trapped underground in past ages, is no longer naturally circulated in the cycle.

Figure 4-2 shows the principal groundwater areas of the United States as depicted by H. E. Thomas.[18] Generally it is evident that the mountain regions in the East and West, the northern Great Plains, and the granitic and metamorphic rock areas of New England and the southern Piedmont do not contain important groundwater supplies.

Aquifers may be generally classified into four categories:

1. Those directly connected to surface supplies which are replenished by gravitational water, and which release water to surface flow. Gravels found in flood plains or river valleys are examples.

2. "Regional" aquifers occurring east of the 100th meridian. These aquifers produce some of the largest permanent groundwater yields and have moderate to high rates of recharge. Good examples are found in the Atlantic and Gulf coastal plain areas.

3. Low-recharge aquifers between the 100th and 120th meridians. These aquifers have relatively little inflow compared to potential or actual drafts. Although storage volumes are often large, the low rate of replenishment indicates the water must be considered more of a minable material than a renewable resource. This possible "limited life" category poses particular problems of development and management.

4. Aquifers subject to saline-water intrusion. These are usually found in the coastal regions but some cases have been recorded in the Western states, notably Arizona.

WATER QUALITY

Water-supply development is concerned with both the quantity and quality of water required to meet the needs of man in an efficient and economical manner. Neither factor can be neglected in a comprehensive study. The usefulness of the maximum available water supply is determined in large part by its quality.

Through the years, quantities of waste have grown until many once-sparkling streams have been degraded to turbid sewers. Such impairment of water quality has resulted in extensive loss of aquatic life and in the destruction of the proper biological balance of streams. In addition, and of utmost importance, pollution has effected an actual decrease in our country's available water resources. If the water is so foul that its treatment for public consumption or industrial use is not economically feasible, then other sources of supply must be sought and the polluted body of water can be considered as much of a loss as if it were physically unavailable.

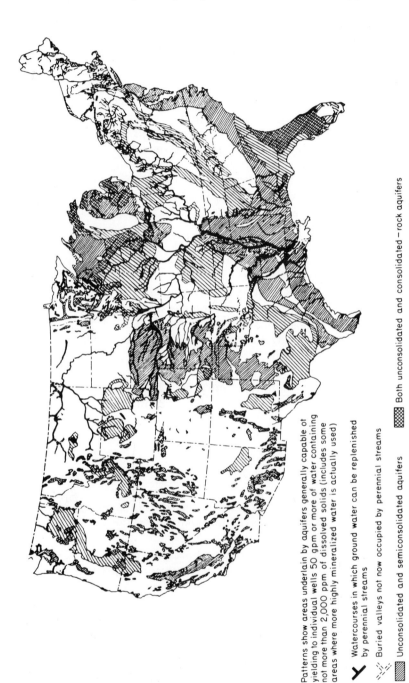

Patterns show areas underlain by aquifers generally capable of yielding to individual wells 50 gpm or more of water containing not more than 2,000 ppm of dissolved solids (includes some areas where more highly mineralized water is actually used)

Watercourses in which ground water can be replenished by perennial streams

Buried valleys not now occupied by perennial streams

Unconsolidated and semiconsolidated aquifers

Consolidated-rock aquifers

Both unconsolidated and consolidated-rock aquifers

Not known to be underlain by aquifers that will generally yield as much as 50 gpm to wells

FIG. 4-2. Groundwater areas in the United States. (From H. E. Thomas, "Water," *The Yearbook of Agriculture*, Washington, D.C.: U.S. Government Printing Office, 1955.)

The quality of precipitation is usually quite high, but once the precipitated water has penetrated the soil with its component minerals and rocks and flowed in streams contaminated by municipalities and industries, its quality may be seriously degraded by bacteria, organic matter, dissolved salts, acids, and possibly radioisotopes.

The drinking-water standards prescribed by the U.S. Public Health Service recommend that the total dissolved solids content for human consumption should not exceed 500 mg/l. The United States Geological Survey states that waters containing more than about 2,000 mg/l dissolved solids are generally unfit for long-term irrigation under average conditions. The usability will depend, however, on the elements present, the soil type, and tolerance of the crop, and may thus vary considerably from the average allowable concentrations. The sodium and potassium balance is particularly important in agricultural waters for example.[3]

Increased emphasis on the quality of our water resources comes in the face of increasing population, accelerated industrial activity, and large-scale pollution.[7] Waste-abatement operations range from simple technical adjustments to the consideration of exceedingly complex social-political-ecological-psychological problems. A complicating factor is that each pollution-abatement problem is different. In addition, the motivations for abatement programs are shifting from the pure health-hazard base to an inclusion of aesthetic valuations. As stated by Renn, "We undoubtedly have more common interest in pleasant living and are less moved by moralistic views. If we don't like dirty water for any reason, we simply don't like it, and we don't argue that it must necessarily be toxic or bad for health. There is profit in offering a more pleasant future and we know it. We take it for granted that we have a right to some minutes of leisure, irresponsibility, and beauty without reproach. In fact, a very large fraction of our economy rests on this presumption."[17]

4-5. GROUNDWATER

Groundwater quality is influenced considerably by the quality of the source. Changes in source waters or degraded quality of normal supplies may seriously impair the quality of the groundwater supply. Sewage and industrial wastes entering an aquifer are major sources of organic and inorganic pollution. Large-scale organic pollution of groundwaters is infrequent, however, since significant quantities of organic wastes usually cannot be easily introduced underground. The problem is quite different with inorganic solutions, since these move easily through the soil and once introduced are removed only with great difficulty. In addition, the effects of such pollution may continue for indefinite periods since natural dilution is slow, and artificial flushing or treatment is generally impractical or too expensive. The number of harmful enteric organisms is generally reduced to tolerable levels by the percolation of water through 6 or 7 ft of fine-grained soil.[5] However, as the water passes through the soil a significant increase in the amounts of dissolved salts may occur. These salts are added by soluble products of soil weathering and of erosion by rainfall and flowing water. Locations downstream from heavily irrigated areas may find that the water they are receiving is too saline for satisfactory crop production. These saline contaminants are difficult to control because removal methods are exceedingly expensive. A possible solution is to dilute with waters of lower salt concentration (sewage-treatment-plant effluent, for example) so that the average water produced by mixing will be suitable for use.

Considerable care should be exercised to protect groundwater storage capacity from irreparable harm through the disposal of waste materials.[6]

4-6. SURFACE WATER

The primary causes of deterioration of surface-water quality are municipal and domestic sewage, industrial wastes (organic, inorganic, heat), and solid and semisolid refuse. A municipality obtaining its water supply from a surface body may find upstream users discharging untreated sewage and toxic chemicals in such quantities as to render the stream unsuitable or too costly to treat for use as a water supply. Waste products discharged by cities and industry can, however, be controlled at the point of initiation. This has been borne out by recent successes in cleaning up such watersheds as the Delaware and Susquehanna in the eastern United States. Fortunately, effluent treatment is assuming increased importance and thousands of industrial plants are now treating their wastes. In 1956, *Chemical and Engineering News* suggested that the chemical industry alone was spending $50 million a year in new water pollution control facilities.

THE WATER BUDGET

In theory, accounting for the water resources of an area is relatively simple. The basic procedure involves the separate evaluation of each factor in the water budget so that a quantitative comparison of the available water resources with the known or anticipated water requirements of the area can be made. In practice, however, the evaluation of the water budget is often quite complex, and extensive and time-consuming investigations are generally required.

Both natural and artificial gains and losses in the water supply must be considered. The primary natural gains to surface bodies are those which result from direct runoff caused by precipitation and effluent seepage of groundwater. Evapotranspiration and unrecovered infiltration are the major natural losses. Dependable dry-season supplies can be increased through diversion from other areas, through low-flow augmentation, through saline water conversion, and perhaps in the future, through induced precipitation. On the other hand, diversions out of the basin will decrease the quantity of water available.

After the gross dependable water supply has been estimated, the net dependable supply may be determined at any point of interest by subtracting the quantity used, detained, or lost as a result of man's activities, from the gross supply. When water is withdrawn from a river, a decrease in flow between the point of withdrawal and the point of return is experienced. As the water is used, part of it will be lost to the atmosphere through various forms of consumption. These consumptive losses are accumulative downstream and effect a permanent decrease in the dependable water supply. Temporary decreases in dependable supply occur along the water course between intake and discharge points. The dependable supply in the reach of watercourse between the two points is thus diminished by the amount of the withdrawal.

A water supply may be considered adequate for present needs but inadequate to provide for future requirements. In many cases it is therefore necessary to predict future water needs based on estimated changes in population, industrial development, agricultural practices, and on changes in water policy and technology which will affect the supply and use of water.[2]

4-7. DEFINITION OF TERMS IN THE WATER BUDGET

The evaluation of problems in water supply and demand requires clear-cut definitions of the various components that comprise the water budget. For this reason some of the most troublesome or confused terms will be defined here.

Consumptive Use. *Water consumption* and *water use* are terms that have frequently been employed indiscriminately and interchangeably. Several definitions of *consumption* or *consumptive use* may be found in the literature. A special committee of the American Water Works Association defines consumptive use as water used in connection with vegetative growth, food processing, or incidental to an industrial process, which is discharged to the atmosphere or incorporated in the products of the process.[20] A slight modification of this definition which includes air-conditioning losses will be adopted here.

Withdrawal Use. The use of water for any purpose which requires that it be physically removed from the source. Depending on the use to which the water is put, a significant percentage may be returned to the original source and then be available for reuse.

Nonwithdrawal Use. The use of water for any purpose which does not require that it be removed from the original source such as water used for navigation.

Nonconsumptive Losses. Certain water losses, though not "consumptive" in the sense of the definition, may have the effect of reducing the available water supply of an area. For example, dead storage (storage below outlet elevations) in impoundments is unavailable for downstream use. Diversion of water from one drainage basin to another represents an additional form of nonconsumptive loss. An example of this is the use of the Delaware River Basin for the municipal supply of New York City. This decreases the total flow in the Delaware River below the point of diversion. New York is required, however, to augment low flows through compensating the downstream interests for diversion losses. Water contaminated or polluted during use which cannot be economically treated for reuse also constitutes a real loss from the total supply.

SURFACE-WATER SUPPLIES

Surface-water supplies may be generally categorized as perennial or continuous unregulated rivers, rivers or streams containing impoundments, or natural lakes. Evaluation of the surface-water resources of an area requires a determination of the general characteristics of the region. The area should be located geographically on the basis of established references. All available data on the climate, hydrology, geology, and topography of the area should be accumulated. The type of industrial, agricultural, and residential development and the predicted growth rates of these factors are necessary information. A description of the principal metropolitan areas and a knowledge of the economy of the region is also important. An evaluation of the natural resources of the area and the impact of their development on the hydrology and economy of the area are additional requirements.

4-8. DRAINAGE AREA DETERMINATION

The hydrologic area must be accurately defined before a water balance can be established. Normally an area of such configuration as to make a rational accounting practical should be sought. A river basin will, under most circumstances, satisfy this requirement.

A river basin or drainage basin may be defined as the area drained by a stream or system of connecting streams such that all stream flow originating in the area is discharged through a single outlet.[16] The basin is completely enclosed by a divide or ridge line which crosses the stream only at the outlet point. Some basins may contain blind drainage areas such as sinks or lakes which are not connected by surface channels to other streams in the basin. These areas are often described as noncontributing to stream flow, although groundwater connections may exist. Subbasins within the major basin are defined by interior divides exactly in the same manner as the major basin.

The drainage area of a basin is defined as the plane area enclosed within its divide. Noncontributing areas are normally deducted from the total and, in like manner, external contributing areas are added to the total. Drainage-area determinations are usually made from Geological Survey or Army Map Service maps and are normally expressed in square miles.

4-9. THE EQUATION OF CONTINUITY APPLIED TO A DRAINAGE BASIN

The model equation with which we could theoretically work to estimate available surface supplies is

$$\Sigma I - \Sigma L = Y \qquad (4\text{-}1)$$

where I = input

L = loss

Y = available yield or stream flow.

The primary inputs are precipitation and groundwater seepage. Artificial inputs such as diversions are generally minor considerations on a basin-wide scale but may be important locally. Principal losses are evapotranspiration and unrecovered infiltration. A reliable quantitative evaluation of this equation is unfortunately all but impossible because of the difficulty encountered in making accurate estimates of the components.

4-10. PRECIPITATION

Data on average annual precipitation, seasonal distribution of precipitation, and annual precipitation variability are available through the U.S. Weather Bureau for the entire United States. In determining the available water supply of an area, precipitation data may be used in the following ways:

1. In the absence of runoff records, an inference as to runoff conditions may be drawn from a knowledge of rainfall characteristics. Numerous rainfall-runoff relationships have been reported in the literature.[16] If rainfall records are available for a catchment area adjacent to a completely gaged basin, runoff on the ungaged basin may be assumed to be 80 to 85 percent of the rainfall ratio (ungaged to gaged) times the runoff of the gaged basin.[12,19] The adjacent drainage basin should, however, possess similar physical characteristics, such as slope, shape, soil, and type, and distribution of rainfall. Great care should be exercised in using such an approach, however, and if development is planned, gaging of runoff should start immediately. Comparison can then be made between the long-term and short-term records for the two basins.

2. Precipitation data may indicate on a seasonal basis critical periods during a year. For example, water requirements for irrigation needs are generally seasonal and they may or may not coincide with periods of low

flow. Knowledge of the seasonal distribution of rainfall provides a means for determining which seasonal water users must share the available water during a specified time period.

3. The frequency of occurrence of droughts can be established by statistical analysis of rainfall data.

4-11. EVAPORATION AND TRANSPIRATION

Evaporation and transpiration are more difficult to measure and consequently are less well known than most hydrologic parameters.[11] Because evaporation is related to differences in vapor pressure, air and water temperatures, wind, atmospheric pressure, and quality of the water, it is subject to wide seasonal and regional fluctuations.

A determination of water yield on the basis of evapotranspiration is subject to gross errors and should be used only when more reliable means are not available. Local data on evaporation or transpiration may be of great value, however, and would be applicable to specific problems such as the estimation of losses from storage reservoirs. Estimates of evaporation are usually made by the energy budget or mass transfer methods. A number of empirical equations based on Dalton's law of partial pressures are reported in the literature.[16,19]

4-12. RUNOFF

A major hydrologic consideration is that of determining the magnitude, distribution, and timing of various runoff events. Maximum and minimum events are both extremely important to the water resources engineer. Floods are significant because they menace both human life and property; droughts are important because of their direct bearing on the development of a dependable water supply.

Floods result primarily from excess volumes of surface runoff. The conditions which may generate these excesses are intense storms, snow melt, and snow melt combined with rainfall. In the United States, floods on the large drainage basins are often due to combinations of rainfall and snow melt, whereas on small basins the greatest floods often result from intense thunderstorms. It is important that the factors which produce floods on a specific basin be determined. Without this knowledge, little reliability can be attached to estimates.

Stream flow is considered to include both surface and subsurface flows that eventually become stream flow. Except for special applications (primarily local), precipitation and evaporation data are either not sufficiently accurate or cannot be intelligently used in Eq. 4-1 to estimate the water yield or available stream flow. Fortunately, stream flow is the one phase of the hydrologic cycle in which water is conveyed within defined boundaries so that reasonable measurements of the volumes involved can be obtained. Other measurements in the hydrologic cycle are less reliable samples of the whole.[16]

4-13. RECORDED STREAM FLOWS

The U.S. Geologic Survey operates over 5,000 gaging stations on important streams in the United States and publishes annual records in the form of Water Supply Papers. For a specific gaging station, the following information can be found: exact geographic location of the station, maximum and minumum flows of record, mean flow of record, mean monthly flows, exact drainage area contributing to the station, and information on upstream regulation, diversion, or withdrawals. From these records an "available water supply" can be determined based on the flow criterion desired. The flow criterion selected will depend largely on the type of information to be obtained from the study. In "water-shortage" problems this criterion will most likely be a low flow such as the minimum annual flow of record, the 95 percent low flow, or some augmented low flow. The selection of this criterion will have to be made by the investigator based on his knowledge of the area and the problem he is facing.

4-14. BASIN CHARACTERISTICS AFFECTING RUNOFF

Important natural characteristics of the basin affecting stream flow are the basin's topographic and geologic features.

Topography determines the slopes and location of drainage channels and the storage capacity of the basin. Channel slope and configuration are directly related to the rate of flow in a basin and the magnitude of the peak flows. A steep watershed will generally indicate a rapid rate of runoff with little storage, whereas relatively flat areas are subject to considerable storage and lower rates of flow.

The soils in a basin affect infiltration capacity and the ability of underground strata to transmit or hold groundwater. A thorough understanding of the characteristics of the underground formations is necessary to properly evaluate these factors.

4-15. NATURAL AND REGULATED RUNOFF

Natural runoff is defined as that runoff which is unaffected by any other than natural influences. Runoff subject to withdrawals by man or artificial storage is defined as *regulated runoff*. An estimate of natural runoff is most significant when minimum flows are the controlling criterion. For example, in comparing the average-maximum-month water use with the minimum annual stream flow of record, the runoff records for the main stream and its tributaries for this minumum-flow period would be used. If an unregulated stream is to be developed as a primary water source, the safe yield will be the lowest dry-weather flow of the stream. Under this condition, the user will always have an adequate supply providing his maximum requirements do not exceed this minimum flow. If during any time interval the expected demands exceed the lowest dry-weather flow, then periods of water shortage can be anticipated unless supplementary supplies are provided.

If stream-flow records for long periods of years are available, and if minimum recorded flows appear in the records prior to periods when consumptive use is considered important, these minimums may be assumed to represent natural runoff. Any regulation of flow at the time must be accounted for, however. If the basin is relatively homogeneous, there may be undeveloped tributaries which will permit estimation of natural runoff on a discharge-per-unit-area basis for the entire basin.

Regulated runoff is normally the type of runoff for which information is available. Many streams for which runoff records are at hand were unregulated at the time they were first gaged. In most cases however, their records have now become seriously affected by artificial regulation from upstream storage works or by the diversion of flows into or out of the stream at points above the gaging station. These withdrawals from the basin or diversions into the basin from outside sources affect the hydrology of the basin. Fortunately, diversions and withdrawals usually lend themselves to accurate estimates since they are for specific purposes and are gaged or can be measured with little difficulty. Examples of diversion uses are as follows:

1. Municipal—the use of the Delaware River for the water supply of New York City
2. Agricultural—the use of the Colorado River to supply irrigation water to California
3. Waste Disposal—the use of the Chicago Drainage Canal to remove waste water from Chicago which originated in Lake Michigan

The safe yield of a stream which is regulated approaches the average annual flow as storage approaches full development. Economical yields are between the safe yields for unregulated and fully regulated flows. Usually safe yields of 75 to 90 percent of the mean annual flow can be realistically developed. Through regulation, the greatest benefits are normally derived from a stream and by means of diversified usage, a method of achieving the maximum economy in the utilization of the water is provided.

4-16. STORAGE

Water may be stored for single or multiple uses such as navigation, flood control, hydroelectric power, agriculture, water supply, pollution abatement, recreation, flow augmentation, and others. Either surface or subsurface storage can be utilized but both necessitate a reservoir which affects the hydrology of a basin.

Reservoirs regulate stream flow for beneficial use by storing water for later release. The term *regulation* can be defined as the amount of water stored or released from storage in a period of time, usually one year. The ability of a reservoir to regulate river flow depends on the ratio of its capacity to the volume of river flow. Evaluation of the regulation provided by existing storage facilities can be determined by studying the records of typical reservoirs. A representative group of reservoirs having detention periods from 0.01 year to 20 years is given by Langbein, with the usable capacity, detention period, and annual regulation of each.[15]

About 190 million acre-ft of water, representing approximately 13 percent of the total river flow, has been made available through reservoir storage development in the United States.[15] The degree of storage development is exceedingly variable but is generally greatest in the Colorado River basin and least in the Ohio River Basin. Substantial increases in water supply can be attained through the development of additional storage but water regulation of this type follows a law of diminishing returns. There are limitations on the amount of storage that can be used. The storage development of the Colorado River Basin for example, may be approaching (if not already in excess of) the maximum useful limit.

Reservoir construction seems to be accelerating with maximum development a definite possibility in the not-too-distant future. Water supply and pollution control appear to be the coming primary objectives of water storage.

RESERVOIRS

Where natural storage in the form of ponds or lakes is not available, artificial impoundments or reservoirs must be constructed if optimum development of the surface supply is to be obtained.

4-17. LOCATING THE RESERVOIR

If artificial storage is to be developed, a suitable site for the construction of the storage works must be selected. Locations affording maximum storage for minimum dam volume are desirable. A wide valley converging on a narrow gorge is especially suitable. The location must also include a satisfactory dam site. This is extremely important, since construction cost is often a controlling factor. The geology of the region must provide a safe foundation for the dam and yield suitable material for construction. The need for a thorough geologic study of the area cannot be over-emphasized. Deep reservoirs are more desirable than shallow ones because of their more favorable surface area to unit-volume ratios. Evaporation losses, shoreline weeds, and mosquito problems are thereby reduced.

If possible, a site where land is relatively inexpensive and free of occupancy by man, roads, and railroads should be selected. Areas sparsely vegetated and free of marshes are desirable, as these conditions may adversely affect the quality of the impounded water. The water source should be of good quality and free of pollution. Tributaries with high sediment yield are undesirable and should be avoided if possible.

4-18. SITE PREPARATION

Optimum site preparation includes removal of highly organic topsoil, cutting down trees and brush, burning grass, draining swamps and removing muck, removing or destroying structures, and removing animal or human excreta. Economic considerations usually dictate that only primary sources of pollution and trees or structures which might stand higher than the water surface be removed.

Stripping practices improve water quality during the initial period of reservoir service but usually in ten or fifteen years there is little difference between stripped and unstripped reservoirs. To control aquatic growths, it is desirable to create a relatively steep shoreline along the reservoir periphery. This can usually be accomplished through excavation or fill.

4-19. SURFACE AREA AND STORAGE VOLUME CONSIDERATIONS

The capacity of a reservoir can be determined from topographic maps of the region to be flooded. Surface areas enclosed by contour lines are normally determined by planimetering. Storage volumes between these contours are then computed by the average-end-area method or some similar procedure. Area-elevation and elevation–storage-volume curves are normally plotted using these computed values. Figure 4-3 illustrates a typical set of such curves which can be used to determine surface areas and volumes for elevations other than those for which contour lines were drawn.

A knowledge of surface areas is important in estimating evaporation losses. Storage volumes must be known if adequate hydrologic computations are to be made. Both quantities have an important bearing on the control of aquatic plant life and the quality of the impounded supply.

4-20. DETERMINATION OF REQUIRED RESERVOIR CAPACITY

The amount of storage that must be provided is a function of the expected demands and the inflow to the impoundment. Mathematically this may be stated as follows:

$$\Delta S = I - O \tag{4-2}$$

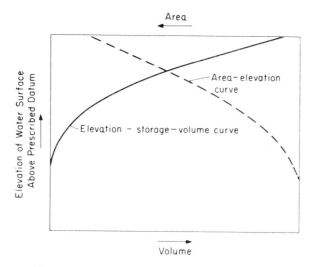

FIG. 4-3. Typical area-elevation and elevation-storage-volume curves for a reservoir.

where ΔS = change in storage volume during some specified time interval
I = total inflow volume during this period
O = total outflow volume during this period

Normally, O will be the draft requirement imposed by the various types of use but it may also include evaporation and transpiration and flood discharges during periods of high runoff when inflow may greatly exceed draft plus available storage, and outflow seepage from the bottom or sides of the reservoir.

Realizing that the natural inflow to any impoundment area is often highly variable from year to year, season to season, or even day to day, it is obvious that the reservoir function must be that of redistributing this inflow with respect to time so that the projected demands are satisfied. This poses a serious problem when one is charged with determining the design storage for a proposed reservoir. The following example will serve to clarify this point.

EXAMPLE 4-1. Find the storage capacity required to provide a safe yield of 67,000 acre-ft per year for the data given in Fig. 4-4.

Solution: Construct tangents at A, B, and C having slopes equal to 67,000 acre-ft per year. Find the maximum vertical ordinate between the inflow mass curve and the constructed draft rates. From Fig. 4-4 the maximum ordinate is found to be 38,000 acre-ft, which is the required capacity.

The significance of this example is not the illustration of the determination of the maximum ordinate but rather the indication that the

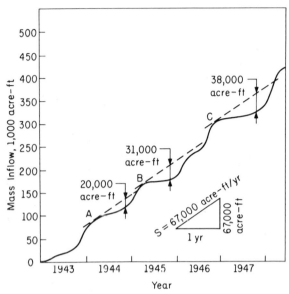

FIG. 4-4. Reservoir capacity for a specified yield
as determined by use of a mass curve.

magnitude of this ordinate depends entirely on the time period chosen. Since the period of record shown covers only five and one-half years, it is easily understood that a design storage of 38,000 acre-ft might be totally inadequate for the next three years, for example. With this in mind it becomes evident that unless the frequency of the flow conditions used in the design is known, little can be said regarding the long- or short-term adequacy of the design.

Example 4-1 also illustrates the fact that the period during which storage must be provided is dependent upon hydrologic conditions. Since reservoir yield is defined as the amount of water which can be supplied during a specific time interval, choice of the interval is critical. For distribution reservoirs a period of one day is often sufficient. For large impounding reservoirs periods of several months, a year, or several years storage may be required.

4-21. METHODS OF COMPUTATION

Several approaches may be taken in the selection of reservoir capacities. Recent advances in computer technology have permitted the application of a few new procedures to the solution of such problems. Manually, or by desk calculator, these computations would previously have been inordinately difficult. Actual or synthetic records of stream flow and a knowledge of the proposed operating rules of the reservoir are fundamental to all solutions. Determination of storage may be accomplished by either graphical or analytical techniques.

Historically, one of the most used methods of determining storage has been the selection of some low-flow period considered to be critical. The most severe drought of record might be selected for example. Once the critical period is chosen, storage is usually calculated by the mass-curve analysis introduced in 1883 by Rippl.[25]

Basically the method involves a determination of the cumulative difference between desired flow and actual flow during the critical period. The method has the shortcoming, however, of yielding a unique solution which may be deceptive in its adequacy. The primary difficulty is the probability that the design storage determined in this manner may be too small or too large for optimum economic or operating efficiency.

Application of the Rippl method is illustrating in Fig. 4-5. Assuming that the reservoir is full at the beginning of the selected dry period, the maximum storage requirement which must be provided to maintain a draft O may be stated mathematically as follows:

$$S = \text{maximum value of } \Sigma(O - I) \qquad (4\text{-}3)$$

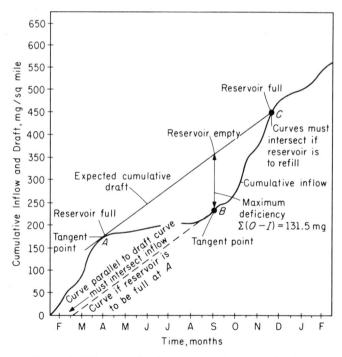

FIG. 4-5. The determination of reservoir storage by the Rippl method.

The quantity $\Sigma(O - I)$ may be determined arithmetically or graphically. The accuracy of the results will be a function of the interval of time for which runoff is recorded. The shorter the period the better the result. Annual, monthly, daily, and (in the case of distribution reservoirs) shorter-period intervals may be used. Normally annual data will yield only crude results since flow variations within a year are usually exceedingly significant. Monthly values are generally considered adequate where inflow is small in comparison to the storage volume. For small reservoirs, short intervals should be selected accordingly.

EXAMPLE 4-2. Consider an impounding reservoir that is expected to provide for a constant draft of 448 mg/sq mi/year. The following record of monthly mean inflow values is representative of the critical or design period. Find the storage requirement.

Month	F	M	A	M	J	J	A	S	O	N	D	J	F
Observed inflow, mg/sq mile	31	54	90	10	7	8	2	28	42	108	92	22	50

Solution: Set up the tabulation of values shown in Table 4-2.

TABLE 4-2
STORAGE REQUIREMENT COMPUTATIONS

(1)	(2)	(3)	(4)	(5)	(6)*
Month	Inflow, I mg/sq mile/month	Draft, O mg/sq mile/month	Cumulative Inflow, $\Sigma I =$ $\Sigma(2)$	Deficiency, $(O - I) =$ $(3) - (2)$	Cumulative Deficiency, $\Sigma(O - I) =$ $\Sigma(5)$
F	31	37.3	31	6.3	0
M	54	37.3	85	−16.7	0
A	90	37.3	175	−52.7	0
M	10	37.3	185	27.3	27.3
J	7	37.3	192	30.3	57.6
J	8	37.3	200	29.3	86.9
A	2	37.3	202	35.3	122.2
S	28	37.3	230	9.3	131.5
O	42	37.3	272	−4.7	126.8
N	108	37.3	380	−70.7	56.1
D	98	37.3	478	−60.7	0
J	22	37.3	500	15.3	0
F	50	37.3	550	−12.7	0

*Only positive values of cumulative deficiency are tabulated.

From Table 4-2 or Fig. 4-5 it can be seen that the maximum cumulative deficiency is 131.5 mg/sq mile, which occurs in September. The number of months of draft is found to be 131.5/37.3 = 3.53, or stated differently, enough water must be stored to supply the region for about 3.5 months.

The preceding example gives a numerical answer to the question posed in determining a design storage. It does not, however, give any expression of the probabilities of shortages or excesses which may result from this design. Normal practice is to use the lowest recorded flow of the stream as the critical period. Obviously this approach overlooks the possibility that a more serious drought might occur with a resultant yield less than the anticipated safe yield.

Present-day designs for impounding reservoirs are normally based on the provision of adequate capacity to meet a natural event having a known recurrence interval while the reservoir is operating under a prescribed set of rules. Often this is the 20-, 50-, or 100-year event. To answer a question of the type "How often will the expected design storage be inadequate to meet a prescribed demand?" the modern engineer must resort to statistical methods and probability theory.

Considerable information is available relative to the probability that droughts of various severities will occur during any single year or during any specified period of years.[23] By applying this type of information the engineer can gain considerable insight into the risks associated with reservoir development. A knowledge of these risks permits an estimate of the numerical odds for any specified yield. The designer may thus evaluate the performance of the reservoir under any set of risks he chooses.

In designing a reservoir to meet a specific draft rate, certain basic information must be at hand. First, the duration of the low flow or critical period of design must be known. Second, the magnitude of the critical low flow must be determined. Third, the frequency of occurrence of the critical event must be known.

The question of the critical period can be answered by investigating a number of low-flow durations and then selecting some duration with which to work. From existing or synthetic stream-flow data, a series of magnitudes of critical flows for the specified duration can be obtained. This information answers the question of magnitude. Finally, by assigning a *recurrence interval* to the critical events, the frequency of the event can be established. Recurrence interval may be defined as the average interval in years between the occurrence of an event of stated magnitude and an equal or more serious event.

In determining the recurrence interval of a runoff event, both annual and partial duration series are used. An annual series is composed of one significant event for each year of record. The nature of the event depends on the object of the study. Usually the event will be a maximum or minimum flow. A *partial duration* series consists of all events exceeding in significance some base value. The two series compare favorably at the larger recurrence intervals, but for the smaller recurrence intervals the partial duration series will normally indicate events of greater magnitude.

If a runoff event (in this case the event of concern is a low flow) has a true recurrence interval of T_R years, then the probability that this magnitude will be equaled or exceeded in any particular year is

$$P = \frac{1}{T_R} \qquad (4\text{-}4)$$

There are two possibilities regarding the event: it either will or will not occur in a specified year. The probability that at least one event of equal or greater significance than the T_R year event will occur in any series of N years is shown in Table 4-3. For example, there exists a probability of 0.22 that the 100-year event will occur in a series of 25 years.

TABLE 4-3

THE PROBABILITY THAT AN EVENT HAVING
A PRESCRIBED RECURRENCE INTERVAL WILL BE
EQUALED OR EXCEEDED DURING A SPECIFIED PERIOD

T_R, years	Period, years					
	1	5	10	25	50	100
2	0.5	0.97	0.999	*	*	*
5	0.2	0.67	0.89	0.996	*	*
10	0.1	0.41	0.65	0.93	0.995	*
50	0.02	0.10	0.18	0.40	0.64	0.87
100	0.01	0.05	0.10	0.22	0.40	0.63

*Values are approximately equal to 1.

An example will serve to illustrate the application of frequency studies in determining the calculated risks of impounding reservoir yields. The example is based primarily on the work of Stall and Neill.[23,26]

EXAMPLE 4-3. The following partial duration series of 30-month low flows is available from 49 years of record on the Little Elk River. This river serves as the input to the Little Elk Reservoir. The drainage area equals 330 sq miles.

30-month flow, in./sq mi	4.95	5.40	6.12	8.90	12.70	13.91	15.10	18.30	21.00	24.15
Rank of events	1	2	3	4	5	6	7	8	9	10

Solution: (a) Determine the recurrence interval in years for this data. Using the relationship

$$T_R = \frac{N}{m} \qquad (4\text{-}5)$$

where T_R = recurrence interval in years
   N = number of years of record
   m = rank of the event arranged in order of magnitude
the tabulation shown in Table 4-4 is obtained.

   (b) Assuming a knowledge of the storage capacity of the Little Elk Reservoir, and using the drought-recurrence intervals determined in (a), a mass-flow analysis will permit determination of the gross reservoir yield for a specific

TABLE 4-4

RECURRENCE INTERVALS FOR A 30-MONTH LOW-FLOW SERIES
FOR LITTLE ELK RIVER

Rank of Event	T_R, years	30-Month Flow, in./sq mi
1	49	4.95
2	24.5	5.40
3	16.3	6.12
4	12.3	8.90
5	9.8	12.70
6	8.2	13.91
7	7.0	15.10
8	6.1	18.30
9	5.4	21.00
10	4.9	24.15

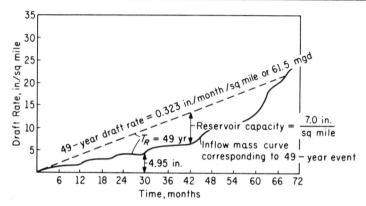

FIG. 4-6. Determination of 49-year draft rate for Example 4-3.

TABLE 4-5

GROSS YIELD FOR A SPECIFIED DROUGHT RECURRENCE INTERVAL
FOR THE LITTLE ELK RIVER

Drought Recurrence Interval, years	Gross Yield, mgd
2	136
4	110
6	100
8	94
10	88
20	76
40	64

recurrence interval. Figure 4-6 shows the procedure for the 49-year event if the reservoir capacity is assumed to be 7.0 in. per sq mile. The values in millions of gallons per day determined in this manner can then be plotted as shown in Fig. 4-7 to obtain the frequency curve of gross yield. Table 4-5 is derived directly from this curve.

(c) The yield-probability curves (dashed curves) in Fig. 4-7 are determined by using a graphical plot of the type data given in Table 4-3. A detailed discussion of this procedure can be found in Ref. 23. Using Fig. 4-7, a plot of the type shown

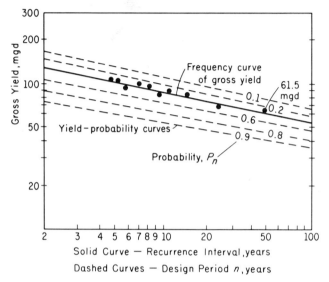

FIG. 4-7. Frequency and yield-probability curves.

in Fig. 4-8 can be easily obtained by replotting the yield-probability curves on arithmetic coordinate paper. This plot permits the direct determination of the probability that various yields will be met by the reservoir.

Consider that the reservoir is to be operated at a design pumpage of 75 mgd. Figure 4-8 will yield the following type of information. There is a probability of 0.8 (or 8 chances out of 10) that the design pumpage will be met for the next five years without failure, a probability of 0.6 that the rate will be met for the next 11 years without failure, and probability of 0.4 that the design pumpage will be met successfully for the next 21 years.

The example illustrates the association of risks with a specified reservoir development. An engineer is thereby offered the opportunity to evaluate the severity of these risks as they relate to a particular draft-storage situation.

In recent years the science of operations research or systems analysis has been applied successfully to some of the problems related to reservoir design and operation. Langbein, Thomas, and Fiering have made notable contributions in this field through their application of the theory of queues.[22,24,27]

Queuing theory, or the theory of waiting lines, offers a new methodology in probability analysis as applied to storage determination. Using a little imagination one may draw an analogy between the water im-

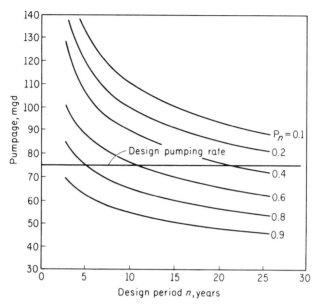

Fig. 4-8. Yield-probability curves for Little Elk
Reservoir.

pounded behind a dam and the waiting line at a ticket counter. One of
the most useful aspects of queuing theory is that it classifies certain factors
which describe water storage. These factors may be summarized as follows:[22]

1. The rate of arrival. For reservoir studies this is simply the inflow.
It represents a time distribution of the arrivals.

2. The queue discipline, which is a rule for setting the priority of
servicing the elements of the queue. Usually the old axiom first come,
first served is the rule, but actually any set of rules may be followed. For
example, in reservoir operation several intakes might be available by
which drafts may be made alternately from different levels so as to tap
water of a desired quality.

3. A service function. This is an operating rule by which the rate of
service of the elements in the queue is defined. The control might be a
fixed reservoir outlet, a manually operated gate, or a set of automatically
operated outlets. The outlet work controls the outflow of the reservoir in
proportion to the head developed and is thus a function of storage.

4. Attrition rate. If a waiting line is long it is not uncommon for
persons to refuse to join the line or to leave the line before they are waited
upon. The analogy to this in reservoir operation is the evaporation loss
which is related to the existing storage at any given point in time. Evaporation rates are dependent on local climate and the reservoir geometry.

Any decision regarding permissible queues or optimum reservoir size must include a consideration of evaporative losses.

The preceding statements indicate the close parallel between queuing theory and reservoir operation. In engineering practice, reservoirs are usually classified in terms of capacity or detention period (capacity divided by average stream flow). In queuing theory, the classification is primarily by the distribution of the inflow and the service function. A duration curve such as shown in Fig. 4-9 usually defines the inflow distribution.

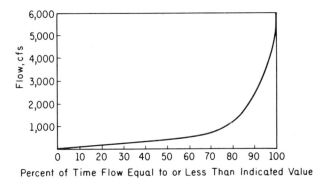

Fig. 4-9. Typical flow-duration curve based on mean daily flows.

Queuing theory relates this duration curve to storage. Figure 4-10 illustrates several types of service functions as discussed by Langbein.[22] Type IA is a linear relationship which provides a minimum low flow and tends to reduce flood peaks. Type IB is typical of a flood-control reservoir which is of the orifice type. The type II service functions are typical of the kind of regulation assumed in most storage analyses where the mass-curve technique is employed. Both exhibit uniform draft rates (these may vary seasonally) except when the reservoir is empty or full. A seasonal kind of rule curve is indicated as type III. The classifications shown in Fig. 4-10 or combinations of them can be readily treated by probability analysis. Several illustrative examples of the application of queuing theory to reservoir design can be found in Ref. 22 and 24. A more complete discussion is beyond the scope of this book.

Regardless of the analytical technique employed in solving reservoir problems, a satisfactory inflow record is essential. If an adequate record is not available at the reservoir site, the record from some other point on the stream or from a nearby stream may be adjusted to provide the required data. Short-period records can be extended by comparison with longer stream-flow records for similar streams or by employing a precipitation runoff relationship.[16]

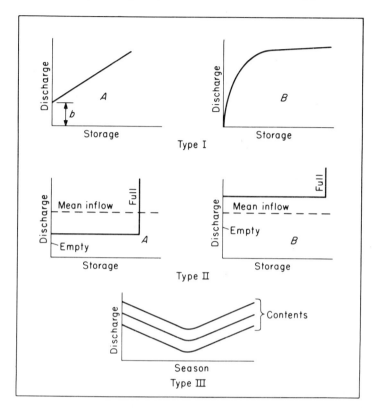

Fɪɢ. 4-10. Three types of service functions. (After Walter J. Langbein, "Queuing Theory and Water Storage," ASCE Proc. Paper No. 1811, Vol. 84, No. HY5, October 1958, pp. 1811–1813.)

4-22. LOSSES FROM STORAGE

The design of an impounding reservoir must include an evaluation of storage losses which may result from natural or artificial phenomena. Natural losses occur through evaporation, seepage, and siltation, while artificial losses are usually the product of withdrawals made to satisfy prior water rights.

Once a dam has been built and the impoundment filled, the exposed water-surface area is increased significantly over that of the natural stream. The resultant effect is that losses are incurred through increased evaporation. In addition, the opportunity for the derivation of runoff from the flooded land is eliminated. On the credit side, gains are made through the catchment of direct precipitation. These phenomena are commonly known as the *water-surface effect*. Net gains, then, usually result in well-watered regions. In arid lands, losses are the typical outcome, since evaporation generally exceeds precipitation.

The magnitude of seepage losses depends mainly on the geology of the region. If porous strata underlie the reservoir valley, considerable losses can occur. On the other hand, where permeability is low, seepage may be negligible. A thorough subsurface exploration is a prerequisite to the adequate evaluation of such losses.

Sedimentation studies are extremely valuable in planning for the development of surface-water supplied by impoundment.[47,29] Since the useful life of a reservoir will be materially affected by the deposition of sediment, a knowledge of sedimentation rates is important in reaching a decision regarding the feasibility of its construction.

The rate and characteristic of the sediment inflow can be controlled by using sedimentation basins, providing vegetative screens, and by employing various erosion-control techniques.[16] Dams can be designed so that part of the sediment load can be passed through or over them. A last resort is the physical removal of sediment deposits. Normally this is not economically feasible.

EXAMPLE 4-4. Determine the expected life of the Lost Valley reservoir. The initial capacity of the reservoir is 45,000 acre-ft, and the average annual inflow is 76,000 acre-ft. A sediment inflow of 176 acre-ft per year is reported. Assume the useful life of the reservoir is exceeded when 77.8 percent of the original capacity is lost.

Solution: The solution is obtained through application of the data given in Fig. 4-11. The results are tabulated in Table 4-6.

TABLE 4-6
DETERMINATION OF THE PROBABLE LIFE OF THE LOST VALLEY RESERVOIR

(1)	(2)	(3)	(4)	(5)	(6)	(7)
Reservoir Capacity, acre-ft	Volume Increment, acre-ft	Capacity Inflow Ratio = $\dfrac{(1)}{76,000}$	Percent Sediment Trapped from Fig. 4-11	Average Percent Sediment Trapped per volume Increment	Acre-ft Sediment Trapped Annually (5) × 176	Number of Years Required to Fill the Volume Increment = (2) ÷ (6)
45,000	5,000	0.59	96.5			
40,000	5,000	0.52	96.1	96.3	169	30
35,000	5,000	0.46	95.8	95.9	169	30
30,000	5,000	0.39	95.0	95.4	168	30
25,000	5,000	0.33	94.5	94.7	167	30
20,000	5,000	0.26	93.0	93.8	165	30
15,000	5,000	0.20	92.0	92.5	163	31
10,000	5,000	0.13	88.0	90.0	158	32

Total number of years of useful life 213

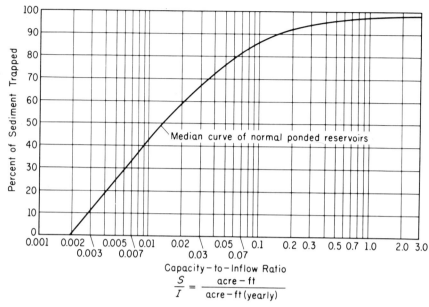

Fig. 4-11. Relationship between reservoir sediment trap efficiency and capacity to inflow ratio. (Developed from data by Brune.[46])

4-23. FLOOD ROUTING

Flood routing is the process whereby a known upstream hydrograph is transferred or routed to a downstream location. Routing techniques play a significant role in planning for flood relief. Impounding reservoirs must have spillway capacities equal to the floods they are expected to handle. To provide safety in design, the flood is often assumed to occur with the reservoir full. Under such circumstances the inflow will back up in the impoundment area and fill the space between the spillway crest and peak flood stage. When this occurs, the maximum spillway head can be developed. In this process some of the flood waters are stored, with the result that the peak rate of flow downstream is decreased.

This retardation of floods by storage is a function of the rate of inflow to the reservoir (I), the available storage above the spillway crest (S), and the rate of outflow from the reservoir (O).

Solutions to this problem are customarily based on a stepwise analysis of hydraulic occurrences. For a specific time interval Δt,

$$O\Delta t = I\Delta t - \Delta S \qquad (4\text{-}6)$$

Usually it is considered that the arithmetic means of the rates of inflow and outflow at the beginning and ending of specified time intervals are good approximations of the average rates. The steps in the mechanical integration are then

$$O\Delta t = \frac{\Delta t(O_n + O_{n+1})}{2} \tag{4-7}$$

$$I\Delta t = \frac{\Delta t(I_n + I_{n+1})}{2} \tag{4-8}$$

$$\Delta S = S_{n+1} - S_n \tag{4-9}$$

Substitution of these quantities in Eq. 4-6 yields

$$\frac{\Delta t(O_n + O_{n+1})}{2} = \frac{\Delta t(I_n + I_{n+1})}{2} - (S_{n+1} - S_n) \tag{4-10}$$

in which outflow and storage are related to spillway head. The form of these relationships is $O = KLH^n$ and $S = CH^m$.[30] Rewriting Eq. 4-10, the following result is obtained:

$$\left[\frac{S_{n+1}}{\Delta t} + \frac{O_{n+1}}{2}\right] = \left[\frac{S_n}{\Delta t} - \frac{O_n}{2}\right] + \left[\frac{I_n + I_{n+1}}{2}\right] \tag{4-11}$$

This equation may be used to determine the reservoir outflow pattern associated with a particular inflow. A more complete treatment can be found in Ref. 28.

GROUNDWATER

Groundwater storage is considerably in excess of all artificial and natural surface storage in the United States, including the Great Lakes.[13] This enormous groundwater reserve sustains the continuing outflow of streams and lakes during prolonged periods which often follow the relatively few runoff-producing rains each year. However, the relation between groundwater and surface storage is one of mutual interdependence. For example, groundwater intercepted by wells as it moves towards a stream represents a real diversion just as if the water had actually been taken from the stream.

Recent increased usage and development of groundwater supplies have stimulated the search for knowledge regarding the occurrence, origin, and movement of these supplies. The study of groundwater is vital. It is also exceedingly complex due to the fact that groundwater location and movement are determined primarily by the geology of the area. This geologic role can not be overemphasized. Groundwater distribution in the United States has been discussed in Sec. 4-4.

Practically all groundwater can be considered as part of the hydrologic cycle even though small amounts may enter the cycle from other origins. Connate water, or water that was entrapped in the pores of sedimentary rock at the time of deposition, is an example.

4-24. THE SUBSURFACE DISTRIBUTION OF WATER

Groundwater distribution may be generally catagorized into zones of aertion and saturation. The saturated zone is one in which all the voids are filled with water under hydrostatic pressure. In the zone of aeration, the interstices are filled partly with air and partly with water. The saturated zone is commonly called the *groundwater zone,* while the zone of aeration may ideally be subdivided into several sub-zones.

1. *Soil-water zone* The soil-water zone begins at the ground surface and extends downward through the major root zone. Its total depth is variable and dependent upon soil type and vegatation. The zone is unsaturated except during periods of heavy infiltration. Three categories of water classification may be encountered in this region: hygroscopic water, which is adsorbed from the air; capillary water, which is held by surface tension; and gravitational water, which is excess soil water draining through the soil.

2. *Intermediate zone.* This zone extends from the bottom of the soil-water zone to the top of the capillary fringe and may vary from non-existence to several hundred feet in thickness. The zone is essentially a connecting link between the near-ground surface region and the near-water-table region through which infiltrating waters must pass.

3. *Capillary zone.* The capillary zone extends from the water table to a height determined by the capillary rise which can be generated in the soil. Considering pore space as representing an idealized capillary tube, the capillary rise hc may be computed by

$$hc = \frac{2\tau}{r\gamma} \cos \lambda \qquad (4\text{-}12)$$

where hc = capillary rise
τ = surface tension
γ = specific weight of water
λ = angle of contact between the meniscus and the tube wall
r = tube radius.

The capillary zone thickness is a function of soil texture and may vary not only from region to region but also within a local area.

4. *Saturated zone.* In the saturated zone groundwater fills the pore spaces completely and porosity is therefore a direct measure of storage volume. Part of this water (specific retention) cannot be removed by pumping or drainage because of molecular and surface-tension forces. The specific retention is the ratio of the volume of water retained against gravity drainage to the gross volume of the soil. Expressed as a percentage, the specific retention is

$$S_r = 100 \frac{W_r}{V} \qquad (4\text{-}13)$$

where W_r = volume of water retained

     V = gross soil volume

The water which can be drained from a soil by gravity is known as the specific yield. It is expressed as the ratio of the volume of water which can be drained by gravity to the gross volume of the soil. Expressed as a percentage,

$$S_y = \frac{100 \ W_y}{V} \qquad (4\text{-}14)$$

where W_y = volume of water drained

     V = gross volume of the soil

Values of specific yield are dependent upon soil particle size, shape and distribution of pores, and degree of compaction of the soil. Average values of specific yield for alluvial aquifers range from 10 to 20 percent. Meinzer and others have proposed numerous procedures for determining specific yield.[31]

4-25. AQUIFERS

An *aquifer* is a water-bearing stratum or formation which is capable of transmitting water in quantities sufficient to permit development. Aquifers may be considered as falling into two categories, confined and unconfined, depending upon whether or not a water table or free surface exists under atmospheric pressure. The storage volume within an aquifer is changed whenever water is recharged to or discharged from an aquifer. In the case of an unconfined aquifer this may be easily determined as

$$\Delta S = S_y \Delta V \qquad (4\text{-}15)$$

where ΔS = change in storage volume

     S_y = average specific yield of the aquifer

     ΔV = volume of the aquifer lying between the original water table and the water table at some later specified time

For saturated, confined aquifers, pressure changes produce only slight changes in storage volume. In this case, the weight of the overburden is supported partly by hydrostatic pressure and partly by the solid material in the aquifer. When the hydrostatic pressure in a confined aquifer is reduced by pumping or other means, the load on the aquifer increases, causing its compression with the result that some water is forced from it. Decreasing the hydrostatic pressure also causes a small expansion which in turn produces an additional release of water. For confined aquifers, the water yield is expressed in terms of a storage coefficient S_c. This storage coefficient may be defined as the volume of water an aquifer takes in or releases per unit surface area of aquifer per unit change in head normal to the surface. Figure 4-12 illustrates the classifications of aquifers.

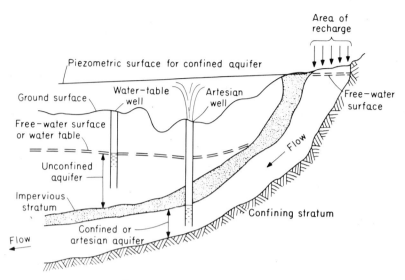

FIG. 4-12. Aquifer classifications.

In addition to water-bearing strata exhibiting satisfactory rates of yield, there are also nonwater-bearing and impermeable strata. An *aquiclude* is an impermeable stratum which may contain large quantities of water but whose transmission rates are not high enough to permit effective development. An aquifuge is a formation which is impermeable and devoid of water.

4-26. FLUCTUATIONS IN GROUNDWATER LEVEL

Any circumstance which alters the pressure imposed on underground water will also cause a variation in the groundwater level. Seasonal factors, changes in stream and river stages, evapotranspiration, atmospheric pressure changes, winds, tides, external loads, various forms of withdrawal and recharge, and earthquakes all may produce fluctuations in the level of the water table or the piezometric surface, depending upon whether the aquifer is free or confined.[10] It is important that the engineer concerned with the development and utilization of groundwater supplies be aware of these factors. He should also be able to evaluate their importance relative to the operation of a specific groundwater basin.

4-27. COMPREHENSIVE GROUNDWATER BASIN DEVELOPMENT

In order to realize the most efficient utilization of groundwater resources, and at the same time afford their maximum development, equilibrium must exist between all waters being withdrawn from and entering any given basin. Economic, legal, and water quality aspects must be carefully considered at the same time.

Assurance of lasting supplies of groundwater may be had only if the capabilities of replenishment are not exceeded. The equation of hydrologic equilibrium is a most useful tool for evaluating the potentialities of a groundwater basin. Mathematically this may be stated as

$$\Sigma I - \Sigma O = \Delta S \qquad (4\text{-}16)$$

where ΣI = summation of all forms of recharge
  ΣO = summation of all forms of discharge
  ΔS = change in storage

Table 4-7 lists the most important forms of recharge and discharge.

TABLE 4-7
RECHARGE AND DISCHARGE CATEGORIES

Recharge Mechanisms	Discharge Mechanisms
1. Influent seepage from streams, ponds, and lakes of natural origin	1. Effluent seepage to lakes, streams, springs, etc.
2. Subsurface inflow	2. Subsurface outflow
3. Precipitation through infiltration	3. Evapotranspiration
4. Artificial recharge (irrigation, reservoirs, water spreading, canal seepage, and injection)	4. Discharge through pumping or other artificial means of collection

The solution to Eq. 4-16 for any particular basin may be exceedingly complex and will in most instances require the careful compilation of considerable data. These data may be classified as follows:

(a) *Surface inflows and outflows.* These may be in the form of streams, rivers, imported and exported waters, and waste waters. All of these forms are measurable by standard methods.

(b) *Precipitation.* Data are available from U.S. Weather Bureau records. Precipitation gages should be located at sufficient points in the area to permit reasonable estimates of mean annual precipitation using either the Isohyetal or Thiessen methods.[28]

(c) *Consumptive uses.* All water released to the atmosphere as a result of evaporation or transpiration is known as consumptive use. This is exceedingly complex to evaluate and necessitates a comprehensive land-use survey of the basin which will indicate the size of the various types of water-consuming areas. Values of consumptive use for each type area must be determined. Essentially these fall into three categories: (1) crops and native vegetation, (2) surface waters, and (3) urban and industrial areas. Unit values of consumptive use for crops and native vegetation may be determined by the Blaney-Criddle method based on available heat.[10] For water surfaces, the use of local evaporation data is recommended. Energy-budget or available-heat methods may also be used. For urban and industrial areas field surveys and information on process design will usually produce the required data although this information is often difficult to obtain.

(d) *Changes in surface storage.* These are determined directly from water level measurements.

(e) *Changes in groundwater storage.* These changes involve both the zone of aeration and the saturated zone. Estimates of the amount of storage change above the water table are exceedingly difficult to obtain, however, and are usually unreliable. To minimize this complexity, periods of storage change are usually selected in which the amount of water in the unsaturated zone is essentially the same at the beginning and end of the period. Estimates of changes in groundwater storage must be founded on a thorough knowledge of the geology of the basin; antecedent information on water levels, pumping, and recharge; a knowledge of the specific yields of unconfined aquifers and of the storage coefficients of confined aquifers.

(f) *Subsurface inflow and outflow.* These are extremely difficult to evaluate as direct measurements cannot be made. Estimates can be obtained using Darcy's law, but these may be very crude.[10] In some cases, inflow and outflow may be assumed equal to zero or may be included in surface flow accountings. Where underground flow from one basin to another is known to occur, the difficulties may be compounded.

4-28. THE SAFE YIELD OF AN AQUIFER

The development engineer must be able to determine the quantity of water that can be produced from a groundwater basin in a given period of time. He must also be able to evaluate the consequences that will result from the imposition of various drafts on the underground supply. A knowledge of the safe yield of an aquifer is therefore exceedingly important. Following are pertinent definitions:

(a) *Safe yield*—the safe yield of a groundwater basin is the quantity of water that can be annually withdrawn without the ultimate depletion of the aquifer.

(b) *Maximum sustained yield*—maximum rate at which water can be withdrawn on a continuing basis from a given source.

(c) *Permissive sustained yield*—maximum rate at which withdrawals can be made legally and economically on a continuing basis for beneficial use without the development of undesired results.

(d) *Maximum mining yield*—total storage volume in a given source which can be withdrawn and used.

(e) *Permissive mining yield*—maximum volume of water which can be withdrawn legally and economically, to be used for beneficial purposes, without causing an undesired result.

After studying these definitions the student should realize that extreme caution must be exercised in the development and utilization of groundwater resources. These resources are finite and not inexhaustible. If drafts are imposed such that the various recharge mechanisms will balance them over a period of time, no difficulty will result. On the other hand, excessive drafts may reduce underground storage volumes to a point at which economic development is no longer feasible. The mining of water as with any other natural resource will ultimately result in exhuastion of the supply. Figure 4-13 indicates those areas in the United States where perennial overdrafts occur.[18]

Methods for determining the safe yield of an aquifer have been proposed by Hill, Harding, Simpson, and others.[10] The Hill method based on groundwater studies in Southern California and Arizona will be presented here.

In the Hill method, the annual change in groundwater table elevation or piezometric surface elevation is plotted against the annual draft. The

Storage progressively depleted

Areas of encroachment of inferior water

Remedial measures undertaken to balance draft and replenishment

? ? ? Insufficient data to be certain that overdraft exists

FIG. 4-13. Groundwater reservoirs with perennial overdraft. (From H. E. Thomas, "Water," *The Yearbook of Agriculture*, Washington, D.C.: U.S. Government Printing Office, 1955.)

points can be fitted by a straight line, providing the water supply to the basin is fairly uniform. That draft which corresponds to zero change in elevation is considered to be the safe yield. The period of record should be such that the supply during this period approximates the long-time average supply. Even though the draft during the period of record may be an overdraft, the safe yield can be determined by extending the line of best fit to an intersection with the zero change in elevation line. An example of this procedure is given in Fig. 4-14.

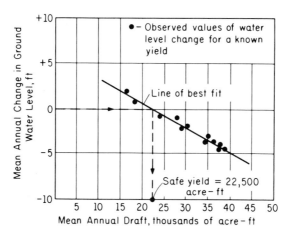

FIG. 4-14. An example of the determination of safe yield by the Hill method.

It should be noted that the safe yield of a groundwater basin may be variable with time. This is because the groundwater basin conditions under which the safe yield was determined are subject to change and these changes will be reflected in the modified value of the safe yield.

4-29. GROUNDWATER FLOW

The rate of movement of water through the ground is of an entirely different magnitude than that through natural or artificial channels or conduits. Typical values range from 5 ft per day to a few feet per year. Methods for determining these transmission rates are primarily based on the principles of fluid flow represented by Darcy's law. Mathematically, this law may be stated as

$$V = kS \qquad (4\text{-}17)$$

where V = velocity of flow
$\quad k$ = a coefficient having the same units as velocity
$\quad S$ = slope of the hydraulic gradient

Darcy's law is limited in its applicability to flows in the laminar region. The controlling criterion is the Reynolds number,

$$N_R = \frac{Vd}{\nu} \tag{4-18}$$

where V = flow velocity
d = mean grain diameter
ν = kinematic viscosity

For Reynolds numbers of less than one, groundwater flow may be considered laminar. Departure from laminar conditions develops normally in the range of Reynolds numbers from 1 to 10, depending on grain size and shape. Under most conditions, with the exception of regions in close proximity to collecting devices, the flow of groundwater is laminar and Darcy's law applies.

EXAMPLE 4-5. (a) Find the Reynolds number for the portion of an aquifer distant from any collection device where water temperature is 50°F ($\nu = 1.41 \times 10^{-5}$ sq ft/sec), flow velocity is 1.0 ft per day, and mean grain diameter is 0.09 in.

(b) Find the Reynolds number for a flow 4 ft from the center line of a well being pumped at a rate of 3,800 gpm if the well completely penetrates a confined aquifer 28 ft thick. Assume a mean grain diameter of 0.10 in., a porosity of 35 percent, and $\nu = 1.41 \times 10^{-5}$ sq ft/sec.

Solution: (a) Using Eq. 4-18,

$$N_R = \frac{Vd}{\nu}$$

where

$$V = \left(\frac{1.0}{86,400}\right) \text{ ft/sec} \qquad d = \left(\frac{0.09}{12}\right) \text{ ft}$$

$$N_R = \frac{1.0}{86,400} \times \frac{0.09}{12} \times \frac{1}{1.41 \times 10^{-5}}$$

$$N_R = 0.0062 \text{ (indicating laminar flow)}$$

(b) Using Eq. 4-18,

$$N_R = \frac{Vd}{\nu} = \frac{Q}{A} \frac{d}{\nu}$$

$$Q = 3800 \times 2.23 \times 10^{-3} = 8.46 \text{ cfs}$$

$$V = 8.46/2\pi rh \times \text{porosity}$$

$$= 8.46/8\pi \times 28 \times 0.35$$

$$= 0.0344 \text{ ft/sec}$$

$$N_R = \frac{0.0344 \times 0.10}{1.41 \times 10^{-5} \times 12} = 20.3 \text{ (indicating turbulent flow)}$$

To compute discharge it is necessary to multiply Eq. 4-17 by the effective cross-sectional area. The equation then becomes

$$Q = pAkS \tag{4-19}$$

where p = porosity or ratio of the void volume to the total volume of the mass expressed as a percentage

A = gross cross-sectional area

and the other terms are as previously defined. By combining k and p into a single term, Eq. 4-18 may be written in its most common form,

$$Q = KAS \qquad (4\text{-}20)$$

where K is known as the coefficient of permeability. A number of ways of expressing K may be found in the literature. The U.S. Geological Survey defines the standard coefficient of permeability K_s as the number of gallons of water per day that will flow through a medium of 1-sq-ft cross-sectional area under a hydraulic gradient of unity at 60°F. The field coefficient of permeability is obtained directly from the standard coefficient by correcting for temperature.

$$K_f = K_s \frac{\mu_{60}}{\mu_f} \qquad (4\text{-}21)$$

where K_f = field coefficient

μ_{60} = dynamic viscosity at 60°F

μ_f = dynamic viscosity at field temperature

An additional term which is much used in groundwater computations is the coefficient of transmissibility T. It is equal to the field coefficient of permeability multiplied by the saturated thickness of the aquifer in feet. Using this terminology, Eq. 4-19 may also be written as

$$Q = T \times \text{section width} \times S \qquad (4\text{-}22)$$

Table 4-8 gives some typical values of the standard coefficient of permeability for a range of sedimentary materials. It should be noted that the permeabilities for specific materials vary widely. Traces of silt and clay can significantly decrease the permeability of an aquifer. Differences in particle orientation and shape can cause striking changes in permeability within aquifers composed of the same geologic material. Careful evaluation of geologic information is absolutely essential if realistic values of permeability are to be used in groundwater-flow computations.

TABLE 4-8
Typical Values of the Standard Coefficient of Permeability for Various Materials

	Material	Approximate Range in K_s, gpd/sq ft
I	Clean gravel	$10^6 – 10^4$
II	Clean sands; mixtures of clean sands and gravels	$10^4 – 10$
III	Very find sands; silts; mixtures of sand, silt, and clay; stratified clays, etc.	$10 – 10^{-3}$
IV	Unweathered clays	$10^{-3} – 10^{-4}$

It is of interest to note that Darcy's equation is analogous to the electrical equation known as Ohm's law,

$$i = \frac{1}{R} E$$

(4-23)

where i = current

R = resistance

E = voltage

The quantities i and Q, K and $1/R$, and E and S are comparable. This equivalency permits the use of electrical models in solving many groundwater flow problems.[10]

4-30. COLLECTION OF GROUNDWATER

The collection of groundwater is accomplished primarily through the construction of wells or infiltration galleries. Numerous factors are involved in the numerical estimation of the performance of these collection works. Some cases are ameneable to solution through the utilization of relatively simple mathematical expressions. Other cases can be solved only through graphical analysis or the use of various kinds of models.[10] Several of the less difficult cases will be discussed here. The student should be cautioned not to be mislead by the simplicity of some of the solutions presented and should observe that many of these are special-case solutions and are not indiscriminately applicable to all groundwater flow situations. A more mature treatment of groundwater and seepage problems may be found in numerous references.[10,32,33]

Flow to an Infiltration Gallery. An infiltration gallery may be defined as a partially pervious conduit constructed across the path of the local groundwater flow such that all or part of this flow will be intercepted. These galleries are often built in a valley area parallel to a stream so that they can convey the collected flow to some designated location under gravity-flow conditions. Figure 4-15 shows a typical cross section through a gallery with one pervious face.

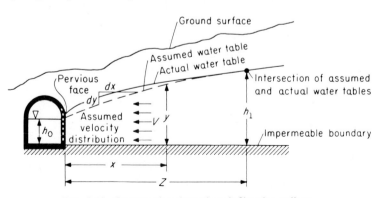

FIG. 4-15. Cross section through an infiltration gallery.

Computation of discharge to an infiltration gallery with one pervious wall (Fig. 4-15) is accomplished in the manner outlined by Dupuit.[34] Several assumptions must be made to effect the solution. They are that the sine and tangent of the angle of inclination of the water table are interchangeable; that the velocity vectors are everywhere horizontal and uniformly distributed; that the soil is incompressible and isotropic and that the gallery is of sufficient length that end effects are negligible. While permitting a solution of the problem, these assumptions do limit the utility of the results.

Following the preceding assumptions and using the notation indicated in Fig. 4-15, the discharge per unit width q at any vertical section becomes

$$q = Ky \frac{dy}{dx} \qquad (4\text{-}24)$$

where K is the coefficient of permeability and y represents the area through which flow takes place. Integrating this expression,

$$\int_0^z q\,dx = \int_{h_0}^{h_1} Ky\,dy \qquad (4\text{-}25)$$

which yields

$$qZ = \frac{K(h_1^2 - h_0^2)}{2} \qquad (4\text{-}26)$$

and the discharge per unit width becomes

$$q = \frac{K}{2Z} (h_1^2 - h_0^2) \qquad (4\text{-}27)$$

This equation indicates that the computed water table is parabolic. This is often called Dupuit's parabola. Figure 4-15 shows that the computed water table differs from the actual water table in an increasing manner as the gallery face is approached. It is therefore apparent that the computed parabola does not accurately describe the real water table. The differences however, are small except near the point of outflow providing the initial assumptions are satisfied. The calculated discharge approximates the true discharge more closely as the ratio of Z/h_1 increases.

Flow to Wells. A well system may be considered to be composed of three elements—the well structure, the pump, and the discharge piping. The well itself contains an open section through which flow enters and a casing through which the flow is transported to the ground surface. The open section is usually a perforated casing or a slotted metal screen which permits the flow to enter and at the same time prevents collapse of the hole. Occasionally gravel is placed at the bottom of the well casing around the screen. Hoffman states that it is not economical to use anything but a properly sized screen for industrial wells.[35]

When a well is pumped, water is removed from the aquifer immediately adjacent to the screen. Flow then becomes established at locations some distance from the well in order to replenish this with-drawal. Due to the resistance to flow offered by the soil, a head loss is encountered and the piezometric surface adjacent to the well is depressed. This is known as the *cone of depression* (Fig. 4-16). The cone of depression spreads until a condition of equilibrium is reached and steady-state conditions are established.

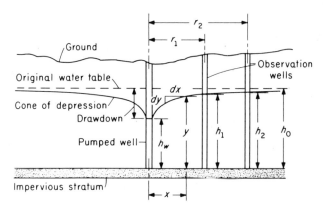

FIG. 4-16. Well in an unconfined aquifer.

The hydraulic characteristics of an aquifer (which are described by the storage coefficient and the aquifer permeability) may be determined by laboratory or field tests. The three most commonly used field methods are the application of tracers, use of field permeameters, and aquifer performance tests.[10] A discussion of aquifer performance tests will be given here along with the development of flow equations for wells.[35,36,42]

Aquifer performance tests may be classified as being either equilibrium or nonequilibrium tests. In the first case the cone of depression must be stabilized in order for the flow equation to be derived. In the second case the derivation includes the condition that steady-state conditions have not been reached. Adolph Thiem published the first performance tests based on equilibrium conditions in 1906.[39]

The basic equilibrium equation for an unconfined aquifer can be de-rived using the notation of Fig. 4-16. In this case the flow is assumed to be radial, the original water table is considered to be horizontal, the well is considered to fully penetrate the aquifer of infinite aereal extent, and steady-state conditions must prevail. Then the flow toward the well at any location x from the well must equal the product of the cylindrical element of area at that section and the flow velocity. Using Darcy's law this becomes

$$Q = 2\pi x y K_f \frac{dy}{dx}$$

(4-28)

where $2\pi xy$ = area at any section
$\quad K_f \, dy/dx$ = flow velocity
$\qquad Q$ = discharge in cubic feet per second
Integrating over the limits specified below,

$$\int_{r_1}^{r_2} Q\,\frac{dx}{x} = 2\pi K_f \int_{h_1}^{h_2} y\,dy \tag{4-29}$$

$$Q \log_e \left(\frac{r_2}{r_1}\right) = \frac{2\pi K_f (h_2^2 - h_1^2)}{2} \tag{4-30}$$

and

$$Q = \frac{\pi K_f (h_2^2 - h_1^2)}{\log_e (r_2/r_1)} \tag{4-31}$$

This equation may then be solved for K_f, yielding

$$K_f = \frac{1055\,Q \log_{10}(r_2/r_1)}{h_2^2 - h_1^2} \tag{4-32}$$

where the $\log_e$ has been converted to the $\log_{10}$, K_f is in gallons per day per square foot, Q is in gallons per minute, and r and h are measured in feet. If the drawdown is small compared with the total aquifer thickness, an approximate formula for the discharge of the pumped well can be obtained by inserting h_w for h_1 and the height of the aquifer for h_2 in Eq. 4-31.

The basic equilibrium equation for a confined aquifer can be obtained in a similar manner, using the notation of Fig. 4-17. The same assumptions apply. Mathematically the flow in cubic feet per second may be determined as follows:

$$Q = 2\pi xmK_f \,\frac{dy}{dx} \tag{4-33}$$

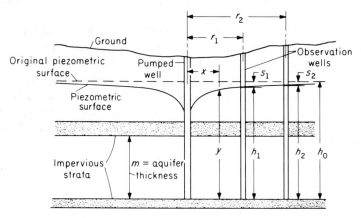

FIG. 4-17. Radial flow to a well in a confined aquifer.

Integrating,

$$Q = 2\pi K_f m \frac{h_2 - h_1}{\log_e(r_2/r_1)} \qquad (4\text{-}34)$$

The coefficient of permeability may be determined by rearranging Eq. 4-34 to the form

$$K_f = \frac{528\,Q\,\log_{10}(r_2/r_1)}{m\,(h_2 - h_1)} \qquad (4\text{-}35)$$

where Q is in gallons per minute, K_f is the permeability in gallons per day per square foot, and r and h are measured in feet.

EXAMPLE 4-6. Determine the permeability of an artesian aquifer being pumped by a fully penetrating well. The aquifer is composed of medium sand and is 90 ft thick. The steady-state pumping rate is 850 gpm. The drawdown of an observation well 50 ft away is 10 ft, and the drawdown in a second observation well 500 ft away is 1 ft.

Solution:

$$K_f = \frac{528\,Q\,\log_{10}(r_2/r_1)}{m(h_2 - h_1)}$$

$$= \frac{528 \times 850 \times \log_{10}(10)}{90 \times (10 - 1)}$$

$$= 554 \text{ gpd/sq ft}$$

For a steady-state well in a uniform flow field where the original piezometric surface is not horizontal, a somewhat different situation than that previously assumed prevails. Consider the artesian aquifer shown in Fig. 4-18. The heretofore assumed circular area of influence becomes distorted in this case. Solution to this problem may be had by application of potential theory, or by graphical means; or, if the slope of the piezometric surface is very slight, Eq. 4-34 may be applied without serious error.

Referring to the definition sketch of Fig. 4-18, a graphical solution to this type of problem will be discussed. First, an orthogonal flow net consisting of flow lines and equipotential lines must be constructed. The construction should be performed so that the completed flow net will be composed of a number of elements which approach little squares in shape. Reference 32 is a good source of information on this subject for the interested student. A comprehensive discussion cannot be provided here.

Once the net is complete, it may be analyzed by considering the net geometry and using Darcy's law. In the definition sketch of Fig. 4-18, the hydraulic gradient is

$$h_g = \frac{\Delta h}{\Delta s} \qquad (4\text{-}36)$$

and the flow increment between adjacent flow lines is

$$\Delta q = K \frac{\Delta h}{\Delta s} \Delta m \qquad (4\text{-}37)$$

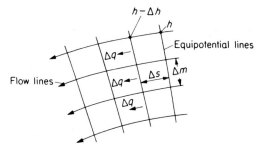

Definition Sketch of a Segment of a Flow Net

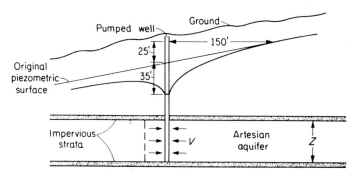

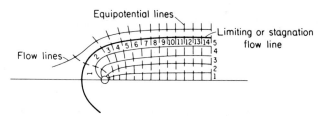

FIG. 4-18. Well in a uniform flow field and flow net definition.

where for a unit thickness, Δm represents the cross-sectional area. If the flow net is properly constructed so that it is orthogonal and composed of little square elements,

$$\Delta m \approx \Delta s \qquad (4\text{-}38)$$

and

$$\Delta q = K \Delta h \qquad (4\text{-}39)$$

Now considering the entire flow net,

$$\Delta h = \frac{h}{n} \qquad (4\text{-}40)$$

where n is the number of subdivisions between equipotential lines. If the flow is divided into m sections by the flow lines, then the discharge per unit width of the aquifer will be

$$q = \frac{Kmh}{n} \tag{4-41}$$

A knowledge of the aquifer permeability and the flow-net geometry permits solution of Eq. 4-41.

EXAMPLE 4-8.   Find the discharge to the well of Fig. 4-18 by using the applicable flow net. Consider the aquifer to be 35 ft thick, K_f to be 3.65×10^{-4} fps, and the other dimensions as shown.

Solution: Using Eq. 4-41,

$$q = \frac{Kmh}{n}$$

where $h = (35 + 25) = 60$ ft
$m = 2 \times 5 = 10$
$n = 14$
$q = \dfrac{3.65 \times 10^{-4} \times 60 \times 10}{14}$

= 0.0156 cfs per unit thickness of the aquifer

The total discharge Q is thus

$$Q = 0.0156 \times 35 = 0.55 \text{ cfs or } 245 \text{ gpm}$$

When a new well is first pumped, a large portion of the discharge is produced directly from the storage volume released as the cone of depression develops.   Under these circumstances the equilibrium equations overestimate permeability and therefore the yield of the well.   Where steady-state conditions are not encountered—as is usually the case in practice—a nonequilibrium equation must be used.   Two approaches can be taken, the rather rigorous method of C. V. Theis, or a simplified procedure such as that proposed by Jacob.[40,41]

In 1935 Theis published a nonequilibrium approach which takes into consideration time and the storage characteristic of the aquifer.[40]   His method utilizes an analogy between heat transfer described by the Biot-Fourier law, and groundwater flow to a well. Theis states that the drawdown(s) in an observation well located at a distance r from the pumped well is given by

$$s = \frac{114.6Q}{T} \int_u^\infty \frac{e^{-u}}{u}\, du \tag{4-42}$$

where T = transmissibility
Q = discharge in gpm

and u is given by

$$u = \frac{1.87\, r^2 S_c}{Tt} \tag{4-43}$$

where S_c = storage coefficient

T = transmissibility

t = time in days since the start of pumping

The integral in Eq. 4-42 is usually known as the well function of u and is commonly written as $W(u)$. It may be evaluated from the infinite series

$$W(u) = -0.577216 - \log_e u + u - \frac{u^2}{2 \times 2!} + \frac{u^3}{3 \times 3!} \cdots \qquad (4-44)$$

The basic assumptions employed in the Theis equation are essentially the same as those for the Thiem equation except for the nonsteady-state condition.

Equations 4-42 and 4-43 can be solved by comparing a log-log plot of u vs. $W(u)$ known as a "type curve," with a log-log plot of the observed data r^2/t vs. s. In plotting the type curve, $W(u)$ is the ordinate and u is the abscissa. The two curves are superimposed and moved about until some of their segments coincide. In doing this, the axes must be maintained parallel. A coincident point is then selected on the matched curves and both plots are marked. The type curve then yields values of u and $W(u)$ for the selected point. Corresponding values of s and r^2/t are determined from the plot of the observed data. Inserting these values in Eqs. 4-42 and 4-43 and rearranging, values for the transmissibility T and the storage coefficient S_c may be found.

Often, this procedure can be shortened and simplified. When r is small and t large, Jacob found that values of u are generally small.[41] Thus the terms in the series of Eq. 4-44 beyond the second term become negligible and the expression for T becomes

$$T = \frac{264 \, Q(\log_{10} t_2 - \log_{10} t_1)}{h_0 - h} \qquad (4-45)$$

which can be further reduced to

$$T = 264 \, Q / \Delta h \qquad (4-46)$$

where Δh = drawdown per log cycle of time $[(h_0 - h)/(\log_{10} t_2 - \log_{10} t_1)]$

Q = well discharge in gallons per minute

h_0 and h are defined as shown on Fig. 4-17, and T is the transmissibility in gallons per day per foot. Field data on drawdown $(h_o - h)$ vs. t are plotted on semilogarithmic paper. The drawdown is plotted on the arithmetic scale as shown on Fig. 4-20. This plot forms a straight line, the slope of which permits the determination of the formation constants using Eq. 4-46 and

$$S_c = \frac{0.3 \, T t_0}{r^2} \qquad (4-47)$$

where t_0 is the time which corresponds to zero drawdown.

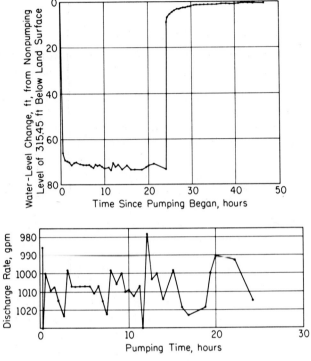

FIG. 4-19. Drawdown and recovery of water level and pumping rate during pumping test at Well I, May 1–2, 1963. (Courtesy of the U.S. Geological Survey.[21])

EXAMPLE 4-9. Using the data given on Figs. 4-19 and 4-20, find the coefficient of transmissibility T and the storage coefficient S_c for the aquifer. Assume $r = 300$ ft.

Solution: A mean discharge rate of 1,010 gpm is determined from the plot of discharge rate vs. pumping time in hours (Fig. 4-19). The value of h is then found graphically as shown on Fig. 4-20. Using Eq. 4-46,

$$T = \frac{264\,Q}{\Delta h} = 264 \times \frac{1010}{5.5}$$
$$= 48,500 \text{ gpd/ft}$$

Using Eq. 4-47,

$$S_c = \frac{0.3\,T t_0}{r^2}$$

and noting that t_0 is in days,

$$S_c = \frac{0.3 \times 48,500 \times 1.59 \times 10^{-3}}{(300)^2}$$
$$= 0.000257$$

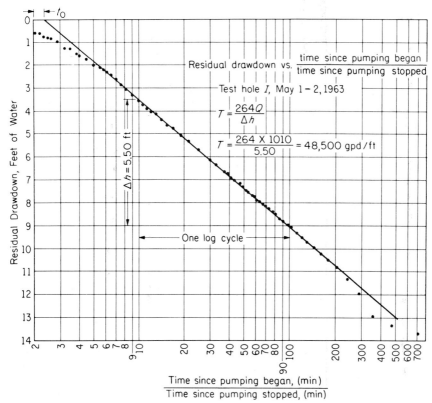

FIG. 4-20. Water-level recovery data for test at Well I on May 1-2, 1963. (Courtesy of the U.S. Geological Survey.)

4-31. BOUNDARY EFFECTS

Only the effect of pumping a single well has been previously considered. If more than one well is pumped in an area, however, a composite effect or interference due to the overlap of the cones of depression will result. In this case the drawdown at any location is obtained by summing the individual drawdowns of the various wells involved. An additional problem is that of boundary conditions. The previous derivations have been based on the supposition of a homogeneous aquifer of infinite aerial extent. A situation such as this is rarely encountered in practice. Computations based on this assumption are often sufficiently accurate, however, providing field conditions closely approximate the basic hypotheses. Boundary effects may be evaluated by using the theory of image wells proposed by Lord Kelvin, through the use of electrical and membrane analogies and through the use of relaxation procedures. For a detailed discussion of these topics the reader is referred to the many references on groundwater flow.[10,32]

4-32. SALT-WATER INTRUSION

Salt-water contamination of fresh-water aquifers presents a serious water-quality problem in island locations; in coastal areas; and occasionally inland, as in Arizona, where some aquifers contain highly saline waters. Because fresh water is lighter than salt water (specific gravity of sea water is about 1.025) it will usually float above a layer of salt water. When an aquifer is pumped, the original equilibrium is disturbed and salt water replaces the fresh water. Under equilibrium conditions a drawdown of 1 ft in the fresh-water table will result in a rise of approximately 40 ft by the salt water. Pumping rates of wells subject to salt-water intrusion are therefore seriously limited.

In coastal areas, recharge wells are somtimes used in an attempt to maintain a sufficient head to prevent sea-water intrusion. Injection wells have been used effectively in this manner in Southern California.

A prime example of fresh-water contamination by sea water is noted in Long Island, New York.[42] During the first part of this century the rate of pumping far exceeded the natural recharge rate. The problem was further complicated because storm-water runoff from the highly developed land areas was transported directly to the sea. This precluded the opportunity for this water to return to the ground. As pumping continued, the water table dropped well below sea level and saline water intruded the aquifer. The result was such a serious impairment of the local water quality that Long Island was forced to transport its water supply from upper New York State.

4-33. GROUNDWATER RECHARGE

The volumes of groundwater replaced annually through natural mechanisms are relatively small because of the slow rates of movement of groundwaters and the limited opportunity for surface waters to penetrate the earth's surface. To supplement this natural recharge process, a recent trend toward artificial recharge has been developing. In 1955 over 700 million gallons of water per day were artifically recharged in the United States.[38] This water was derived from natural surface sources, returns from air conditioning, industrial wastes, and municipal water supplies. The total recharge volume was equal, however, to only about 1.5 percent of the groundwater withdrawn that year. In California, for example, artificial recharge is presently a primary method of water conservation. During the 1957–1958 period a daily recharge volume of about 560 million gallons was reported for 63 projects in that state alone.[38]

Numerous methods are employed in artificial recharge operations. One of the most common plans is the utilization of holding basins. The usual practice is to impound the water in a series of reservoirs arranged so that the overflow of one will enter the next, and so on. These artificial storage works are generally formed by the construction of dikes or levees. A second method is the modified stream bed which makes use of the natural water supply. The stream channel is widened, leveled, scarified, or treated by a combination of methods to increase its recharge capabilities. Ditches and furrows are also used. The basic types of arrangement are the contour type, in which the ditch follows the contour of the ground; the lateral type, in which water is diverted into a number of small furrows from the main canal or channel; and the tree-shaped or branching type, where water is diverted from the primary channel into successively smaller canals and ditches. Where slopes are relatively flat and uniform, flooding provides an economical means of recharge. Normal practice is to spread the recharge water over the ground at relatively small depths so as not to disturb the soil or native vegetation. An additional method is the use of injection wells. Recharge rates are normally less than pumping rates for the same head conditions, however, due to clogging which is often encountered in the area adjacent to the well casing.[37] Clogging may result from the entrapment of fine aquifer particles, from suspended material in the recharge water which is subsequently strained out and deposited in the vicinity of the well screen, from air binding, from chemical reactions between recharge and natural waters, and from bacteria. For best results the recharge water should be clear, contain little or no sodium, and be chlorinated.

Richter and Chun have outlined several factors worthy of consideration relative to the selection of artificial recharge project sites.[38] Essentially they are availability and character of local and imported water supply; factors relating to infiltration rates of the native soils; operation and maintenance problems; net benefits; water quality; and legal considerations.

CONCURRENT DEVELOPMENT OF GROUNDWATER AND SURFACE-WATER SOURCES

The maximum practical conservation of our water resources is based on the coordinated development of groundwater and surface-water supplies. Geologic, hydrologic, economic, and legal factors must be carefully considered.

Concurrent utilization is primarily founded on the premise of transference of impounded surface water to groundwater storage at optimum rates.[43,44] Annual water requirements are generally met by surface storage while groundwater storage is used to meet cyclic requirements covering periods of dry years. The operational procedure involves a lowering of groundwater levels during periods of below-average precipitation and a subsequent raising of levels during wet years. Transfer rates of surface waters to underground storage must be large enough to assure that surface-water reservoirs will be drawn down sufficiently to permit impounding significant volumes during periods of high runoff. To provide the required maximum transfer capacity, methods of artificial recharge such as spreading, ponding, injecting, returning flows from irrigation, or other techniques must be used.

The coordinated use of groundwater and surface-water sources will result in the provision of larger quantities of water at lower costs. As an example, it has been found that the conjunctive operation of the Folsom Reservoir (California) and its groundwater basin yields a conservation and utilization efficiency of approximately 82 percent as compared with about 51 percent efficiency for the operation of the surface reservoir alone.[45] There is little doubt that the inclusion of groundwater resources should be given very careful consideration in future planning for large-scale water development projects.

In general, the analysis of a conjunctive system consisting of a dam and an aquifer requires the solution of three fundamental problems. The first is to establish the design criteria for the dam and the recharge facilities. The second is to determine the service area for the combined system. Finally, a set of operating rules which define the reservoir drafts and pumpages to be taken from the aquifer are required. A mathematical model for an analysis such as this has been proposed by Buras.[43]

REFERENCES

1. E. A. Ackerman and G. O. Lof, *Technology in American Water Development* (Baltimore: The Johns Hopkins Press, 1959).

2. Harold E. Babbitt, James J. Doland, and John L. Cleasby, *Water Supply Engineering* (New York: McGraw-Hill Book Co., Inc., 1962).

3. H. F. Dregne and H. J. Maker, "Irrigation Well Waters of New Mexico," Agricultural Experiment Station, New Mexico State University, Bull. 386 (1954).

4. M. S. Hantush, "Preliminary Quantitative Study of the Roswell Ground Water Reservoir, New Mexico," New Mexico Institute of Mining and Technology, Socorro, New Mexico, 1957.

5. Jack Hirshleifer, J. DeHaven, and J. Milliman, *Water Supply-Economics, Technology, and Policy* (Chicago: University of Chicago Press, 1960).

6. L. Koenig, "Disposal of Saline Water Conversion Brines—An Orientation Study," *U.S. Office Saline Water, Saline Water Res. Develop. Progr. Rept.* No. 20 (1958).

7. J. M. McKee, "We Need Researchers," *Eng. News-Record* (October 1962).

8. Charles R. Renn, "Sources of Information and Research in Industrial Waste Treatment," *Proc. 2d Annual Symp. Ind. Waste Control* (Baltimore: The Johns Hopkins Press, 1961).

9. W. M. Sanders, J. J. Lentz, D. W. Duttweiler, and others, "Heat Dissipation in Flowing Streams," The Johns Hopkins University, Dept. of Sanitary Engineering, Baltimore, 1962.

10. David K. Todd, *Ground Water Hydrology* (New York: John Wiley and Sons, Inc., 1960).

11. G. S. Benton et al., "Measuring Evapotranspiration from Atmospheric Data," *Proc. Am. Soc. Civil Engrs., J. Hydraulics Div.,* Paper 1035 (1956).

12. C. V. David et al., *Handbook of Applied Hydraulics,* 2d ed. (New York: McGraw-Hill Book Co., Inc., 1952).

13. J. G. Ferris, "Ground Water," *Mech. Eng.* (January 1960).

14. J. C. Geyer and G. M. Fair, *Water Supply and Waste-Water Disposal* (New York: John Wiley and Sons, Inc., 1954).

15. W. B. Langbein, "Water Yield and Reservoir Storage in the United States," U.S. Geological Survey Circular (1959).

16. R. K. Linsley, M. A. Kohler, and J. L. H. Paulhus, *Applied Hydrology* (New York: McGraw-Hill Book Co., Inc., 1949).

17. Charles E. Renn, "Sources of Information and Research in Industrial Waste Treatment," *Proc. 2d Annual Symp. Ind. Waste Control* (Baltimore: The Johns Hopkins Press, 1961).

18. H. E. Thomas, "Underground Sources of Water," *The Yearbook of Agriculture, 1955* (Washington, D.C.: U.S. Government Printing Office, 1956).

19. G. M. Fair and J. C. Geyer, *Water Supply and Waste-Water Disposal* (New York: John Wiley and Sons, Inc., 1954).

20. Task Group A4, D1, "Water Conservation in Industry," *J. Am. Water Works Assoc.,* vol. 45 (December 1958).

21. G. C. Doty, "Water Supply Development at the National Aeronautics and Space Agency Apollo Propulsion System Development Facility, Dona Ana County, New Mexico," U.S. General Services Administration, Open File Report (October 1963).

22. W. B. Langbein, "Queuing Theory and Water Storage," *Proc. Am. Soc. Civil Engrs., J. Hydraulics Div.,* no. HY5 (October 1958).

23. John B. Stall and James C. Neill, "Calculated Risks of Impounding Reservoir Yield," *J. Hydraulics Div., Am. Soc. Civil Engrs.,* vol. 89, no. HY1 (January 1963).

24. Myron B. Fiering, "Queuing Theory and Simulation in Reservoir Design," *J. Hydraulic Div., Am. Soc. Civil Engrs.,* vol. 87, no. HY6 (November 1961).

25. W. Rippl, "The Capacity of Storage Reservoirs for Water Supply," *Proc. Inst. Civil Engrs. (London),* vol. 71 (1883), p. 270.

26. John B. Stall, "Reservoir Mass Analysis by a Low-Flow Series," *J. Sanit. Eng. Div., Am. Soc. Civil Engrs.,* vol. 88, no. SA5 (September 1962).

27. Harold A. Thomas, Jr., "Queuing Theory of Stream Flow Regulation Applied to the Cost-Benefit Analysis of a Multipurpose Reservoir," Private Communication to the Harvard Water Resources Program, Harvard University, Cambridge, Mass., Nov. 20, 1959.

28. C. O. Wisler and E. F. Brater, *Hydrology* (New York: John Wiley and Sons, Inc., 1959).

29. G. M. Brune and R. E. Allen, "A Consideration of Factors Influencing Reservoir Sedimentation in the Ohio Valley Region," *Trans. Am. Geophys. Union,* vol. 22 (1941), pp. 649–655.

30. G. M. Fair and J. C. Geyer, *Elements of Water Supply and Waste-Water Disposal* (New York: John Wiley and Sons, Inc., 1958).

31. O. E. Meinzer, "Outline of Methods for Estimating Ground Water Supplies," *U.S. Geol. Surv. Water Supply,* Washington, D.C. Paper 638C (1932).

32. M. E. Harr, *Groundwater and Seepage* (New York: McGraw-Hill Book Co., Inc., 1962).

33. M. Muskat, *The Flow of Homogeneous Fluids Through Porous Media* (Ann Arbor, Mich.: J. W. Edwards, Inc., 1946).

34. Jules Dupuit, "Etudes theoriques et pratiques sur le mouvement des eaux," 2d ed. (Paris, 1863.)

35. John F. Hoffman, "Field Tests Determine Potential Quantity, Quality of Ground Water Supply," *Heating, Piping, Air Cond.* (August 1961).

36. John F. Hoffman, "Well Location and Design," *Heating, Piping, Air Cond.* (August 1963).

37. David K. Todd, "Ground Water Has to be Replenished," *Chem. Eng. Progr.,* vol. 59, no. 11 (Nov., 1963).

38. R. C. Richter and R. Y. D. Chun, "Artificial Recharge of Ground Water Reservoirs in California," *Proc. Am. Soc. Civil Engrs., J. Irrigation Drainage Div.,* vol. 85, no. IR4 (December 1959).

39. G. Thiem, *Hydrologische Methodern* (Leipzig: Gebhart, 1906), pp. 56.

40. C. V. Theis, "The Relation Between the Lowering of the Piezometric Surface and the Rate and Duration of Discharge of a Well Using Ground Water Storage," *Trans. Am. Geophys. Union,* vol. 16 (1935), pp. 519–524.

41. H. H. Cooper, Jr. and C. E. Jacob, "A Generalized Graphical Method for Evaluating Formation Constants and Summarizing Well-Field History," *Trans. Am. Geophys. Union,* vol. 27 (1946) pp. 526–534.

42. John F. Hoffman, "How Underground Reservoirs Provide Cool Water for Industrial Uses," *Heating, Piping, Air Cond.* (October 1960).

43. Nathan Buras, "Conjunctive Operation of Dams and Aquifers," *J. Hydraulics Div., Am. Soc. Civil Engrs.,* vol. 89, no. HY6 (November 1963).

44. F. B. Clendenen, "Z Comprehensive Plan for the Conjunctive Utilization of a Surface Reservoir with Underground Storage for Basin-Wide Water Supply Development: Solano Project, California," D. Eng. thesis (University of California, Berkeley, California, 1959), p. 160.

45. "Ground Water Basin Management," *Am. Soc. Civil Engrs. Manual of Engineering Practice,* No. 40 (New York: American Society of Civil Engineers, 1961).

46. G. M. Brune, "Trap Efficiency of Reservoirs," *Trans. Am. Geophys. Union,* vol. 34 (June 1953), pp. 407–418.

47. R. K. Linsley and J. B. Franzini, *Water Resources Engineering* (New York: McGraw-Hill Book Co., Inc., 1964).

PROBLEMS

4-1. Water quality may be affected by (a) suspended solids, (b) radioactive materials, (c) dissolved solids, (d) physical properties, and (e) biological properties. Give examples of how these factors might influence each other in water and sewage flows.

4-2. A refinery uses 8×10^6 gal of water per day. Fifty percent of this flow is discharged to a nearby stream as a concentrated waste containing 3,000 ppm (parts per million) dissolved solids. The stream has a watershed of 100 sq miles and a mean annual flow rate of 1 cfs/sq mile. Will the water downstream of the refinery meet the U.S. Public Health Service standards regarding recommended total dissolved solids for (a) drinking purposes? (b) irrigation purposes? Assume that the stream normally contains 25 ppm dissolved solids.

4-3. Compare the amounts of water required by the various users in your state. What is the relative worth of water in its various uses?

4-4. A mean draft of 120 mgd is to be developed from a 200-sq-mile catchment area. At the flow line the reservoir is estimated to be 4,300 acres. The annual rainfall is 35 in., the mean annual runoff is 14 in., and mean annual evaporation is 54 in. Find the net gain or loss in storage this represents. Compute the volume of water evaporated. State this figure in a form such as the number of years the volume could supply a given community, etc.

4-5. Discuss how you would go about collecting data for an analysis of the water budget of a region. What agencies would you contact? What other sources of information would you seek out?

4-6. For some area of your choice, make a plot of mean monthly precipitation vs. time. Explain how this fits the pattern of seasonal water uses for the area. Will the form of precipitation be an important consideration?

4-7. Given the following 10-yr record of annual precipitation, plot a rough precipitation frequency curve. Tabulate the data to be plotted and show the method of computation. *Data:* annual precipitation in inches: 26, 21, 30, 24, 28, 20, 18, 25, 19, 22. NOTE: Frequency in percent of years $= 1/T_R \times 100$.

4-8. What are some of the factors that determine rate of evaporation? Write a brief discussion of the evaporation process.

4-9. What is the purpose of a flood-control reservoir? In view of this, what should be remembered concerning use of the captured flood waters by irrigators, etc?

4-10. Outline a procedure for estimating the size of a multipurpose reservoir for a particular area, indicating what factors should be considered.

4-11. State all the possible uses for which surface supplies might be developed. List some conflicting uses. Explain.

4-12. Discuss the preparation of a new reservoir site to insure cleanliness and satisfactory operating conditions.

4-13. Given the following elevation-area information for an existing reservoir, plot an area-elevation curve. From this curve, compute the total storage volume and incremental storage volume of the reservoir so that you can plot an elevation–storage-volume curve.

Elevation, above mean sea level, ft	1,835	1,840	1,860
Area, acres	0	1,000	4,000

1,880	1,900	1,920	1,940	1,960	1,975
6,000	9,000	12,000	18,000	27,000	35,000

4-14. Find the storage requirement arithmetically if a uniform draft of 680,000 gpd/sq mile from a specific stream is to be maintained. The following record of average monthly runoff values is given:

Month	A	M	J	J	A	S	O	N	D	J	F	M	A	M	J
Runoff, mg/sq mile	96	118	49	6	4	3	1	2	20	9	68	97	28	59	38

4-15. Solve Prob. 4-14 graphically and compare the results.

4-16. Using the information given in Table 4-3, plot recurrence interval in years as the ordinate, design period in years as the abscissa, and construct a series of recurrence interval–design period–probability lines for probabilities that an event will *not* be exceeded during the design period. Use arithmetic coordinate paper. NOTE: To conform to this, probabilities in the table must be subtracted from 1.0. Where sufficient information is not provided by the table, probabilities may be computed using $P_n = (1 - 1/T_R)^n$, where n = design period in years.

4-17. The following partial duration series of 20-month low-flows is available from 56 years of record on the Lentz River. The river supplies the Lentzville Reservoir which has a drainage area of 350 sq miles.

20-month flow, in./sq mi. 5.6, 7.8, 4.9, 12.7, 19.3, 13.1, 16.2, 3.8, 6.9, 7.1
Find the recurrence interval for these events.

4-18. Consider that in Prob. 4-17 the various low flows have been plotted and for the reservoir capacity of 8 in./sq mile (350 sq mile), the gross yield values were found to be 180, 173, 164, 152, 140, 135, 122, 103, 89, and 69 mgd. Graphically determine a gross yield–recurrence interval curve and plot yield-probability curves. For a reservoir supply of 80 mgd, what is the probability of satisfying this requirement if the design period is (a) 10 yr and (b) 20 yr?

4-19. Given the following 57-month record of mean monthly discharge, find the magnitude of the 20-month low flow.

Consecutive average monthly flows, cfs. 10, 12, 14, 16, 19, 21, 18, 16, 18, 25, 28, 32, 34, 35, 30, 28, 20, 23, 20, 18, 16, 14, 12, 13, 14, 13, 12, 11, 12, 13, 14, 13, 12, 11, 10, 9, 10, 9, 8, 7, 6, 5, 6, 7, 8, 9, 10, 9, 8, 6, 7, 8, 12, 16, 17, 12, 10

4-20. Find the expected life of a reservoir having an initial capacity of 50,000 acre-ft. The average annual inflow is 70,000 acre-ft and a sediment inflow of 206 acre-ft yr is reported. Consider the useful life of the reservoir to be exceeded when 80 percent of the original capacity is lost. Use 5,000-acre-ft volume increments. Obtain values of percent sediment trapped from Fig. 4-11.

4-21. What precautions might be taken to avoid or minimize silting when planning a reservoir?

4-22. Given the following data relating mean annual change in groundwater level to mean annual draft, find the safe yield.

Mean annual change in groundwater level, ft	+1	+2	−1	−3	−4	+1.5	+1.2	−2.6
Mean annual draft, thousands of acre-ft	22	20	29	38.5	42.5	20	21	35

4-23. What is the Reynolds number for flow in a soil when the water temperature is 52°F, velocity is 0.8 ft/day, and mean grain diameter 0.08 in.?

4-24. A 12-in. well fully penetrates a confined aquifer 100 ft thick. The coefficient of permeability is 600 gpd/sq ft. Two test wells located 30 ft and 100 ft away show a difference in drawdown between them of 8 ft. Find the rate of flow delivered by the well.

4-25. Determine the permeability of an artesian aquifer being pumped by a fully penetrating well. The aquifer is composed of medium sand and is 110 ft thick.

The steady-state pumping rate is 1,100 gpm. The drawdown in an observation well 60 ft away is 11 ft, and the drawdown in a second observation well 500 ft away is 1 ft. Find K_f in gallons per day per square foot.

4-26. Consider a confined aquifer with a coefficient of transmissibility $T = 695$ cu ft/day/ft. At $t = 5$ min the drawdown $= 6$ ft, at 50 min, $s = 22.4$ ft, at 100 min, $s = 27.0$ ft. The observation well is 60 ft away from the pumping well. Find the discharge of the well.

4-27. What is meant by a combination of wells? Why must this problem be treated in a different manner from that of the single well?

4-28. Assume an aquifer is being pumped at a rate of 275 gpm. The aquifer is confined and the pumping test data are given below. Find the coefficient of transmissibility T and the storage coefficient S. $r = 50$ ft.

Time, since pumping started, min	1.5	2.6	4.0	7.0	10.0	100.0
Drawdown s, ft	4.9	7.0	8.0	10.5	12.6	27.0

4-29. Given the following data:

$$Q = 60,000 \text{ cu ft/day} \qquad t = 30 \text{ days}, r = 1 \text{ ft}$$
$$T = 650 \text{ cu ft/day/ft} \qquad S_c = 6.4 \times 10^{-4}$$

Consider this to be a nonequilibrium problem. Find the drawdown s. Note for

$$u = 8.0 \times 10^{-9} \qquad W(u) = 18.06$$
$$u = 8.2 \times 10^{-9} \qquad W(u) = 18.04$$
$$u = 8.6 \times 10^{-9} \qquad W(u) = 17.99$$

4-30. A 24-in. well penetrates a body of free groundwater 45 ft in depth. The slope of the water table is 2.5×10^{-3}. The coefficient of permeability of the water-bearing material is 6.5×10^{-4} fps. The well is pumped long enough to establish a constant drawdown of 18 ft. (a) Estimate the diameter of the circle of influence (b) Compute the discharge.

4-31. Discuss how you would evaluate the practicality of practicing groundwater recharge by spreading at a given location. What factors would you have to consider?

chapter 5

Transportation and Distribution of Water

It is the purpose of this chapter to acquaint students with the varied aspects of transporting and distributing water. An attempt is made to develop techniques for handling certain hydraulic problems which are more or less unique to this subject.

THE TRANSPORTATION PROBLEM

The controlled movement of water from one point to another for the purpose of serving man's needs may be considered broadly as the transportation of water. This general definition will be modified here to reserve the concept of transportation for the bulk movement of water for relatively long distances. A prime example is the transportation of water from an impounding reservoir to a water-treatment plant. Once the water reaches the treatment works and has been processed, its movement to the individual consumer will then be classified as distribution.

Numerous types of conveyances are employed in the transportation of water. They are all categorized as aqueducts and may take the form of pipelines, tunnels, flumes, open channels, and siphons. Flow may occur under pressure or at atmospheric conditions.

Before considering specific hydraulic features and the design details of transportation works, several examples of major transportation systems will be briefly discussed to indicate the scope of these works.

5-1. THE AQUEDUCTS OF ANCIENT ROME

Few of us have not seen pictures of or heard comments about the aqueducts of ancient Rome. These conduits usually were formed of brick and stone and were covered by an arch to keep the water cool and free of impurity. The invert of the conveyance was normally coated with mortar to seal it. The aqueducts were built above ground where possible, but when necessity required they ran underground, through tunnels, or overhead on arched structures. An idea of the size and quantity of flow carried by several of them is indicated in Table 5-1.

TABLE 5-1
DATA ON SOME OF THE ROMAN AQUEDUCTS
DURING THE TIME OF FRONTINUS[1]

Aqueduct	Approximate Date	Length of Conduit (Roman Miles $\simeq$ 5,000 ft)	Approximate Flow, mgd	Remarks
Appia	312 B.C.	11	16.7	Mostly underground
Marcia	144 B.C.	62	42.8	54 miles underground
Claudia	A.D. 50	46.5	42.1	36 miles underground
Anio Nova	A.D. 52	58.8	43.3	49 miles underground passed over arches 109 ft high

These figures serve to show that large-scale water transportation feats are not new. The quantities of water transported by the Romans are significant even on today's scale. The flow delivered by the aqueduct Appia, for example, would easily serve most present-day American cities of about 30,000 population.

5-2. THE CANADIAN RIVER PROJECT

Modern examples of first-magnitude water transportation undertakings are the Canadian River Project in Texas and the California State Water Project.

The Canadian River project was initiated in March 1962 with construction of the Sanford Reservoir which will impound more than 2.4 million acre-ft of water.[2] This supply will ultimately serve eleven cities in the Texas Panhandle. Flows from the reservoir will be transported a maximum distance of 322 miles by pipeline. The transportation system is illustrated in Fig. 5-1. It is to be built under ten contracts, the first of which involves the construction of 56 miles of 72-, 78-, and 96-in. reinforced-concrete and steel-cylinder pipe. This first section will run from the Sanford Dam to the city of Amarillo. Also included in the initial contract are four steel surge tanks and a 44-acre, 18-ft maximum depth, regulating reservoir at Amarillo. Flows will have to be pumped to an elevation of 760 ft above the mean expected level of the reservoir. To meet this requirement and other pumping needs, a series of pumping stations will be required.

5-3. THE CALIFORNIA STATE WATER PROJECT

The California State Water Project is probably the best example that can be given to demonstrate man's attempt to solve the problem of unequal distribution of water over the earth's surface. About 70 percent of California's water supply is generated in the northern part of the state while about 77 percent of the state's water needs are in the south. In addition, the population of the state is experiencing rapid increases.

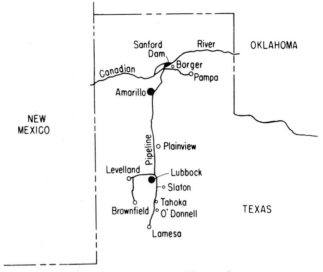

FIG. 5-1. The Canadian River project.

The overall objectives of the California water plan are to evaluate the current degree of water development, to estimate ultimate water requirements, and to determine means for providing the necessary water. In 1959 impetus to a segment of this plan was provided when the legislature adopted the Burns-Porter Act to finance the state water project.

This massive transportation undertaking is the largest in the world. It will deliver about 4 million acre-ft of water annually to areas in the Sacramento Valley, San Francisco Bay region, San Joaquin Valley, and Southern California.[3] Upon completion, the project will include 16 reservoirs having a combined storage in excess of 6 million acre-ft. There will be 662 miles of aqueduct and eight power plants capable of producing more than 5 billion kilowatt hours of energy annually.

The primary storage facility is the 3.5 million acre-ft Oroville Reservoir located on the Feather River (see Fig. 5-2). When complete, this dam will tower over 700 ft and be the highest of its type in the United States.

Water released from the Oroville dam will flow down the Feather River into the Sacramento River and then on to the Sacramento-San Joaquin Delta. From that point it will be transported by the California Aqueduct (maximum capacity of 10,000 cfs) to a location south of Bakersfield where it will be pumped across the Tehachapi Mountains. This mountain crossing will involve a lift of about 2,000 ft which is unprecedented in the United States. A series of tunnels six miles long and about 17 to 20.5 ft in diameter will be used to convey the water over the higher elevation of the mountains.[4]

1. Upper Feather River Reservoirs
2. Oroville Facilities
3. North Bay Aqueduct
4. Delta Project
5. South Bay Aqueduct
6. San Luis Project (joint with United States)
7. Coastal Aqueduct
8. Castaic Reservoir
9. Cedar Springs Reservoir
10. Perris Reservoir

FIG. 5-2. California's state water project. (Courtesy of the California Department of Water Resources.)

South of the Tehachapis the aqueduct follows the south side of Antelope Valley and the Mohave Desert to Cedar Springs Reservoir. It then turns south and passes through a tunnel in the San Bernardino Mountains, down Devils Canyon, and then in an underground pipeline to the Perris Reservoir. About 450 miles separate the Delta Pumping Plant from the Perris Reservoir (Fig. 5-2). A cross section of the California Aqueduct is given in Fig. 5-3.

5-4. TYPES OF AQUEDUCTS

It has been stated previously that a variety of types of conduit can be used for transporting water. The final selection rests on such factors as topography, head availability, construction practices, economic considerations, and water quality. In addition, the transported water must be safeguarded against pollution by other inferior water sources. This is a

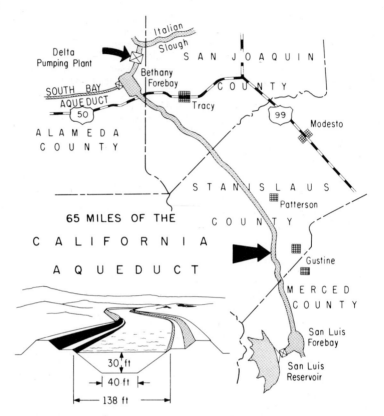

FIG. 5-3. The California Aqueduct. (Courtesy of the California Department of Water Resources.)

special problem when open channels or conduits operating at low pressure are used.

Open Channels. Open channels are conduits designed to convey water under conditions of atmospheric pressure. By this definition, the hydraulic gradient and free-water surface are coincident. If the channel is supported on or above the ground, it is classified as a flume. Open channels may be covered or open and may take on a variety of shapes.

Hydraulically, the most economical cross section is a semicircle since the maximum hydraulic radius for a specific cross-sectional area is obtained for this shape. In practice, however, this section is usually approximated with an easier-to-construct-and-maintain trapizoidal section. In unlined channels, side slopes generally vary from about $1\frac{1}{4}$ to $2\frac{1}{2}$ to 1, horizontal to vertical, depending on the type of soil encountered. Figure 5-3 illustrates a trapezoidal canal section used in California.

The choice of an open channel as the means of conveyance will usually be predicated on suitable topographic conditions which permit gravity flow with minimal excavation or fill. If the channel is unlined, the perviousness of the soil must be considered relative to seepage losses. Other considerations of importance are the potential pollution hazard and evaporative losses.

Many modern open channels are lined with concrete, bituminous materials, butyl rubber, vinyl, synthetic fabrics, or other products to reduce the resistance to flow, minimize seepage, and lower maintenance costs. Flumes are usually constructed of concrete, steel or timber.

Pipelines. Pipelines are usually built where topographic conditions preclude the use of canals. Since this type of conduit is operated under pressure, the overall length of the line will normally be less than that of a canal connecting the same terminals. A pipeline may be laid above or below ground or be partly buried.

Circular cross sections are generally chosen for pressure conduits as stresses can be economically carried under tension. Others types of sections (oval, horseshoe, etc.) have also found use. Their choice depends primarily on special local conditions and on structural and economic considerations.

Most modern pressure conduits are built of concrete, steel, cast iron, or asbestos cement.

Pipelines used in important transportation systems may require gate valves, check valves, air-release valves, drains, surge control equipment, expansion joints, insulation joints, manholes, and pumping stations. These appurtenances are provided to insure safe and efficient operation, provide for easy inspection, and facilitate maintenance. Check valves are normally located on the upstream side of pumping equipment and at the beginning of each rise in the pipeline to prevent backflow. Gate valves are often spaced about 1,200 ft apart so that the intervening section of line can be drained for inspection or repair and on either side of a check valve to permit its removal for inspection or repair. Air-release valves are needed at the high points in the line to release trapped gases and to vent the line to prevent vacuum formation. Drains are located at low points to permit removal of sediment and allow the conduit to be emptied. Control equipment is used to protect against hydraulic surge, commonly called water hammer. Surge tanks or quick-opening valves provide the most common forms of relief from this problem.

Tunnels. Where it is not practical or economical to lay a pipeline on the surface or provide an open trench for underground installation, a tunnel is selected. Tunnels are well suited to mountain or river crossings. They may be operated under pressure or act as open channels. Tunnels may be lined or unlined, depending on the material through which they are driven. Linings may be required to prevent the walls of the tunnel from collapsing either inward or outward. The former condition would require consideration where low pressure operation is to be experienced. For high pressure tunnels the latter case would usually control.

5-5. HYDRAULIC CONSIDERATIONS

The analysis of flows in an aqueduct system is carried out through the application of the basic principles of open-channel and closed-conduit hydraulics. It is assumed that the student already has been exposed to these concepts in his courses in hydraulics or fluid mechanics.

Except for sludges, most flows may be treated hydraulically in the same manner as clean water even though considerable quantities of suspended material are being carried. The Hazen-Williams and Manning formulas are the equations used extensively in water transportation problems. The Hazen-Williams formula is used primarily for pressure conduits, while the Manning equation has found its major application in open-channel problems. Both equations are applicable when normal temperatures prevail, a relatively high degree of turbulence is developed, and ordinary commercial materials are used.[5] The Hazen-Williams equation may be expressed in the following form:

$$V = 1.318\, CR^{0.63} S^{0.54} \qquad (5\text{-}1)$$

where V = velocity in feet per second
   C = coefficient which is a function of the material and age of the conduit
   R = hydraulic radius in feet (flow area divided by the wetted perimeter)
   S = slope of the energy gradient in feet per foot of length

For circular conduits flowing full, the equation may be restated as

$$Q = 0.279\, CD^{2.63} S^{0.54} \qquad (5\text{-}2)$$

where Q = flow in mgd
   D = pipe diameter in feet.

Some values of C for use in the Hazen-Williams formula are given in Table 5-2. Charts and nomographs which facilitate the solution of the equation are given in most books on hydraulics.

The Manning equation is stated in the following form.

$$V = \frac{1.49}{n}\, R^{2/3} S^{1/2} \qquad (5\text{-}3)$$

where V = velocity of flow in feet per second
   n = a coefficient of roughness
   R = hydraulic radius in feet
   S = slope of the energy gradient

TABLE 5-2
SOME VALUES OF THE
HAZEN-WILLIAMS COEFFICIENT

Pipe Material	C
New cast iron	130
5-year-old cast iron	120
20-year-old cast iron	100
Average concrete	130
New welded steel	120
Asbestos cement	140

The equation is applicable as long as S does not materially exceed 0.10. In channels having nonuniform roughness, an average value of n is selected. Where the cross-sectional roughness changes considerably as in a channel with a paved center section and grassed outer sections, common practice is to compute the flow for each section independently and sum these flows to obtain the total. As in the case of the Hazen-Williams equation, numerous tables, charts, and nomographs are available to permit rapid computations. Values of n for use in Manning's equation are indicated in Table 5-3.

TABLE 5-3
VALUES OF MANNING'S ROUGHNESS COEFFICIENT

Material	n
Concrete	0.013
Cast-iron pipe	0.015
Vitrified clay	0.014
Brick	0.016
Corrugated metal pipe	0.022
Bituminous concrete	0.015
Uniform firm sodded earth	0.025

The head lost as a result of pipe friction can be computed by solving Eq. 5-1 or Eq. 5-3 for S and multiplying by the length of the pipeline. A slightly more direct method is to use the Darcy-Weisbach equation.

$$h_L = f \frac{LV^2}{D2g} \qquad (5\text{-}4)$$

where h_L = head loss
L = length of the pipe
D = pipe diameter
f = friction factor
V = flow velocity

The friction factor is related to the Reynolds number and the relative roughness of the pipe. For conditions of complete turbulence, Fig. 5-4 relates the friction factor to pipe geometry and characteristics.

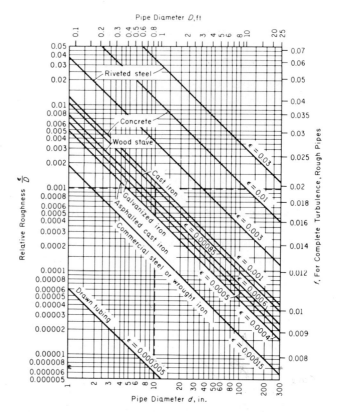

FIG. 5-4. Relative roughness of pipe materials and friction factors for complete turbulence. (Courtesy of the Crane Co., Chicago.)

In transportation systems, the pipe friction-head loss is usually predominant and other losses can ordinarily be neglected without serious error. In short pipelines such as found in water-treatment plants, the minor losses may be exceedingly important. If there is doubt, it is always best to include them. Minor losses result from valves, fittings, bends, and changes in flow characteristics at inlets and outlets. For turbulent-flow conditions, minor losses are customarily expressed as a function of velocity head. Adequate information is available from manufacturers and other sources on losses in various types of valves and fittings.[5,6]

EXAMPLE 5-1. Consider that water is pumped 10 miles from a reservoir at elevation 100 ft to a second reservoir at elevation 230 ft. The pipeline connecting the reservoirs is 48 in. in diameter and is constructed of concrete with an absolute roughness of 0.003. If the flow is 25 mgd and the efficiency of the pumping station is 80 percent, what will be the monthly power bill if electricity costs 1 cent per kilowatt hour?

Solution: 1. Writing the energy equation between a point on the water surface of the reservoir (A) and a point on the water surface of reservoir (B), the following equation is obtained.

$$Z_A + \frac{P_A}{W} + \frac{V_A^2}{2g} + H_p = Z_B + \frac{P_B}{W} + \frac{V_B^2}{2g} + H_L$$

2. Letting $Z_A = 0$, and noting that $P_A = P_B =$ atmospheric pressure, and $V_A = V_B = 0$ for a large reservoir, the equation reduces to

$$H_p = Z_B + H_L$$

where $H_p =$ head developed by the pump

$H_L =$ total head lost between A and B including pipe friction and all minor losses

3. Using Fig. 5-4, determine the value of f as 0.0182.

4. Using Eq. 5-4, find the pipe friction-head loss. Assuming that the minor losses are negligible in this problem, this is equal to H_L.

$$H_L = f\left(\frac{L}{D}\right)\left(\frac{V^2}{2g}\right)$$

V must be determined before Eq. 5-4 can be solved.

$$V = \frac{Q}{A} = \frac{25 \times 10^6 \times 1.55}{\pi \times 4 \times 10^6} = 3.09 \text{ ft/sec}$$

$$H_L = 0.0182 \times \frac{5,280 \times 10}{4} \times \frac{(3.09)^2}{64.4}$$

$$= 35.6 \text{ ft}$$

5. $H_p = (230 - 100) + 35.6$
   $= 130 + 35.6 = 165.6 \text{ ft-lb/lb}$

the energy imparted by the pump to the water.

6. The power requirement may be computed as

$$P = Q\gamma H_p$$
$$= 25 \times 1.55 \times 62.4 \times 165.6 = 400,000 \text{ ft-lb/sec}$$

7. For 80 percent efficiency, the power requirement is

$$\frac{400,000}{0.80} = 500,000 \text{ ft-lb/sec}$$

8. $5.00 \times 10^5 \times 3.766 \times 10^{-7} = 18.8 \times 10^{-2} \text{ kwh/sec}$

The number of kwh per 30-day month is then

$$18.8 \times 10^{-2} \times 30 \times 864 \times 10^2 = 485,000 \text{ kwh month}$$

9. The monthly power cost is therefore $485,000 \times 0.01 = \$4,850.00$.

5-6. DESIGN OF TRANSPORTATION SYSTEMS

The design of transportation systems involves primarily a determination of hydraulic adequacy, structural adequacy, and economic efficiency. The required waterway area is a function of the flow to be carried, the head available, the character of the conduit material, and limiting velocities.

Locating the Aqueduct.   The location of an aqueduct is based on engineering and economic considerations. Since the terminal locations are dictated by the source of supply and the region to be served, the problem becomes one of finding the most practical and economic route between them. The choice of location has an obvious bearing on the type of aqueduct that can be built. Aqueducts built to grade require topography such that cut-and-cover operations can be closely balanced. Pressure aqueducts, on the other hand, can follow the topography and often permit the choice of a direct route. Pumping costs in such cases would have to be included in making economic comparisons with conduits constructed along the hydraulic grade line. Material and construction costs must also be balanced against length. The most direct route is not always the least expensive.

Determining the Size and Capacity of the Conduit.   The size and configuration of the aqueduct finally selected will in all probability be variable along the route. The choice of section depends on the hydraulic loading, external loading and economic considerations.

Once the stage has been reached where the actual conduit design is required, a decision will have been made as to the quantities of water to be transported along its various reaches. This information will be derived by the methods outlined in Chap. 3 and will answer the question of the required capacity.

For a given type aqueduct (pipe, tunnel, flume, canal) the size will usually be determined on the basis of hydraulic, economic and construction considerations. Occasionally construction practices dictate a minimum size in excess of that required to handle the flow under the prevailing hydraulic conditions (available head). This condition would most likely be encountered where a tunnel was involved. Hydraulic factors which control the design are the head available and permissible velocities. Available heads are affected by reservoir drawdown and local pressure requirements. Where the head is in excess of that needed to transport the water, power development might be economical. Limiting velocities are based on the character of the water to be transported and the need to protect transmission lines against excessive pressures which might be developed through hydraulic surge. Where silt is transported with the water, minimum velocities of about 2.5 fps should be maintained. Maximum velocities must preclude pipe erosion or hydraulic surge problems. Upper limits are usually between 10 and 20 fps. A normal range of 4 to 6 fps is common.

Where power generation is involved, pumping costs or power values and conduit costs jointly determine the conduit size. For single gravity-flow pipelines the size should be determined such that all of the head available is consumed by friction.

EXAMPLE 5-2. Determine the dimensions of a rectangular concrete channel which is to carry 600 cfs with a hydraulic slope of 0.08 ft/1000 ft. The section is to be of smooth concrete. Assume a mean velocity of 3 fps.

Solution: 1. Using Manning's equation, Eq. 5-3,

$$V = \frac{1.49}{n} R^{2/3} S^{1/2}$$

$$R^{2/3} = \frac{V \times n}{1.49 \times S^{1/2}}$$

$$= \frac{3 \times 0.013}{1.49 \times (0.00008)^{1/2}}$$

$$= 2.94$$

$$R = 5.0 \text{ ft}$$

2. The most efficient channel will be one in which R is a maximum or the wetted perimeter P is a minimum. For a rectangular channel,

$$P = 2d + b$$

$$= 2d + \frac{A}{d}$$

Differentiating P with respect to d and setting the equation equal to zero permits determination of the minimum value of P.

3. $\dfrac{dP}{dd} = 2 - \dfrac{A}{d^2} = 0$

Substituting the product of the channel width and the depth of flow for A,

$$2 - \frac{bd}{d^2} = 0 \qquad \text{and} \qquad b = 2d$$

4. $A = \dfrac{Q}{V} = \dfrac{600}{3} = 200 \text{ sq ft}$

5. $A = bd = 2d^2 = 200$

$$d^2 = 100$$
$$d = 10 \text{ ft}$$
therefore
$$b = 20 \text{ ft}$$
and

$$R = \frac{A}{P} = \frac{200}{40} = 5, \text{ as indicated in Step 1}$$

Determining the Most Economical Aqueduct. In any aqueduct system, hydraulic head has a real economic value. It costs money to produce the head at the upstream end of the system because head can be used for increased flow, for power production, or a combination of these factors.

A definite relationship always exists between aqueduct size, hydraulic gradient, and the value of head. In some cases construction costs are related to the elevation of the hydraulic gradient. The elevation of the gradient also affects pumping costs and power-production values, as does the slope of the hydraulic gradient. In long lines composed of different types of conduits passing through varied topography, a means of coordinating conduit types, choosing dam elevations, and selecting pump lifts or power drops is important. This problem can be approached through a joint application of hydraulic and economic principles.[7,10]

In any conduit, sufficient hydraulic slope must exist to obtain the required flow. Steep slopes generate high velocities with smaller conduit requirements. When sufficient fall is available, steep slopes are often economical. On the other hand, if head can be generated only by pumping or through construction of a dam, flatter slopes calling for larger conduits are probably necessary to reduce the cost of the lift. Apparently, then, some combination of lift and slope will yield the optimum economy.

Usually in designing water-transmission lines some controlling feature establishes the elevation of the line at a specified point. Examples of possible governing features are dam heights, tunnel locations, terminal reservoirs, and hilltops. These controls are valuable aids in carrying out the overall system design.

Basic principles of the economic location of a pipeline are given in Fig. 5-5. Water is to be pumped from reservoir *A* to a second reservoir *M*. Consider first the use of the pump line *AB* and the grade tunnel *BD*. The water must be pumped to a height great enough at *B* so that the hydraulic gradient in the tunnel *BD* will permit economic construction. The required tunnel size can be arrived at by using the plot of cost versus slope in Fig. 5-5. Curve *AB* gives the total cost of tunnel for any specified hydraulic gradient. The curve is obtained by selecting various hydraulic slopes, determining the tunnel size required to transmit the required flow at that slope, and then computing costs for the various sizes. Curve *CD* represents the capitalized cost of raising water to heights which correspond to the several tunnel slopes. Summing curves *AB* and *CD* gives the combined cost curve. Point *F* indicates the minimum combined cost and thus permits determination of the optimum hydraulic gradient as shown in the figure. Projecting the gradient upstream from *D* establishes the height of pumping lift and allows the grade tunnel *BD* to be designed.

The most economical gradient can also be obtained without the use of curve *EFG*. To do this, select any arbitrary point on the pumping curve *CD* and construct a tangent at this point. Then construct a tangent to curve *AB* whose slope is the reverse of that of the tangent to *CD*. If the two points of tangency do not lie on approximately the same vertical, select a new starting point and repeat the procedure. At the tangent point *T'* (Fig. 5-5), the slope of the tangent is numerically equal to the cost of an

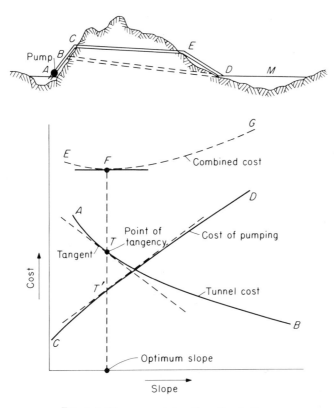

FIG. 5-5. The economic location of a pipeline.

additional foot of head. When information on this cost is available from other sources, *CD* need not be drawn since the tangent is determined directly from the cost of a foot of head.

Consider now the alternative aqueduct *ACED* in Fig. 5-5. The question arises, Is it more economical to pump to *C* and then carry the flow through the shorter tunnel *CE*, or to pump to *B* and use the longer tunnel *BD*? This problem may be solved by making trial estimates. First, assume the control point to be at *E*. An estimate is then prepared for line *ACED* in the manner previously indicated and compared with the one made for *ABD* where the control was assumed at *D*. If the total aqueduct cost plus the capitalized cost of pumping is less for *ACED* than for *ABD*, the critical point is *E*. If this is not the case, the control will be at *D*.

When the head loss between two points in an aqueduct is fixed, it may be most economical to divide this amount unequally between the various types of conduits used.

The division will be determined largely by economic considerations. For example, since tunnel costs are often very high, it may be best to build the smallest possible tunnel and thereby consume a disproportionate share of the head available in this particular reach.

If an aqueduct is to be constructed of several different types of conduits and if the total head loss is fixed, application of the principles of Lagrange's method of undetermined multipliers will permit an evaluation of the most economical distribution of head loss,[8] which occurs when the ratios of change in cost Δc to change in head Δh are equal for each type of conduit. The total available head H is equal to the sum of the various component losses or $H = \Sigma h$.

Application of this theory will be illustrated with the aid of Fig. 5-6. First, it is necessary that a set of curves of cost vs. head loss be plotted for each conduit type. These curves are derived from data obtained by designing the conduit types for various conditions of head loss and then estimating their cost. Example 5-2 would be typical of one such computation. Second, a series of parallel tangents drawn to each curve will be constructed by trial and error so that the sum of the individual head losses for each conduit equals the total available head. The ratio $\Delta c/\Delta h$ will be equal for all conduits when the tangents are parallel. This

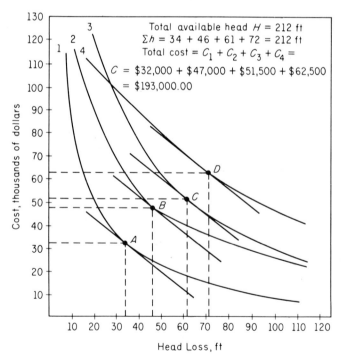

Total available head $H = 212$ ft
$\Sigma h = 34 + 46 + 61 + 72 = 212$ ft
Total cost $= C_1 + C_2 + C_3 + C_4 =$
$C = \$32,000 + \$47,000 + \$51,500 + \$62,500$
$= \$193,000.00$

Fig. 5-6. Graphical determination of the minimum cost of an aqueduct composed of four conduit types.

situation, along with the condition $\Sigma h = H$, satisfies the requirements for the most economical design.

EXAMPLE 5-3. Using the data supplied in Fig. 5-6 find the most economical division of the total head of 212 ft and the minimum aqueduct cost.

Solution: 1. By repeated trial, find the set of tangents A, B, C, and D such that $\Sigma h = H$.

2. Find the related costs $C1$, $C2$, $C3$, and $C4$ by projecting the points of tangency to intersections with the cost axis.

3. Numerical solutions are found on Fig. 5-6.

The method of parallel tangents just discussed will yield the required economic information providing that the total head loss is known.

Referring to Fig. 5-7, assume it is necessary to design an aqueduct system between a reservoir at A and a lake at G where power production is required. An investigation of the route indicates that the best arrange-

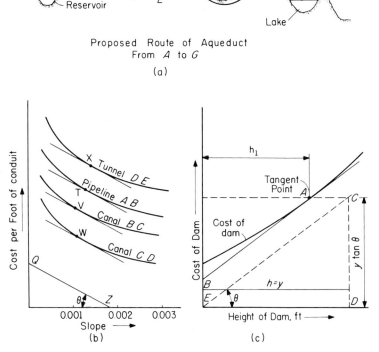

FIG. 5-7. Economic study of an aqueduct.

ment is a pipeline between A and B, a canal between B and D, and a tunnel between D and E. Assume further that a power drop is necessary at F. Determine the conduit gradients and their location for the optimum system.

Suppose that the tunnel DE is a controlling factor and that point E will fix the vertical location of the aqueduct. The most economical slopes may then be determined in the following manner:[10]

1. Plot a set of curves showing cost per linear foot of conduit versus slope for the various types of conduit (Fig. 5-7b). Note that these curves must correspond to the designated design discharge.

2. Plot a cost curve for the dam (Fig. 5-7c). Assume some trial height of dam h_1 and construct a tangent at the intersection of the ordinate constructed at h_1 with the cost curve (point A). The slope of this tangent represents the cost of an added foot of dam height at h_1.

3. Lay off the line QZ on Fig. 5-7b such that the tan θ equals the cost of an additional foot of dam at the trial height h_1. This slope is determined from the inclination of the tangent at point A in Fig. 5-7c but with the slope reversed.

4. Construct tangents to the cost curves AB, BC, CD, and ED in Fig. 5-7b. These tangents are all drawn parallel to QZ. The locations of the tangent points T, V, W, and X permit determination of the optimum economical slopes for each type of conduit.

5. Using the slopes defined by the tangents, and the known or assumed elevation at E, compute the required elevation of the dam at A.

6. Compare the computed dam height with h_1. If there is considerable difference, repeat the procedure outlined until a satisfactory solution is obtained. In this manner the most economical combination of dam height, conduit size, and corresponding hydraulic gradient is established between the dam and the assumed fixed point E.

7. From E to G the optimum system will have to be resolved through a consideration of the value of power developed in the power drop FG. To accomplish this, a procedure simular to that already illustrated is followed. Begin by assuming a trial power drop FG. This tentatively establishes point F. Estimate the value of a foot of head resulting from this drop. A plot similar to that of Fig. 5-7c, or an analytical procedure, may be used.

8. Plot cost curves for the types of conduits required between E and F. On this plot construct a new line similar to QZ which has tan θ equal to the value of a foot of head at F.

9. Draw parallel tangents to the cost curves and find the most economical slopes as before.

10. Using these slopes, find the actual elevation at F. If the power drop found in this manner differs enough to indicate an important change

in the value of a foot of head at F, repeat the procedure until satisfactory agreement is obtained.

A method for determining the optimum hydraulic grade line which does not require the assumption of control points (points at which the elevation of the hydraulic gradient is known) has been developed by E. E. Jackson and R. M. Edmonston for use in designing the Feather River Project in California.[7] The method appears to have particular merit, especially where pumping is involved.

The method is based on the Euler-Lagrange equation[9]

$$\frac{\partial f}{\partial y} - \frac{d}{dx}\left(\frac{\partial f}{\partial y'}\right) = 0 \tag{5-5}$$

which in this case governs the selection of the most economical grade line.

The equation is a perfectly general relationship applicable to any location on any type of conduit structure in the aqueduct. The terms in the equation are defined as follows:[7]

f = cost per foot of the conduit

y = elevation of the hydraulic grade line at some specified location

x = distance along the conduit measured from any origin

$y' = \dfrac{dy}{dx}$, the hydraulic gradient

$\dfrac{\partial f}{\partial y}$ = rate of change of unit conduit cost with respect to change in elevation of the hydraulic gradient at a specific location.

$\dfrac{\partial f}{\partial y'}$ = rate of change of unit conduit cost with respect to change of the hydraulic grade line (Numerically, it equals the value of a foot of head at any given point. The value of a foot of head N as defined by Hines is the cost of conveying the design flow through one foot of lift.[10] For a pumping plant, the cost of a foot of head equals the capitalized cost of pumping the design flow through a foot of lift. This includes· the incremental cost of the additional plant capacity required for the higher lift.)

$\dfrac{d}{dx}\left(\dfrac{\partial f}{\partial y'}\right)$ = rate of change of the value of a foot of head with respect to change in location along the aqueduct

This equation is the model for establishing the optimum hydraulic gradient. In practice it is not solved analytically but serves as an expression of the basic principle to follow in evaluating the various factors considered in an economical aqueduct design. Jackson and Edmonston give a more complete treatment of the theoretical aspects of this relationship.

In practice, the method can be applied in the following fashion:[7]

1. Determine the relationship between the unit costs of the various

types of conduit and the hydraulic gradient. This can be accomplished by plotting cost per foot of conduit as the ordinate versus hydraulic gradient as the abscissa. This gives a plot similar to that of Fig. 5-5.

2. Estimate the value of a foot of head N at some control point such as a pumping plant, a power plant, or a dam. Figure 5-7c illustrates this approach.

3. Using the information developed in Steps 1 and 2, make rough approximations of the optimum hydraulic gradient for each type of conduit. The method of tangents can be used for this.

4. Select a trial starting elevation of the hydraulic gradient after the first pumping lift.

5. Using a topographic map select a tentative route for the aqueduct, and combining it with field inspections, tentatively select the types of conduits to be utilized.

6. Plot the ground profile of the selected route.

7. Where there is an afterbay reservoir following the initial lift, determine a value of a foot of head N which includes the N of the pumping plant plus the cost of raising the afterbay elevation 1 ft.

8. From the value of N at the afterbay and the conduit cost curves, find the optimum gradient of the first type of conveyance reach. This will be determined by the tangent method as previously illustrated. Project this gradient ahead until N has changed by at least $1,000.

9. Using the value of N at the end of the first gradient, set a new gradient for the following reach. Repeat this process until the next pumping station or power plant is reached.

10. At the second pumping or power plant compare the value of N obtained in the preceding manner with the known value of a foot of head at that plant. If the computed value differs by more than 5 percent from the known value, choose a higher or lower starting elevation for the hydraulic grade line and begin again.

11. The procedure may be repeated several times as mapping and cost data are refined.

The conduit sizes established by the hydraulic gradients determined in this manner are the most economical for a specified set of operating rules over a particular ground profile. Note that not more than two end conditions may be met. These conditions might be known values of N or fixed elevations of the hydraulic gradient at the ends of a line.

Strength Considerations. Water-conveyance structures are required to resist numerous forces such as those resulting from water pressure within the conduit, hydraulic surge (transient internal pressure generated when the velocity of flow is rapidly reduced), external loads, forces at bends or changes in cross section, expansion and contraction, and flexural stresses.

Only those factors which are of a hydraulic nature will be discussed here. The other considerations may be handled in a manner similar to that of numerous problems in structural analysis. For a discussion of these topics the reader is referred to the ample literature on pipe and structural loadings available through the many manufacturers of these products.

Internal Pressure.   Internal pressures in conduits are caused by static pressure and/or hydraulic surge. These internal pressures cause circumferential tensile stresses in the pipe walls and thereby are important factors in designing pipe-wall thicknesses. Tensile stress may be approximated by the relationship

$$S_t = \frac{PR}{t} \tag{5-6}$$

where S_t = tensile stress

P = internal pressure

R = internal pipe radius

t = pipe-wall thickness

Hydraulic Surge.   A sudden decrease in the flow velocity in pipelines is accompanied by pressure increases which may in some cases cause rupture of the pipe. It is important that engineers be able to analyze problems of this nature and provide the necessary surge relief measures.

Consider a long pipe of uniform diameter connected to a reservoir at its upper end. If a valve in this line is suddenly closed, particles of water immediately adjacent to the valve will have their velocities reduced from a steady-state velocity v to zero at the instant of closure. If pipe walls and water were perfectly inelastic (rigid), the whole mass of water would be immediately brought to rest and result in infinite pressure being developed in the closed system.   This condition does not happen since water is slightly compressible and the pipe walls are elastic.   Large pressure increases may be generated, however, and these rises cause concern.

To clarify the concepts that are to follow, it will be assumed that the water in the pipeline is divided into an infinite number of increments or *laminae* of equal mass.[22]   At the moment the valve closes, the lamina adjacent to it is compressed through the conversion of its kinetic energy. As fluid compression proceeds, the pipe wall surrounding the lamina is expanded; the adjacent lamina experiences the same effect, and so in turn do the remaining laminae back to the reservoir. After the lamina at the inlet end of the line has been compressed, the entire system is filled with fluid at rest and under increased pressure. If the pipe is of length L and the time required for the compression of the last lamina after closure of the valve is T, then the relationship

$$c = \frac{L}{T} \tag{5-7}$$

yields the celerity c of a pressure wave that has moved up the pipeline from the valve to the reservoir. Once the last lamina has been brought to rest, the kinetic energy will have been converted to pressure energy and stored in the elastic deformation of the fluid and pipe material. This may be considered to conclude the first period of the initial cycle of events.

After compression of all the laminae in the pipe is complete, the energy stored in the pipe walls and the fluid will initiate flow once again but in the opposite direction. Once all the laminae are set in motion, pressures will have returned to normal and the fluid will be moving toward the reservoir with its original velocity. The pipe wall will no longer be distended. This completes the second period.

As the fluid moves away from the closed valve and toward the reservoir, its kinetic energy will be expended in decreasing the fluid pressure to a subnormal value. The fluid will then come to rest at a pressure below normal.

The fourth period is one in which flow is reestablished toward the valve. Due to the subnormal pressure condition at the completion of the third period, water begins to enter the pipe from the reservoir. Pressures are restored to normal and flow again takes place in its original direction and with the original velocity. Thus, a cycle of four movements has occurred during a period of time equal to $4L/c$. Additional cycles follow but these are continually dampened by viscous friction until static conditions prevail.

The engineer is interested in the magnitude of the excess pressure which results during this course of events. Figure 5-8 will be used in the development of an expression for the excess pressure p_e^{22}. At the instant the valve closes, the volume $ABCD$ is compressed into volume $EFGH$, the pipe is distended to radius $R + \Delta R$ and the original volume is shortened by the amount dL'. The change in volume V may be expressed as

$$\Delta V = \pi R^2 dL' - 2\pi R \Delta R\, dL \qquad (5\text{-}8)$$

Then, since the volume modulus of elasticity of water is given by

$$K = \frac{p_e}{\Delta V/V} \qquad (5\text{-}9)$$

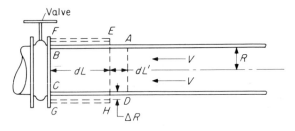

FIG. 5-8. Analysis of hydraulic surge.

where K = volume modulus of elasticity (300,000 psi is commonly used)
   V = volume

K may be rewritten as

$$K = \frac{p_e \, \pi R^2 (dL + dL')}{\pi R^2 dL' - 2\pi R \Delta R dL} \qquad (5\text{-}10)$$

where p_e is the intensity of the excess pressure. Using Eq. 5-6, the stress produced in the pipe wall by this pressure is $S_t = p_e R / t$. For an elongation of the pipe circumference equal to ΔS, the modulus of elasticity of the wall will be given by the ratio of the stress to the strain, or

$$E = \frac{S_t}{\Delta S / 2\pi R} = \frac{2\pi p_e R^2}{t \Delta S} \qquad (5\text{-}11)$$

Using the fact that circumference is a direct function of radius,

$$\frac{\Delta S}{2\pi R} = \frac{\Delta R}{R} \qquad (5\text{-}12)$$

and

$$\Delta S = 2\pi \Delta R \qquad (5\text{-}13)$$

Substituting in Eq. 5-11,

$$\Delta R = \frac{p_e R^2}{t E} \qquad (5\text{-}14)$$

Considering that the volume $ABCD$ was brought to rest by the action of pressure, it may be said that this occurred through the action of the force $p_e \pi R^2$. The rate of deceleration of the volume $ABCD$ is determined by

$$a = \frac{\text{force}}{\text{mass}} = \frac{p_e \pi R^2}{\rho \pi R^2 (dL + dL')} \qquad (5\text{-}15)$$

As the volume $ABCD$ comes to rest it is compressed and the location of its center of gravity shifts by a distance $dL'/2$. In uniformly decelerating a mass having an initial velocity v, the space traversed by the mass is

$$L = \frac{v^2}{2a} \qquad (5\text{-}16)$$

Using this relationship and Eq. 5-15 we may write

$$\frac{dL'}{2} = \frac{v^2 \pi R^2 (dL + dL') \rho}{2\pi R^2 p_e} \qquad (5\text{-}17)$$

then making the substitution $dL' = v \, dT$ and rearranging,

$$p_e = \frac{\rho v (dL + dL')}{dT} \qquad (5\text{-}18)$$

Considering that dL' is extremely small compared with dL, it may be neglected, yielding

$$p_e = \rho v \frac{dL}{dT} \tag{5-19}$$

where dL/dT is the celerity of the pressure wave c.

In order to solve Eq. 5-19 a way to evaluate dL/dT must be found. The needed relationship can be obtained by again considering Eq. 5-10. If the value of ΔR from Eq. 5-14 is substituted and the value of p_e from Eq. 5-18 is used to eliminate $(dL + dL')$,

$$K = \frac{p_e \pi R^2 (dL + dL')}{\pi R^2 dL' - 2\pi R\, p_e R^2 \Delta L / tE} \tag{5-10}$$

and

$$K = \frac{p_e (dL + dL')}{dL' - 2Rp_e dL/tE}$$

$$dL' - \frac{2R\, p_e\, dL}{tE} = \frac{p_e}{K}(dL + dL')$$

$$\frac{dL'}{p_e} - \frac{2R\, dL}{tE} = \frac{p_e(dL + dL')\, dT}{K\rho v(dL + dL')}$$

$$\frac{dL'}{dT} - \frac{2R}{tE}\frac{dL}{dT}p_e = \frac{p_e^2}{K\rho v}$$

then substituting for p_e its value from Eq. 5-19, and since $dL'/dT = v$ and $dL/dT = c$,

$$v - \frac{2R}{tE}\rho v c^2 - \rho \frac{v c^2}{K} = 0$$

and

$$c = \sqrt{\frac{K}{\rho}}\sqrt{\frac{1}{1 + KD/Et}} \tag{5-20}$$

where D is the pipe diameter.

To determine the excess pressure p_e, Eq. 5-20 may be substituted for dL/dT in Eq. 5-19 to yield

$$p_e = \rho v \sqrt{\frac{K}{\rho}}\sqrt{\frac{1}{1 + KD/Et}} \tag{5-21}$$

The total pressure which develops at the valve immediately after an instantaneous closure is therefore $p_e + p$, where p is the static pressure in the pipe.

The preceding derivation was for the case of instantaneous closure. Looking back at the four periods discussed, it will be seen that the maximum pressure is maintained at the valve for the first two periods, or for a time $2L/c$. If the valve is closed gradually but within this period, Eq. 5-21 is applicable. For closure times longer than $2L/c$, Joukovsky has proposed the following equation [11]

$$p_m \cong p_e \frac{2L}{cT_c} \tag{5-22}$$

where p_m is the maximum pressure for a closure time $T_c > 2L/c$. It has been shown that this relation errs on the side of safety since it yields values greater than the actual pressure.

Recent advances in the application of the digital computer have stimulated the solution of this problem by making use of the basic partial differential equations which describe the transient phenomena. The general form of these equations is

$$\frac{\partial H}{\partial T} = - \left(\frac{c^2}{g}\right) \frac{\partial v}{\partial x} \tag{5-23}$$

$$\frac{\partial H}{\partial x} = - \left(\frac{1}{g}\right) \frac{\partial v}{\partial T} \tag{5-24}$$

where H = pressure head equal to p/γ
   x = length of the pipe over which peak head will occur (measured from the valve)

and the other variables are defined as before. Numerical methods are usually employed to effect simultaneous solutions of the equations for ΔH and Δv for assumed values of Δx and ΔT. A more complete discussion of these solutions is given by Morris.[5]

One of the ways to guard pipelines against hydraulic surge is to construct surge tanks which relieve the excess pressure. These devices also serve to minimize the danger of negative pressure if a valve is suddenly opened. Figure 5-9 shows a surge tank constructed on the South Bay Aqueduct in California. Figure 5-10 illustrates the operation of a simple surge tank.

In Fig. 5-10, assume that water is flowing in the direction indicated with a velocity v, and a friction head loss H_f. If the valve at A is closed quickly, water will rise in the surge tank to an elevation $S + H_f$ above the level of the original hydraulic gradient. Using the relation $F = ma$, we may write the unsteady flow energy equation

$$-\rho g (S + H_f)A_p = \rho A_p L \frac{dv}{dT} \tag{5-25}$$

and rearranging,

$$\frac{dv}{dT} = - \frac{g}{L} \left[S + f\left(\frac{L}{D}\right)\left(\frac{v_0^2}{2g}\right) \right]$$

or

$$\frac{dv}{dT} = - \left(\frac{Sg}{L} + \frac{Fv_0^2}{2D}\right) \tag{5-26}$$

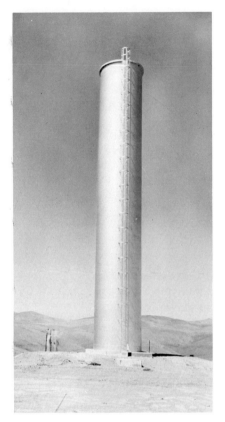

FIG. 5-9. South Bay Aqueduct surge tank, used to take excess water from pipeline during periods of high pressure. (Courtesy of the California Department of Water Resources.)

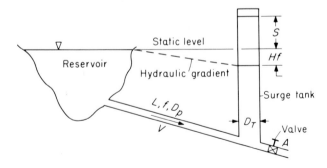

FIG. 5-10. Schematic diagram of a simple surge tank.

The continuity equation can be written as

$$A_p v = A_T \frac{dS}{dT} \tag{5-27}$$

where A_p = cross-sectional area of the pipeline

A_T = cross-sectional area of the tank

If the pipeline is not long, friction losses may be neglected and Eq. 5-26 becomes

$$\left(\frac{dv}{dS}\right)\left(\frac{dS}{dT}\right) = -\frac{Sg}{L} \tag{5-28}$$

Inserting the value of dS/dT from Eq. 5-27, the equation becomes

$$\frac{dv}{dS} = -\left(\frac{A_T}{A_p v}\right)\left(\frac{g}{L}\right)S \tag{5-29}$$

Integrating this equation,

$$\int_{v_0}^{v_t} v\, dv = -\left(\frac{A_T}{A_p}\right)\left(\frac{g}{L}\right)\int_0^S S\, dS$$

$$v_t^2 = v_0^2 - \left(\frac{A_T}{A_p}\right)\left(\frac{g}{L}\right)S^2 \tag{5-30}$$

This equation relates the velocity at any time T to the original pipe velocity and the surge. When $v_t = 0$, the surge will be a maximum. Then

$$S_{max} = v_0 \sqrt{\left(\frac{A_p}{A_T}\right)\left(\frac{L}{g}\right)} \tag{5-31}$$

This equation is reasonably accurate and will yield conservative values for S_{max}. If the pipeline is long, friction should not be neglected and the following equation relating surge and time obtains,

$$\frac{d^2 S}{dT^2} + \left(\frac{f}{2D_p}\right)\left(\frac{A_T}{A_p}\right)\left(\frac{dS}{dT}\right)^2 + \left(\frac{g}{L}\right)\left(\frac{A_p}{A_t}\right)S = 0 \tag{5-32}$$

Numerical or graphical methods may be applied to effect a solution.[5]

Generally, surge tanks are open at the top and built high enough so they will not overflow. Where very high heads are encountered, the simple surge tank may not be practical. In this case some modification such as a restricted entrance or a closed top with an air cushion to absorb part of the pressure is often used. Differential surge tanks are sometimes built. They are constructed with a center riser having a diameter about the same as that of the pipe, with openings to admit water to the main tank. Because the oscillations in the riser and main tank are out of phase, the damping action is accomplished more quickly.

Anchorages. Pipelines are anchored to resist overstressing of joints in bends or on steep gradients, and to control temperature effects.

Figure 5-11 illustrates the forces exerted on a pipe bend by an anchorage. Consider the pipe to be horizontal so that the action of gravity is excluded. Also, since the length of the bend is short, neglect friction losses. The x component of the resultant force is therefore

$$F_x = P_1 A_1 - P_2 A_2 \cos\alpha - \rho Q(V_2 \cos\alpha - V_1) \tag{5-33}$$

and in the y direction,

$$F_y = P_2 A_2 \sin\alpha + \rho Q V_2 \sin\alpha \tag{5-34}$$

where P_1 and P_2 = intensity of pressure at sections 1 and 2
V_1, V_2 = velocities at the two sections

and the other terms are as indicated in Fig. 5-11.

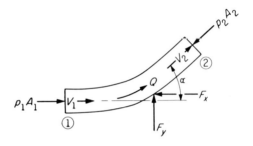

FIG. 5-11. Definition sketch for determination of force exerted on pipe bends.

EXAMPLE 5-4.   Find the total force an anchorage must exert on a pipe bend 36 in. in diameter curving through an angle of 60 degrees. Assume $P_1 = P_2 = 50$ psi and $Q = 50$ cfs.

Solution:

$$F_x = 50 \times \frac{\pi(36)^2}{4} - 50 \times \frac{\pi(36)^2}{4} \times 0.50 - 1.94 \times 50\left(7.07 \times \frac{1}{2} - 7.07\right)$$

$$= 50,700 - 25,350 + 342$$

$$= 25,692 \text{ lb} \qquad\qquad Ans.$$

$$F_y = 50 \times \frac{\pi 36^2}{4} \times 0.866 + 1.94 \times 50 \times 7.07 \times 0.866$$

$$= 43,900 + 594$$

$$= 44,494 \text{ lb}$$

$$F = \sqrt{F_x^2 + F_y^2} = 51,379 \text{ lb} \qquad\qquad Ans.$$

DISTRIBUTION SYSTEMS

Water-distribution systems are ordinarily designed to adequately satisfy the water requirements for some combination of domestic, commercial, industrial, and fire-fighting purposes. The system should be capable of meeting the demands placed on it at all times and at satisfactory pressures. Pipe systems, pumping stations, storage facilities, fire hydrants, house service connections, meters, and other appurtenances are the main elements of the system.

5-7. TYPES AND SYSTEMS

Distribution systems may be generally classified as grid systems, branching systems, or some combination of these. The configuration of the system is dictated primarily by street patterns, topography, degree and type of development of the area, and location of treatment and storage works. Figure 5-12 illustrates the basic patterns which evolve.

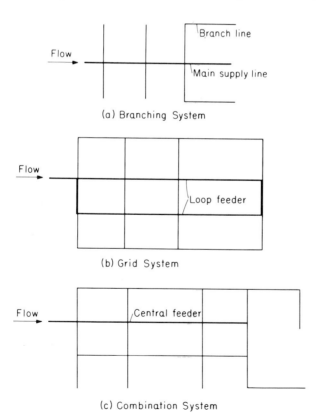

(a) Branching System

(b) Grid System

(c) Combination System

FIG. 5-12. Water-distribution system patterns.

The grid system has the decided advantage hydraulically of providing flow at any point from more than one direction. The branching system does not permit this type of circulation since it has numerous terminals or dead ends. A grid or combination system also has the advantage of permitting the use of loop feeders which supply an area from more than one direction.

In locations where sharp changes in topography occur (hilly or mountainous regions) it is common practice to divide the distribution system into two or more service areas or zones. Thus there are independent high- and low-service areas. This precludes the difficulty of extremely high pressure in low-service areas in order to maintain reasonable pressures in the high-service areas. Common practice is to interconnect the various systems for emergency use. Under normal conditions of operation the interconnections are closed off by gate valves.

5-8. PRESSURE AND CAPACITY

The performance of a distribution system can be judged on the basis of the pressures available in the system for a specific rate of flow.[13,19] Pressures should be great enough to adequately meet consumer and fire-fighting needs. At the same time they should not be excessive, since the development of pressure head is an important cost consideration. In addition, as pressures increase, leakage increases, and money is then spent to transport and process a product which is wasted. Because the investment in a distribution system is exceedingly large, it is important that the design be optimized economically.

For business or downtown areas, pressures of 60 to 75 psig (pounds per square inch, gage) are normal. Residential areas usually are adequately serviced by pressures of 40 to 50 psig. Where hydrant pressures sufficient to directly supply fire hoses are required, pressures in excess of 100 psig are not uncommon. The advent of the modern motor pumper has generally eliminated this need, however.

In large tower buildings it is often necessary to provide booster pumps to elevate the water to upper floors. Storage tanks are usually provided at the highest level and distribution is made directly from them.

The capacity of the distribution system is determined on the basis of an evaluation of the various normal municipal water needs plus fire demands as outlined in Chap. 3. Pipe sizes should be selected so that excessive velocities with their accompanying high pressure drops and potential hydraulic-surge characteristics are avoided. Once the flow has been determined, pipe sizes can be selected by assuming velocities of from 3 to 5 fps.

Where fire-fighting requirements are to be met, a minimum diameter of 6 in. is common. The National Board of Fire Underwriters recommends 8 in. as a minimum diameter but will permit 6-in. pipes in grid systems providing the length between connections does not exceed 600 ft. Where fire-fighting is not a requirement, pipes 4 in. in diameter and less are sometimes used. Normally, 4-in. pipe is not used because of the relatively large losses of head involved. The initial economy in selecting a small pipe is usually offset materially by the higher costs of maintaining adequate pressures in such systems.

5-9. HYDRAULIC DESIGN OF DISTRIBUTION SYSTEMS

In order to effect the hydraulic design of a water-distribution system, information must be available on the anticipated local rates of water consumption; the manner in which these design flows are distributed geographically; and the required pressure gradients for the system.

The answer to the first question is obtained in the manner already indicated in Chap. 3. It should be reemphasized that the designer ought to investigate both the maximum day rate plus fire protection and the maximum hourly rate to determine which will govern the design.

The spatial distribution of consumption can be estimated by studying population densities, and commercial and industrial use patterns, which are known or predicted for the region. Consider the design of a feeder to an area composed of residential, commercial, and industrial users. In investigating the peak hour for example, it will be important to have the predicted hydrograph for each type of user so that the specific hour in which the summation of the three component flows is greatest will be used for the design. Students are cautioned that the regional maximum hour might well coincide with the residential maximum within the region, but not coincide with the commercial or industrial peaks, or vice versa. For this reason, information on the hourly variation of water use for all users is extremely valuable. Once the water consumption has been estimated, it is usual practice to consider it to be concentrated at specified points on the feeder-main system. Computations based on the concentration of consumption in this manner normally appear to correlate well with field observations.

Distribution systems are usually designed so that reasonably uniform pressures prevail. Where important differences in land elevation are encountered, various high- and low-service zones are often designated. A pressure of 30 psi is normally considered to be the minimum desirable in any area with the exception that during a serious fire it may be permissible to allow the pressure to drop to about 20 psi. Main feeders should be designed for pressures between 40 and 75 psi whenever possible.[13]

Perhaps the most useful methods of pipe-network analysis are (1) the Hardy Cross method, (2) the method of sections, and (3) the equivalent-pipe method which is often used with the Hardy Cross analysis. The

Hazen-Williams pipe-flow formula is commonly used in all of these. The tedious solutions to some of the approaches lend themselves especially well to electric analyzers and digital computers. More will be given on this in Sec. 5-11.

The Equivalent-Pipe Method.   The analysis of a distribution system is often expedited by first skeletonizing the system. This might involve the replacement of a series of pipes of varying diameter with one equivalent pipe or replacing a system of pipes with an equivalent pipe. An equivalent pipe is one in which the loss of head for a specified flow is the same as the loss in head of the system which it replaces. For any system there are theoretically an infinite number of equivalent pipes. An example will illustrate the method of analysis.

EXAMPLE 5-5.   Considering the pipe system shown in Fig. 5-13, replace (a) pipes BC and CD with an equivalent 12-in. pipe and (b) the system from B to D with an equivalent 20-in. pipe.

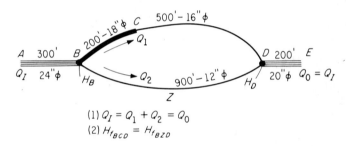

$$(1)\ Q_I = Q_1 + Q_2 = Q_0$$
$$(2)\ H_{f_{BCD}} = H_{f_{BZD}}$$

FIG. 5-13. Diagram for Example 5-5.

Solution: (a) Assume a discharge through BCD of 8 cfs. Using the Hazen-Williams nomograph (Fig. 5-14) find the head loss for $BC = 6.1$ ft/1,000 ft and for $CD = 11$ ft/1,000 ft.

The total head loss between B and D is therefore

$$6.1 \times \frac{200}{1,000} + 11.0 \times \frac{500}{1,000} = 6.72 \text{ ft}$$

Using a discharge of 8 cfs, Fig. 5-14 indicates a head loss of 45 ft/1,000 ft for a 12-in. pipe. The equivalent length of 12-in. pipe is therefore

$$L_{12} = \frac{6.72 \times 1,000}{45} = 149 \text{ ft}$$

(b) Assume a total head loss between B and D of 5.0 ft. For the 12-in. equivalent pipe this is 33.5 ft/1,000 ft and for the 900 ft of 12-in. pipe it is 5.5 ft/1,000 ft. Using these values and Fig. 5-14, the discharges for the two pipes are found to be 6.8 and 2.6 cfs, respectively. The total flow is thus 9.4 cfs at a

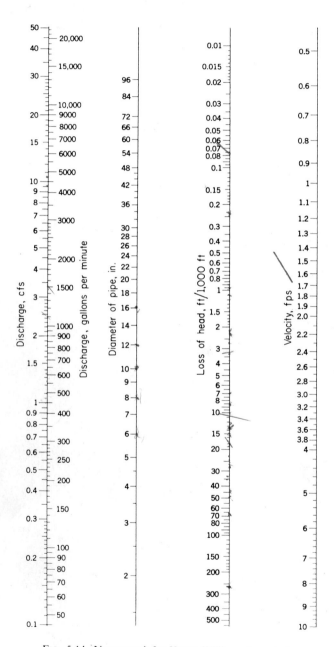

FIG. 5-14. Nomograph for Hazen-Williams formula in
which C = 100.

head loss of 5 ft. For this discharge, a 20-in. pipe will have a head loss of 4.8 ft/1,000 ft. The equivalent 20-in. pipe to replace the whole system will be

$$\frac{5}{4.8} \times 1,000 = 1,042 \text{ ft long}$$

The Method of Sections. A useful tool in making approximate checks of the adequacy of a specified distribution system for a prescribed mode of operation is the method of sections developed by Allen Hazen.

The manner in which this procedure is employed (with the aid of Fig. 5-15) follows.

1. Determine the quantity of water which is to be drawn off along the network for various uses, including fire-fighting. Indicate the approximate remaining flow the system must handle at locations where there is a significant change in total flow (Fig. 5-15).

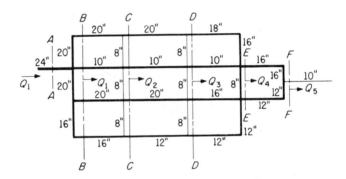

Note: Between *A-A*, and *C-C*, the system must be able to handle Q_1, between *C-C* and *D-D*, Q_2, between *D-D* and *E-E*, Q_3, etc. Q_1-Q_2, is representative of the draft between *B-B* and *C-C*.

FIG. 5-15. Illustration of the use of method of sections in pipe network analysis.

2. Cut the network at any location considered in need of investigation by a series of lines such as shown. These cutting lines may be straight or curved. They are usually drawn approximately normal, at any point, to a direction which is considered to be critical. Common practice is to cut the initial trial sections at right angles to the general direction of flow.

3. Evaluate the capability of the distribution system to support the indicated flow of each cut section. To do this it is expeditious to first tabulate the various pipes cut in the primary direction of flow giving size and material. Then on the basis of a knowledge of the available or as-

sumed hydraulic gradient, determine the capacity of each individual pipe which has been cut. For distribution networks, hydraulic gradients between 1 and 3 ft/1,000 ft are common.

4. Total the individual flows and compare them with the flow that is to be handled. For example, referring to Fig. 5-15, the computed flows through two 20-in., one 10-in., and one 16-in. pipe at section *B-B* must be compared to Q_1.

5. If in Step 4 Q_1 exceeds the computed capacity of the system, the system will have to be supplemented to meet this deficiency.

6. Select pipes to be added to the system by using the known or assumed hydraulic gradient and the additional increment of flow to be added. The location of the supplementary pipes should be made on a basis of a knowledge of the entire network in such a manner as to optimize the improvement to the system.

The Hardy Cross Method. The analysis of a simple hydraulic system such as that shown in Fig. 5-13 presents little difficulty. A slightly more complex system is shown in Fig. 5-16. The method of equivalent pipes

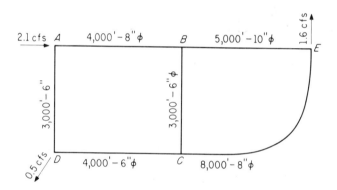

FIG. 5-16. Simple pipe network analyzed by the Hardy Cross method.

will fail to yield a solution in this case because there are crossover pipes (pipes which operate in more than one circuit) and a number of withdrawal points throughout the system.

This type of network may be solved by using the Hardy Cross method of network analysis.[15] The procedure permits the accurate computation of the rates of flow through the system and the resulting head losses in the system. It is a relaxation method by which corrections are applied to assumed flows or assumed heads until the system is hydraulically balanced.

The Hardy Cross analysis is based primarily on the hydraulic axioms that (1) in any system continuity must be preserved, and (2) the pressure at any junction of pipes is single valued. Referring to the simple network of Fig. 5-17, the elements of the procedure can be explained. First the system must be defined in terms of pipe size, length, and roughness. Then for any inflow Q_1, the system can be balanced hydraulically only if $H_{f_{BCD}} = H_{f_{BZD}}$. This restriction limits the possibilities to only one value of Q_1 and Q_2 which will satisfy the conditions.

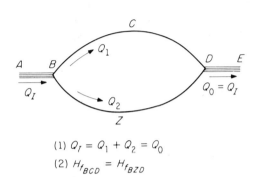

(1) $Q_I = Q_1 + Q_2 = Q_0$

(2) $H_{f_{BCD}} = H_{f_{BZD}}$

Fig. 5-17. Sketch illustrating the derivation of the Hardy Cross method.

Derivation of the basic equation for balancing heads by correcting assumed flows will now be given for the loop of Fig. 5-17.[15] First find the required inflow Q_I. Then arbitrarily divide this flow into components Q_1 and Q_2. The only restriction on the selection of these values is that $Q_1 + Q_2 = Q_I$. An attempt should be made however, to select realistic values. Since the procedure involves a number of trials, the amount of work involved will be dependent upon the accuracy of the value originally selected. For example, in the network shown, BCD is considerably larger in diameter than BZD. A logical choice would therefore assume that Q_1 will be larger than Q_2. The final solution to the problem will be the same regardless of the original choice but much more rapid progress results from reasonable initial assumptions.

After Q_1 and Q_2 have been chosen, $H_{f_{BCD}}$ and $H_{f_{BZD}}$ can be computed using the Hazen-Williams or some other pipe flow formula. Remembering that the Hazen-Williams equation is of the form

$$Q = 0.279 CD^{2.63} S^{0.54} \qquad [5\text{-}2]$$

the equation may be rewritten as

$$Q = K_a S^{0.54} \qquad (5\text{-}35)$$

where K_a is a constant when we are dealing only with a single pipe of specified size and material. Rearranging this equation and substituting

H_f/L for S,

$$H_f = KQ^n \tag{5-36}$$

where $n = 1.85$ in the Hazen-Williams equation. Equation 5-36 is convenient for expressing head loss as a function of flow in network analyses.

If the computed values of $H_{f_{BCD}}$ and $H_{f_{BZD}}$ are not equal (which is usually the case on the first trial) a correction must be applied to the initial values. Call this correction ΔQ. If, for example, $H_{f_{BCD}} > H_{f_{BZD}}$ then the new value for Q_1 will be $Q_1 - \Delta Q = Q_1'$ and the new value for Q_2 must be $Q_2 + \Delta Q = Q_2'$. The corresponding values of head loss will be $H'_{f_{BCD}}$ and $H'_{f_{BZD}}$. If ΔQ is the true correction, then

$$H'_{f_{BCD}} - H'_{f_{BZD}} = 0 = K_1(Q_1 - \Delta Q)^n - K_2(Q_2 + \Delta Q)^n$$

The binomials may be expanded as follows:

$$K_1(Q_1^n - n\Delta Q\, Q_1^{n-1} + \cdots) - K_2(Q_2^n + n\Delta Q\, Q_2^{n-1} + \cdots) = 0$$

If ΔQ is small, the terms in the expansion involving ΔQ to powers greater than one can safely be neglected. Therefore,

$$K_1 Q_1^n - nK_1 \Delta Q\, Q_1^{n-1} - K_2 Q_2^n - nK_2 \Delta Q Q_2^{n-1} = 0$$

Substituting $H_{f_{BCD}}$ for $K_1 Q_1^n$, $H_{f_{BZD}}$ for $K_2 Q_2^n$, and rewriting the terms KQ^{n-1} as $K\dfrac{Q^n}{Q}$,

$$H_{f_{BCD}} - \Delta Q n K_1 \frac{Q_1^n}{Q_1} - H_{f_{BZD}} - \Delta Q n K_2 \frac{Q_2^n}{Q_2} = 0$$

$$H_{f_{BCD}} - H_{f_{BZD}} = \Delta Q n \left(\frac{H_{f_{BCD}}}{Q_1} + \frac{H_{f_{BZD}}}{Q_2} \right)$$

and

$$\Delta Q = \frac{H_{f_{BCD}} - H_{f_{BZD}}}{n(H_{f_{BCD}}/Q_1 + H_{f_{BZD}}/Q_2)} \tag{5-37}$$

Expanding this expression to the more general case, the equation for the flow correction ΔQ becomes

$$\Delta Q = -\frac{\Sigma H}{n\Sigma(H/Q)} \tag{5-38}$$

Application of this equation involves an initial assumption of discharge and a sign convention for the flow. Either clockwise or counterclockwise flows may be considered positive, and the terms in the numerator will bear the appropriate sign. For example, if the counterclockwise direction is considered positive, then all H values for counterclockwise flows will be positive and all H values for clockwise flows will be negative. The denominator, however, is the absolute sum without regard to sign convention. The correction ΔQ has a single direction for all pipes in the loop and thus the sign convention must also be considered in applying the correction. Example 5-6 illustrates the application of the procedure to a network problem.

EXAMPLE 5-6. Given the network, the inflow at *A*, and outflows at *B*, *C*, and *D* in Fig. 5-18, find the flows in the individual pipes comprising the network.

Solution: The computational procedure is given in Table 5-4. The final flows are shown on Fig. 5-18.

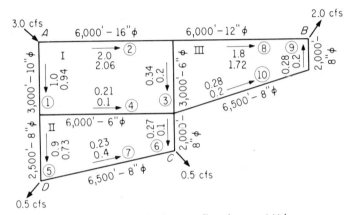

Note: Clockwise direction considered positive. Flows shown are initial assumption and final corrected value.

FIG. 5-18. Pipe network analyzed by the Hardy Cross method.

It should be noted that since pipes 3 and 4 appear in more than one loop, they are subject to the combined correction for loops I and III and I and II respectively.

A similar procedure to that just discussed is to assume values of *H* and then balance the flows by correcting the assumed heads. The mechanics of the two methods are the same and the applicable relationship

$$\Delta H = -\frac{n \Sigma Q}{\Sigma Q / H} \tag{5-39}$$

can be derived in a manner similar to that for Eq. 5-38. The number of trials required for the satisfactory solution of any problem using Eq. 5-38 or Eq. 5-39 depends to a large extent on the accuracy of the initial set of assumed values and on the desired degree of accuracy of the results.

In using the Hardy Cross method to analyze large distribution systems, it is often useful to reduce the system to a skeleton network of main feeders.[13] Where the main-feeder system has a very large capacity relative to that of the smaller mains, field observations indicate that this type of *[handwritten annotation: "will decrease # of iterations" with arrow pointing to the $\Delta Q/2$ column; "$\dfrac{\Delta Q}{2}$" written above column 11]*

TABLE 5-4
COMPUTATIONS FOR EXAMPLE 5-6

Trial I and Trial II

(1) Loop No.	(2) Pipe No.	(3) Pipe Diam., in.	(4) Length, ft	(5) Q, cfs	(6) H_L, ft	(7) H_L/Q	(8) $n\Sigma\,H_L/Q$	(9) ΣH_L	(10) ΔQ	(5) Q_1	(6) H_L	(7) H_L/Q	(8) $n\Sigma\,H_L/Q$	(9) ΣH_L	(10) ΔQ	(11) $\Delta Q/2$
I	1	10	3,000	−1.0	− 6.9	6.9	90.3	+ 0.15	−0.002	−1.0	− 6.9	6.9	171.5	−8.13	+0.05	
	2	16	6,000	+2.0	+ 4.92	2.46			−0.002	+2.0	+ 4.92	2.46			+0.05	
	3	6	3,000	+0.2	+ 4.05	20.30			+0.12	+0.32	+ 9.45	29.5			+0.03	
	4	6	6,000	−0.1	− 1.92	19.2			−0.19	−0.29	−15.6	53.8			+0.09	
II	4	6	6,000	+0.1	+ 1.92	19.2	102.5	−19.42	+0.19	+0.29	+15.6	53.8	153.1	+5.6	−0.09	
	6	8	2,000	+0.1	+ 0.16	1.6			+0.19	+0.29	+ 1.4	4.83			−0.04	
	7	8	6,500	−0.4	− 7.8	19.5			+0.19	−0.21	− 2.4	11.43			−0.04	
	5	8	2,500	−0.9	−13.7	15.2			+0.19	−0.71	− 9.0	12.69			−0.04	
III	3	6	3,000	−0.2	− 4.05	20.3	81.7	+ 9.8	−0.12	−0.32	− 9.45	29.5	109.9	−1.85	−0.03	
	8	12	6,000	+1.8	+16.2	9.0			−0.12	+1.68	+14.4	8.58			+0.02	
	9	8	2,000	−0.2	− 0.7	3.5			−0.12	−0.32	− 1.6	5.0			+0.02	
	10	8	6,500	−0.2	− 2.28	11.4			−0.12	−0.32	− 5.2	16.25			+0.02	

Trial III and Trial IV

(1) Loop No.	(2) Pipe No.	(5) Q, cfs	(6) H_L, ft	(7) H_L/Q	(8) $n\Sigma\,H_L/Q$	(9) ΣH_L	(10) ΔQ	(5) Q_1	(6) H_L	(7) H_L/Q	(8) $n\Sigma\,H_L/Q$	(9) ΣH_L	(10) ΔQ	(11) $\Delta Q/2$
I	1	−0.95	− 6.3	6.64	154.8	+ 2.55	−0.016	−0.966	− 6.59	6.83	163.5	−4.50	+0.027	−0.94
	2	+2.05	+ 5.1	2.48			−0.016	+2.034	+ 5.09	2.51			+0.027	+2.06
	3	+0.35	+11.85	33.90			−0.047	+0.303	+ 9.0	29.70			+0.038	+0.34
	4	−0.20	− 8.1	40.50			−0.048	−0.248	−12.0	48.30			+0.035	−0.21
II	4	+0.20	+ 8.1	40.50	133.8	− 4.31	+0.048	+0.248	+12.0	48.30	146.3	+1.14	−0.035	+0.21
	6	+0.25	+ 1.08	4.32			+0.032	+0.282	+ 1.30	4.61			−0.008	+0.27
	7	−0.25	− 3.51	14.1			+0.032	−0.218	− 2.92	13.4			−0.008	−0.23
	5	−0.75	−10.00	13.33			+0.032	−0.718	− 9.24	12.85			−0.008	−0.73
III	3	−0.35	−11.85	33.90	116.3	− 3.57	+0.047	−0.303	− 9.0	29.70	106.2	+1.16	−0.038	−0.34
	8	+1.70	+14.38	8.46			+0.031	+1.731	+15.25	8.80			−0.011	+1.72
	9	−0.30	− 1.44	4.80			+0.031	−0.269	− 1.2	4.46			−0.011	−0.28
	10	−0.30	− 4.68	15.61			+0.031	−0.269	− 3.89	14.48			−0.011	−0.28

skeletonizing yields reasonable results. Where no well-defined feeder system is apparent serious errors may result from skeletonizing. Figure 5-19 illustrates a skeletonized distribution network consisting of arterial mains only. Figure 5-20 shows how a portion of the distribution system of Fig. 5-19 (that part lying within the dashed rectangle) looked before skeletonizing. A more complete discussion of such procedures is given by Reh.[13] The analysis of a large network may also be expedited by balancing portions of the system successively instead of analyzing the whole network simultaneously.

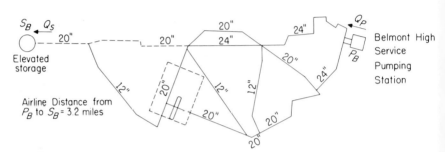

FIG. 5-19. Arterial piping network of Belmont High Service District, Philadelphia. (Courtesy of the Civil Engineering Department, University of Illinois.)

Normally, minor losses are neglected in network studies but they can easily be introduced as equivalent lengths of pipe when it is felt that they should be included. Where C values are determined from field measurements they invariably include a component due to the various minor losses encountered. McPherson gives a good discussion of local losses in water distribution networks.[14]

The construction of pressure contours helps to isolate shortcomings in the hydraulic performance of distribution systems. Contours are often drawn with intervals of 1 to 5 ft of head loss but may have other intervals depending on local circumstances. For a given set of operating rules applicable to a particular network, the pressure contours indicate the distribution of head loss and are helpful in showing regions where head losses are excessive. Figure 5-21 illustrates contours constructed for a distribution network.

Computations for a given network may be reduced considerably by making use of the proportional-flow method outlined by McPherson when studies of different inputs and outflows are needed.[12] In applying the technique, demands are first concentrated at key points in the network and a solution effected in the normal manner. Then if the inputs and demands on the system are changed in a truly proportional manner, a new set of pipe flows and head losses may be readily obtained. McPherson

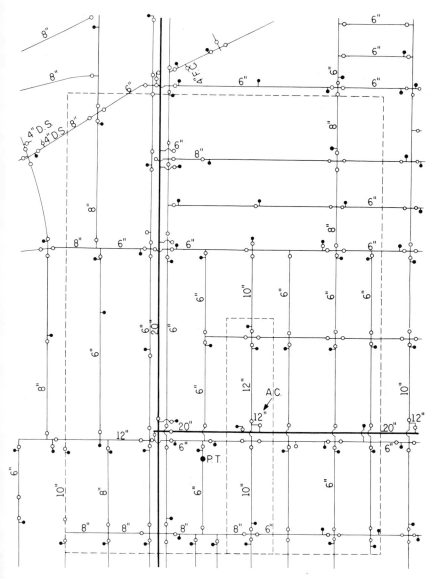

FIG. 5-20. Intermediate Grid Sector, Belmont High Service District, Philadelphia. (Courtesy of the Civil Engineering Department, University of Illinois.)

states that *proportional load* may be defined as the design assumption that each consolidated demand on the system fluctuates about its mean value in direct proportion to the manner in which the total system load fluctuates. Note that the assumption of proportional loading is not always realistic and in such cases the procedure outlined here does not apply.

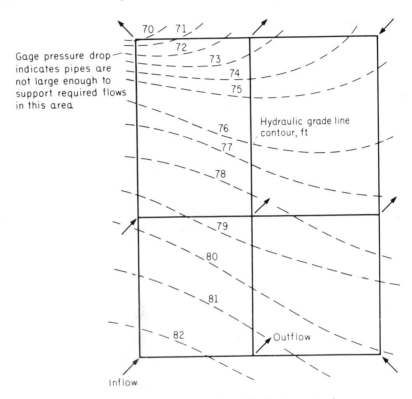

FIG. 5-21. Pressure contours for a distribution network.

The significance of this condition can best be illustrated by referring to Fig. 5-17. In the simple network pictured we may state that

(1) $Q_I = Q_0 = Q_1 + Q_2$
(2) $H_1 - H_2 = 0$ or $K_1 Q_1^n - K_2 Q_2^n = 0$

Solving these equations simultaneously,

$$Q_1 = A Q_I \quad \text{and} \quad Q_2 = B Q_I \tag{5-40}$$

where A and B are constants for the system. Thus it can be seen that if Q_I is doubled, then Q_1 and Q_2 are also doubled. Extending this thinking to a slightly more complex system having several outflows in place of the single one Q_0, as in the network of Fig. 5-17, the same reasoning holds true, providing the drafts and the inflow are all increased or decreased by the same percentage. New values for Q_1, Q_2, etc. may then be found by using a set of equations such as Eq. 5-40 without the need for making a complete network analysis.

McPherson has shown that under proportional-loading conditions the head loss of a complex network can be reduced to the following equation:[12]

$$\frac{\Sigma h}{Q_d^m} = \Phi \left(\frac{Q_p}{Q_d}\right)^n \qquad (5\text{-}41)$$

where h = loss in head between an input and some point in the district (such as an elevated storage location)

Q_d = demand placed on the network

Q_p = input rate at the point from which h is referenced

To determine values for Φ and n, only two network balances (computations) are required. If $Q_p = Q_d$, which is the case when there is no equalizing storage (see sec. 5-12), Φ can be determined by a single network balance. For more detailed information on proportional loading the student should refer to McPherson's work.

5-10. SYSTEM LAYOUT AND DESIGN

The design of a water-distribution network involves the selection of a system of pipes so that the predicted design flows can be carried with head losses which do not exceed those deemed necessary for adequate operation of the system. Normally the design flows should be based on estimated future requirements since a distribution system is expected to provide effective service for many years (often as long as 100 years). A logical sequence of design and layout operations is as follows:

1. Obtain a development plan for the area to be serviced. The plan should show the final street layout, building lots, and the type and value of structures to be placed on them.

2. Sketch the tentative location of all water mains which will be required to supply the area. The completed drawing should differentiate between proposed feeder mains and smaller service mains. The various pipelines comprising the system should be interconnected at intervals of 1,200 ft or less. Looped feeder systems are desirable and should be used wherever possible. Two small feeder mains running parallel several blocks apart are preferable to a single large main with an equal or slightly larger capacity than the two mains combined. Usually only a single main is laid in each street, although special circumstances may require other arrangements. Most major municipalities have well-established standards for positioning the distribution network.

3. Using estimated values of the anticipated design flows, select appropriate pipe sizes by assuming velocities of from 3 to 5 fps. Label each pipe with the selected diameter, length, and expected flow.

4. Mark the position of building service connections, fire hydrants, and valves. Service connections form the link between the distribution system and the individual consumer. Normally the practice is one

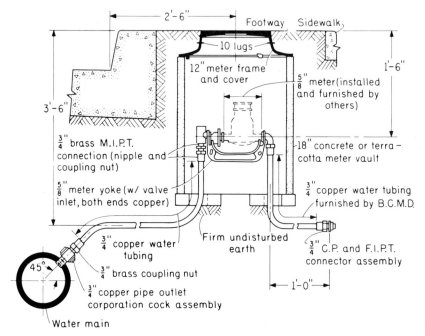

FIG. 5-22. Typical installation of ¾ in.-metered domestic service.   (Courtesy Baltimore County, Maryland, Department of Public Works.)

customer per service pipe.   Figure 5-22 illustrates the details of a typical service connection for a private residence.   Fire hydrants are located to provide complete protection to the area covered by the distribution system.   Recommendations regarding average area per hydrant for various populations and required fire flow are given by the National Board of Fire Underwriters.   Hydrants generally should not be farther than 500 ft apart.   Common practice in positioning hydrants is to construct a circle whose diameter is approximately 160 percent of the optimum hose length, using the hydrant as a center.   Complete coverage results when the entire area is covered by at least one circle.

Street intersections are particularly efficient locations for hydrants. Where blocks are long, intermediate locations may be required.   Figure 5-23 illustrates a typical fire-hydrant setting.   Valve locations should permit sections of the distribution system to be taken out for maintenance without seriously curtailing service over large areas.   They should be placed between feeder mains and service mains and on all pipes connected to fire hydrants.   Accepted practice is to use three valves at crosses and two at tees, and space them so that the maximum length of pipe uncontrolled by valves is not greater than about 1,200 ft.

5. Using the Hazen-Williams or some other appropriate method,

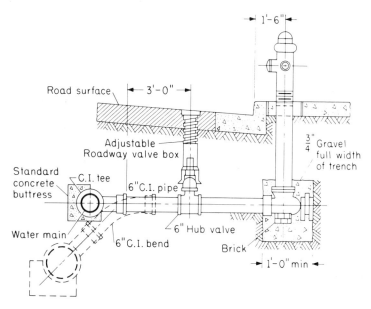

Fig. 5-23. Typical fire-hydrant setting.   (Courtesy Baltimore County, Maryland, Department of Public Works.)

compute pressures at key points in the distribution system.   From this information construct a map of pressure contours.   Kincaid presents detailed information on requirements prior to a thorough network analysis.[16]

6. Revise the initial trial network as necessary to get adequate operating pressures. The pressure-contour map will help select those parts of the system not adequately sized.

It must be emphasized here that although the network analysis yields very reliable results for the case studied, the results are no better than the initial assumptions of inputs, takeoffs, and pipe roughness.

5-11.   EVALUATION OF EXISTING SYSTEMS

Existing distribution networks can be analyzed for performance by conducting pressure surveys and hydrant flow tests. From recorded system pressures at selected observation points, pressure contours can be constructed for any gaged mode of operation. The data obtained in this manner give the performance for conditions which are in existence at the time of the gaging only and do not yield information on other modes of operation. Pressure surveys conducted during periods when demands are expected to be high are of particular value. A hot summer day preceded by a dry spell would be typical of such a period.

To determine the operation of the network during periods of fire demand, hydrant flow tests are conducted. In conducting these tests a centrally located hydrant is usually selected at which pressure is gaged. Flows are then measured at several surrounding hydrants and the pressure variation of the central hydrant is recorded for the various rates of flow at the group of test hydrants. This type of investigation demonstrates the magnitude of pressure drop possible for a given fire-fighting load.

5-12. SYSTEM ANALYZERS

In recent years the application of computers in balancing pipe networks has permitted studies on a scope previously unattainable. The computer cannot actually do anything miraculous but it does provide solutions almost instantaneously.

Distribution networks are expensive, they are expected to provide service for long periods, and their performance is often the factor which determines whether the water utility operates at a profit or loss. For these reasons it is important that in large metropolitan areas at least, the inefficient and exceedingly time-consuming methods of hand calculation be replaced by the use of computers.[14]

The two main types of computer are the analog computer and the digital computer. The first deals with continuous physical variables, while the second is concerned only with numerical values. The analog computer acts as a physical model of the system to be studied and produces results which are limited in accuracy only by the physical elements of the model. The digital computer is theoretically limited in accuracy only by the reliability of the original input data.

The most impressive analog computer is the McIlroy Fluid Network Analyzer. The McIlroy Analyzer makes use of Fluistors, which are non-linear resistances. The voltage drop E for a Fluistor with a direct current I is given by

$$E = RI^m \qquad (5\text{-}42)$$

where R is the resistance. Any value of m between 1.85 and 2.00 can be approximated by the judicious selection of Fluistors. It is evident that Eq. 5-42 is in a form identical to that of Eq. 5-36, $H = KQ^n$. As a result of this analogy, a d-c network can be developed to simulate any desired hydraulic network. Once the system is energized, measured voltages and currents, converted into units of discharge and head loss can be read directly. A more detailed discussion of the McIlroy Analyzer can be found in several of the references at the end of the chapter.[14,17,18]

Solutions of the Hardy Cross method by digital computer involve a computation of the flow correction

$$\Delta Q = -\frac{\Sigma H}{n\Sigma(H/Q)} \qquad [5\text{-}37]$$

for each loop of the network after an initial assumption of flows has been made. Repeated sets of corrections are computed and applied until a satisfactorily balanced system is attained. The process of repeated trials is known as the iterative convergence technique. *Feedback* is the term applied to the modification of an initial value by some fraction of the corresponding output. The Hardy Cross procedure can be said to apply a feedback operation to sequential calculations, a procedure extremely well suited to the digital computer.

A review of the merits of the various computers used in distribution network balancing is presented by McPherson and Radziul.[19] The McIlroy Analyzer has the advantage of yielding a direct analogy of the system being investigated. The operation of the equipment is such that system inputs (from pumps or storage) are raised from zero to full system capacity, whereas drafts are set initially at full load values. This procedure is particularly valuable in design analysis since it can indicate system deficiencies at less than design rates. In such a case, revisions in the system piping can be made prior to any detailed test runs. Using the McIlroy Analyzer, trial changes can be made very rapidly, and unsatisfactory arrangements eliminated quickly and directly. The analyzer also has great value in studying pumping station and service reservoir performance.

Using the iteration process combined with a convergence technique, the digital computer adjusts an initial set of flow rates to any desired degree of balance. The information obtained from the computer is usually in the form of tabulated head loss and directional flow rate for individual pipe branches. The data obtained must be transferred to a map of the network and then summed algebraically so that the net result can be attained. Input data must be modified if changes in loading are to be studied.

5-13. DISTRIBUTION RESERVOIRS AND SERVICE STORAGE

Distribution reservoirs provide service storage to meet the widely fluctuating demands often imposed on a distribution system, to provide storage for fire-fighting and emergencies, and to equalize operating pressures. They are either elevated or at or just below ground level.

The main categories of storage reservoirs are surface reservoirs, standpipes, and elevated tanks. Surface reservoirs may be built below the existing ground level or constructed by balancing cut and fill. Common practice is to line the reservoir with concrete, gunite, asphalt, or an asphaltic membrane. Large reservoirs are often built of concrete with vertical walls which must also act as retaining walls to resist earth pressure when the reservoir is empty. Surface reservoirs may be covered or uncovered. Whenever possible a cover should be considered for the prevention of contamination of the water supply by animals or humans and to prevent the growth of algae. If the reservoir is to be left open, fencing is a necessity.

Standpipes or elevated tanks are normally employed where the construction of a surface reservoir would not provide sufficient head. A standpipe is essentially a tall cylindrical tank whose storage volume includes an upper portion (the useful storage) which is above the entrance to the discharge pipe, and a lower portion (supporting storage). This lower portion acts only to support the useful storage and provide the required head. For this reason standpipes over 50 ft high are usually uneconomical. Steel, concrete, and wood are used in the construction of standpipes and elevated tanks. When it becomes more economical to build the supporting structure for an elevated tank than to provide for the supporting storage in a standpipe, the elevated tank is used. A good discussion of the construction details and characteristics of various kinds of distribution reservoirs is given by Babbitt, Doland, and Cleasby.[20]

Distribution reservoirs should be located strategically for maximum benefits. Normally the reservoir should be near the center of use, but in large metropolitan areas a number of distribution reservoirs may be located at key points. Reservoirs providing service storage must be high enough to develop adequate pressures in the system they are to serve. A central location decreases friction losses by reducing the distance from supply point to the area served. Positioning the reservoir so that pressures may be approximately equalized is an additional consideration of importance. Figure 5-24 will illustrate this point. The location of the tank as shown in part *a* results in a very large loss of head by the time the

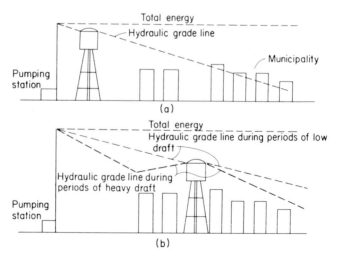

FIG. 5-24. Pressure distribution as influenced by the location of a distribution reservoir.

far end of the municipality is reached. Thus pressures too low will prevail at the far end or excessive pressures will be in evidence at the near end. In part *b* it is seen that pressures over the whole municipal area are much more uniform for periods of both high and low demand. Note that during periods of high demand the tank is supplying flow in both directions (being emptied), while during periods of low demand the pump is supplying the tank and the municipality.

The amount of storage to be provided is a function of the capacity of the distribution network, the location of the service storage, and the use to which it is to be put. When water-treatment facilities are required, it is preferable to operate them at a uniform rate such as the maximum daily rate. It is also usually desirable to operate pumping units at constant rates. Demands on the system in excess of these rates must therefore be met by storage, previously defined as operating storage. Requirements for fire-fighting purposes should be sufficient to provide fire flows for 10 to 12 hr in large communities and for two or more hours in smaller ones. Emergency storage is provided to sustain the community's needs during periods when the inflow to the reservoir is shut off, for example through a failure of the supply work, failure of pumping equipment, or need to take a supply line out of service for maintenance or repair. The length of time the supply system is expected to be out of service dictates the amount of emergency storage to be provided. Emergency storage volumes sufficient to last for several days are common.

The amount of storage required for emergency and fire-fighting purposes is readily computed once the time period over which these flows are to be provided has been selected.[21] An emergency storage of 3 days for a community of 8,000 having an average use rate of 150 gpcd is 3 × 150 × 8,000 = 3.6 million gallons. From Table 3-4 it can be seen that a fire flow of 2,750 gpm must be provided for a duration of 10 hr. This means a total fire-fighting storage of 1.65 million gallons. To the sum of these values, an additional equalizing or operating storage requirement would be added. The determination of this volume is slightly more complex and needs further explanation.

To compute the required equalizing or operating storage, a mass diagram or hydrograph indicating the hourly rate of consumption is required. The procedure to be used in determining the needed storage volume is then:

1. Obtain a hydrograph of hourly demands for the maximum day. This may be obtained through a study of available records, by gaging the existing system during dry periods when lawn sprinkling demands are high, or by using available design criteria such as presented in Chap. 3 to predict a hydrograph for some future condition of development.

2. Tabulate the hourly demand data for the maximum day as shown in Table 5-5.

TABLE 5-5
HOURLY DEMAND FOR THE MAXIMUM DAY

Time	Average Hourly Demand Rate, gpm	Hourly Demand, gallons	Cumulative Demand, gallons	Hourly Demand as a Percent of Average	Average Hourly Demand Minus Hourly Demand (286,250) − (col. 3) −	+
1	2	3	4	5	6	7
12 p.m.	0	0	0	0	−	−
1 a.m.	2,170	130,000	130,000	45.4		156,250
2	2,100	126,000	256,000	44.1		160,250
3	2,020	121,000	377,000	42.3		165,250
4	1,970	118,000	495,000	41.3		168,250
5	1,980	119,000	614,000	41.6		167,250
6	2,080	125,000	739,000	43.17		161,250
7	3,630	218,000	957,000	76.2		68,250
8	5,190	312,000	1,269,000	108.9	25,750	
9	5,620	337,000	1,606,000	117.8	50,750	
10	5,900	354,000	1,960,000	123.6	67,750	
11	6,040	363,000	2,323,000	126.7	76,750	
12	6,320	379,000	2,702,000	132.4	92,750	
1 p.m.	6,440	387,000	3,089,000	135.2	100,750	
2	6,370	382,000	3,471,000	133.4	95,750	
3	6,320	379,000	3,850,000	132.4	92,750	
4	6,340	381,000	4,231,000	133.0	94,750	
5	6,640	399,000	4,630,000	139.5	112,750	
6	7,320	439,000	5,069,000	153.3	152,750	
7	9,333	560,000	5,629,000	195.5	273,750	
8	8,320	499,000	6,128,000	174.4	212,750	
9	5,050	303,000	6,431,000	105.8	16,750	
10	2,570	154,000	6,585,000	53.8		132,250
11	2,470	148,000	6,733,000	51.7		138,250
12	2,290	137,000	6,870,000	47.9		149,250
Totals		6,870,000			1,466,500	1,466,500

$$\text{Average hourly demand} = \frac{6,870,000}{24} = 286,250 \text{ gallons}$$

3. Find the required operating storage by using mass diagrams such as in Fig. 5-25 and 5-26, the hydrograph of Fig. 5-27, or the values tabulated in column 6 of Table 5-5.

The required operating storage is found by using a mass diagram with the cumulative pumping curve plotted on it. Figure 5-25 illustrates this diagram for a uniform 24-hr pumping rate. Note that the total volume pumped in 24 hr must equal the total 24-hr demand and thus the mass curve and cumulative pumping curve must be coincident at the origin and at the end of the day. Next construct a tangent to the mass curve which is parallel to the pumping curve at point *A* in the figure. Then draw a second parallel tangent to the mass curve at point *C* and drop a vertical from *C* to an intersection with tangent *AB* at *B*. The required storage is equal to the magnitude of the ordinate *CB* measured on the

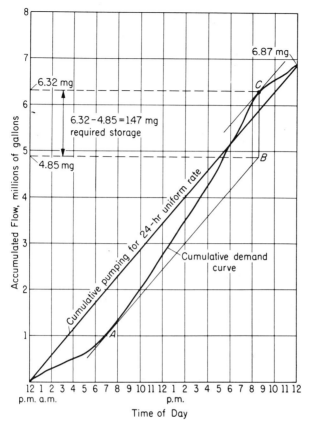

FIG. 5-25. Operating storage for 24-hr pumping determined by use of the mass-diagram.

vertical scale. In the example shown, the necessary storage volume is found to be 1.47 million gallons for a 24-hr pumping period.

Students should recognize that the reservoir is full at *A*, empty at *C*, is filling whenever the slope of the pump curve exceeds that of the cumulative demand curve, and is being drawn down when the rate of demand exceeds the rate of pumping.

It is often desirable to operate an equalizing reservoir so that pumping will take place at a uniform rate but for a period less than 24 hr. In small communities for example, it is often advantageous to pump only during the normal working day. It may also be more economical to operate the pumping station at off-peak periods when electric power rates are low.[21]

Figure 5-26 illustrates the operation of a storage reservoir where pumping occurs during the period between 6 a.m. and 6 p.m. only. To

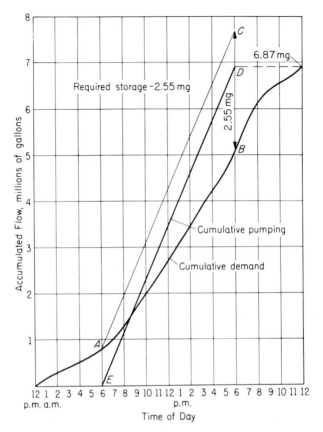

FIG. 5-26. Mass-diagram determination of equalizing
storage for 12-hr pumping.

find the required storage in this case, construct the cumulative pumping
curve *ED* so that the total volume of 6.87 mg is pumped uniformly
from 6 a.m. to 6 p.m.   Then project point *E* vertically upward to an
intersection with the cumulative demand curve at *A*.   Construct line *AC*
parallel to *ED*.   Point *C* will be at the intersection of line *AC* with
the vertical extended upward from 6 p.m. on the abscissa.   The required
storage equals the value of the ordinate *CBD*.   Numerically it is 2.55 mg
and exceeds the storage requirement for 24-hr pumping.

Another graphical solution to the storage problem may be obtained
as outlined in Fig. 5-27.   The figure is a plot of the demand hydrograph
for the maximum day.   For uniform 24-hr pumping, the pumping rate will
be equal to the mean hourly demand.   This is shown as line *PQ*.   The
required storage is then obtained by planimetering or determining in some

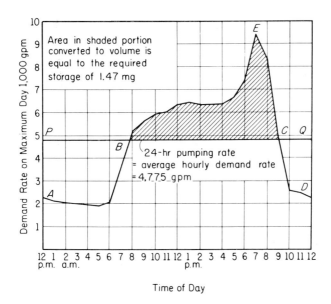

Area in shaded portion converted to volume is equal to the required storage of 1.47 mg

24-hr pumping rate = average hourly demand rate = 4,775 gpm

Fig. 5-27. Graphical determination of equalizing storage.

other manner the area between curve *BEC* and line *PQ*. Conversion of this area to units of volume yields the required storage of 1.47 mg.

The required storage for 24-hr pumping may also be determined by summing either the plus or minus values of column 6 in Table 5-5.

Unless pumping follows the demand curve or demand hydrograph, storage will be required. Figure 5-27 shows that a maximum pumping rate of about 9,400 gpm will be required with no storage, whereas if storage is provided a maximum pumping rate of 4,775 gpm (about 50 percent of that required with storage) will suffice. This example tends to illustrate the economics of providing operating storage.

Variable-rate pumping is normally not economical. In practice it is common to provide storage and pumping facilities so that pumping at the average rate for the maximum day can be maintained. On days of lesser demand, some pumping units will stand idle. Another operational procedure is to provide enough storage for pumping at the average rate for the average day, with idle reserve capacity, and then to overload all available units on the maximum day. Provision of pumping and storage capacity to meet peak demands experienced for a few hours only every few years has been found to be economically impractical.

Analyses of distribution systems are commonly concerned with the pipe network, topographic conditions, pumping-station performance, and the operating characteristics of the distribution storage. One, all, or any combination of these features may be the object of study. Where multiple sources of supply operate under variable-head conditions, the hydraulic balancing of the system becomes more complex. The simple system of Fig. 5-28 illustrates this point.

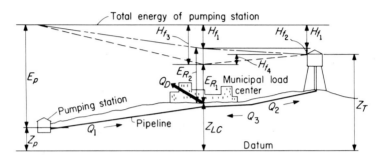

FIG. 5-28. Sketch illustrating the modes of operation of a distribution system.

Considering that the demand for water by the municipal load center fluctuates hourly, it is evident there are essentially two modes of operation of the given distribution system. When municipal requirements are light, such as in the early morning hours, the pumping station will meet these demands and in addition supply the reservoir. The solution of the problem may then be had by writing the equations

$$(1) \qquad Q_1 - Q_D = Q_2$$

$$(2) \qquad Z_p + E_p = Z_{LC} + E_{R_2} + H_{f_1}$$

$$(3) \qquad Z_{LC} + E_{R_2} = Z_T + H_{f_2}$$

$$(2 + 3) \qquad H_{f_1} + H_{f_2} = E_p + Z_p - Z_T$$

where

$$
\begin{aligned}
Q_1 &= \text{flow from the pump} \\
Q_D &= \text{municipal demand} \\
Q_2 &= \text{flow to the tank} \\
Z_p, Z_{LC}, Z_T &= \text{elevations above the arbitrary datum } (Z_T = \text{eleva-} \\
&\quad \text{tion of water surface in tank}) \\
E_p &= \text{the energy produced by the pump} \\
E_{R_2} &= \text{residual energy of the load center (pressure head} \\
&\quad \text{plus velocity head)} \\
H_{f_1}, \text{etc.} &= \text{friction-head losses}
\end{aligned}
$$

If Q_d, Z_p, Z_{LC}, and Z_T are specified, the equations may be solved by selecting values of E_{R_2} and then solving for H_{f_1} and H_{f_2}. When a solution is reached such that equation $(2 + 3)$ is satisfied, Q_1 and Q_2 may be computed.

When demands are high, both the tank and the pump will supply the community. The direction of flow will then be reversed in the line from the tank to the pump and the applicable equations will be

(1) $$Q_1 + Q_3 = Q_D$$

(2) $$Z_p + E_p = Z_{LC} + E_{R_1} + H_{f_3}$$

(3) $$Z_{LC} + E_{R_1} + H_{f_4} = Z_T$$

Again, an assumed value for E_R will be taken and trial solutions carried out until equation (1) is satisfied. Note that the foregoing illustration is a simple case since Z_T has been specified. Actually, since Z_T fluctuates with time, it is necessary to have information on storage volume available vs. water elevation in the tank so that at any specified condition of draft, the actual value for Z_T can be determined and used in the computations.

Water-distribution systems generally are considered to be a composite of four basic constituents: the pipe network, storage, pump performance, and the pumping station and its suction source. These components must be integrated into a functioning system for various schedules of demand. A thorough analysis of each system must be made to insure that it will operate satisfactorily under all anticipated combinations of demand and hydraulic-component characteristics. The system may work well under one set of conditions but will not necessarily be operable under some other set. A comprehensive system balance requires an hourly simulation of performance for the expected operating schedule.[12,14]

There is an infinite number of possible arrangements of the basic components in a distribution system. The hydraulic analyses applicable to each system are, however, common to all, and have been illustrated in detail in this chapter.

PUMPING

Pumping equipment forms an important part of the transportation and distribution facilities for water and wastes. Requirements vary from small units used to pump only a few gallons per minute to large units capable of handling several hundred cubic feet per second. The two primary types of pumping equipment of interest here are the centrifugal pump and the displacement pump. Air-lift pumps, jet pumps, and hydraulic rams are also used in special applications. In water and sewage works the centrifugal pump finds the widest use. Centrifugal pumps have a rotating element (impeller) which imparts energy to the water. Displacement pumps are often of the reciprocating type where a piston draws water into a closed chamber and then expels it under pressure. Reciprocating pumps are widely used to handle sludge in sewage-treatment works.

Electrical power is the primary source of energy for driving pumping equipment but gasoline, steam, and diesel power are also used. Often a standby engine powered by one of these forms is included in primary pumping stations to operate in emergency situations when electric power fails. For a known discharge and total pump lift, the theoretical horsepower (hp) required may be found by using

$$\text{hp} = \frac{Q\gamma H}{550} \tag{5-43}$$

where Q = discharge in cubic feet per second
        γ = specific weight of water
        H = total lift in feet
        550 = conversion from foot-pounds per second to horsepower

The actual horsepower required is obtained by dividing the theoretical horsepower by the efficiency of the pump and driving unit.

Anticipated operating conditions of the system must be known to effectively design a pumping station. A knowledge of the total dynamic head, TDH, against which the pump must operate is needed. The TDH is composed of the difference in elevation between the pump center line and the elevation to which the water is to be raised, the difference in elevation between the level of the suction pool and the pump center line, the frictional losses encountered in the pump, pipe, valves and fittings, and the velocity head. In addition to a knowledge of the total head, the characteristics of various pumping units (a function of the size and speed of the pump and the pump design) must be known. Figure 5-29 illustrates a series of pump-characteristic curves for a particular pump operated at three different speeds. These curves relate head, discharge, and efficiency of the unit at a specified speed. At no flow, the head is known as the *shutoff head*. The pumphead may rise slightly or fall from the shutoff value as discharge increases. Ultimately, however, the head for any centrifugal pump will fall with increase in flow. At maximum efficiency, the discharge is known as the *normal* or *rated* discharge of the pump. Varying the pump discharge by throttling will lower the efficiency of the unit. By changing the speed of the pump, discharge can be varied within a certain range without a loss of efficiency. The most practical and efficient approach to the variable-flow problem is to provide two or more pumps in parallel so that the flow may be carried at close to the peak efficiency of the units which are operating.

The normal range of efficiencies for centrifugal pumps is between 50 and 85 percent, although efficiencies in excess of 90 percent have been reported. Pump efficiency usually increases with the size and capacity of the pump.

Operating characteristics for a wide range of pump sizes and speeds are available from pump manufacturers. Special equipment manufac-

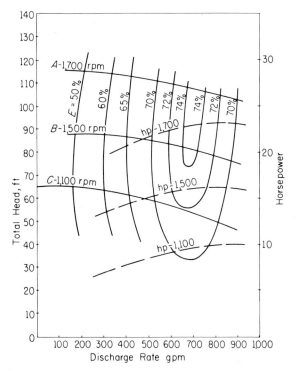

FIG. 5-29. Typical characteristic curves for a centrifugal pump at several speeds.

tured to satisfy the prescribed requirements of the customer must customarily satisfy an acceptance test after it has been installed.

Babbitt, Doland, and Cleasby give a detailed discussion of a variety of pump types.[20]

REFERENCES

1. Peter C. G. Isaac, "Roman Public Works, Engineering," University of Durham, King's College Department of Civil Engineering, Bull. 13 (February 1958).

2. Anonymous, "Canadian River Project Moves Ahead," *Public Works* (April 1963).

3. William E. Warne, "The Big Flow," *California*, Magazine of California State Chamber of Commerce (December 1963).

4. Alfred R. Golze, "The California Water Program in 1964," Paper presented before American Right-of-Way Association, Sacramento Chapter 27, Sacramento, Calif., January 15, 1964.

5. Henry M. Morris, *Applied Hydraulics in Engineering.* (New York: The Ronald Press Co., 1963).

6. "Flow of Fluids Through Valves, Fittings, and Pipe," Crane Co., Chicago, Ill., Tech. Paper no. 410 (1957).

7. J. M. Edmonston and E. E. Jackson, "The Feather River Project and the Establishment of the Optimum Hydraulic Grade Line for the Project Aqueduct," Los Angeles, Calif.

8. I. S. Sokolnikoff and E. S. Sokolnikoff, *Higher Mathematics for Engineers and Physicists* (New York: McGraw-Hill Book Co., Inc., 1941.)

9. Robert Weinstock, *Calculus of Variations*. International Series in Pure and Applied Mathematics (New York: McGraw-Hill Book Co., Inc., 1952).

10. Julian Hinds, "Economic Water Conduit Size," *Eng. News-Record* (January 1937).

11. N. Joukowsky, "Water Hammer" (translated by Miss O. Simin), *Proc. Am. Water Works Assoc.*, vol. 24 (1904), pp. 341–424.

12. M. B. McPherson, "Generalized Distribution Network Head Loss Characteristics," *Proc. Am. Soc. Civil Engrs.*, *J. Hydraulics Div.*, vol. 86, no. HY1 (January 1960).

13. Carl W. Reh, "Hydraulics of Water Distribution Systems," *Proc. Sanit. Engrs. Conf.*, University of Illinois, Eng. Expt. Sta., Circ. 75 (February 1962).

14. M. B. McPherson, "Applications of System Analyzers: A Summary," *Proc. Sanit. Engrs. Conf.*, University of Illinois, Eng. Expt. Sta., Circ. no. 75 (February 1962).

15. Hardy Cross, "Analysis of Flow in Networks of Conduits or Conductors," University of Illinois, Bull. 286 (November 1936).

16. R. G. Kincaid, "Analyzing Your Distribution System," *Water Works Engr.*, vol. 97, nos. 2, 6, 10, 16, 21 (January, March, May, August, October 1944).

17. Malcom S. McIlroy, "Direct Reading Electric Analyzer for Pipeline Networks," *J. Am. Water Works Assoc.*, vol. 42, no. 4 (April 1950).

18. V. A. Appleyard and F. P. Linaweaver, Jr., "The McIlroy Fluid Analyzer in Water Works Practice," *J. Am. Water Works Assoc.*, vol. 49, no. 1 (January 1957).

19. M. B. McPherson and J. V. Radziul, "Water Distribution Design and the McIlroy Network Analyzer," *Proc. Am. Soc. Civil Engrs.*, vol. 84, Paper 1588 (April 1958).

20. Harold E. Babbitt, James J. Doland, and John L. Cleasby, *Water Supply Engineering* (New York: McGraw-Hill Book Co., Inc., 1962).

21. John E. Kiker, "Design Criteria For Water Distribution Storage," *Public Works* (March 1964).

22. George E. Russell, *Hydraulics* (New York: Holt, Rinehart and Winston, Inc., 1957).

PROBLEMS

5-1. Water is pumped 8 miles from a reservoir at elevation 150 ft to a second reservoir at elevation 275 ft. The pipeline connecting the reservoirs is 48 in. in diameter. It is concrete and has an absolute roughness of 0.003. If the flow is 22 mgd and pumping station efficiency is 80 percent, what will be the monthly power bill if electricity costs one cent per kilowatthour?

5-2. A reservoir at elevation 600 ft is to supply a second reservoir at elevation 350 ft. The reservoirs are connected by 1,300 ft of 24-in. cast-iron pipe and 2,600 ft of 20-in. cast-iron pipe in series. What will be the discharge delivered from the upper reservoir to the lower one?

5-3. Consider that the water needs of a city for the next 30 years may be met by constructing a single 10-in. main for the first 15 years followed by a second 10-in. main for the next 15 years. At this time both mains will be in service. An alternate solution is to build one 18-in. line which will serve the entire 30-year period. Consider that the cost per foot installed is $13 for the first 10-in. line, $14.25 for the next 10-in. line, and $17.25 for the 18-in. line. The combined interest and amortization rate is 6.5 percent per year. Find the most economical method of meeting the community water requirements.

5-4. It is necessary to pump 5,170 gpm of water from a reservoir at elevation 980 ft to a tank whose bottom is at an elevation of 1,200 ft. The pumping unit is located at elevation 970. The suction pipe is 24 in. in diameter and very short, so that head losses may be neglected. The pipeline from the pump to the upper tank is 350 ft long and is 20 in. in diameter. Consider the minor losses in the line to equal 2.0 ft of water. The maximum depth of water in the tank is 36 ft and the supply lines are cast iron. Find the maximum lift of the pump and the horsepower required for pumping if the pump efficiency is 71 percent.

5-5. If a flow of 5 cfs is to be carried by a 10,000-ft cast-iron pipeline without exceeding a head loss of 125 ft, what must the pipe diameter be?

5-6. A 48-in. water main carries 81 cfs and branches into two pipes at point A. The branching pipes are 36 in. in diameter and 24 in. in diameter and they are 2,800 ft and 6,300 ft long respectively. These pipes rejoin at point B and become again a single 48-in. pipe. If the friction factor is 0.022 for the 36-in. pipe and 0.023 for the 24-in. pipe, what will be the discharge in each branch?

5-7. Water is pumped from a reservoir whose surface elevation is 1,300 ft to a second reservoir whose surface elevation is 1,360 ft. The connecting pipeline is 5,000 ft long and 12 in. in diameter. If the pressure during pumping is 83 psi at a point midway on the pipe at elevation 1,210 ft, find the rate of flow and the power exerted by the pumps. Also, plot the hydraulic grade line. Assume $f = 0.022$.

5-8. Water flows through a smooth horizontal drawn tube at a rate of 115 cfm. The pressure drop in 1,200 ft is 21.3 psi. Find the pipe diameter. -

5-9. A concrete channel 20 ft wide at the bottom is constructed with side slopes of 2 horizontal to 1 vertical. The slope of the energy gradient is 1 in 1,300 and the depth of flow is 4.5 ft. Find the flow velocity and the discharge.

5-10. A rectangular channel is to carry 250 cfs. The mean velocity must be approximately 2.5 ft/sec. The channel bottom should be about twice the channel depth. Find the channel cross section and the required channel slope.

5-11. A rectangular channel carries a flow of 14 cfs per foot of width. Plot a curve of specific energy vs. depth. Compute the minimum value of specific energy and the critical depth. What are the alternate depths for $E_s = 5.0$?

5-12. A water transmission line is to connect point A with points B, C, and D in succession. The line must be capable of carrying 175 mgd with a total head loss not to exceed 35 ft. Use a Hazen-Williams C of 100. Line AB is 32,000 ft, line *BC* is 21,000 ft, and line *CD* is 13,000 ft. Find the most economical diameter for each of the three sections of pipe.

	Size of Pipe, in.					
	84	96	108	120	132	144
Pipe	Dollar Cost per Foot of Pipe, Installed					
AB	73	86	98	121	142	180
BC	96	110	129	160	175	230
CD	129	138	163	190	201	275

5-13. How would you go about making an economic decision between instal-lation of a 12-in. pipeline at a cost of $13 per foot vs. the cost of a 4-in. pipeline at the cost of $9.25 per foot if both lines are to be exactly equal in length, and deliver the same flow at the same terminal head? Assume that there is a pumping station at the head of the line.

5-14. A water-transportation system is to consist of a tunnel, a pipeline, and a canal. Given the cost vs. head loss data below, find the most economical division of the total head of 120 ft.

Head Loss, ft	10	20	30	40	50	60	70	80
	Cost, thousands of dollars							
Tunnel..........	—	120	98	80	60	53	49	46
Pipeline........	—	105	76	53	47	43	40	39
Canal..........	110	55	35	29	26	23	20	19

5-15. Assume a valve on a 48-in. diameter pipe closes very quickly. The original flow velocity was 4.5 fps. Use values of $E = 30 \times 10^6$ psi, $K = 306 \times 10^3$ psi, and $t = 0.25$ in. Find the excess pressure p_e.

5-16. The velocity in a 24-in. cast-iron pipe ($E = 12 \times 10^6$) is changed from 2.5 fps to 0 in 0.30 sec when a valve 1,200 ft from a reservoir is closed. Assume a pipe-wall thickness equal to 3.4 in. Find the excess pressure due to closure.

5-17. Find the magnitude and direction of the total force an anchorage must exert on a pipe bend 24-in. in diameter curving through an angle of 45 degrees. Assume $p_1 = p_2 = 42$ psi and $Q = 16$ cfs.

5-18. Determine an equivalent pipe for the system shown in the accompany-ing diagram.

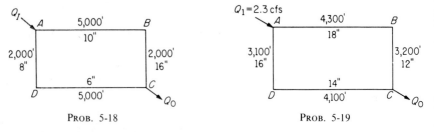

PROB. 5-18   PROB. 5-19

5-19. From the accompanying diagram, compute (a) the total head loss from *A* to *C*, (b) P_a if $P_c = 23$ psi, and (c) the flow in each line.

5-20. Write a computer program for solving Prob. 5-19.

5-21. In the system shown, determine the flow distribution by a Hardy Cross analysis. Find sizes of pipes, *EF*, and *GF*. Use a Hazen-Williams *C* = 100.

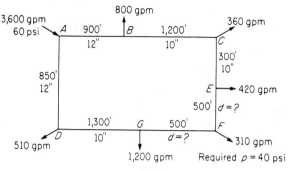

PROB. 5-21

5-22. Compute the flow in the lines of the diagram shown. Assume that the elevation at *A* is 1,300 ft and the elevation at *D* is 1,245 ft. The pressure at *D* is 35 psi. Find the pressure at *A*.

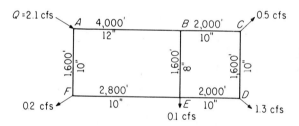

PROB. 5-22

5-23. In the diagram shown, P_A = 65 psi and P_C = 47 psi. Find the discharge in all lines and determine the size of lines *BC* and *CD*.

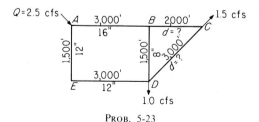

PROB. 5-23

5-24. Given the accompanying pipe network, use the method of sections and evaluate the capability of the system for supporting the indicated flows. If necessary, show the size and location of pipes to be added or replaced. Flow crossing A–A must equal 3.0 cfs, that crossing B–B equals 3.0 cfs, C–C equals 2.2 cfs, D–D equals 1.3 cfs, and E–E equals 0.6 cfs.

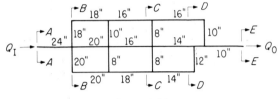

PROB. 5-24

5-25. Derive Eq. 5-39.

5-26. Given the pipe layout shown, determine the length of an equivalent 16-in. pipe.

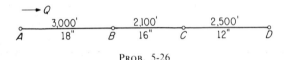

PROB. 5-26

5-27. Given the pipe layout shown, find the diameter of an equivalent 2,000-ft pipe.

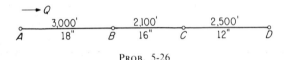

PROB. 5-27

5-28. Consider the accompanying sketch. Determine the design flows, required pipe sizes, residual pressures at all takeoff points, and pipe materials.

A, B, C, D, E = drinking fountains
F = inflow point
G = club house
  4 sinks
  2 urinals
  4 toilets
  4 showers
  2 fountains

Note: E stands for elevation

PROB. 5-28

5-29. Given the following average hourly demand rates in gallons per minute, find the uniform 24-hr pumping rate and the required storage.

12 p.m.	0	5 a.m.	1,775
1 a.m.	1,860	6 a.m.	1,810
2 a.m.	1,830	7 a.m.	3,100
3 a.m.	1,800	8 a.m.	4,900
4 a.m.	1,760	9 a.m.	5,400

10 a.m.	5,870	6 p.m.	7,000
11 a.m.	6,100	7 p.m.	8,900
12 a.m.	6,200	8 p.m.	8,600
1 p.m.	6,350	9 p.m.	5,200
2 p.m.	6,320	10 p.m.	2,100
3 p.m.	6,300	11 p.m.	2,000
4 p.m.	6,400	12 p.m.	1,900
5 p.m.	6,590		

5-30. Solve Prob. 5-29 if the period of pumping is from 6 a.m. to 6 p.m. only.

5-31. Solve Prob. 5-29 by the method outlined in Fig. 5-27, assuming 24 hr pumping.

5-32. Use the data given in Prob. 5-29 and add a fire-flow requirement of 4.5 mgd. Refer to Fig. 5-28 and assume that this flow requirement can be delivered to the city by the pumping station-tank system shown. The pipeline from the pumping station to the town is 28 in. in diameter and 5 miles long, and the pipeline from the town to the tank is 26 in. in diameter and 3.5 miles long. Elevations are 430 ft at the pump center line, 580 ft at the ground surface in the town, 650 ft at the ground surface at the tank, and 710 ft at the bottom of the tank. The tank is 30 ft high and contains a total of 1.47 mg storage. Find the pressure in town during the peak average hour plus fire flow if the pumping station can maintain a maximum pressure of 130 psi and the tank is half full.

chapter 6

Sewerage and Drainage Systems

The engineer is as much concerned with the collection and transportation of storm-water runoff and waste flows as he is with the transportation and distribution of water to be processed or used for drinking purposes. The engineering importance of the conveyance systems for these flows is indicated by their costs. In 1963 the Committee on Urban Hydrology of the American Society of Civil Engineers stated that the probable direct capital cost of urban drainage works would be about $25 billion in the next 40 years and that the per capita costs are often in excess of $100.[11]

The collection and movement of surface drainage and waste flows from residential, commercial, and industrial areas pose problems of a different nature than those for water supply discussed in Chap. 5. Waste must be transported from the point of collection to the treatment or disposal area as quickly as possible to prevent development of septic conditions. In addition, waste flows are highly variable and contain coarse solids which may be floating or suspended. Storm-water runoff is characterized by exceedingly rapid changes in rate of flow during periods of precipitation. These flows commonly carry various forms of debris from the drainage area.

HYDRAULIC CONSIDERATIONS

Sewerage and drainage systems are usually designed as open channels except where lift stations are required to overcome topographic barriers. The hydraulic problems associated with these flows are complicated in some cases by the quality of the fluid, the highly variable nature of the flows, and the fact that an unconfined or free surface exists. Open-channel flow occurs through the force of gravity. The forces retarding flow are derived from viscous shear along the channel bed with both the Reynolds number and the Froude number involved. Open-channel flow may be either laminar or turbulent but since the case of laminar flow is exceedingly rare in engineering practice it will not be considered here.

6-1. FUNDAMENTAL CONSIDERATIONS FOR THE CONDITION OF UNIFORM FLOW

If flow in an open channel is steady (fluid properties do not change with time) and uniform (cross-sectional area, depth, and velocity are translated uniformly downstream), equilibrium between viscous and gravity forces must exist. Referring to Fig. 6-1, an application of the momentum theorem parallel to the channel bottom yields

$$P_1 A_1 + \gamma A dx \sin \alpha - \tau_0 P_w dx - P_2 A_2 = 0$$

where $P_1 = P_2$

$A_1 = A_2$

P_w = wetted perimeter

The average value of the channel shearing stress, or average unit tractive force, is thus

$$\tau_0 = \gamma RS \tag{6-1}$$

where γ = specific weight of water

R = hydraulic radius equal to A/P_w

S = slope of the channel bottom

It should be noted that d is the vertical distance from the channel bottom to the water surface, whereas d' is the normal depth. If the channel does not drop by more than 14 ft/100 ft, y and y' agree within 1 percent and d will be used to describe the depth. The slope of the channel bed is also theoretically equal to the drop in elevation per horizontal distance in con-

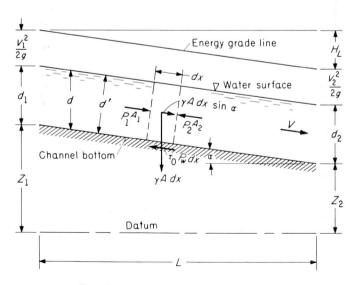

FIG. 6-1. Uniform flow in an open channel.

trast to the value of sin *a*. For slopes less than 0.14, however, the sine and tangent of α do not differ by more than 1 percent and for all practical purposes may be considered equal.

The energy equation written between sections 1 and 2 of Fig. 6-1 is

$$Z_1 + d_1 + \frac{V_1^2}{2g} = Z_2 + d_2 + \frac{V_2^2}{2g} + H_L \tag{6-2}$$

where Z = elevation above an arbitrary datum in feet
   d = flow depth in feet
   V = average velocity in fps
   H_L = total head lost between the two sections

In reality, the units of all the terms in Eq. 6-2 are foot-pounds per pound of fluid flowing. For uniform flow, $d_1 = d_2$ and $V_1 = V_2$, so Eq. 6-2 reduces to the form

$$Z_1 - Z_2 = H_L$$

or

$$\Delta Z = SL$$

where S is the slope of the energy gradient (and in the case of uniform flow, the slope of the channel bottom also) and L is the length between sections.

The velocity of flow in an open channel is generally determined by using Manning's equation,

$$V = \frac{1.49}{n} R^{2/3} S^{1/2} \tag{5-3}$$

which has been discussed in Chap. 5. Table 5-3 gives values of the roughness coefficient *n* for various materials used in open channels. Figure 6-2 is a nomograph which facilitates the solution of the equation when $n = 0.013$. Values obtained from the nomograph may be adjusted to other values of *n* by making the applicable proportional correction.

Many sanitary sewers and storm drains are circular in cross section and thus it is cumbersome to compute values for the hydraulic radius and the cross-sectional area for conditions when the pipe is flowing partially full. Figure 6-3 is useful in computing partial flow values from full flow conditions. Example 6-1 illustrates this technique.

EXAMPLE 6-1. Given: discharge flowing full 16 cfs, velocity 8 fps. Find: velocity and depth of flow when $Q = 10$ cfs.

Solution: Enter chart at $10/16 = 62.5$ percent of value for full section. Obtain depth of flow = 57.5 percent of full flow depth and velocity = $1.05 \times 8 = 8.4$ fps.

The depth at which uniform flow occurs in an open channel is termed the *normal depth*, d_n. This depth may be computed by using Manning's

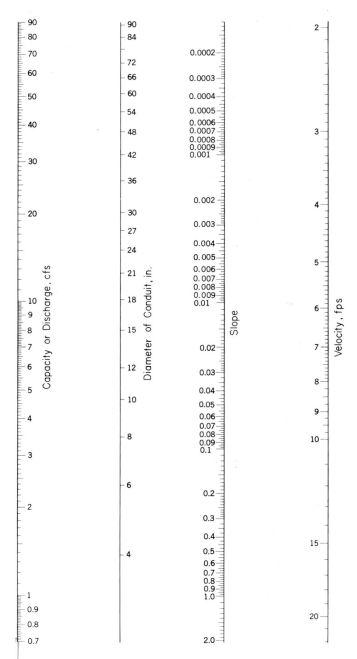

FIG. 6-2. Nomograph based on Manning's formula in which
$n = 0.013$.

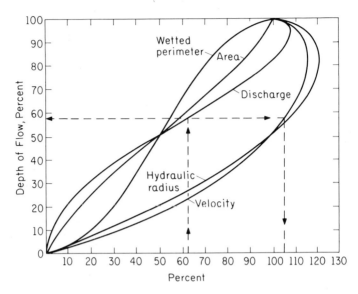

FIG. 6-3. Hydraulic elements of a circular section.

equation for discharge after A and R have been translated into functions of depth. The solution for d_n is often obtained through a trial-and-error procedure.

For a specified channel cross-section and discharge there are three possible values for the normal depth, all dependent on the channel slope. Uniform flow for a given discharge may occur at critical depth, at less than critical depth, or at greater than critical depth. Critical depth occurs when the specific energy is a minimum. Specific energy is defined as

$$E_s = d + \frac{V^2}{2g} \qquad (6\text{-}3)$$

where d = depth of flow
V = mean velocity

Flow at critical depth is highly unstable and designs indicating flow at or near critical depth are to be avoided. For any value of E_s above the minimum, two alternate depths of flow are possible. One is greater than critical depth, the other less than critical depth. The former case indicates subcritical flow, the latter, supercritical flow. Critical depth for a channel can be found by taking the derivative of Eq. 6-3 with respect to depth, setting this equal to zero, and solving for d_c. For mild slopes the normal depth is greater than d_c and subcritical flow prevails. On steep slopes the normal depth is less than the critical depth and flow is supercritical. Once the critical depth has been computed, critical velocity is easily obtained.

Critical velocity for a channel of any cross section can be shown to be

$$V_c = \sqrt{g \frac{A}{B}} \qquad (6\text{-}4)$$

where V_c = critical velocity
      A = cross-sectional area of the channel
      B = width of the channel at the water surface
The critical slope can then be found by using Manning's equation.

In practice, uniform flows are encountered only in long channels after a transition from nonuniform conditions. Nevertheless, a knowledge of uniform-flow hydraulics is extremely important as numerous varied flow problems are solved through partial applications of uniform-flow theory. A basic assumption in gradually varied flow analyses, for example, is that energy losses are considered to be the same as for uniform flow at the average depth between two sections along the channel which are closely spaced.

6-2. GRADUALLY VARIED FLOW AND SURFACE PROFILES

Gradually varied flow results from gradual changes in depth which take place over relatively long reaches of a channel. Abrupt changes in the flow regime are classified as rapidly varied flow and will be discussed later. Problems in gradually varied flow are widespread and represent the majority of flows in natural open channels and many of the flows in man-made channels. They can be caused by such factors as change in channel slope, in cross-sectional area, or in roughness, or by obstructions to flow such as dams, gates, culverts, bridges, etc. The pressure distribution in gradually varied flow is hydrostatic and the streamlines are considered to be approximately parallel.

The significance of gradually varied flow problems may be illustrated by considering the following case. Assume that the maximum design flow for a uniform rectangular canal will occur at a depth of 8 ft under uniform-flow conditions. For these circumstances the requisite canal depth, including 1 ft of freeboard, will be 9 ft. Now consider that a gate is placed at the lower end of this canal. Assume that at maximum flow, the depth immediately upstream from the gate will have to be 12 ft in order to produce the required flow through the gate. The depth of flow will then begin decreasing gradually in an upstream direction and approach the uniform depth of 8 ft. Obviously, unless the depth of flow is known all along the channel the channel depth cannot be designed.

Determination of the water-surface profile for a given discharge in an open channel is of importance in solving many engineering problems. There are 12 classifications of water-surface profiles, or *backwater curves*

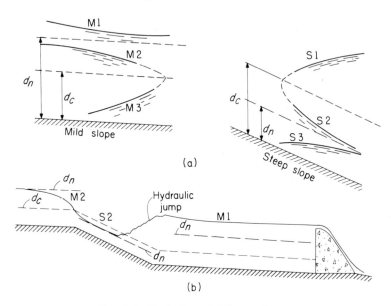

FIG. 6-4. Gradually varied flow profiles.

as they are commonly called.[1] Figure 6-4 illustrates several of these and also a typical change which might take place in the transition from one type of flow regime to another. For any channel, the applicable backwater curve will be a function of the relationship between the actual depth of flow and the normal and critical depths for the channel. For example, in Fig. 6-4*b* at the upstream end, the flow is known to be at less than normal depth. The applicable backwater curve is thus an M2 curve. Often it is helpful to sketch the type curves for a given problem before attempting to effect an actual solution. In doing this, the type curves given in Fig. 6-4 are useful. Additional type curves are presented by Posey and Woodward.[1]

Numerous procedures have been proposed for computing backwater curves. The one to be discussed here is known as the direct step method. Referring to Fig. 6-1 and assuming the datum to be raised to elevation Z_2, the energy equation may be written

$$Z_1' + d_1 + V_1^2/2g = d_2 + V_2^2/2g + H_J$$

where $Z_1' = Z_1 - Z_2$ and the other terms are as defined previously. A rearrangement of this equation yields

$$\left(\frac{V_2^2}{2g} + d_2\right) - \left(\frac{V_1^2}{2g} + d_1\right) = Z_1' - H_L$$

or

$$E_2 - E_1 = S_c L - \overline{S}_e L$$

so that

$$L = \frac{E_2 - E_1}{S_c - \overline{S}_e} \tag{6-5}$$

where E_2, E_1 = values of specific energy at sections 1 and 2
$\quad\quad\quad S_c$ = slope of the channel bottom
$\quad\quad\quad \overline{S}_e$ = the slope of the energy gradient

The value of S_e is obtained by assuming that (1) the actual energy gradient is the same as that obtained for uniform flow at a velocity equal to the average of the velocities at sections 1 and 2 (this can be found using Manning's equation) or (2) the slope of the energy gradient is equal to the mean of the slopes of the energy gradients for uniform flow at the two sections. The procedure in using Eq. 6-5 is to select some starting point where the depth of flow is known. A second depth is then selected in an upstream or downstream direction and the distance from the known depth to this point computed. Then, using the second depth as a reference, a third is selected and another length increment calculated, etc. The results obtained will be reasonably accurate provided the selected depth increments are small, since the energy loss assumptions are fairly accurate under these conditions.

EXAMPLE 6-2. Water flows in a rectangular concrete channel 10 ft wide, 8 ft deep, inclined at a grade of 0.10 percent. The channel carries a flow of 245 cfs and has a roughness coefficient n of 0.013. At the intersection of this channel with a canal, the depth of flow is 7.5 ft. Find the distance upstream to a point where normal depth prevails and determine the surface profile.

Solution: Using Manning's equation and the given value of discharge, the normal depth is found to be 4 ft. The critical depth y_c is determined by solving Eq. 6-4 after rearranging and substituting by_c for A and b for B, where b equals the width of the rectangular channel. Then,

$$V_c = \sqrt{g\left(\frac{by_c}{b}\right)}$$

$$= \sqrt{gy_c}$$

$$y_c = \frac{V_c^2}{g} = \frac{Q^2}{A^2 g}$$

$$y_c^3 = \frac{Q^2}{gb^2}$$

$$y_c = \sqrt[3]{\frac{Q^2}{gb^2}} \tag{6-6}$$

Substituting the given values for Q and b,

$$y_c = \sqrt[3]{\frac{(245)^2}{32.2 \times (10)^2}}$$

and
$$y_c = 2.65 \text{ ft}$$

Since $y > y_n > y_c$, an M1 profile will depict the water surface. The calculations then follow the procedure indicated in Table 6-1.

By Table 6-1, the distance upstream from the junction to the point of normal depth is 6,210 ft. The surface profile therefore can be plotted by using the values in columns 1 and 13 of the table. In practice greater accuracy could be obtained by using smaller depth increments, such as 0.25 ft, but the computational procedure would be the same.

6-3. HYDRAULIC JUMP

The hydraulic jump is an illustration of rapidly varied flow and of considerable interest to the hydraulic engineer. A jump may occur in a channel of any slope and often is in evidence at the foot of spillways and downstream from sluice gates. Flow prior to the jump is supercritical; after the jump it is subcritical. Relationships between conditions before and after the jump may be obtained through application of the continuity, energy, and momentum equations. For a rectangular channel having a horizontal slope, the depth after the jump may be calculated using

$$y_2 = -\frac{y_1}{2} \pm \sqrt{\frac{y_1^2}{4} + \frac{2V_1^2 y_1}{g}} \tag{6-7}$$

where y_1 and y_2 = depths before and after the jump respectively
$\qquad V_1$ = the upstream velocity.

For slopes less than 0.10 this equation gives good results. On slopes steeper than 0.10 a different method of solution is required.[3] The depths y_2 and y_1 are commonly known as conjugate depths or sequent depths.

Location of the hydraulic jump may be determined by considering the surface profiles in the region of the jump and by fitting the conjugate depths to these profiles.

6-4. CHANNEL TRANSITIONS

Transitions are important in the design of open channels. They are constructed to provide for changes in size, grade, shape and alignment of conduits; to minimize head losses; and to control the flow regime. In sewerage and drainage works, manholes, junction boxes, and special custom-designed structures are the primary kinds of transitions. Changes in size and grade of drainage conduits are frequent. Because these and other changes have a pronounced effect on the surface profile and the energy gradient, knowledge of the hydraulic performance of transition structures is fundamental to efficient and economical design.

Figure 6-5 illustrates the changes in surface profile which take place at a transition in size or grade of sewer. Head losses which occur in drain-

TABLE 6-1

CALCULATIONS FOR THE SURFACE PROFILE OF EXAMPLE 6-2

1	2	3	4	5	6	7	8	9	10	11	12	13
y	A	V	$V^2/2g$	$E = d + \dfrac{V^2}{2g}$	P	R	$R^{4/3}$	$S_e = \dfrac{V^2}{(1.49)^2 R^{4/3}/n^2}$	$\bar{S}_e$	ΔE	$S_c - \bar{S}_e$	$\Delta L = \dfrac{\Delta E}{S_c - \bar{S}_e}$
7.5	75	3.27	0.166	7.666	25	3.0	4.33	0.000188				
7.0	70	3.50	0.191	7.191	24	2.91	4.15	0.000225	0.000207	0.475	0.000793	598
6.0	60	4.08	0.259	6.259	22	2.73	3.82	0.000333	0.000279	0.932	0.000721	1,292
5.0	50	4.90	0.374	5.374	20	2.50	3.40	0.000539	0.000436	0.885	0.000564	1,570
4.0	40	6.12	0.582	4.582	18	2.22	2.90	0.000984	0.000762	0.792	0.000238	3,328

$$L = \Sigma \Delta L = \overline{6,788}$$

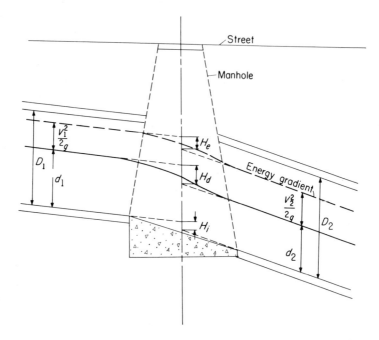

FIG. 6-5. Schematic diagram indicating shift in the hydraulic and energy gradients in a manhole.

age works are important since they affect the location of the hydraulic gradient. If the gradient is contained within the channel configuration as indicated in the figure, there is no problem. Many storm-drainage systems are designed to operate surcharged (under pressure) at times, however. In such cases the elevation of the hydraulic gradient in the manholes or other structures which open to the ground surface is above the top of the pipes and may reach street level. This condition is not compatable with good design practice, which normally requires that the hydraulic gradient be maintained some minimum depth below the ground surface. Imposing such a restriction precludes the possibility of water backing up into the street as a result of developing the head required for a particular design flow. For some designs the head lost in manholes and similar structures is high, and special transitions are useful to minimize these losses. A comprehensive treatment of the design of special transitions can be found in references listed at the end of the chapter.[4,5,7]

For the transition accomplished by the manhole of Fig. 6-5, the following relationships are evident:

$$H_d + \frac{V_1^2}{2g} = \frac{V_2^2}{2g} + H_e$$

or

$$H_d = H_e + \frac{\Delta V^2}{2g} \tag{6-8}$$

where H_d is the change in elevation of the hydraulic gradient (or the water surface in this case) when measured as the difference in elevation between the normal flow depths projected to the center line of the manhole, and H_e is the energy loss in the transition. The value of H_e is usually small and normally considered to be a function of the change in velocity head, or

$$H_e = K\Delta\left(\frac{V^2}{2g}\right)$$

Hinds has indicated values of K varying from 0.1 upward when velocities increase through the transition, and values upwards of 0.2 when the velocity decreases through the transition, providing the flow is subcritical.[5] For rapid flows, K is considered to increase approximately as the square of the velocity ratios.

If a prescribed loss in energy is selected, the drop in invert across the structure may be determined as follows:

$$H_i + d_1 + \frac{V_1^2}{2g} = H_e + \frac{V_2^2}{2g} + d_2$$

$$H_i = H_e + \Delta\left(d + \frac{V^2}{2g}\right)$$

or

$$H_i = K\Delta\left(\frac{V^2}{2g}\right) + \Delta\left(d + \frac{V^2}{2g}\right) \tag{6-9}$$

where H_i is the drop in invert as measured at the centerline of the manhole and its sign may be either positive or negative. Negative values indicate a rise in the invert but this is not done in practice. In such cases the invert is made continuous. Commonly, in sewer designs a fixed value will be used for the drop at all transitions and the change in hydraulic gradient computed accordingly. A number of rules for determining invert drops in manholes where a change in conduit size takes place are reported by Fair and Geyer.[8] A comprehensive study of pressure changes at storm-drain junctions is presented by Sangster, Wood, Smerdon, and Bossy.[6]

6-5. CURVED CHANNELS

Special consideration must be given channels which are not linear in their alignment. Where curves or bends are encountered, the water surface is inclined so that the depth of flow on the outside of the bend exceeds that on the inside wall. Outer walls must therefore be higher than inner walls for specific discharges. An additional factor is that diagonal waves are encountered in bends where supercritical flow prevails. These waves may be of such magnitude as to indicate the need for corrective measures, for example, superelevating the channel bottom in combination with a spiral transition to minimize their effect.[24] Wave heights may also be reduced by the use of diagonal sills.

Figure 6-6 illustrates the flow around an open-channel bend. Considering a unit length of channel centered at section *A-A*, equilibrium is maintained between the net pressure force and the centrifugal force acting on this volume of fluid. The total pressure acting at the inner wall of the

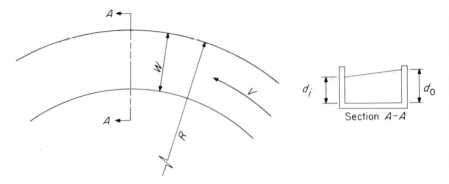

FIG. 6-6. Flow in a curved open channel.

channel is $\gamma d_i^2/2$ and that at the outer wall is $\gamma d_o^2/2$. The centrifugal force is equal to the product of the fluid mass and the normal or radial acceleration of the fluid V^2/r, where r is the radius of curvature. Equating the pressure and centrifugal forces, the following expression is obtained.

$$\frac{\gamma d_o^2}{2} - \frac{\gamma d_i^2}{2} = \rho W \frac{d_i + d_o}{2} \left(\frac{V^2}{r}\right) \tag{6-10}$$

where W is the channel width, V is the tangential linear velocity, and the other terms are as previously defined. This equation may be transformed to,

$$\frac{\gamma}{2} (d_o + d_i)(d_o - d_i) = \frac{\gamma}{2} (d_o + d_i) \frac{W}{g}\left(\frac{V^2}{r}\right)$$

which simplifies to

$$d_o - d_i = \frac{W}{g}\left(\frac{V^2}{r}\right) \tag{6-11}$$

Equation 6-11 permits determination of the slope of the water surface in the bend and is applicable to channels of any cross section. The difference in depths computed by Eq. 6-11 may be underestimated by as much as 20 percent if variations in curvature and a nonuniform velocity distribution are considered. For known velocity distributions, the cross section may be divided into parts and the depth change computed individually for them, then summed for the entire width.

6-6. VELOCITY CONSIDERATIONS

It has been stated previously that storm-water runoff and sewage or waste flows differ in nature from drinking-water supplies. First, sewage must be moved as swiftly as possible to prevent septicity and second, if velocities are too high, conduit erosion may result. In general, both maximum and minimum velocities are prescribed for waste-transportation systems.

Maximum velocities are determined primarily on the basis of the erodability of the channel material. Normally, velocities in excess of 20 fps are to be avoided in concrete or tile sewers and whenever possible velocities of 10 fps or less should be used. Specially lined inverts are sometimes employed to combat channel erosion. The average value of the channel shearing stress is related to both erosion and sediment deposition. The manner in which the tractive force is related to velocity may be indicated using Eq. 6-1.

$$\tau_0 = \gamma RS \qquad [6\text{-}1]$$

The flow velocity is a function of R and S and may be written in the form of the Chézy formula[8]

$$V = C \sqrt{RS} \qquad (6\text{-}12)$$

where C is the Chézy coefficient, equal to $1.49 R^{1/6}/n$ as evaluated by Manning. Substituting for R and S in Eq. 6-1, the relation between V and τ_0 is obtained:

$$\tau_0 = \gamma \left(\frac{V}{C}\right)^2 \qquad (6\text{-}13)$$

From this formula it can be seen that tractive force per unit area varies as the square of the velocity.

Minimum velocities are required to prevent deposition of organic or inorganic materials within the channel. These minimum velocities are commonly called *self-cleansing velocities*. In sanitary sewers, velocities in excess of 2.5 fps are desirable and velocities less than 2 fps should be avoided except where there is no alternative.

For a given sediment, the velocity at which frictional resistance is overcome and the material moved along must be determined if deposition is to be prevented. A number of relationships have been developed, all based on the relationship between the drag force acting on the sediment layer and the resistive force which tends to prevent motion of the particles.

Neglecting friction between particles, the intensity of the resistance to motion of the particles is a function of their weight in water per unit surface area. This may be stated as

$$(\gamma_s - \gamma)\frac{V}{A}$$

where γ_s = specific weight of the particles
γ = specific weight of water
V = particle volume
A = surface area
The expression may also be written as

$$K(\gamma_s - \gamma)d$$

where K is a measure of particle shape and cohesiveness and the effectiveness of scour. The resistive force must be balanced by the drag force acting on the particle thus

$$\gamma RSA = KA(\gamma_s - \gamma)d$$

and

$$S = \frac{K}{R}\frac{\gamma_s - \gamma}{\gamma}d \qquad (6\text{-}14)$$

in which S is the minimum slope at which the conduit will be self-cleansing. Substitution of this value of S in the Chézy equation yields

$$V_m = C\sqrt{K\frac{\gamma_s - \gamma}{\gamma}d} \qquad (6\text{-}15)$$

where V_m is the minimum velocity for self-cleansing, and C is selected with consideration given to the presence of solids in the flow. The value of K must be found experimentally. Values ranging from 0.04 for the initiation of scour to more than 0.8 for effective cleansing have been reported.[10]

If nonflocculating particles have mean diameters between 0.05 and 0.5 mm, the minimum velocity may be determined using[9]

$$V_m = \left[25.3 \times 10^{-3}\text{g}\frac{d(\rho_s - \rho)}{\rho}\right]^{0.816}\left(\frac{D\rho_m}{\mu_m}\right)^{0.633} \qquad (6\text{-}16)$$

where V_m = minimum velocity in fps
d = mean particle diameter in feet
D = pipe diameter in feet
ρ_m = mean mass density of the suspension in pounds per cubic foot
ρ_s = particle density in pounds per cubic foot
μ_m = viscosity of the suspension in pounds of mass per foot second
ρ = liquid mass density in pounds per cubic foot
The value of ρ_m may be determined by using

$$\rho_m = X_v\rho_s + (1 - X_v)\rho \qquad (6\text{-}17)$$

where X_v is the volumetric fraction of the suspended solids.

DESIGN OF SANITARY SEWERS

The design of sanitary sewers involves (1) the application of the principles outlined in Chap. 3 to determine the design flows and (2) the application of hydraulic engineering principles to devise adequate conveyances for transporting these flows.

6-7. HOUSE AND BUILDING CONNECTIONS

Connections from the main sewer to houses or other buildings are commonly constructed of vitrified clay, concrete, or cast-iron pipe. Building connections are usually made on about a 2 percent grade with 6-in. or larger pipe. Grades less than 1 percent are to be avoided; likewise extremely steep grades.

6-8. COLLECTING SEWERS

Collecting sewers gather flows from individual buildings and transport the material to an interceptor or main sewer. Local standards usually dictate the location of these sewers but they are commonly located under the street paving on one side of the storm drain, which is usually centered. The collecting sewer should be capable of conveying the flow of the present and anticipated population of the area it is to serve. Design flows are the sum of the peak domestic, commercial, and industrial flows and infiltration. The collecting sewer must transport this design flow when flowing full. Grades requiring minimum excavation while maximum and minimum restrictions on velocity are satisfied are best. Manholes are normally located at changes in direction, grade, pipe size, or at intersections of collecting sewers. For 8-, 10-, or 12-in. sewers, manholes spaced no further than about 400 ft apart permit inspection and cleaning when necessary. For larger sizes, the maximum spacing can be increased.

6-9. INTERCEPTING SEWERS

Intercepting sewers are expected to carry flows from the collector sewers in the drainage basin to the point of treatment or disposal of the sewage. These sewers normally follow valleys or natural stream beds of the drainage area. When the sewer is built through undeveloped areas, precaution should be taken to insure the proper location of manholes for future connections. For 15- to 27-in. sewers, manholes are constructed at least every 600 ft; for larger sewers, increased spacing is common. Manholes or other transition structures are usually built at every change in pipe size, grade or alignment. For large sewers, horizontal or vertical curves are sometimes constructed. Grades should be designed so that the criteria regarding maximum and minimum velocities are satisfied.

6-10. MATERIALS

Collecting and intercepting sewers are constructed of asbestos cement sewer pipe, cast-iron pipe, concrete pipe, vitrified clay pipe, and brick. Care should be exercised in designing the system so that permissible structural loadings are not exceeded for the material selected. Information on pipe loading is readily available from the Clay Products Association, the Portland Cement Association, Cast Iron Pipe Manufacturers, and others.

6-11. SYSTEM LAYOUT

The first step in designing a sewerage system is to establish an overall system layout which includes a plan of the area to be sewered showing roads, streets, buildings, other utilities, topography, soil type, and the cellar or lowest floor elevation of all buildings to be drained. Where part of the drainage area to be served is undeveloped and proposed development plans are not yet available, care must be taken to provide adequate terminal manholes which can later be connected to the system constructed serving the area. If the proposed sewer connects to an existing one, an accurate location of the existing terminal manhole giving invert elevation, size, and slope is essential.

On the drainage-area plan just described, a tentative layout of collecting sewers and the intercepting sewer or sewers should be made. When feasible, sewer location should minimize the length required while providing service to the entire area. Length may be sacrificed if the shorter runs would require costlier excavation. Normally, the sewer slope should follow the ground surface so waste flows can follow the approximate path of the area's surface drainage. In some instances it may be necessary to lay the sewer slope in opposition to the surface slope or to pump wastes across a drainage divide. This situation can occur when a developer buys land lying in two adjacent drainage basins and, for economic or other reasons, must sewer the whole tract through only one basin.

Intercepting sewers or trunk lines are located to pass through the lowest point in the drainage area (the outlet) and to extend through the entire area to the drainage divide. Normally they follow major natural drainage ways and are located in a designated right of way or street. Land slopes on both sides should be toward the intercepting sewer. Lateral or collecting sewers are connected to the intercepting sewer and proceed upslope to the drainage divide. Collecting sewers should be located in all streets or rights-of-way within the area to provide service throughout the drainage basin. Figure 6-7 illustrates a typical sewer layout. Note that the interceptor sewer is located in the stream valley and collector sewers transport flows from the various tributary areas to the interceptor.

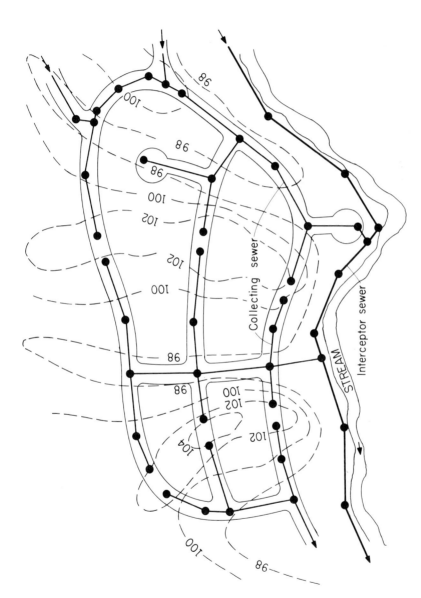

FIG. 6-7. Typical layout for design of a sewerage system.

6-12. HYDRAULIC DESIGN

The hydraulic design of a sanitary sewer can be carried out in a systematic manner. Figure 6-8 is typical of the way in which data can be organized to facilitate computations. The essential elements of hydraulic design require that peak design flows be carried by the pipe flowing full at velocities great enough to prevent sedimentation yet small enough to prevent erosion. To minimize head losses at transitions and eliminate backwater effects, the hydraulic gradient must not change abruptly or slope in a direction adverse to the flow at changes in horizontal direction, pipe size, or quantity of flow. Sewers are usually designed to closely follow the grade of the ground surface or street paving under which they are laid. In addition, the depth of cover should be kept as close to the minimum as effective hydraulic design will permit to minimize excavation costs. The sewer cannot, of course, conflict with other subsurface utilities or structures.

Pipe sizes are determined in the following manner. A profile of the proposed sewer route is drawn and the hydraulic gradient at the downstream end of the sewer noted (normally the elevation of the hydraulic gradient of the sewer being met). Where discharge is to a treatment plant or open body of water, the hydraulic gradient is the elevation of the freewater surface at this point. At the beginning elevation of the hydraulic gradient, a tentative gradient approximately following the ground surface is drawn upstream to the next point of control (usually a manhole). Exceptions to this occur when the surface slope is less than adequate to provide cleansing velocities, where obstructions preclude using this slope, or where adequate cover cannot be maintained. Using the tentative gradient slope, a pipe size is then selected which comes closest to carrying the design flow under full flow conditions. Usually, a standard size pipe is not found that will carry the maximum flow exactly at full depth with this gradient. Common practice is then to select the next larger size, modify the slope, or both. The choice will depend upon a comparison of pipe-cost savings vs. excavation costs, and on additional local conditions such as other utilities which may control the vertical location of the sewer being designed.

After the first section of pipe has been designed, the hydraulic gradient at its upstream end is then used as a beginning point for the next section, and so on. Where significant changes in flow, direction, velocity, or any combination of these occur at manholes, it is important that the head lost in the manhole structure be computed and added to the elevation of the hydraulic gradient at the entrance to the outflow pipe. This total value then serves as the initial elevation of the hydraulic gradient for the succeeding section upstream. An example of the design of a storm-drainage system given later in the chapter will illustrate the procedure described here.

JOB NAME _____ J. O. _____ DISTRICT _____ DATE _____

PREPARED BY _____ OF _____ SHEET _____ OF _____

CHECKED BY _____ (FIRM)

Area Symbol	Area Acres	Population Density		Population		Non-Domestic Average Flow (MGD)		Average Sewage Flow (MGD)		Peak Flow (MGD)		Infil-tration MGD	Peak Industrial Waste Flow, MGD		Design Flow, MGD		Approx. Grade	Tent-ative Size	Velocity	
		Pres.	Ult.	Pres.	Ult.	Pres.	Ult.	Pres.	Ult.	Pres.	Ult.		Pres.	Ult.	Pres.	Ult.			+	++
(1)	(2)	(3)	(4)	(5)	(6)	(7)*	(8)*	(9)	(10)	(11)	(12)	(13)	(14)**	(15)**	(16)	(17)	(18)	(19)	(20)	(21)

NOTES: Where columns 7, 8, 14 and 15 are used, show calculations on back of form

* includes average sewage flow from institutional, industrial, and commercial establishments

** Use this column as described under II-B-2-b, Sanitary Sewer Section

+ Velocity based upon present average sewage flow

++ Velocity based upon ultimate peak design flow

APPROVED

DIRECTOR

DIVISION OF ENGINEERING

REVIEWED

DATE

BALTIMORE COUNTY DEPARTMENT OF PUBLIC WORKS

STANDARD SANITARY SEWER DESIGN

FLOW TABULATION FORM

Revised

Date | By

Fig. 6-8. Typical computation sheet for sanitary sewer design. (Courtesy of the Baltimore County Department of Public Works, Towson, Maryland.)

6-13. PROTECTION AGAINST FLOOD WATERS

Because the volume of sewage is extremely small compared with flood flows, it is important that sewers be constructed to prevent admittance of large surface-runoff volumes. This will preclude overloads on treatment plants with their resultant reduction in degree of treatment or complete elimination of treatment in some instances.

Where interceptor sewers are built along stream beds, manhole stacks frequently are raised above some design flood level such as the 50-year level. In addition, the manhole structures are waterproofed. Where stacks cannot be raised, watertight manhole covers are employed. Such measures as these keep surface drainage into the sewer at a minimum.

6-14. INVERTED SIPHONS

An inverted siphon is a section of sewer which is constructed below the hydraulic gradient due to some obstruction and operates under pressure. The term *depressed sewer* is actually more appropriate, since no real siphon action is involved. Usually, two or more pipes are needed for a siphon in order to handle flow variability. Normally the water-surface elevation at the entrance and exit to a siphon is fixed. Under these conditions the hydraulic design consists of selecting a pipe or pipes which will carry the design flow with a head loss equivalent to the difference in entrance and exit water-surface elevations. A transition structure is generally required at the entrance and exit of the depressed sewer to properly proportion or combine the flows.

The minimum flow in a siphon must be great enough to prevent deposition of suspended solids. Normally, velocities less than 3 ft/sec are unsatisfactory. When the siphon is required to handle flows which vary considerably during any 24-hr period, it is customary to provide two or more pipes. A small pipe is provided to handle the low flows; intermediate flows may be carried by the smallest pipe and a larger pipe. Maximum flows may require the use of three or more pipes. By subdividing the flow in this manner, adequate cleansing velocities are assured for all flow magnitudes. The entrance transition structure is designed to properly channel the flow into the various pipes. Figure 6-9 illustrates a typical transition structure.

DESIGN OF STORM-DRAINAGE SYSTEMS

Rapid and effective removal of storm runoff was a luxury not found in many cities of the early nineteenth century. Today, however, the modern city dweller has come to think of this as an essential service. Urban drainage facilities have progressed from crude ditches and stepping stones to the present intricate coordinated systems of curbs, gutters, inlets, and underground conveyances.

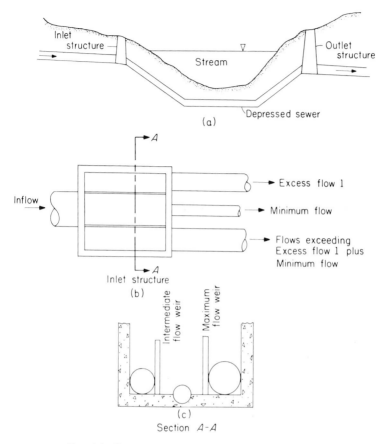

Fig. 6-9. Sketch of an inverted siphon or depressed sewer.

Handling surface runoff on urban drainage areas is a complex and costly undertaking with several primary difficulties—notably quantity and variability. Volumes of surface runoff can be exceedingly large during intense storms, yet such storms may occur on only a very infrequent basis. This poses the problem of building-drainage works which perhaps are used for only a short time. The costly nature of urban drainage work has already been mentioned in this chapter (the 1963 statement of the Committee on Urban Hydrology of the American Society of Civil Engineers).

6-15. HYDROLOGIC CONSIDERATIONS

The hydrologic phase of urban drainage design is concerned with determining the magnitude, distribution, and timing of the various runoff events. Maximum events are of utmost importance since they are the basis for design of major structures. In some cases a knowledge of peak flow will suffice, whereas if storage or routing considerations are important, the volume and distribution must also be known.

Runoff which occurs in any drainage area is a function of both the climate of the locality and the physical characteristics of the area. Factors which may be pertinent in precipitation-runoff relationships include precipitation type, rainfall intensity, duration, and distribution; storm direction; antecedent precipitation; initial soil moisture conditions; soil type; evaporation; transpiration; and the size, shape, slope, elevation, directional orientation, and land-use characteristics of the drainage area. Indirect and artificial drainage must also be considered when applicable.

A brief study of these items should be sufficient proof that the hydrologic problem is complex. If urban drainage works are to effectively and economically serve the areas for which they are designed, considerable emphasis must be placed on the determination of accurate and reliable estimates of flow. Unfortunately, it is all too common that months are spent on the structural design of hydraulic conveyances while only meager computations are made of the flow magnitudes on which these designs are based. Except in the case of very important structures, computations are often founded on formulas of questionable reliability, or on the assumption of a past maximum flow plus a factor of safety. Indiscriminate and general use of the Talbot formula for culvert design in highway engineering is a prime example. The greatest number of hydraulic failures have been caused by faulty determinations of runoff magnitude, not by structural inadequacies.

Peak flows result from excess surface-runoff volumes. The conditions which may generate these excesses are intense storms, snow melt, and snow melt combined with rainfall. Maximum flows on urban areas in the United States usually result from high intensity short-duration rainfall of the thunderstorm type, whereas floods on large drainage basins are habitually caused by a combination of rainfall and snow melt. The particular factors which produce maximum flow on a specific drainage area must be determined if reasonable reliability is to be accorded the estimated quantities of discharge.

6-16. THE DESIGN FLOW

Design flow may be defined as the maximum flow which a specified structure can pass safely. It is significant that the first question to be answered in relation to the design flow is its probability of occurrence. Should a drainage system be designed to carry the maximum possible flow, the 5 percent, the 1 percent, or some other chance discharge? Once this question has been answered, the magnitude of flow having the selected "design" frequency must be determined. Note particularly that there is little relationship between the normal life of the drainage works and the frequency of the design flow.

Table 6-2 shows, for example, that there is a 22 percent chance that the 100-year storm will occur in any 25-year period. This is good reason for questioning the design of a structure for a life expectancy of 25 years, then using design flows expected on the average of once in 25 years or less. If such a design is used, the chances are good that the structure will be damaged, destroyed or at least overloaded before it has served its useful life.

TABLE 6-2

THE PROBABILITY THAT AN EVENT HAVING A PRESCRIBED RECURRENCE INTERVAL WILL BE EQUALED OR EXCEEDED DURING A SPECIFIED PERIOD

T_R, years	Period, years					
	1	5	10	25	50	100
1	1.0	1.0	1.0	1.0	1.0	1.0
2	0.5	0.97	0.999	*	*	*
5	0.2	0.67	0.89	0.996	*	*
10	0.1	0.41	0.65	0.93	0.995	*
50	0.02	0.10	0.18	0.40	0.64	0.87
100	0.01	0.05	0.10	0.22	0.40	0.63

*Values are approximately equal to 1.

Selection of a design frequency must be based on consideration of potential damage to human life, property damage, and inconvenience. Human life cannot be judged in terms of monetary values. If it is apparent that failure of a proposed drainage system or structure will imperil human lives, the design should be appraised accordingly. Property damage is a purely economic consideration and design flows can be determined on the basis of the limiting size flow against which it is economically practical to protect. Inconvenience is an intangible quantity for the most part but can be related to economic values under many circumstances and should also be heeded in selecting a design frequency.

6-17. PROCEDURES FOR ESTIMATING RUNOFF

Procedures used in estimating runoff magnitude and frequency can be generally categorized as (1) empirical approaches, (2) statistical or probability methods, and (3) methods relating rainfall to runoff.

Historically, numerous empirical equations have been developed for use in the prediction of runoff. Most of them have been based on the correlation of only two or three variables, and at best given rough approximations. Many are applicable only to specific localities—a fact that should be carefully considered before they are used. In most cases the frequency of the computed flow is unknown. Formulas of this type are useful only where a more reliable means is not available and then only with a complete understanding of the relationship and the exercise of due caution. Many of these relationships are of the form

$$Q = KA^n \tag{6-18}$$

where Q = discharge (usually in cubic feet per second)
  K = coefficient reflecting rainfall and runoff characteristics
  A = drainage area
  n = a constant

Statistical analyses provide good results if sufficient records are available and where no significant changes in stream regimen are experienced or expected in the future. Estimates generally are based on the use of duration or probability curves. In applying these curves, the larger the sample population the greater the validity of the estimate. For example, a determination of the 10-year peak flow based on records of only 10 years might be seriously in error whereas the same answer computed from a 100-year record would yield good results. About ten independent samples normally can be expected to provide satisfactory estimates of maximum flow magnitudes of any frequency. The need for long-term records emphasizes the limitation inherent in the use of probability methods since extreme values expected to occur only on the average of once in 50 to 100 years or more are not often obtainable within the available record. They must therefore be determined by extrapolation of the probability curve, an extremely dangerous undertaking. Most streams in the United States do not have reliable gaging records longer than 50 years and only a few urban areas have even limited reports. An example will illustrate the use of a frequency distribution of runoff as a tool in prediction.

EXAMPLE 6-3. Consider the 20-year record of maximum annual stream flows shown in Table 6-3. Plotting these values on log-probability paper vs. percent of years during which runoff was equal to or less than the indicated value shows the peak flow expected once in 2 and 15 years. The data are organized in Table 6-3, and the solution is given in Fig. 6-10.

Solution: It can easily be seen from Fig. 6-10 that if some relatively infrequent runoff, such as the 100-year runoff, is to be determined, large errors resulting from the extrapolation of the fitted curve might result. Obviously, the greatest reliability can be placed on those estimates which fall within the limits of the original data. Even then it should be understood that if the physical character of the drainage area is materially modified, such changes could invalidate the use of past records for predicting future events.

TABLE 6-3
DATE FOR EXAMPLE 6-3

Ranked 24-hr Maximum Annual Flood Flows, cfs	Rank, K	Percentage of Total Occurrences Having Values Equal To or Greater Than the Stated Value $= \dfrac{100K*}{n+1}$
26.7	20	95.3
33.0	19	90.5
34.8	18	87.7
37.8	17	80.9
42.9	16	76.2
46.8	15	71.4
49.5	14	66.7
50.4	13	61.9
53.4	12	57.1
54.3	11	52.3
55.5	10	47.7
64.2	9	42.9
66.9	8	38.1
72.0	7	33.3
84.0	6	28.5
119.2	5	23.8
126.0	4	19.1
129.0	3	14.3
139.2	2	9.5
190.8	1	4.8

*Use of this relationship gives recognition to the fact that values both greater and less than the observed maximum and minimum are expected to occur.[13]

Of the methods relating runoff to rainfall, the most used are the unit hydrograph method and the "rational method," or some modification of these.

The unit hydrograph method is an extremely valuable tool for estimating runoff magnitudes of different frequencies which may occur on a specific stream.[15] In order to use this approach it is necessary to have continuous records of runoff and precipitation for the particular drainage area. Determinations must be made of infiltration capacity variations throughout the year. The method is limited to areas for which precipitation patterns do not vary markedly. On large drainage basins, hydrographs must be developed for the various reaches and then synthesized into a single design flow at the critical location.

A unit hydrograph represents the runoff volume of 1 in. from a specified drainage area for a particular rainfall duration. A separate unit hydrograph is theoretically required for every possible rainfall length of interest. Ordinarily, however, variations of ±25 percent from any duration are considered acceptable. In addition, unit hydrographs for short periods can be synthesized into hydrographs for longer durations.

Once a unit hydrograph has been derived for a particular drainage area and rainfall duration, the hydrograph for any other storm of equal

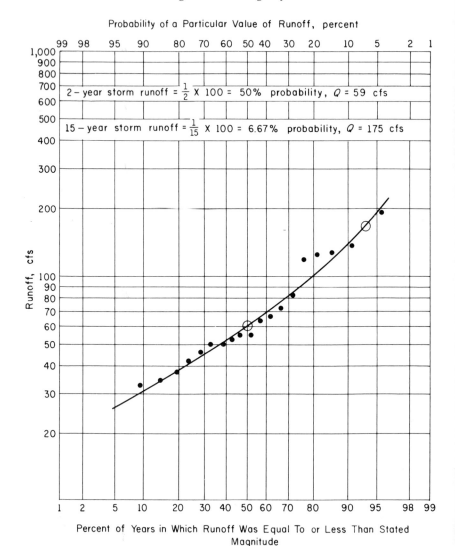

FIG. 6-10. Graphical runoff determination using a probability curve.

duration can be obtained. This new hydrograph is developed by applying the unit hydrograph theorem that the ordinates of all hydrographs resulting from equal unit time rains are proportional to the total direct runoff from that rain. The condition may be stated mathematically as

$$\frac{Q_s}{V_s} = \frac{Q_u}{1} \qquad (6\text{-}19)$$

where Q_s = magnitude of a hydrograph ordinate of direct runoff having a volume equal to V_s in inches at some instant of time after the start of runoff

$\quad Q_u$ = ordinate of the unit hydrograph having a volume of one inch at the same instant of time

Storms of reasonably uniform rainfall intensity, having a duration of about 25 percent of the drainage area lag time (difference in time between the center of mass of rainfall and center of mass of resulting runoff) and producing a total runoff of 1 in. or more, are most suitable in deriving a unit hydrograph.

Essential steps in the development of a unit hydrograph are as follows:

1. Analysis of the stream-flow hydrograph to permit separation of the surface runoff from the groundwater flow. It can be accomplished by any one of several methods.[14]

2. Measure the total volume of surface runoff (direct runoff) from the storm producing the original hydrograph. The volume is equal to the area under the hydrograph after the groundwater flow has been removed.

3. Divide the ordinates of the direct runoff by the total direct runoff volume in inches. The resulting plot of the answers versus time is a unit graph for the basin.

4. Finally, the effective duration of the runoff-producing rain for this unit graph must be found. The answer can be obtained by a study of the hyetograph of the storm used.

The steps listed are used in deriving the unit hydrograph from an isolated storm. Other procedures are required for complex storms or in developing synthetic unit graphs when few data are available. Unit hydrographs may also be transposed from one basin to another under certain circumstances. An example will serve to illustrate the derivation and application of the unit hydrograph.

EXAMPLE 6-4. Using the hydrograph given in Fig. 6-11, derive a unit hydrograph for the 3-sq-mile drainage area. Then, from this unit hydrograph, derive a hydrograph of direct runoff for the rainfall sequence given in Table 6-5.

Solution: The steps for solving are as follows:

1. Separate the base or groundwater flow so that the total direct runoff hydrograph may be obtained. As stated previously, a number of procedures are reported in the literature. A common method is to draw a straight line AC which begins when the hydrograph starts an appreciable rise and ends where the recession curve intersects the base flow curve. The most important point here is to be consistent in methodology from storm to storm.

2. Determine the duration of the effective rainfall (rainfall that actually produces surface runoff). The effective rainfall volume must be equivalent to the volume of direct surface runoff. Usually the unit time of the effective rainfall

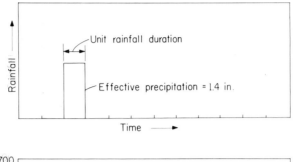

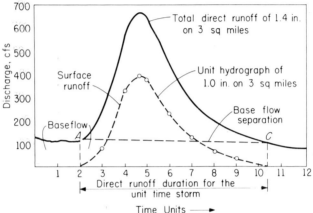

Fig. 6-11. Illustration of the derivation of a unit hydrograph from an isolated storm.

will be 1 day, 1 hr, 12 hr, or some other interval appropriate for the size drainage
area studied. As stated before, the unit storm duration should not exceed about
25 percent of the drainage area lag time. The effective portion of the rainstorm
for this example is given in Fig. 6-11 along with its duration. The effective volume
is 1.4 in.

3. Project the base length of the unit hydrograph down to the abscissa giving
the horizontal projection of the base flow-separation line AC. It should be noted
that the unit hydrograph theory assumes that for all storms of equal duration,
regardless of intensity, the period of surface runoff is the same.

4. Tabulate the ordinates of direct runoff at the peak rate of flow and at
sufficient other positions to determine the hydrograph shape. Note that the direct
runoff ordinate is the ordinate above the base flow-separation line.

5. Compute the ordinates of the unit hydrograph by using Eq. 6-19. In this
example the values are obtained by dividing the direct runoff ordinates by 1.4.
Table 6-4 outlines the computation of the unit hydrograph ordinates.

6. Using the values from Table 6-4, plot the unit hydrograph as shown on
Fig. 6-11.

TABLE 6-4

DETERMINATION OF A UNIT HYDROGRAPH FROM AN ISOLATED STORM

1	2	3	4	5
Time Unit	Total Runoff, cfs	Base Flow, cfs	Total Direct Runoff, (2) − (3), cfs	Unit Hydrograph Ordinate, (4) ÷ 1.4, cfs
1	110	110	0	0
2	121	121	0	0
3	230	120	110	78.7
4	578	118	460	328
4.7	666	116	550	393
5	645	115	530	379
6	434	114	320	229
7	293	113	180	129
8	202	112	90	64.2
9	160	110	50	35.7
10	117	105	12	8.6
10.5	105	105	0	0
11	90	90	0	0
12	80	80	0	0

7. Using the derived ordinates of the unit hydrograph, determine the ordinates of the hydrographs for each consecutive unit rainfall period as given in Table 6-5.

8. Determine the synthesized hydrograph for unit storms 1-3 by plotting the three hydrographs and summing the ordinates. The procedure is indicated on Fig. 6-12.

The unit hydrograph method provides the entire hydrograph resulting from a particular storm and offers certain definite advantages over

TABLE 6-5

UNIT HYDROGRAPH APPLICATION

1	2	3	4*		
Time Unit Sequence	Rain Unit Number	Effective Rainfall, in.	Hydrograph Ordinates for Rainfall Units 1-3		
			1	2	3
1	1	0.7	55.1	—	—
2	2	1.7	229	134	—
2.7	3	1.2	275	—	—
3	—	—	265	558	94.3
3.7	—	—	—	668	—
4	—	—	161	644	393
4.7	—	—	—	—	472
5	—	—	90.5	389	455
6	—	—	44.9	219	275
7	—	—	25.0	109	155
8	—	—	6.0	60.7	77
9	—	—	—	14.6	42.8
10	—	—	—	—	10.3

*Values in column 4 obtained by multiplying values in colum 3 by unit hydrograph ordinates.

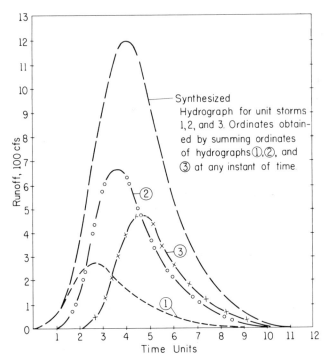

FIG. 6-12. Synthesized hydrograph derived by the unit
hydrograph method.

procedures which produce peak flows alone. It has the disadvantage of
requiring both rainfall and runoff data for its derivation and of being
limited in its application to a particular drainage basin. A number of
refinements to the procedure may be found in the literature.[14-17] Procedures for producing synthetic unit hydrographs covering areas where
adequate records are not available have also been derived.[14]

The other rainfall-runoff relationship which will be discussed here is
known as the "rational method." It was first proposed in 1889 and is
currently the most used method in this country for computing quantities
of storm-water runoff.[18] The rational formula relates runoff to rainfall
in the following manner

$$Q = cia \tag{6-20}$$

where Q = peak runoff rate in cfs

c = runoff coefficient which is actually the ratio of the peak runoff
rate to the average rainfall rate for a period known as the
time of concentration

i = average rainfall intensity in inches per hour for a period equal
to the time of concentration

a = drainage area in acres

It should be noted that the assignment of units of cfs to Q is satisfactory for all practical purposes, since 1.008 cfs equals 1 in. of rainfall in 1 hr on an area of 1 acre.

Assumptions basic to the rational method are (1) the maximum run-off rate to any design location is a function of the average rate of rainfall during the time of concentration and (2) the maximum rate of rainfall occurs during the time of concentration. The variability of the storm pattern is not taken into consideration. The time of concentration t_c is defined as the flow time from the most remote point in the drainage area to the point in question. Usually it is considered to be composed of an overland flow time or, in most urban areas, an inlet time plus a channel flow time.

The channel flow time can be estimated with reasonable accuracy from the hydraulic characteristics of the sewer. Normally the average full-flow velocity of the conveyance for the existing or proposed hydraulic gradient is used. The channel flow time is then determined as the flow length divided by the average velocity.

The inlet time consists of the time required for water to reach a de-fined channel such as a street gutter, plus the gutter flow time to the inlet. Numerous factors, such as rainfall intensity, surface slope, surface roughness, flow distance, infiltration capacity, and depression storage, affect inlet time. Because of this, accurate values are difficult to obtain. Design inlet flow times of from 5 to 30 min are used in practice. In highly developed areas with closely spaced inlets, 5-to-15-min inlet times are common, for similar areas with flat slopes, 10-to-15-min periods are common, and for very level areas with widely spaced inlets, inlet times of 20 to 30 min are frequently used.[18]

Inlet times are also estimated by breaking the flow path into various components, such as grass, asphalt, etc., then computing individual times for each surface and adding them. In theory this would seem desirable but in practice, there are so many variables affecting the flow that the reliability of computations of this type is questionable. The standard procedure is to use inlet times which have been found through experience to be applicable to the various types of urban areas.

Izzard found the concentration time for small experimental plots without developed channels to be

$$t_c = \frac{41b\,L_o^{1/3}}{(ki)^{2/3}} \qquad (6-21)$$

where t_c = time of concentration in minutes
     b = coefficient
    L_o = overland flow length in feet
    k = rational runoff coefficient (see Table 6-7)
    i = rainfall intensity in inches per hour during time t_c[19]

The equation is valid only for laminar flow conditions where the product iL_o is less than 500. The coefficient b is found by using

$$b = \frac{0.0007i + C_r}{S_o^{1/3}} \qquad (6\text{-}22)$$

where S_o = surface slope
$\quad C_r$ = a coefficient of retardance
Values of C_r are given in Table 6-6.

TABLE 6-6
IZZARD'S RETARDANCE COEFFICIENT C_r

Surface	C_r
Smooth asphalt	0.007
Concrete paving	0.012
Tar and gravel paving	0.017
Closely clipped sod	0.046
Dense bluegrass turf	0.060

The runoff coefficient C is the component of the rational formula which requires the greatest exercise of judgment by the engineer. It is not amenable to exact determination, since it includes the influence of a number of variables, such as infiltration capacity, interception by vegetation, depression storage, and antecedent conditions. As used in the rational equation, the coefficient C represents a fixed ratio of runoff to rainfall, while in actuality it is not fixed and may vary for a specific drainage basin with time during a particular storm, from storm to storm, and with change in season. Fortunately, the closer the area comes to being impervious the more reasonable the selection of C becomes. This is true since for highly impervious areas C approaches unity, and for these areas the nature of the surface is much less variable for changing seasonal, meterological, or antecedent conditions. The rational method therefore is best suited for use on urban areas where a high percentage of imperviousness is common.

At present there is no precise method for evaluating the runoff coefficient C although some modern research is being directed toward this end.[20] Common engineering practice is to make use of average values of the coefficient for various surface types which are normally found in urban regions. Table 6-7 lists some values of the runoff coefficient as reported in the American Society of Civil Engineers' *Manual on the Design and Construction of Sanitary and Storm Sewers.*[18]

Figure 6-13 relates the rational C to imperviousness, soil type, and lawn slope. This graph is used in designing storm drains in Baltimore County, Maryland. Most engineering designers make use of information reported in similar tabular or graphical form, inserting local conditions of experience and practice.

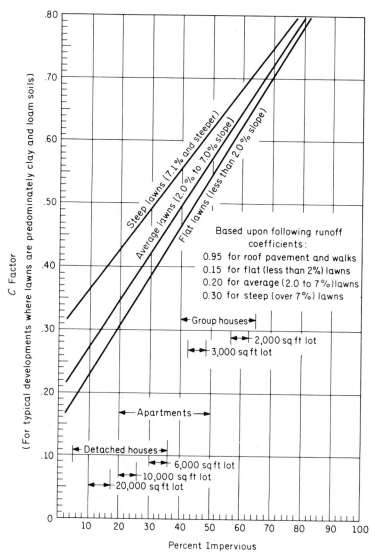

Fig. 6-13. C Factors for typical developments with clay soils. (Courtesy of the Baltimore County Department of Public Works, Towson, Maryland.)

In applying the rational method, a rainfall intensity i must be used which represents the average intensity of a storm of given frequency for the time of concentration. The frequency chosen is largely a matter of economics. Factors related to the choice of a design frequency have already been discussed. Frequencies of 1 to 10 years are commonly used where residential areas are to be protected. For higher-value districts,

TABLE 6-7
SOME VALUES OF THE RATIONAL COEFFICIENT C[18]

Surface Type	C Value
Bituminous streets	0.70 to 0.95
Concrete streets	0.80 to 0.95
Driveways, walks	0.75 to 0.85
Roofs	0.75 to 0.95
Lawns; sandy soil	
Flat, 2 percent	0.05 to 0.10
Average, 2 to 7 percent	0.10 to 0.15
Steep, 7 percent	0.15 to 0.20
Lawns; heavy soil	
Flat, 2 percent	0.13 to 0.17
Average, 2 to 7 percent	0.18 to 0.22
Steep, 7 percent	0.25 to 0.35

10- to 20-year or higher return periods often are selected. Local conditions and practice normally dictate the selection of these design criteria.

After t_c and the rainfall frequency have been ascertained, the rainfall intensity i is usually obtained by making use of a set of rainfall intensity-duration-frequency curves such as shown on Fig. 6-14. Entering the curves on the abscissa with the appropriate value of t_c and then projecting upward to an intersection with the desired frequency curve, i can be found by projecting this intersection point horizontally to an intersection with the ordinate. If an adequate number of years of local rainfall records is available, curves similar to Fig. 6-14 may be developed. Other-

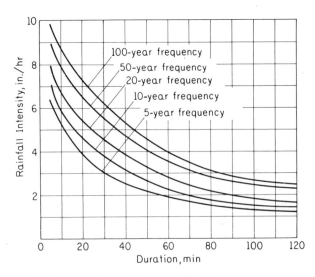

FIG. 6-14. Typical intensity-duration-frequency curves.

wise, data compiled by the Weather Bureau, the Department of Commerce, the Department of Agriculture, and other government agencies which are available for numerous localities and regions can be used.

Generally, the rational method should be used only on areas that are smaller than about 2 sq miles (approximately 1,280 acres) in size. For areas larger than 100 acres, due caution should be exercised. Most urban drainage areas served by storm drains become tributary to natural drainage channels or large conveyances before they reach 100 acres or more in size, however, and for these tributary areas the rational method can be put to reasonable use.

6-18. STORM-WATER INLETS

Storm-water inlet capacity is a subject which has received little emphasis in the design of storm-drainage systems for highways and streets. It is, nevertheless, a consideration of great importance because regardless of the adequacy of the underground drainage system, proper drainage cannot result unless storm water is quickly and efficiently collected and introduced into the system.

A reliable knowledge of the behavior of storm-water inlets has broad implications: overdesign and inefficient use of the drainage system due to inadequate inlets can be avoided; debris and leaf stoppage of inlets can be reduced; and traffic interference on streets and highways can be minimized.

No specific inlet type can be considered best for all conditions of use. Street grade, cross-slope, and depression geometry affect the hydraulic efficiency. Eliminating stoppages or minimizing traffic interference often take precedence over hydraulic considerations in design.

Ideally, a simple opening across the flow path is the most effective type of inlet structure. Construction of this type would be impractical and unsafe, however, and the opening must therefore be covered with a grate or located in the curb. Unfortunately, grates obstruct the fall of water and often serve to collect debris, while curb openings are not in the direct path of flow. Nevertheless, a compromise of this type must be made.

Increasing the street cross-slope will increase the depth of flow of the gutter, gutter depressions will concentrate flows at the inlet, and curb and gutter openings can be combined. These and other modifications provide increased inlet capacities although some of them are not compatible with high-volume traffic.

Numerous inlet designs are seen across the United States, most of which have been developed from the practical experience of engineers or by rule-of-thumb procedures. The hydraulic capacity of many of these designs is totally unknown and estimates frequently are considerably in error. Only in recent years have laboratory studies been conducted to produce efficient designs and develop a better understanding of inlet behavior.[21,23]

Four major types of inlets are being built: curb inlets, gutter inlets, combination inlets, and multiple inlets. A multitude of varieties is possible in each classification. A brief general description of the basic types follows.

(a) Curb inlet—a vertical opening in the curb through which gutter flow passes.

(b) Gutter inlet—a depressed or undepressed opening in the gutter section through which the surface drainage falls, covered by one or more grates.

(c) Combination inlet—an inlet composed of both curb and gutter openings which acts as an integrated unit. Gutter openings may be placed directly in front of the curb opening (contiguous combination inlet) or may be placed upstream or downstream of the gutter opening (offset inlet). Combination inlets may be depressed or undepressed. Figure 6-15 depicts a typical combination inlet. Figure 6-16 relates the capacity of the inlet to the percent gutter slope.

(d) Multiple inlets—closely spaced interconnected inlets acting as a unit. Identical inlets end to end are called "double inlets."

Several general design recommendations regarding storm-water inlets may be made. The final selection of the optimum inlet type for a specific location will necessarily have to be based on the exercise of engineering judgment relative to the importance of clogging, traffic hazard, safety, and cost. In general use cross-slopes that are as steep as possible considering traffic safety and comfort. Locate and design the inlets so there will be a 5 to 10 percent bypass in gutter flow. This greatly increases the inlet capacity. The bypass flow should not be great enough to inconvenience pedestrians or vehicular traffic, however. On streets where parking is permitted or where vehicles are not expected to travel near the curb, use contiguous combination curb-and-gutter inlets with longitudinal grate bars, or build depressed gutter inlets if clogging is not a problem. Where clogging is important, use depressed curb inlets if the gutter flow is small. For large flows, use depressed combination inlets with the curb opening upstream. On streets having slopes in excess of 5 percent where traffic passes close to the curb, use deflector inlets if road dirt will not pack in the grooves. For flat slopes or where dirt is a problem, use undepressed gutter inlets or combination inlets with longitudinal bars only. For streets having flat grades or sumps (lows), pitch the grade toward the inlet on both ends. This will have the effect of providing a sump at the inlet. For true sump locations, use curb openings or combination inlets. The total open area and not the size and arrangement of bars is important because the inlet will act as an orifice. Nor-

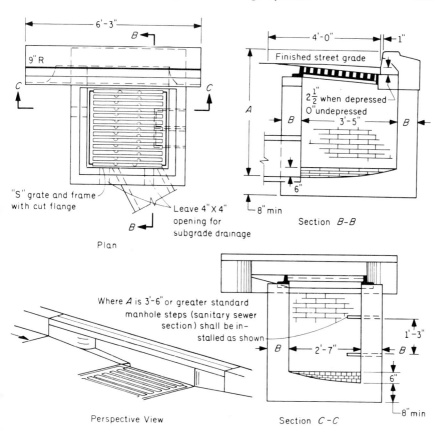

FIG. 6-15. Baltimore type S combination inlet. (Courtesy of the Baltimore County Department of Public Works, Towson, Maryland.)

mally sump inlets should be overdesigned because of the unique clogging problems which develop in depressed areas.

Inlets should be constructed in all sumps and at all street intersections where the quantity of flow is significant, or where nuisance conditions warrant such construction. Inlets are required at intermediate points along streets where the curb and gutter capacity would be exceeded without them. Inlet capacities should be equal to or greater than the design flows. As shown in Fig. 6-16, inlet capacity is related to gutter slope and must be taken into account when selecting an inlet for a specific location.

Rapid and efficient removal of surface runoff from streets and highways is exceedingly important for maximum safety and minimum nuisance. Street grade, crown slope, inlet type, grate design, and tolerable bypass flow are all important factors in the selection of inlet structures

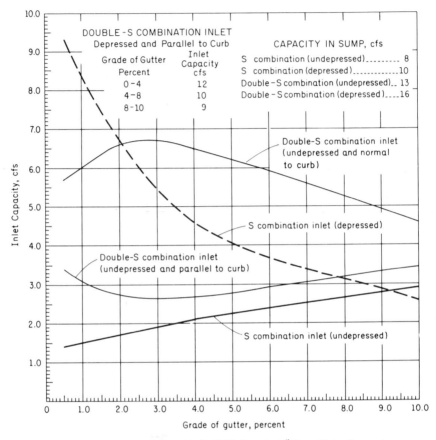

Curves based on data from 1952-1953 Report of "Storm Water Research Committee," Johns Hopkins University, Institute of Cooperative Research.[21]

Inlet capacities have been reduced for the estimated effect of debris partially clogging the inlet by 20 percent (on slopes).

Capacities based on Standard 7-3/16 in. curb and gutter and 1-18 average crown slope for a distance of approximately 5 ft from face of curb.

FIG. 6-16. Inlet-capacity curves for type S combination inlets. (Courtesy of the Baltimore County Department of Public Works, Towson, Maryland.)

to do a specific job. Reliable information on the hydraulic performance of various inlet works is essential if effective designs are to be made.

6-19. SYSTEM LAYOUT

Storm-drainage systems may be closed-conduit, open-conduit, or some combination of the two. In most urban areas, the smaller drains frequently are closed conduits, and as the system moves downstream, open channels are often employed. Because quantities of storm-water runoff are usually quite large when contrasted with flows in most water mains and sanitary sewers, the drainage works needed to carry these flows are also quite large and occupy an important position from the standpoint of utilities placement. Common practice is to build the storm drains along the center line of the street, then offset the water main to one side and the sanitary sewer to the other.

In order to produce a workable system layout, a map of the area is needed showing contours, streets, buildings, other existing utilities, natural drainage ways, and areas for future development. As in the case of the sanitary sewer system, the storm drains will lie principally under the streets or in designated drainage rights of way. The entire area to the physical divide should be served by the drain or by an extension of it.

In laying out the drainage system, the first step is to tentatively locate all the necessary inlet structures. Once this has been done, a skeleton pipe system connecting all the inlets within a particular drainage area is drawn along with the location of all manholes, wye branches, special bend or junction structures, and the outfall.

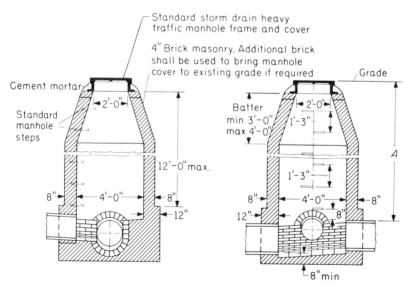

FIG. 6-17. Typical storm-drainage manhole details. (Courtesy of the Baltimore County Department of Public Works, Towson, Maryland.)

Customarily a manhole or junction structure will be required at all changes in grade, pipe size, direction of flow, and quantity of flow. Figure 6-17 illustrates the details of a typical manhole. Storm drains are usually not built smaller than 12 in. in diameter, because pipes of lesser size tend to clog readily with debris and therefore present serious malfunction problems. Maximum manhole spacing for pipes 27 in. and under should not exceed about 600 ft. For larger pipes, no maximum is prescribed and the normal requirements for structures should provide access to the drain for inspection, cleaning, or maintenance.

6-20. HYDRAULIC DESIGN OF URBAN STORM-DRAINAGE SYSTEMS

Basic principles outlined at the beginning of the chapter are sufficient to adequately design an urban drainage system. Calculations for the drainage area shown in Fig. 6-18 are presented in detail to illustrate the mechanical procedure and the rational method as applied to an actual design problem. The overall Mextex area is an urban residential area made up of single-family dwellings and is divided into 8 subareas which are tributary to individual storm-water inlets.

EXAMPLE 6-5.   Design a storm-drainage system to carry the flows from the 8 inlet areas given in Fig. 6-18. It will be assumed that a 10-year frequency rainfall satisfies the local design requirements. Assume clay soil to be predominant in the area with average lawn slopes.

Solution: The steps for solving are as follows:
1. Prepare a drainage-area map showing drainage limits, streets, impervious areas, and direction of surface flow.
2. Divide the drainage area into subareas tributary to the proposed storm-water inlets (Fig. 6-18).
3. Compute the acreage and imperviousness of each area.
4. Calculate the required capacity of each inlet, using the rational method. Assume a 5-min inlet time to be appropriate and compute inlet flows for a rainfall intensity of 7.0 in./hr. This is obtained by using the 10-year frequency curve on Fig. 6-14 with a 5-min concentration time. Appropriate C values are obtained from Fig. 6-13 by entering the graph with the calculated percentage imperviousness (the percent of the inlet area which is covered by streets, sidewalks, drives, roofs, etc.), projecting up to the average lawn slope curve and reading C on the ordinate. Computations for the inlet flows are tabulated in Table 6-8.
5. Select the type inlets required to adequately drain the flows in Table 6-8. The choice will be based on a knowledge of the street slopes and their relation to various inlet capacities. Inlet capacity curves such as given in Fig. 6-16 would be used. For the purposes of this example, no actual selections will be made but the student should recognize that this is the next logical step and an exceedingly important one.
6. Beginning at the upstream end of the system, compute the discharge to be carried by each successive length of pipe, moving downstream. These calculations are summarized in Table 6-9. Note that at each point downstream where a new flow is introduced, a new time of concentration must be determined as well as new values of C and drainage area size. As the upstream inlet areas are

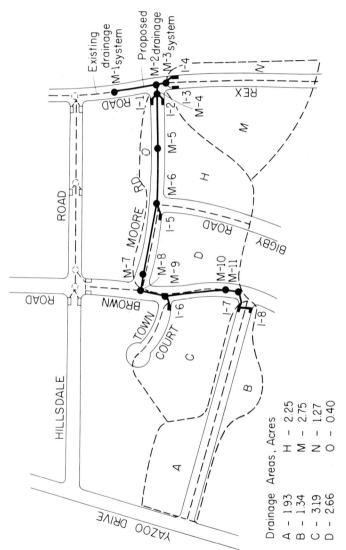

Drainage Areas, Acres

A - 1.93   H - 2.25
B - 1.34   M - 2.75
C - 3.19   N - 1.27
D - 2.66   O - 0.40

FIG. 6-18. Plan view of Mextex storm-drainage system.

TABLE 6-8
REQUIRED STORM-WATER INLET CAPACITIES FOR EXAMPLE 6-5

1	2	3	4	5	6	7
Inlet	Area Designation	Area Acres	Percent Impervious	C	Rainfall Intensity	Q, cfs (3) × (5) × (6)
I-1	O	0.40	49	0.57	7.0	1.59
I-2	H	2.25	20	0.35	7.0	5.52
I-3	M	2.75	26	0.40	7.0	7.70
I-4	N	1.27	26	0.40	7.0	3.55
I-5	D	2.66	26	0.40	7.0	7.43
I-6	C	3.19	24	0.38	7.0	8.48
I-7	A	1.93	23	0.37	7.0	4.99
I-8	B	1.34	29	0.42	7.0	3.93

combined to produce a larger tributary area at some design point, a revised C value representing these combined areas must be obtained. Usually the procedure is to take a weighted average of all the individual C values of which the larger area is composed. For example, when computing the flow to be carried by the pipe from M-9 to M-8, the tributary area is A + B + C = 6.46 acres, and the composite value of C will be

$$C = \frac{\Sigma c_i a_i}{\Sigma a_i} = \frac{0.37 \times 1.93 + 0.42 \times 1.34 + 0.38 \times 3.19}{6.46} = 0.38$$

At the design location the value of t_c will be equal to the inlet time at I-8 plus the pipe flow time from I-8 to M-9 (see Table 6-9), which must be known to permit solving the rainfall intensity to be used in computing the runoff from composite area A + B + C.

7. Using the computed discharge values, select tentative pipe sizes for the approximate slopes given in column 8 of Table 6-9. Once the pipe sizes are known, flow velocities between input locations can be determined. Normally these velocities are approximated by computing the full flow velocities for maximum discharge at the specified grade. These velocities are then used to compute channel flow time for estimating the time of concentration. If upon completing the hydraulic design enough change has been made in any concentration time to alter the design discharge, new values of flow should be computed. Generally this will not be the case.

8. Using the pipe sizes selected in Step 7, draw a profile of the proposed drainage system. Begin the profile at the point farthest downstream, which can be an outfall into a natural channel, an artificial channel, or an existing drain as in the case of the example. In constructing the profile, be certain that the pipes have at least the minimum required cover. Normally 1.5 to 2 ft is sufficient. Pipe slopes should conform to the surface slope wherever possible. At all manholes indicate the necessary change in invert elevation as prescribed in Sec. 6-4 or by some other procedure. In this example where there is no change in pipe size through the manhole, a drop of 0.2 ft will be used. Where the size decreases upstream through a manhole, the upstream invert will be set above the downstream invert a distance equal to the difference in the two diameters. In this

TABLE 6-9

COMPUTATION OF DESIGN PIPE FLOWS FOR THE STORM-DRAINAGE SYSTEM OF EXAMPLE 6-5

Pipe Section	Tributary Area	Area, acres	Flow Time, min			Rainfall Intensity, i	C	Q, cfs	Pipe			
			Inlet	Pipe	Total				Slope, percent	Size, in.	Full-Flow Velocity, fps	Length, ft
I-8-I-7	B	1.34	5	0.10	5	7.0	0.42	3.93	1.0	15	5.2	30
I-7-M-11	A + B	3.27	5	0.13	5.10	7.0	0.39	8.93	1.0	18	5.9	46
M-11-M-10	A + B	3.27		0.24	5.23	—	0.39	8.93	1.0	18	5.9	85
M-10-M-9	A + B	3.27		0.37	5.47	—	0.39	8.93	2.0	18	8.1	178
I-6-M-9	C	3.19	5	—	5	7.0	0.38	8.48	1.0	18	5.9	40
M-9-M-8	A + B + C	6.46		0.21	5.80	6.9	0.38	16.90	1.8	21	8.5	110
M-8-M-7	A + B + C	6.46		0.11	6.01	—	0.38	16.90	1.8	21	8.5	57
M-7-M-6	A + B + C	6.46		0.47	6.12	—	0.38	16.90	1.6	21	8.1	230
I-5-M-6	D	2.66	5	—	5	7.0	0.40	7.43	2.0	15	7.4	19
M-6-M-5	A + B + C + D	9.12		0.38	6.59	6.8	0.39	24.20	2.0	24	10.0	230
M-5-M-4	A + B + C + D	9.12		0.42	6.97	—	0.39	24.20	1.9	24	9.8	247
I-1-M-4	0	0.40	5	—	5	7.0	0.57	1.59	3.0	15	9.0	19
I-2-M-4	H	2.25	5	—	5	7.0	0.35	5.52	3.0	15	9.0	17
M-4-M-2	A + B + C + D + O + H	11.77		0.05	7.39	6.6	0.39	30.3	1.5	27	9.4	29
I-3-M-3	M	2.75	5	—	5	7.0	0.40	7.70	2.0	15	7.4	15
I-4-M-3	N	1.27	5	—	5	7.0	0.40	3.55	2.0	15	7.4	20
M-3-M-2	M + N	4.02		—	5	7.0	0.40	11.30	1.8	18	7.8	37
M-2-M-1	A + B + C + D + O + H + M + N	15.79		—	7.44	6.6	0.39	40.6	1.4	30	9.8	176

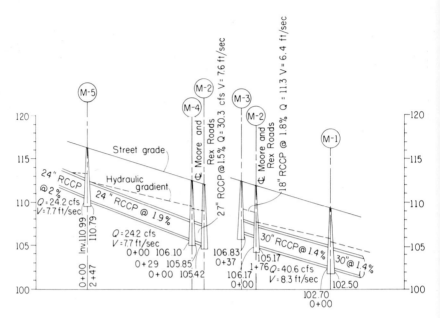

Fig. 6-19. Profile of part of the Mextex storm drain, showing the hydraulic gradient.

way the crowns are kept at the same elevation.   A part of the profile of the drainage system in the example is given in Fig. 6-19.

9. Compute the position of the hydraulic gradient along the profile of the pipe. If this gradient lies less than 1.5 ft below the ground surface, it must be lowered to preclude the possibility of surcharge during the design flow. Note that the value of 1.5 ft is arbitrarily chosen here. In practice, local standards indicate the limiting value. Hydraulic gradients may be lowered by increasing pipe sizes, decreasing head losses at structures, by designing special transitions, by lowering the system below ground, or by some combination of these means.

Computations for a portion of the hydraulic gradient of the example will now be given. Head losses in the pipes are determined by applying Manning's equation, assuming $n = 0.013$ in this example. Head losses in the structures will be determined by using the relationships defined in Figs. 6-20 and 6-21. These curves were developed for surcharged pipes entering rectangular structures but may be applied to wye branches, manholes, and junction chambers as pictured on the curves.[22] The "*A*" curve is used to find entrance and exit losses, the "*B*" curve to evaluate the head loss due to an increased velocity in the downstream direction. The loss is designated as the difference between the head losses found for the downstream and upstream pipe ($V_{h-2} - V_{h-1}$). In cases where the greatest velocity occurs upstream, the difference will be negative and may be applied to offset other losses in the structure. The "*C*" loss results from a change in direction in a manhole, wye branch, or bend structure. The "*D*" loss is related to the effects produced by the entrance of secondary flows into the structure. Several examples of the use of these curves are shown on Figs. 6-20 and 6-21.

Computations for the hydraulic gradient shown in Fig. 6-19 are as follows:

(a) Begin at the elevation of the hydraulic gradient at the upstream end of the existing 30-in. reinforced-concrete culvert pipe (RCCP). This elevation is 105.50. The existing hydraulic gradient is shown on Fig. 6-19.

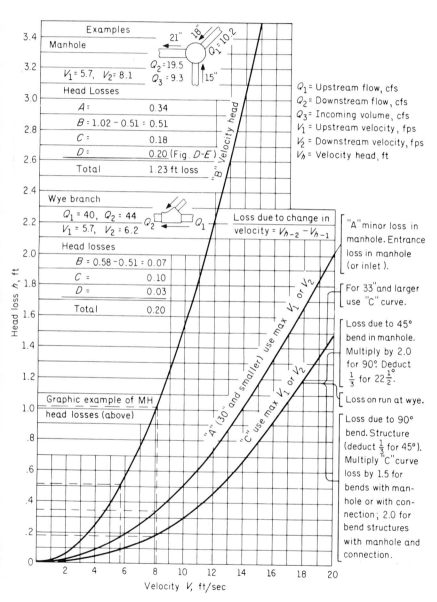

FIG. 6-20. Types A, B, and C head losses in structures. (Courtesy of the Baltimore County Department of Public Works, Towson, Maryland.)

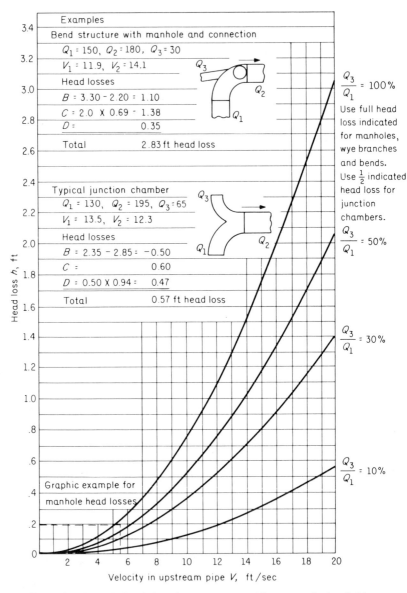

FIG. 6-21. Type C head loss in structures. (Courtesy of the Baltimore County Department of Public Works, Towson, Maryland.)

(b) Compute the head losses in manhole M-1 using Figs. 6-20 and 6-21.

$$A \text{ loss} = 0.36 \text{ ft } (V = 8.3 \text{ ft/sec} = Q/A)$$
$$B \text{ loss} = 0; \text{ no change in velocity, } V_1 = V_2$$
$$C \text{ loss} = 0; \text{ no change in direction}$$

D loss = 0; no secondary flow
Total = 0.36 ft

The hydraulic gradient therefore rises in the manhole to an elevation of 105.50 + 0.36 = 105.86 ft, plotted in M-1 on Fig. 6-19.

(c) Compute the head loss due to friction in the 30-in. drain from M-1 to M-2. Assume n = 0.013. Using Manning's equation, the head loss per linear foot of drain is

$$S = \frac{(nV)^2}{2.21 R^{4/3}}$$ (6-23)

and from M-1 to M-2,

$$S = \frac{(0.013 \times 8.3)^2}{2.21 \times 0.534} = 0.0166$$

The total frictional head loss is therefore

$$hf = S \times L = 0.0116 \times 176 = 1.73 \text{ ft}$$

Elevation of the hydraulic gradient at the downstream end of M-2 is thus 105.86 + 1.73 = 107.59 ft. This elevation is plotted on Fig. 6-19, and the hydraulic gradient in this reach is drawn in.

(d) Compute the head losses in M-2.

A = 0.36 (V = 8.3 ft/sec)
B = 1.07 − 0.90 = 0.17 (V_2 = 8.3, V_1 = 7.6 = Q/A for 27-in. drain)
C = 0.20 × 2.0 (multiply by 2 for 90 degree bend in manhole—
       see Fig. 6-19) = 0.40
D = 0.22 for Q_3/Q_1 = 11.3/30.3 = 37 percent

Total head loss in M-2 equals 1.15 ft and the elevation of the hydraulic gradient in M-2 is therefore 107.59 + 1.15 = 108.74 ft.

(e) Compute the friction head loss in the section of pipe from M-2 to M-3.

$$S = \frac{(0.013 \times 6.4)^2}{2.21 \times 0.272} = 0.0113$$

$$hf = 0.0113 \times 37 = 0.42 \text{ ft}$$

Elevation of the hydraulic gradient at the downstream end of M-3 is therefore 108.74 + 0.42 = 109.16 ft. Plot this point on the profile and draw the gradient from M-2 to M-3.

Students should realize that the hydraulic gradient in this example was computed under the assumption of uniform flow. In closed conduit systems, if the pipes are flowing full or the system is surcharged (the usual design flow conditions), this method will produce good results. Where open conduits are used, or in partial-flow systems, the hydraulic gradient can be determined by computing surface profiles in the manner described in Sec. 6-2.

Computations for the remainder of the hydraulic gradient are identical to those just given and will not be presented. It should be noted that none of the gradients shown in Fig. 6-19 come within 1.5 ft of the surface, so that no revisions are needed. If too close to the surface, it would be necessary to modify all or a portion of the system to lower the gradient. This could be accomplished by reducing head losses, by increasing the depth of the system, or both. The choice would depend primarily on cost.

REFERENCES

1. S. M. Woodward and C. J. Posey, *Hydraulics of Steady Flow in Open Channels* (New York: John Wiley and Sons, Inc., 1955).

2. R. M. Olson, *Essentials of Engineering Fluid Mechanics* (Scranton, Pa.: International Textbook Co., 1961).

3. C. E. Kindsvater, "The Hydraulic Jump in Sloping Channels," *Trans. Am. Soc. Civil Engrs.*, vol. 109 (1944).

4. Ven Te Chow, *Open-Channel Hydraulics* (New York: McGraw-Hill Book Company, Inc., 1959).

5. Julian Hinds, "The Hydraulic Design of Flume and Siphon Transitions," *Trans. Am. Soc. Civil Engrs.*, vol. 92 (1928).

6. W. M. Sangster, A. W. Wood, E. T. Smerdon, and H. G. Bossy, "Pressure Changes at Storm Drain Junctions," Eng. Expt. Sta., University of Missouri, Columbia, Missouri, Eng. Series Bull. no. 41.

7. Hunter Rouse (ed.), *Engineering Hydraulics* (New York: John Wiley and Sons, Inc., 1950).

8. G. M. Fair and J. C. Geyer, *Elements of Water Supply and Waste-Water Disposal* (New York: John Wiley and Sons, Inc., 1958).

9. K. E. Spells, *Trans. Inst. Chem. Engrs.* (*London*), vol. 33 (1955).

10. T. R. Camp, "Design of Sewers to Facilitate Flow," *Sewage Works J.*, vol. 18 (1946).

11. Anonymous, *Newsletter Hydraulics Div., Am. Soc. Civil Engrs.* (August 1963).

12. H. M. Morris, *Applied Hydraulics in Engineering* (New York: The Ronald Press Company, 1963).

13. G. M. Fair and John C. Geyer, *Water Supply and Waste-Water Disposal* (New York: John Wiley and Sons, Inc., 1954).

14. R. K. Linsley, Jr., M. A. Kohler, and J. L. H. Paulhus, *Applied Hydrology* (New York: McGraw-Hill Book Company, Inc., 1949), pp. 387–411, 444–464.

15. L. K. Sherman, "Streamflow From Rainfall by the Unit Hydrograph Method," *Eng. News-Record*, vol. 108 (1932), pp. 501–505.

16. J. E. Nash, "Systematic Determination of Unit Hydrograph Parameters," *J. Geophys. Res.*, vol. 64 (1959), pp. 111–115.

17. B. S. Barnes, "Consistency in Unitgraphs," *Proc. Am. Soc. Civil Engrs., J. Hydraulics Div.*, vol. 85 (August 1959), pp. 39–61.

18. "Design and Construction of Sanitary and Storm Sewers," *Am. Soc. Civil Engrs. Manual of Engineering Practice*, No. 37 (New York: American Society of Civil Engineers, 1960).

19. C. F. Izzard, "Hydraulics of Runoff from Developed Surfaces," *Proc. Highway Research Board*, vol. 26 (1946), pp. 129–150.

20. John C. Schaake, "Report No. XI of the Storm Drainage Research Project," The Johns Hopkins University, Dept. Sanitary Engineering, Baltimore, Md. (September 1963).

21. ———, "The Design of Storm Water Inlets," The Johns Hopkins University, Dept. Sanitary Engineering and Water Resources, Baltimore, Md. (June 1956).

22. ———, "Baltimore County Design Manual," Baltimore County Dept. of Public Works, Bur. of Eng., Towson, Md., 1955.

23. Richard J. Wasley, "Hydrodynamics of Flow into Curb-Opening Inlets," Dept. Civil Engineering, Stanford University, Stanford, California, Tech. Rept. 6, 1960.

24. R. T. Knapp, "Design of Channel Curves for Supercritical Flow," *Trans. Am. Soc. Civil Engrs.*, vol. 116 (1951).

PROBLEMS

6-1. Waste water flows in a rectangular concrete channel which is 6 ft wide and 3.5 ft deep. The design flow is 38 cfs. Find the critical depth and critical velocity. Also find the slope of the channel if the flow velocity is to be 2 fps.

6-2. An 18-in. sewer pipe flowing full is expected to carry 4 mgd. The n value is 0.011. The minimum flow is $1/12$ that of the maximum. Find the depth and velocity at minimum flow.

6-3. The sewage from an area of 360 acres is to be carried by a circular sewer at a velocity not less than 2.0 fps. Manning's $n = 0.013$. The population density is 15 persons per acre. Find the maximum hourly and minimum hourly flows. Determine the pipe size required to handle these flows and the required slope.

6-4. Water flows in a rectangular concrete channel 9 ft wide and 7.5 ft deep. The channel invert has a slope of 0.10 percent and the n value applicable is 0.013. Flow carried by the channel is 183 cfs. At an intersection of this channel with a canal, the depth of flow is 6.8 ft. Find the distance upstream to a point where normal depth prevails. Plot the surface profile.

6-5. A 48-in. sewer ($n = 0.013$) laid on a 0.20 percent grade carries a flow of 20 mgpd. At a junction with a second sewer the sewage depth is 36 in. above the invert. Plot the surface profile back to the point of uniform depth.

6-6. A hydraulic jump occurs in a flat-bottomed canal. The depth before the jump is 0.5 ft and the discharge is 4 cfs per foot of channel width. Find the depth of flow after the jump.

6-7. Determine the minimum velocity and gradient required to transport $3/16$-in. gravel through a 36-in. diameter pipe, given $n = 0.013$ and $K = 0.05$.

6-8. By arbitrarily designating some pipe size as the minimum allowable, it is not always possible because of grade restrictions, etc., to maintain minimum velocities at all depths of flow. Does this necessarily mean that a gradual buildup of deposited solids will occur? What measures can be taken to alleviate this problem?

6-9. An inverted siphon is to carry a minimum dry-weather flow of 1.2 cfs, a maximum dry-weather flow of 3.3 cfs, and a storm flow of 46.0 cfs in three pipes. Select the proper diameters to assure velocities of 3.0 fps in all pipes. Make a neat detailed sketch of your design. Assume the siphon goes under a highway with a 3-ft drop and is 60 ft long.

6-10. Given the following 25-year record of maximum annual stream flows, plot these values vs. percent of years during which runoff was equal to or less than the indicated value on log-probability paper. Find the peak flow expected on the average of (a) once every 5 years and (b) once every 15 years.

24-Hr Maximum Annual Flood Flows, cfs

240	193	88	55	43
205	131	76	51	38
215	142	65	52	35
198	123	67	49	32
185	117	53	47	29

6-11. How would you go about deriving a synthetic unit hydrograph? What experimental data would be required? How would you derive a prediction equation for some hydrograph parameter?

6-12. Given the following storm pattern, unit storm, and unit hydrograph, determine the composite hydrograph.

Unit storm = 1 unit of rainfall for 1 unit of time
Actual storm: Time units   1   2   3   4
Pattern: Rainfall units   1   2   4   3
Unit hydrograph—triangular with base length = 4 time units;
time of rise = 1 time unit, and maximum ordinate = $\frac{1}{2}$ rainfall unit height

6-13. Given a unit rainfall duration of one time unit, an effective precipitation of 1.3 in., and the following hydrograph and storm sequence, determine (a) the unit hydrograph and (b) the hydrograph for the given storm sequence.

Storm Sequence

Time units	1	2	3	4
Precipitation, in.	0.3	0.9	1.8	1.3

Hydrograph

Time units	1	2	3	4	4.5	5	6	7	8	9	10	11	12	13
Flow, cfs	90	89	210	500	600	570	430	315	190	130	95	75	65	64

6-14. Do Prob. 15-13 if the storm sequence is as follows:

Storm Sequence

Time units	1	2	3
Precipitation, in.	0.6	1.3	1.7

6-15. Compute the design flows for the pipes shown in the accompanying sketch.

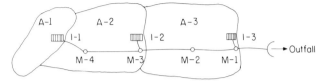

PROB. 6-15

I-1 to M-4, M-4 to M-3, M-3 to M-2, M-2 to M-1, and M-1 to outfall by the rational method

$$A\text{-}1 = 1 \text{ acre}, \quad c_1 = 0.4$$
$$A\text{-}2 = 2 \text{ acres}, \quad c_2 = 0.5$$
$$A\text{-}3 = 3 \text{ acres}, \quad c_3 = 0.6$$

Given pipe flow times are I-1 to M-3 1 min and M-3 to M-1 1.5 min.

6-16. You are called upon to design the storm-water drains for a subdivision. The rational method of design is to be employed. State clearly and in logical order the information which you would gather, the use to which you would put the data, and each successive step in design from the upper inlet to the lower end of the line where the drain discharges into a stream.

6-17. Discuss the theory of the rational method and state and explain its deficiencies.

6-18. Discuss the selection of inlet type, the location of inlets, and the importance of this.

6-19. In providing drainage for a community to be located along a stream, what would be one of your first major considerations?

6-20. Discuss the head losses in a drainage system. Can these be predicted accurately? Is there a need for further research?

6-21. Discuss the economic considerations involved in drainage design.

6-22. Discuss the frequency of floods and rainfall intensities. Does the 10-year storm frequency actually indicate the 10-year discharge frequency?

6-23. You are asked to design the sanitary sewer for a subdivision. State clearly, and in logical order, the information you would gather, the use to which you would put the data, and each successive step in design from the upper terminal manhole to the outflow point in the area.

6-24. Given the data below, design a section of sanitary sewer to carry these flows at a minimum velocity of 2 fps. Assume that the minimum depth of the sewer below the street must be 9 ft and that an n value of 0.013 is applicable. Make a plan and profile drawing.

Manholes	Distance Between Manholes, ft	Flow, gpm	Street Elevations at Manholes, ft
A to B	180	1,200	A—976
B to C	320	1,300	B—972
C to D	390	2,000	C—966
D to E	275	2,300	D—960
E to F	400	2,900	E—956
			F—951

NOTE: The invert into manhole F must be 939 ft. Assume an invert drop of 0.2 ft across each manhole.

6-25. For an inlet area of 1.3 acres, having an imperviousness of 0.41, and a clay soil, find the peak rate of runoff for the 5-, 10-, and 20-year storms.

6-26. Using the manhole spacing-elevation data given in Prob. 6-24 and the data below, design a storm-drainage system such that manhole A is at the upper end of the drainage area and manhole F is replaced by an outfall to a stream. The outfall invert elevation is equal to 940.3 ft. Design for the 5-year storm.

Inflow Point	Incremental Area Contributing to Inflow Point, acres	Impreviousness of Areas, percent
A to B	2.6	41
B to C	3.1	46
C to D	3.8	39
D to E	2.9	48

Total area = 12.4 acres.

chapter 7

Examination of Water and Waste

7-1. PURPOSES OF EXAMINATION

Water and wastes are examined to evaluate their treatability, treatment effectiveness, and quality.

Sewage is analyzed to determine those constituents that may cause difficulties in treatment or disposal, as an aid in plant operation, and in selecting the correct degree and type of treatment. Plant effluents are investigated to measure their strength and to determine the constituents of the final waste. Receiving waters are tested to evaluate their ability to accept a pollutional load and to indicate the degree of self-purification which occurs in a given reach. The strength of sewage is usually measured by its nuisance-producing potentialities—odor, solids content, and appearance. The yardstick that measures much of the nuisance potential is the biochemical oxygen demand or BOD. This is the amount of oxygen required by the bacteria to reduce some of the organic matter in a waste under standard conditions (see Sec. 10-6).

Water to be used for a public supply must be potable (drinkable), i.e., not contain pollution. Pollution can be defined as the presence of any foreign substance (organic, inorganic, radiological, or biological) which tends to degrade the water quality and constitute a hazard or impair the usefulness of the water.[2] Routine analyses of developed water sources are made usually to determine acceptability of the water for domestic and industrial uses. Results of these analyses also indicate the kind of corrective treatment which should be considered for specific applications of the water. The complete analysis of a potential water source should include a sanitary survey and physical, chemical, and biological analysis.

Methods of collection and analysis must be standardized if results obtained by different laboratories are to be comparable. In the United States, *Standard Methods for the Examination of Water and Wastewater* has been published jointly by the American Public Health Association, the American Water Works Association, and the Water Pollution Control Federation. These methods have also been accepted by the American

Chemical Society. No attempt will be made here to describe or explain the various analysis procedures. The reader can acquaint himself with the techniques involved by reading *Standard Methods.* The objective here is to explain the reasons for conducting the different examinations and to indicate the significance of the analytical results in the light of accepted standards.

7-2. SANITARY SURVEY

Sanitary surveys of water and waste waters include (1) surveys of the conditions under which water is processed and (2) observations and examinations of certain properties of the water in its natural or artificial field environment.

A survey to determine the characteristics of sewage should supply information concerning the following: (1) the source, whether domestic or industrial, and if industrial, the types of industries and industrial waste treatment, if any; (2) variations in the rate of flow; (3) the strength and condition of the sewage; (4) the amount of infiltration and storm water carried by the sewer, if any; and (5) other factors that affect the characteristics of the sewage.

Surveys are made of receiving streams for gross qualities such as unsightly floating matter, sludge banks, growths of sewage fungi and other biological indicators of pollution. Physical properties such as temperature are evaluated in the field. Fixing of chemical constituents—for example, carbon dioxide and dissolved oxygen—is also carried out at the site.

Sanitary surveys are made not only of the source of a water supply but of the water-supply system as well. These surveys uncover environmental conditions that may affect the potability and treatability of the water being considered. Increasing pollution problems point up the need for additional attention to the quality of source waters. Abatement and control of pollution at the source will significantly aid in producing a high-quality water. A periodic survey of water-distribution systems is necessary to control physical defects or other health hazards in the system.

7-3. SAMPLING

Because the environmental engineer is often called upon to collect samples or advise on sampling techniques, a knowledge of correct procedures is important.

A 2-liter portion is adequate for most physical and chemical analyses. Larger volumes may be required for special determinations. Separate portions should be collected for chemical and bacteriological examination since the methods of collection and handling are quite different. The shorter the time interval between collection of a sample and its analysis, the more reliable the results. Immediate field analysis is required for certain constituents and physical characteristics to assure dependable results since changes in composition of the sample may occur in transit to the laboratory.

It is difficult to state exactly how much time can be allowed between the collection of a sample and its analysis. A potable water specimen may ordinarily be held for a much longer period than a raw-sewage sample. The following maximum limits are suggested in *Standard Methods* as reasonable for physical and chemical analyses:

Unpolluted waters . . . . 72 hr
Slightly polluted waters . . . . 48 hr
Polluted waters . . . . 12 hr

The time and place of sampling and analysis should be recorded on the laboratory report. If the portions have been preserved by an additive or deviations made from the procedures outlined in *Standard Methods*, these facts should be recorded on the report.

Certain cations such as iron and copper are subject to loss by adsorption on, or ion exchange with, the walls of glass bottles. Also, pH and carbon dioxide are subject to change in transit. These changes in pH-alkalinity-carbon dioxide balance can cause calcium carbonate to be precipitated and underestimates of total hardness and calcium may result.

The microbiologic activity of a sample can produce changes in the nitrate-nitrite-ammonia balance in biochemical oxygen demand (BOD). Color, odor, and turbidity may change significantly between time of sampling and time of laboratory analysis.

It is impossible to prescribe absolute rules for the prevention of all changes that might take place in a sample bottle. The sample should be collected and stored consistent with the character of the laboratory examinations to be made. Often much time and trouble can be saved if the person collecting the samples and the laboratory analyst will confer in advance on the best technique for collecting and storing the samples.

7-4. REPRESENTATIVE SAMPLES

Care must be taken to obtain a specimen that is truly representative of existing conditions. The sample bottle should be rinsed two or three times with the water to be sampled prior to filling. No general recommendations can be made as to the number or places of sampling, since details of collection vary considerably with local conditions. Care should be exercised in identifying every sample bottle, preferably by attaching an appropriately inscribed tag or label. The record needed includes all information pertinent to the purpose of the sample, such as the name of the collector, date, hour, and exact location of the source.

Prior to collecting samples from a water-distribution system, pipes should be flushed for a sufficient period of time to insure that the sample represents the supply. Samples from wells should be taken only after the well has been pumped for a sufficient period of time to reach equilibrium if the test is to represent the groundwater that feeds the well.

Samples collected from a stream may vary with depth, stream flow and distance from shore. An "integrated" portion from top to bottom in the middle of the stream is generally representative of stream flow. A grab sample (a single sample) can be collected at middepth in the middle of the stream.

Because the quality of water in lakes and reservoirs is subject to considerable variation, the choice of location and depth of sampling depends upon local conditions and the purpose of the investigation. Lakes and reservoirs are affected by rainfall, runoff, wind, and seasonal stratification.

In testing influents and effluents from sewage-treatment plants, a composite made up of several grab samples taken at different times is usually desired. If the character of the waste is constant, only a grab sample is necessary, but normally both the character and rate of flow are variable. Under these conditions the collection of a representative sample is difficult. A survey should obtain data on the average concentrations of pollutants over an 8- to 24-hr period from a composite portion, and the concentrations at high and low rates of flow from grab samples.

Composite specimens are prepared from a series of grab samples or from an automatic sampler. A series of grab samples might be taken every 20 min and an amount proportional to the flow rate at the sampling time is placed in the composite container. For example, 1 ml may be taken for each gallon per minute of flow.

It is better to obtain too large a sample rather than one too small as the analyst may wish to make check determinations or run additional tests. Special preservation methods are necessary for portions that are not to be analyzed immediately. Cooling is the most common technique, but special chemicals are added for certain tests. Instructions regarding sampling procedures for specific tests are given in *Standard Methods*.

7-5. EXPRESSION OF RESULTS

Analytical results may be expressed either as milligrams per liter (mg/l) or as parts per million (ppm). Assuming that 1 liter of water or sewage weighs 1 kg, the number of milligrams per litter is equivalent to the number of parts per million. For industrial wastes having a specific gravity different from water, the specific gravity should be given when milligrams per liter are used. When the concentration is less than 1 mg/l, it is convenient to express the result in micrograms per liter (μg/l) or parts per billion (ppb). Where the concentration is greater than 10,000 mg/l, the results may be expressed in percent (1 percent is equivalent to 10,000 mg/l).

Results expressed in mg/l may be converted to ppm by the formula

$$\text{ppm by weight} = \frac{mg/l}{S} \qquad (7\text{-}1)$$

where S = specific gravity.

The results of analyses of polluted waters or evaluations of plant operations are expressed on a weighted basis which includes the concentration and volume rate of flow. Rate of flow is expressed in either cubic feet per second (cfs) or million gallons per day (mgpd). These weighted results may be expressed as pounds per 24 hr or as population equivalents based on biochemical oxygen demand (BOD). The units are calculated as follows:

$$\text{Pounds per 24 hours (lb/24 hr)} = (mg/l) \times mgpd \times 8.34 \qquad (7\text{-}2)$$

or

$$\text{lb/24 hr} = (mg/l) \times cfs \times 5.39 \qquad (7\text{-}3)$$

$$\text{Population equivalent} = (mg/l \text{ of 5 day BOD}) \times mgpd \times \frac{8.34}{0.17} \qquad (7\text{-}4)$$

Test results for color and turbidity are recorded in units of color and turbidity. Hydrogen-ion concentration is expressed in terms of pH value. Bacteriological results are stated in terms of the plate count per milliter or the most probable number (MPN) of coliform bacteria per hundred milliliter.

7-6. STANDARD TESTS

Many of the analyses employed in the examination of samples of water and sewage are identical, but the information sought is used for different purposes. The usual objective of a water analysis is to determine the acceptability of the water for its intended use and as a guide in treatment. The normal purpose of a waste analysis is to learn the composition, concentration, and condition of the waste.

Waters are classified as potable or polluted, safe or unsafe, pure or impure, hard or soft, corrosive or uncorrosive, sweet or sour. Sewage is classified as strong or weak, fresh or septic, putrescible or non-putrescible, domestic or industrial, to mention but a few.

Standard Methods describes the following tests which are performed on waters and wastes. Tests that are not normally a part of a sanitary analysis are printed in italics.

Water in the Absence of Gross Pollution.

Physical and Chemical Examination:

    Temperature, turbidity, color, taste, and odor

    Residue, solids after evaporation (total, *filterable, nonfilterable;* and for each solid the fixed portion and the loss on burning)

Solids by electrolytic conductivity
Hardness by calculation from a mineral analysis and by the versenate (EDTA titration) method
Acidity, including mineral acids, alkalinity (phenolphthalein and total), pH value, carbon dioxide (free and *total*), *bicarbonate ion, carbonate ion,* and *hydroxide*
Silica
Copper, lead, aluminum, iron, *chromium, manganese,* and *zinc*
Magnesium, calcium, sodium, and potassium
Nitrogen, *ammonia, albuminoid, organic, nitrite,* and nitrate
Chloride, *iodide* and fluoride
Phosphate, *orthophosphate, total phosphate,* and *polyphosphate*
Sulfate, sulfide, and *sulfite*
Arsenic, boron, cyanide, selenium, barium,* cadmium,* and *silver**
Alkyl benzene sulfonate (*surfactants*), phenols
Chlorine, free available, *monochloramine, dichloramine, nitrogen trichloride,* and chlorine demand
Tannin and *lignin*
Oxygen, dissolved, biochemical demand, chemical demand and *ozone*
Oil and *grease*
Biological Examination:
Plate count
Coliform group, group density, and *differentiation of coliform Enterococcus group*
Examination and enumeration of microscopic organisms
Radiologic Examination:
Alpha and gross beta (total, suspended, and dissolved)
Strontium, total radioactive, and strontium 90

Examination of Waste Water
Physical and Chemical Examination:
Temperature, *turbidity,* color, and odor
Residue, by evaporation, total, dissolved, suspended, and settleable (for each solid the volatile and fixed portion)
Acidity, alkalinity, and pH value
Nitrogen, ammonia, nitrate, nitrite, and *organic*
Chloride and *sulfide*
Chlorine, residual, and demand
Grease
Alkyl benzene sulfonate (surfactants)
Oxygen, dissolved, demand chemical, and demand biochemical

---

*Barium, cadmium, and silver are not in the eleventh edition of *Standard Methods* but are listed in the 1962 Public Health *Drinking Water Standards.*

Biological examination:
   *Examination and identification of some microorganisms common
      in wastes*
Radiologic Examination:
   Same as for water

NATURE AND SIGNIFICANCE OF COMMON TESTS

7-7. PHYSICAL TESTS

Physical tests are performed to evaluate such factors as temperature, turbidity, taste, odor, and color.

Temperature. Elevated temperatures have a deleterious effect on water and materially affect the rates of chemical and biological activity. The important physical properties dependent upon temperature are density, viscosity, vapor pressure, and surface tension. Temperature readings are used in the calculation of the various forms of alkalinity and affect the saturation values of solids and gases that are or can be dissolved in water.

High-temperature wastes are common in industry and their sudden discharge into a stream may result in a direct fish kill. As water temperature rises it contains less DO (dissolved oxygen), but aquatic organisms require more DO to maintain a normal existence at elevated temperatures. High temperature wastes in sewers accelerate undesirable chemical and biological reactions. Bacterial action and natural purification processes are also speeded up at higher temperatures and may cause depletion of oxygen.

Hot waste discharges usually can be controlled by storage holding basins or evaporative cooling using a spray system. Pennsylvania has recommended that industry limit waste-water heat content so that the stream at the point of discharge will not rise above 93°F.[3]

Taste and Odor. Psychologists state that there are only four true taste sensations—sour, sweet, salty, and bitter. Other sensations usually ascribed to the sense of taste are actually odors. Taste and odor frequently occur together and may be due to the presence of foreign substances in the water, either organic or inorganic, and to living organisms. Inorganic salts of iron, zinc, manganese, copper, sodium, and potassium can be detected by taste and are not accompanied by odor. Household detergents alone do not cause taste and odor.[4] Detergents are generally accompanied by other contaminants from domestic or industrial sources and the tastes and odors must be attributed to these contaminants. Chlorine derivatives of phenol compounds produce tastes and odors at minimal concentrations and much research has been done on these compounds.

Baker lists the threshold odor levels for 32 organic chemicals.[5] The extreme average values for the chemicals he tested ranged from 0.006 mg/l for *n*-Butyl mercaptan to 14,700 mg/l for ally chloride.

Measurements of taste and odor intensity are made by diluting the sample with odor and taste-free water to the threshold value. Keenness of taste and odor perception varies with individuals and is by no means absolute.

Actinomycetes are unicellular, filamentous microorganisms closely accosicated with bacteria. They are widely distributed in nature and account for a large part of the normal microbial population of soils and lake and river muds.[6] They produce earthy odors in waters and these odors can be carried into water sources by runoff from the surrounding soil environment. The chemical structures of the odoriferous concentrates have not been determined but the extreme intensity of the actinomycete odor has been demonstrated.

Biologic odors in water supplies are of two distinct types and origins: (1) those resulting from metabolic activity of the organisms and (2) those resulting from decomposition of the organisms after death. The chemical compounds causing typical algal odors are produced during metabolism and subsequently released to the water.[7] A number of chemical compounds are involved in the odoriferous material.

Hydrogen sulfide is odor producing and frequently found in ground water. Concentrations of less than 4 mg/l do not present much of a removal problem; however, in southern California some groundwaters containing as much as 20 to 30 mg/l of hydrogen sulfide are being used for potable supplies.[8]

Hydrogen sulfide is one of the primary causes of odors found in sewage in transit and in sewage-treatment plants. In sewers it is a considerable nuisance and very costly to eliminate. Many environmental factors are involved in the complex development of hydrogen sulfide in a sewer with the resultant production of destructive sulfuric acid.

Hydrogen sulfide is obnoxious and in sufficient quantities may be toxic to humans, animals, and plants. It is detectable in minute amounts and becomes toxic to humans at concentrations of 0.2 percent after a few minutes' exposure. A 4.3 percent concentration of hydrogen sulfide is reported to be explosive and destructive to many materials used in constructing collection and treatment systems.[9]

Taste and odor tests are used as a check on the quality of finished and raw water, for control of taste and odor through water-treatment plant operation, and as a means of tracing the sources of contamination.

The odor of sewage provides a valuable measure of its condition whether fresh, stale, or septic; it may also indicate the presence of certain industrial wastes. Odors from wastes or from their decomposition products may change an entire stream valley from a pleasant area into one having little or no recreational value.

Turbidity. Turbidity measurements are normally restricted to water. Turbidity is caused by the presence of suspended matter, such as clay, silt, finely divided organic matter, plankton, and other microscopic organisms. Turbidity is an expression of the optical property of the sample which causes light to be scattered and absorbed. It is not a direct equivalent of the amount of suspended matter, as light interference is a function of surface area.

Turbidity, not necessarily a dangerous characteristic, is objectionable from the standpoint of appearance for domestic use of water and its control is essential for many industrial applications. The U.S. Public Health Service Drinking Water Standards recommends that turbidity should not exceed 5 units. Most modern water-treatment plants produce water with a turbidity of 1 unit or less. The turbidity unit is based upon a suspension prepared from diatomaceous earth, to contain 1 g of silica per liter and have a turbidity of 1,000. From this standard, dilutions are prepared with distilled water.

Color. The term *color* means the color of the liquid from which turbidity has been removed. "Apparent color" is used to describe the color resulting from substances in solution and also that due to suspended matter.

The decay of large quantities of organic matter introduces appreciable color into the water and may cause a substantial reduction in dissolved oxygen. Intense color occurs in water draining from swamps and areas of deciduous forests. Industrial wastes may contain many coloring substances.

Any degree of color is objectionable to water consumers. The degree of difficulty in removing color depends upon the color source and on the characteristics of the water. Color is reduced by storage and the bleaching action of sunlight. The apparent color of sewage reflects its strength and condition; fresh sewage is gray, septic sewage is black, while other coloring indicates industrial waste. Table 7-1 gives the recommended upper limits for certain physical characteristics of potable water.

TABLE 7-1
PHYSICAL CHARACTERISTICS, PUBLIC HEALTH SERVICE STANDARDS FOR DRINKING WATER

Turbidity	5 units
Color	15 units
Threshold odor number	3

Residue. Total solids, or residue on evaporation, are important as an index of the concentration of the principal constituents of water, and more especially, of sewage. "Total residue" is the term applied to the material left in a container after the evaporation of a sample of water or waste and its subsequent drying. This total residue includes "nonfilterable residue" or that portion of the total residue retained by a filter. "Filterable residue" is the portion of the total residue which passes through a filter. Weighing the residues after ignition determines the fixed residues. The loss on weight by ignition is the volatile residue. Since organic matter burns, the loss on ignition is a rough measure of the organic matter present. Settling of the sample for a given period before making the residue determination permits evaluation of the settleable residue. The results of this separation, as well as the determination of the amount of suspended matter, are generally most important in waste analyses. Residues are usually referred to as "solids." In the operation of waste-treatment works, the volumetric determination of settleable solids in an Imhoff cone is of some value.

7-8. CHEMICAL TESTS

"Drinking water shall not contain impurities in concentrations which may be hazardous to the heatlh of the consumers. It shall not be excessively corrosive to the water supply system. Substances used in its treatment shall not remain in the water in concentrations greater than required by good practice. Substances which may have deleterious physiological effect, or for which physiological effects are not known, shall not be introduced into the system in a manner which would permit them to reach the consumer."[2]

The chemical substances listed in Table 7-2 should not be present in a water supply in excess of the listed concentrations where a more suitable supply is available.

Presence of the substances listed in Table 7-3 in excess of the concentrations noted shall constitute grounds for rejection of the supply.

Semiannual examinations should be made for these substances. More frequent examinations are required if there is cause to believe that the prescribed limits may be exceeded.

Alkyl Benzene Sulfonate (ABS). This surfactant is a synthetic organic chemical having high residual affinity at one end of its molecule and low residual affinity at the other. The market for cleansing agents has changed since 1948 from a "soap" market to one dominated by synthetics. During 1962, about 80 percent of the 4.8 billion lb of cleansing agents sold in the United States, or approximately 20 lb per person, were synthetics.[10]

Contamination of drinking-water supplies with surfactants results from their disposal as domestic and industrial wastes. Such contamination is appearing in supplies from both surface waters and groundwater.

TABLE 7-2
Upper Recommended Limits of Impurities, Public Health Service Drinking Water Standards, 1962

Substance	Concentration, mg/l
Alkyl benzene sulfonate (ABS)	0.5
Arsenic (As)	0.01
Chloride (Cl)	250.
Copper (Cu)	1.
Carbon chloroform extract (CCE)	0.2
Cyanide (CN)	0.01
Fluoride (F)	(see Table 7-4)
Iron (Fe)	0.3
Manganese (Mn)	0.05
Nitrate* (NO_3)	45.
Phenols	0.001
Sulfate (SO_4)	250.
Total dissolved solids	500.
Zinc (Zn)	5.

*In areas in which the nitrate content of water is known to be in excess of the listed concentration, the public should be warned of the potential dangers of using the water for infant feeding.

Surfactants may be divided into two broad chemical classifications, ionic and nonionic. Ionic types may be anionic or cationic. Alkyl benzene sulfonate is a typical anionic surfactant—in fact, more than 75 percent of the surfactants in household detergents are of this type. Alkyl benzene sulfonate may be represented by the structure shown.

$$
\begin{array}{c}
\text{C}_{12}\text{H}_{25} \\
\text{SO}_3\text{Na}
\end{array}
\qquad (7\text{-}5)
$$

It produces off-taste and frothing in waters containing more than 1 mg/l. The off-taste has been described as oily, fishy, or perfume-like. Alkyl

TABLE 7-3
Upper Limits of Impurities, Public Health Service Drinking Water Standards

Substance	Concentration, mg/l
Arsenic (As)	0.05
Barium (Ba)	1.0
Cadmium (Cd)	0.01
Chromium (Hexaralent) (Cr^{+6})	0.05
Cyanide (CN)	0.2
Fluoride (F)	(see Table 7-4)
Lead (Pb)	0.05
Selenium (Se)	0.01
Silver (Ag)	0.05

benzene sulfonate itself is essentially odorless but the off taste and odor characteristics may rise from the degradation of products associated with the ABS. Since the concentration of ABS in municipal sewage is of the order of 10 mg/l, waters containing ABS are likely to have at least 10 percent of sewage origin for each mg/l of ABS present.

Detergents lower the surface tension of water and in sewage-treatment plants cause or contribute to foaming, thereby creating operational problems where the activated sludge process is used, or at points of hydraulic turbulence.

Legislation has been introduced in the House of Representatives and U.S. Senate to require certain standards of decomposibility of synthetic detergents imported into the United States or shipped in interstate commerce. Some state and municipal laws have been enacted making it unlawful to use, sell, or possess hard detergent soaps after January 1, 1965. The practical consequences of these actions are awaited with interest. Such legislation will be very difficult to enforce, and satisfactory decomposibility standards have not been established. The detergent manufacturers are now in the process of converting to soft detergents.

Arsenic. The U.S. Public Health Service has set a limit on the concentration of arsenic in drinking water because of the widespread use of inorganic arsenic in insecticides and its presence in animal foods. Normal human blood contains approximately 0.064 mg of arsenic per 100 ml and arsenic is found in many foods in varying amounts. Neither trivalent or pentavalent arsenic is known to be an essential or beneficial element in human metabolism.

The ingestion of as little as 100 mg of arsenic usually results in severe poisoning. A considerable portion is retained by the body at low intake levels and a single dose may require 10 days for complete disappearance. There is evidence to support the view that arsenic may be carcinogenic. The incidence of skin cancer was reported to be unusually high in areas of England where arsenic at a level of 12 mg/l was present in drinking water. Successful application of the standard test for arsenic requires considerable practice.

Barium. No study appears to have been made of the amount of barium that can be tolerated in drinking water. Standards have been arbitrarily set because of the seriousness of the toxic effect of barium on the heart, blood vessels, and nerves. Barium occurs naturally in some groundwater as the carbonate salt.

Cadmium. Cadmium apparently is biologically a nonessential, nonbeneficial element with high toxic potential. It is an industrial wastewater hazard from electroplating and from galvanizing iron. The standard method for determining cadmium is highly sensitive and great care must be used to see that all sampling vessels are thoroughly clean. Polyethylene vessels are recommended.

Chromium. The acceptable limit of 0.05 mg/l for chromium as hexavalent chromium ion was set in the 1946 Drinking Water Standards because it was the lowest amount analytically determinable at that time. Chromium is another biologically nonessential but highly toxic element whose tolerable level is not known. Special precautions are necessary in sampling and storing it in order to minimize adsorption on the walls of the container.

Reduction and removal of much of the chromate that reaches waste-treatment plants with secondary treatment is probable. Large doses of chromate will pass through conventional treatment but it is believed that activated sludge units could be designed to remove all of the hexavalent chromium, even in large doses.

Chloride, Sulfate, and Dissolved Solids. Chlorides are widely distributed in nature. They are present in mineral deposits and ocean water which contain about 18,000 mg/l of chlorides. The Dead Sea and the Great Salt Lake have about 150,000 mg/l of chlorides. Chlorides are important in water supply principally because of the salty taste.

There is a great difference between a detectable concentration and an objectionable concentration of the neutral salts. Apparently acclimatization is particularly important. More than 100 public water supplies in the United States provide water with greater than 2,000 mg/l of dissolved solids. Transients and casual visitors certainly find these mineralized waters almost intolerable to the taste, but many local residents actually profess to enjoy them.

Sodium and magnesium sulfate are well-known laxatives, the standard dose for both Glauber salt ($Na_2SO_4 \cdot 10H_2O$) and Epsom salt ($MgSO_4 \cdot 7H_2O$) being about 2 g. Calcium sulfate is less active as a laxative. These medicinal effects are most effective on newcomers, as one becomes acclimated to these waters in a relative short time.

Highly mineralized waters are reported to have an effect on the quality of foodstuffs and coffee. The tests for sulfate and chloride are significant in identifying the nature of noncarbonate hardness in water. Natural fresh waters have a low chloride content and an increase above the normal for an area is an indication of possible pollution from domestic wastes.

Copper. Copper is an essential element in human metabolism. A normal diet provides only a little more than is required. An additional supplement from water would ensure an adequate supply.

Copper imparts some taste to water and small amounts are generally regarded as nontoxic. The drinking-water standard is based on the limit that might impart an undesirable taste.

Copper is used for controlling algae and is present in some industrial wastes. Where large quantities are used in industry, the wastes may contain a sufficient amount to interfere with biological treatment processes.

Presence of more than 0.01 mg/l of copper in the dilution water for the BOD test seriously influences the results.

The copper ion has a tendency to be adsorbed on the surface of a sample container so that specimens must be analyzed as soon as possible after collection. If storage is necessary, a preservative should be added.

Cyanide. The cyanide standards for water appear to be based on the toxicity for fish and not for man. Cyanide in doses of 10 mg or less is readily converted to thiocyanate in the body.

Secondary sewage treatment should reduce the cyanides that reach the plant. Proper chlorination in water treatment under neutral or alkaline conditions will reduce the cyanide to a level below recommended limits.

Fluoride. Small concentrations of fluorides in drinking water reduce the prevalence of dental caries. Excessive amounts of fluorides are definitely associated with the mottling of teeth. Fluorides, therefore, must be regarded as both a beneficial and a dangerous mineral.

Fluoridation has become firmly established as an effective and economical public health measure. The process is recommended as a proven scientific procedure and as an accepted adjunct of water-treatment processes.

Figure 7-1 does not include over 7 million people using naturally fluoridated water in 1962.

The recommended control limits on fluoride are based upon the average temperature of the area. Where fluoride is naturally present in

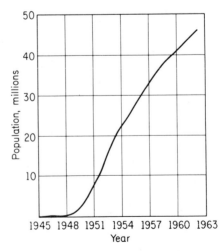

FIG. 7-1. Population using fluoridated water in the United States and Canada, 1945–1962.

drinking water, the concentration should not average more than the appropriate upper limit of Table 7-4. If the natural fluoride content is greater than two times the optimum values in Table 7-4, the supply should be rejected or a defluoridation process incorporated in the treatment.

TABLE 7-4
FLUORIDE CONTROL LIMITS, PUBLIC HEALTH SERVICE
DRINKING WATER STANDARDS

Annual Average of Maximum Daily Air Temperatures*	Recommended Control Limits— Fluoride Concentrations, mg/l		
	Lower	Optimum	Upper
50.0–53.7	0.9	1.2	1.7
53.8–58.3	0.8	1.1	1.5
58.4–63.8	0.8	1.0	1.3
63.9–70.6	0.7	0.9	1.2
70.7–79.2	0.7	0.8	1.0
79.3–90.5	0.6	0.7	0.8

*Based on temperature data obtained for a minimum of 5 years.

Several fluorine compounds are available for water treatment, namely sodium fluoride, hydrofluoric acid, hydrofluocilicic acid, and sodium silicofluoride. Sodium fluoride and sodium silicofluoride are the most widely used. Water apparently has no fluorine demand, and all fluorine added is indicated by the standard tests.

The courts of ten states have held that fluoridation of public water supplies does not infringe on the constitutional or legal rights of an individual. These decisions were rendered by the courts of last resort in California, Louisiana, Ohio, Oklahoma, Oregon, Washington, and Wisconsin and by trail courts in Maryland, Pennsylvania, and North Dakota.[11] These decisions are strengthened by the fact that the U.S. Supreme Court has refused to review some of these decisions for the stated reason that no substantial Federal constitutional question is involved. Only one court has ever rendered an opinion adverse to fluoridation and in that case the decision was promptly reversed by the state supreme court, the U.S. Supreme Court refusing to review the case.

Opponents of fluoridation have alleged that the procedure violates constitutional rights such as religious freedom and other liberties. They have argued that fluoridation represents the unlicensed practice of medicine and dentistry and is mass medication. Every conceivable legal and constitutional objection to fluoridation has been argued unsuccessfully in the courts.

Iron and Manganese. Iron and manganese are highly objectionable constituents in water supplies for either domestic or industrial use. Iron compounds are generously distributed in nature, are common constituents of plant matter, and are present in soil and rocks. Iron is one of the principal materials for water pipes, and iron compounds are used as coagulants in water treatment. It imparts a brown color to laundry and containers and appreciably affects the taste of beverages.

Iron gives water a taste described as bitter. The daily nutritional requirement for iron is 1 to 2 mg but a greater intake is necessary as a result of poor body absorption. Diets normally contain about 16 mg of iron per day.

As the permissible limit for iron is only a small fraction of the amount normally consumed, it is not likely to have any toxicologic effect. The standard is based on quality control for taste and laundry staining.

Many of the problems related to iron are also in evidence for manganese, except that this latter metal is less common in nature. Many exercise the opinion that water should be delivered to the consumer free of manganese although this is not practical, since 0.05 mg/l is the least amount that can be detected with common equipment.

Lead, Selenium, Silver, and Zinc. Lead is a cumulative poison if taken into the body in excess of certain relatively small amounts. Depending on the dose, it can be lethal if taken for either brief or prolonged exposures. The daily intake of lead that can be tolerated without effect is not precisely known. Since 1940 the lead content in potable waters has been reduced by a factor of one-half to one-fifth because the practice of using lead pipe and fittings has steadily decreased. Nevertheless, many plumbing codes still permit the use of lead pipe. The body intake of lead from other sources, primarily the air, has increased during this period. Because the other sources of lead intake into the body are unregulated, presence of lead in the excess of the minimum amount of 0.05 mg/l in water constitutes grounds for rejection of the supply.

Selenium is toxic to both man and animals. Recent reports indicate that selenium may increase the incidence of dental caries and be carcinogenic.

The addition of silver to certain waters as a disinfectant is a primary reason for establishing a standard. The chief effect of silver in the body is cosmetic, i.e., it produces a permanent blue-gray discoloration of the skin, eyes, and mucous membranes.

Zinc is an essential and beneficial element in human metabolism, although zinc salts act as gastrointestinal irritants. A standard on zinc is necessary because of its undesirable esthetic effects.

Removal of heavy metals from liquid waste is relatively simple but expensive. The salts of some of the heavy metals including lead and zinc have been reported to affect trickling filter and activated sludge processes.

Nitrate. Serious illness of infants and occasionally death have been reported following ingestion of waters containing nitrate. Nitrate poisoning appears to be confined to infants during their first few months of life.

Adults drinking the water are not usually affected but breast-fed babies of mothers drinking the water may be poisoned. Cows drinking high-nitrate water may produce milk sufficiently loaded with nitrate to result in infant poisoning. Adults and animals can be poisoned by high concentrations of nitrate.

The present methods of analysis employed for nitrate are not satisfactory and a new standard is needed. At present there are no methods of economically removing excess amounts of nitrate from water. It is important that the public be notified when a surplus quantity of nitrate is present so that other sources of water may be used for infant feeding.

Phenols. Phenols are notorious for producing tastes and odors, which are intensified upon chlorination in water supplies. Removal of phenols from water is difficult, and various procedures have been tried such as adsorption, oxidation, and extraction. Phenols are not injurious to health at the levels normally encountered. Since the standard tests are not sensitive to all phenolic compounds, they usually underestimate the amount present. The most effective way to control phenols in water supplies is to limit their introduction at the source.

7-9. WATER HARDNESS

Hardness of water is caused principally by the elements calcium and magnesium, and sometimes by iron, manganese, strontium, and aluminum. These latter elements are seldom present in potable waters in sufficient amounts to have much significance in hardness determinations, although they are often present in sufficient quantity to cause other undesirable effects on the water. For this reason it will be assumed that hardness is caused entirely by calcium and magnesium.

Much of the calcium and magnesium present in natural water is in the form of bicarbonates, sulfates, and sometimes as chlorides and nitrates. Hardness-producing materials react with soaps before a lather is developed and thus require more soap for a given laundry purpose. Hard waters also deposit scale in boilers and hot-water systems.

Hardness is referred to as temporary or permanent. Temporary hardness is that removed by boiling, whereas permanent hardness is that remaining after boiling. Temporary hardness is normally caused by bicarbonates of calcium and magnesium. Permanent hardness is caused principally by calcium sulfate, which is precipitated at temperatures above 300°F. Carbonate hardness is due to the carbonates and bicarbonates of calcium and magnesium. Noncarbonate hardness is made up of the sulfates, chlorides, and nitrates of calcium and magnesium. Sulfates may be the only noncarbonate hardness found in a sample.

The standard method of analysis for hardness gives results in terms of $CaCO_3$. Alkalinity is also expressed in terms of $CaCO_3$. A report showing a water to have a hardness of 125 mg/l does not indicate just what compounds cause the hardness but only that the hardness is equivalent to that produced by 125 mg/l of $CaCO_3$.

The most accurate method for determining hardness is to compute it from the results of a chemical analysis. The cations of calcium and magnesium and other hardness-producing cations, if they are present in significant amounts, are converted to their $CaCO_3$ equivalent.

EXAMPLE 7-1. Calculate the total hardness of a water having the following analysis:

Free CO_2 .... 15 mg/l as CO_2
Calcium .... 70 mg/l as Ca^{++}
Magnesium....................................... 25 mg/l as Mg^{++}
Bicarbonate alkalinity .... 200 mg/l as $CaCO_3$

Solution:

Equivalent weight of $CaCO_3$ = 50.04
Equivalent weight of Ca = 20.04
Equivalent weight of Mg = 12.16

Total hardness as $CaCO_3$ = mg/l of Ca as $CaCO_3$ + mg/l of Mg as $CaCO_3$

$$\text{Total hardness} = \frac{50.04}{20.04} \times 70 + \frac{50.04}{12.16} \times 25 = 277.7 \text{ mg/l as } CaCO_3$$

Total hardness may also be determined by the versenate (EDTA tritration) method.

Carbonate hardness is determined by calculation from the results of the carbonate and bicarbonate alkalinity determinations. When the carbonate and bicarbonate alkalinity, expressed in terms of $CaCO_3$, is greater than the total hardness, carbonates or bicarbonates of sodium or potassium are present. These compounds do not cause hardness. In this case, the carbonate hardness would be equal to the total hardness. Where the sum of the carbonate and bicarbonate alkalinities is less than the total hardness, this sum is equal to the carbonate hardness, and the difference between this sum and the total hardness is the noncarbonate hardness.

Differentiation between carbonate and noncarbonate hardness is important in water analysis. The temporary hardness produced by the presence of bicarbonates (or complex carbonates) can be alleviated by boiling the water. Boiling decomposes the bicarbonates or complex carbonates and brings about the precipitation of the alkaline earth cations as carbonates:

$$X^{++}(HCO_3^-)_2 \rightarrow X^{++}CO_3^{--} + CO_2 + H_2O \qquad (7\text{-}6)$$

$$H_2[X(CO_3)_2] \rightarrow X^{++}CO_3^{--} + CO_2 + H_2O \qquad (7\text{-}7)$$

The calcium and magnesium, once precipitated, no longer interfere with the action of soaps. The deposits formed are soft and easily removed.

Permanent hardness is usually due to sulfates which are unaffected by boiling at normal pressures. Even though the hardness of a given water supply may be wholly temporary, it is not feasible to soften large volumes by boiling.

EXAMPLE 7-2. Calculate the temporary and permanent hardness of the water sample in Example 7-1.

Solution:

Total hardness = 277.7 mg/l as $CaCO_3$
Bicarbonate alkalinity = 200 mg/l as $CaCO_3$

Total hardness > bicarbonate alkalinity; therefore the temporary hardness is equal to the alkalinity, or 200 mg/l as $CaCO_3$.

The permanent hardness is equal to the total hardness less the temporary hardness, or 77.7 mg/l as $CaCO_3$.

7-10. ALKALINITY AND ACIDITY

The alkalinity of water may be defined as its capacity for neutralizing acids. Determinations of alkalinity and its forms are of interest in water softening, coagulation, and corrosion control. Alkalinity is normally due to the presence of bicarbonate and carbonate ions, but occasionally it may be due to hydroxide. To distinguish between the kinds of alkalinity present in a sample and to determine the amounts of each, a titration is made with a standard acid. The titration is carried successively to the bicarbonate and carbonic acid equivalence points, indicated electrometrically or by means of a color indicator. The color indicators used are phenolphthalein and methyl orange. Phenolphthalein gives a pink color only in the presence of hydroxide or normal carbonate. A change from pink to colorless occurs at a pH value of 8.3. Methyl orange is yellow in the presence of any of the three types of alkalinity and red in the presence of acid. The change in color occurs at a pH value of approximately 4.4, and this information is used to calculate the total alkalinity.

Phenolphthalein and total (methyl orange) alkalinity determinations offer a means for the stoichiometric classification of the three principal forms of alkalinity present in normal waters. This classification assumes that the entire alkalinity is due to bicarbonate, carbonate, and hydroxide. Carbonate alkalinity may be present with either hydroxide or bicarbonate alkalinity, but hydroxide and bicarbonate cannot be present together in the same sample. Phenolphthalein alkalinity is caused by hydroxide, or carbonate, or both. Total alkalinity by methyl orange may be due to any of the three alkalinities. Table 7-5 represents the five alkalinity conditions possible in a sample.

TABLE 7-5
ALKALINITY RELATIONSHIPS

Result of Titration	Hydroxide Alkalinity	Carbonate Alkalinity	Bicarbonate Alkalinity
$P = 0$	0	0	T
$P < \frac{1}{2}T$	0	$2P$	$T - 2P$
$P = \frac{1}{2}T$	0	$2P$	0
$P > \frac{1}{2}T$	$2P - T$	$2(T - P)$	0
$P = T$	T	0	0

P = phenolphthalein alkalinity.
T = total alkalinity.

The following conditions are possible according to Table 7-5:

1. Carbonate alkalinity is present when the phenolphthalein alkalinity is not zero but is less than the total alkalinity.

2. Hydroxide alkalinity is present if the phenolphthalein alkalinity is more than half the total alkalinity.

3. Bicarbonate alkalinity is present if the phenolphthalein alkalinity is less than half the total alkalinity.

Acidity in water is usually due to carbon dioxide, mineral acids, and hydrolized salts. Most waters are alkaline although they may contain free carbon dioxide (CO_2). Because of this condition, many waters contain both acidity and alkalinity, in which case the acidity must be due to carbon dioxide. Waters affected by mine drainage or industrial wastes may contain various acids.

The concentration of carbon dioxide in normal surface water is approximately 1 mg/l. Greater amounts may be present due to the decomposition of organic matter or from groundwater. Care must be exercised in the collection and analysis of water samples containing concentrations of carbon dioxide in amounts greater than 1 mg/l because of possible loss to the atmosphere. This loss of CO_2 will change the pH value but the alkalinity determination is not affected.

7-11. OXYGEN

Surface waters of good quality should be saturated with dissolved oxygen. The concentration of dissolved oxygen in distilled water exposed to normal air at various temperatures is shown in Table 7-6.

The concentration of dissolved oxygen (DO) in water is a significant index of its sanitary quality. The dissolved oxygen test indicates the amount of molecular dissolved oxygen in water. All of the other tests that use the word "oxygen" in reporting chemical analyses refer to the oxidation capabilities of the water sample. The normal tests include the biochemical oxygen demand (BOD), and the oxygen consumed-dichromate (COD). A BOD test gives the amount of molecular oxygen required by bacteria to reduce the carbonaceous material. The COD test provides a measure of some of the organic matter in a sample. Only a part of the organic matter reacts with the dichromate and the test is not selective between biologically reducable and stable material. The COD test has

TABLE 7-6

SATURATION VALUES OF DISSOLVED OXYGEN IN FRESH AND SEA WATER EXPOSED TO AN ATMOSPHERE CONTAINING 20.9 PERCENT OXYGEN UNDER A PRESSURE OF 760 MM OF MERCURY*

(Calculated by G. C. Whipple and M. C. Whipple from measurements of C. J. J. Fox)

Tempera-ture, °C	Dissolved Oxygen (mg/l) for Stated Concentrations of Chloride, mg/l					Difference per 100 mg/l Chloride
	0	5,000	10,000	15,000	20,000	
0	14.62	13.79	12.97	12.14	11.32	0.0165
1	14.23	13.41	12.61	11.82	11.03	.0160
2	13.84	13.05	12.28	11.52	10.76	.0154
3	13.48	12.72	11.98	11.24	10.50	.0149
4	13.13	12.41	11.69	10.97	10.25	.0144
5	12.80	12.09	11.39	10.70	10.01	.0140
6	12.48	11.79	11.12	10.45	9.78	.0135
7	12.17	11.51	10.85	10.21	9.57	.0130
8	11.87	11.24	10.61	9.98	9.36	.0125
9	11.59	10.97	10.36	9.76	9.17	.0121
10	11.33	10.73	10.13	9.55	8.98	.0118
11	11.08	10.49	9.92	9.35	8.80	.0114
12	10.83	10.28	9.72	9.17	8.62	.0110
13	10.60	10.05	9.52	8.98	8.46	.0107
14	10.37	9.85	9.32	8.80	8.30	.0104
15	10.15	9.65	9.14	8.63	8.14	.0100
16	9.95	9.46	8.96	8.47	7.99	.0098
17	9.74	9.26	8.78	8.30	7.84	.0095
18	9.54	9.07	8.62	8.15	7.70	.0092
19	9.35	8.89	8.45	8.00	7.56	.0089
20	9.17	8.73	8.30	7.86	7.42	.0088
21	8.99	8.57	8.14	7.71	7.28	.0086
22	8.83	8.42	7.99	7.57	7.14	.0084
23	8.68	8.27	7.85	7.43	7.00	.0083
24	8.53	8.12	7.71	7.30	6.87	.0083
25	8.38	7.96	7.56	7.15	6.74	.0082
26	8.22	7.81	7.42	7.02	6.61	.0080
27	8.07	7.67	7.28	6.88	6.49	.0079
28	7.92	7.53	7.14	6.75	6.37	.0078
29	7.77	7.39	7.00	6.62	6.25	.0076
30	7.63	7.25	6.86	6.49	6.13	.0075

*For other barometric pressures the solubilities vary approximately in proportion to the ratios of these pressures to the standard pressures.

value where toxic substances interfere with biological activity. Correlation studies between the BOD tests and COD tests have not been fruitful. Oxygen demand is covered more completely in Sec. 10-6.

A water saturated with oxygen may or may not be polluted but is not likely to be contaminated with heavy concentrations of oxidizable matter. Methods of continuously monitoring the DO concentrations in streams have proved valuable from the regulatory point of view in indicating waste overloads.

Oxygen is essential to the corrosion of iron (see Sec. 9-5) and its control in water systems either by deactivation (removal of the oxygen) or by inhibitors is normally required.

The artificial reaeration of streams to increase their working capacity for self-purification is being studied with new interest. Reaeration of oxygen-depleted waters is being successfully developed as a supplementary method of alleviating critically low levels of dissolved oxygen in some Wisconsin streams.[12] Reaeration by means of cascades, weirs, and related modifications of turbulent natural aeration processes can be used. Of the methods studied thus far, the hydroturbine aeration technique has been most effective. It consists of introducing air into the water flow in the turbine. The Wisconsin studies indicate a turbine power-production loss of less than 5 percent with reaeration taking place.[12]

Use of pure oxygen in the treatment of sewage by the activated-sludge process has been recommended as economically justified, particularly for large plants in confined areas.[13] Employing pure oxygen allows a much higher solids content which can be used to increase treatment efficiency or reduce the size of the plant.

7-12. HYDROGEN-ION CONCENTRATION

Determination of the degree of ionization of water is essential in water and waste treatment analysis. The hydrogen-ion concentration in a solution is normally expressed in terms of pH, which is the negative logarithm of the hydrogen-ion concentration when expressed as moles per liter.

$$pH = -\log_{10}(H^+) \qquad (7\text{-}8)$$

A knowledge of the hydrogen-ion concentration is necessary to properly design chemical and biological unit processes, and to evaluate the reactions in disinfection of water supplies.

Pure water is weakly ionized and may function as a weak acid or a weak base, that is,

$$H_2O \rightleftharpoons H^+ + OH^- \qquad (7\text{-}9)$$

Extent of the ionization is very small at room temperature. The concentration of the H^+ and OH^- ions at equilibrium is equal to 10^{-7}

mole per liter at 24°C. The following relation exists according to the law of mass action:

Molar concentration of cations times the molar concentration of anions is equal to a constant.

$$(OH^-)(H^+) = K_w$$

This constant K_w, termed the ion product of water, has a value 10^{-14} (mole per liter)^2 at 24°C.

Pure water being neutral, the concentration of the H^+ ions is 10^{-7} mole per liter, and from Eq. 7-8 the $pH = -\log_{10}(H^+) = -\log_{10}(10^{-7}) = 7$. The range of concentrations of either H^+ or OH^- in an aqueous solution is very great. These concentrations range a hundred million millionfold, from 10^{-14} to 10^0. The pH therefore will have a range from 1 to 14. Solutions with a pH less than 7.0 are acid and those with a pH greater than 7.0 are alkaline. As pH values deviate from pH 7 the acidity or alkalinity increases but not in direct proportion to the pH value, since pH is a log function. A solution with a pH of 4 is 100 times as acid as one with a pH of 6, for example.

7-13. RADIOLOGICAL

The effects of radiation on human beings are viewed as harmful, and any unnecessary intake of radioactive material in water should be avoided. Development of the nuclear industry and nuclear weapons testing has caused an increase of radioactivity in the environment. The 1962 Drinking Water Standards established limits for radium 226 and strontium 90. Iodine 131 is not found in significant quantities in public water supplies frequently enough to warrant a limit, and strontium 89 levels are not likely to be significant unless strontium 90 levels are also high.

Above-average levels of radium 226 generally occur only in unusual situations. Certain ground waters have naturally occurring radium 226, and there is a possibility of pollution from industrial discharges. The principal source of strontium 90 thus far has been fallout due to weapons testing. The permissible level of $10\,\mu\mu c/l$ is substantially greater than the highest level found in public water supplies to date. The increased use and wide variety of radionuclides will require continued surveillance by regulatory authorities.

The removal of radioactive materials from either surface waters or groundwater starts before the water enters the treatment process. In surface water, the physical process of sedimentation reduces particulate activity. The extent of this reduction is dependent upon the stream turbulence and size of the particles. Many silts have ion-exchange capabilities and can reduce the level of soluble activity. Biologic processes may be effective in reducing the radiochemical concentration, and some forms of algae have been known to concentrate radiophosphorus by factors up to 10^5.[14] These benefits by natural processes are only temporary because the radioactivity is merely stored in the stream and not removed. During periods of increased turbulence the bottom sediments are resuspended and plants and animals die, returning the activity they contained to the stream.

Percolating ground water normally undergoes some natural treatment. Filtration is effective on particulate substances and some ion-exchange probably takes place with soluble material. Many minerals have good ion-exchange properties, especially some of the clays. The actual degree of decontamination attained depends upon the chemical and physical properties of the radioactive material and the geology of the area.

The radiologic quality of water is further improved by conventional treatment processes. Radioactive materials are retained in sludges, filter backwash water, and ion-exchange resins. However, special handling problems may be required.

7-14. BACTERIOLOGICAL

Most bacteria in water are derived from contact with air, soil, living or decaying plants or animals, mineral sources, and fecal excrement. Some of the most common types of bacteria which may be present in water include the coliform group, fecal streptococcus, fluorescent bacteria, chromogenic bacteria, proteus group, spore-producing rods, and archromobacter.[15] Many of these bacteria are without sanitary significance because they die rapidly in water, come from unknown sources, are widely distributed in air or soil, or have no known or suspected association with pathogenic organisms.

A variety of procedures have been used in the last 100 years to measure the bacteriological quality of water. These biological tests and procedures include the following:

1. The total plate count on gelatin at 20°C and on agar at 37°C.
2. The specific identification of pathogenic bacteria.
3. Use of the coliform group as a sewage-pollution indicator.
4. Checking the fecal streptococcus group to indicate fecal pollution.
5. Examining *Clostridium perfringens* as an indicator of pollution.
6. Employing miscellaneous indicators including bacteriophage tests, serological methods, and identification of other specific bacteria and virus.

The plate count is not required in defining a safe standard for potable waters by the "1962 Drinking Water Standards." It is useful however as a routine quality control test in the various water treatment processes and as a method for estimating the sanitary conditions of basins, filters, distribution systems, or equipment.

The specific identification of pathogenic bacteria as pollution indicators requires extremely large samples and a wide variety of media and methods to exclude all the various pathogens which could be present. Neglecting the expense, the time required for this test procedure would greatly reduce the usefulness of the results. Such a group of test procedures is not applicable to the frequent routine sampling of water supplies.

The coliform group is considered a reliable indicator of the adequacy of treatment for bacterial pathogens. The 1962 Drinking Water Standards reaffirms this standard and includes all of the aerobic and facultative anaerobic, gramnegative, nonspore-forming, rod-shaped bacilli which ferment lactose with gas production within 48 hr at 35°C in the coliform group.

This coliform grouping includes organisms that differ in biochemical and serologic characteristics and in their natural sources and habitats. *Escherichia coli* is characteristically an inhabitant of the intestines of man and animals. *Aerobactor aerogenes* and *Aerobactor cloacae* are frequently found in various types of vegetation and as deposits in the distribution system. The intermediate-aerogenes-cloacae (IAC) subgroups are found in fecal discharges but normally in smaller numbers than *E. coli*. All of the coliform group except *E. coli* are commonly found in soil and in waters polluted in the past.

Organisms of the IAC group tend to survive longer in water than do *E. coli* and are more resistant to chlorination. The relative survival times of the coliform subgroups may be used to distinguish recent from less recent pollution. Waters that have been newly polluted will show an *E. coli* density greater than the IAC density. Polluted waters that have not lately received fecal material will tend to have a higher IAC group density than *E. coli*. There is considerable confusion and controversy regarding both the advantages and disadvantages claimed for *E. coli* as an indicator of recent pollution. *Standard Methods* lists a tentative standard for differentation of coliform group organisms. Section 7-15 gives more detail on coliform-density measurements.

The fecal streptococci are characteristic of fecal pollution and are consistently present in the feces of all warm-blooded animals.[16] They do not multiply in water as sometimes occurs with the coliform group, therefore the presence of fecal streptococci in water indicates fecal pollution with a density equal to or less than that originally present. Improved methods and media are needed for the routine analysis of the streptococcal group which is not recognized as an official test procedure in the United States, although *Standard Methods* lists a tentative procedure for enterococcus. The fecal streptococci tests have application in stream-pollution investigations.

Clostridium perfringens is widely distributed over the earth's surface and uniformly present in the intestinal tract of warm-blooded animals.[17]

The spores have a long survival time in water and are resistant to chemical treatment and natural purification. The presence of spores in deep wells indicates a direct connection between the surface and the underground water source. Methods of isolation and identification are unsatisfactory for routine use. There is no test for *Clostridium perfringens* in *Standard Methods*.

Numerous other biological indicators of pollution have been suggested by various investigators—for example, bacteriophage tests. Phage types in water cannot be interpreted with our current knowledge and therefore have little use as evidence of pollution. Agglutination tests have been propounded for the serological separation of the coliform group. Difficulty has been encountered in duplication of these tests.

7-15. THE COLIFORM GROUP—FERMENTATION TUBE TEST

The coliform group of bacteria possesses the faculty of fermenting lactose or lauryl tryptose broth and producing gas. This offers a simple, visible evidence of a member of the coliform group. Some other bacteria also ferment the broth under certain conditions and combinations and additional growth reactions must be used to confirm the presence of a coliform. The number of coliform organisms in human feces is very great, the daily per capita excretion varying from 125 to 400 billion. The total number of bacteria in fecal matter that can be counted by simple bacteriological techniques is approximately one thousand times greater still. The U.S. Public Health Service 1962 Drinking Water Standards limit the number of coliforms for potable water to less than 1 per 100 ml, or 40 coliforms per gallon. To reach this figure of 40 coliforms per gallon by dilution would require a very large volume of clean water. Assuming 400 billion coliforms per capita day in summer and 100 gpcd sewage produced, the approximate dilution factor would be $(400 \times 10^9)/(40 \times 10^2) = 10^8$ or 100 million. This means that every gallon of sewage would have to be diluted with 100 million gallons of clean water to be acceptable as drinking water. Actually the number of coliforms is materially reduced by death from nonnormal environment, by removal and destruction in waste-treatment process, and by their removal and destruction in water treatment. Nevertheless, the large numbers of coliform organisms are a good indicator of bacterial pollution.

Figure 7-2 shows the anticipated reduction in coliform bacteria in a stream for various types of waste-water treatment. There is some question at the lower end of the activated sludge plant curve and the authors suggest that the dashed portion more nearly represents the anticipated reduction.[18] This dashed portion was arrived at by interpolation of data between primary and biological treatment with postchlorination. The figure also includes dashed lines at the 1,000 and 5,000 coliforms per 100 ml.

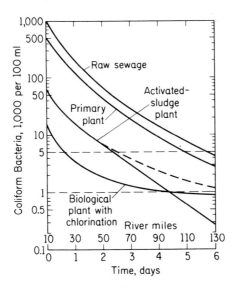

Fig. 7-2. Anticipated reductions in coliform bacteria in a stream for various types of waste-water treatment. (After F. W. Kittrell and S. A. Furfari, "Observations of Coliform Bacteria in Streams," *Water Pollution Control Federation*, vol. 35, no. 11 (November 1963), p. 1379.

These values are typical coliform limits used by a number of state and interstate water-pollution control authorities. The 1,000 coliforms per 100 ml criterion is used for waters where body-contact sports such as swimming and skiing take place. The 5,000 coliforms per 100 ml standard is used for waters that serve as sources for municipal supply and aquatic recreation exclusive of body-contact sports. Using the graph, Fig. 7-2, activated-sludge treatment improves approximately 50 miles of the river as compared to primary treatment for a raw water-supply source. It requires approximately 60 river miles to reduce the coliform count to 5,000 per 100 ml for effluent from an activated-sludge plant and roughly 110 river miles for an effluent from primary treatment.

The standard of less than 1 coliform bacteria per 100 ml of sample does not exclude the possibility of intestinal infection but it is a practical economic degree of acceptability. The test for organisms of the coliform group is simple to perform and can be done by routine laboratory personnel.

The minimum number of samples to be collected from the distribution system and examined each month is given in Fig. 7-3 and should be

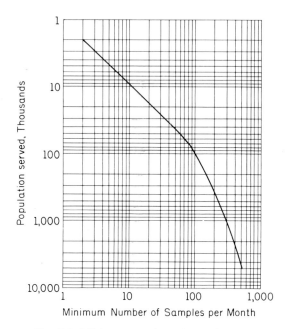

FIG. 7-3. Minimum number of samples per
month required by U.S. Public Health Service
Water Standards, 1962.

in accordance with the following: for a population under 25,000, to the
nearest 1; 25,001 to 100,000, to the nearest multiple of 5; and over
100,000, to the nearest multiple of 10.

Tests for coliform bacteria are made on raw water and water as it
passes through the treatment process and give an indication of its sanitary quality. Coliform bacteria density measurements are made on bathing waters, shellfish waters, and some industrial water. Various state
health departments normally divide surface waters suitable for public
drinking supplies into two or more classes, depending upon the degree of
treatment needed. Since the standard adopted is based upon the number
of coliform organisms per unit volume of the sample, the coliform test
is used over a broad range in water quality. It is important not only
to know that coliform organisms are present but also to determine the
probable number per unit volume in the water. Polluted waters must be
diluted in order to calculate the probable number of organisms. Figure 7-4 illustrates a scheme for making these dilutions.

Tests for the presence and density of coliform organisms utilize the
inoculation of lactose broth or lauryl tryptose broth by multiple portions
of a series of decimal dilutions of a water sample. The number of portions
planted and the range of dilutions made will depend upon the apparent

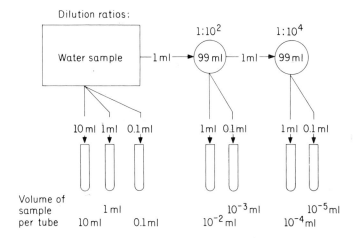

FIG. 7-4. Preparation of dilutions of a water sample for the coliform-density test.

quality of the water under examination and on the records of previous samples. Practical considerations limit the size of the largest portion to 100 ml.

The test sequence is divided into three parts, the presumptive, the confirmed, and the completed test. Figures 7-5 and 7-6 outline the sequence of steps in running the analysis. All examinations for drinking-water purposes should be carried through the confirmed part and occasionally a run should be carried through the completed portion to check the effectiveness of the testing procedure. Analysis other than for drinking water requires only the presumptive test.

7-16. MOST PROBABLE NUMBER (MPN)

The most probable number of coliform organisms in a water sample is the density more likely to produce a particular result. A number of portions of different size of the water sample are examined for the presence of coliform organisms. It is assumed that variations in the distribution of coliform organisms will follow a probability curve and that the MPN can be determined from the following expression:[19, 20]

$$Y = \frac{1}{a} [(1 - e^{-N_1\lambda})^p (e^{-N_1\lambda})^q][(1 - e^{-N_2\lambda})^r (e^{-N_2\lambda})^s]$$

$$[(1 - e^{-N_3\lambda})^t (e^{-N_3\lambda})^u] \qquad (7\text{-}10)$$

where N_1, N_2, N_3 = sizes of portions examined, in milliliters

p, r, t = number of portions of respective sizes giving positive tests for coliforms

q, s, u = number of portions of respective sizes giving negative tests for coliforms

λ = concentrations of coliforms per mililiter

Y = probability of occurrence of a particular result

e = base of Napierian logarithms, 2.718

a = a constant for any particular set of conditions and therefore may be omitted in computation of λ

EXAMPLE 7-3. What is the most probable number of coliform organisms per 100 ml as determined by the following series of observations: five 10-ml tubes

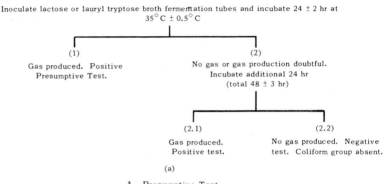

Inoculate lactose or lauryl tryptose broth fermentation tubes and incubate 24 ± 2 hr at 35°C ± 0.5°C

(1) Gas produced. Positive Presumptive Test.

(2) No gas or gas production doubtful. Incubate additional 24 hr (total 48 ± 3 hr)

(2.1) Gas produced. Positive test.

(2.2) No gas produced. Negative test. Coliform group absent.

(a)

A. Presumptive Test

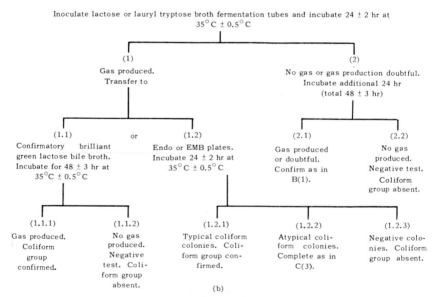

Inoculate lactose or lauryl tryptose broth fermentation tubes and incubate 24 ± 2 hr at 35°C ± 0.5°C

(1) Gas produced. Transfer to

(2) No gas or gas production doubtful. Incubate additional 24 hr (total 48 ± 3 hr)

(1.1) Confirmatory brilliant green lactose bile broth. Incubate for 48 ± 3 hr at 35°C ± 0.5°C

or

(1.2) Endo or EMB plates. Incubate 24 ± 2 hr at 35°C ± 0.5°C

(2.1) Gas produced or doubtful. Confirm as in B(1).

(2.2) No gas produced. Negative test. Coliform group absent.

(1.1.1) Gas produced. Coliform group confirmed.

(1.1.2) No gas produced. Negative test. Coliform group absent.

(1.2.1) Typical coliform colonies. Coliform group confirmed.

(1.2.2) Atypical coliform colonies. Complete as in C(3).

(1.2.3) Negative colonies. Coliform group absent.

(b)

B. Confirmed Test

FIG. 7-5. Schematic outline of presumptive and confirmed test.

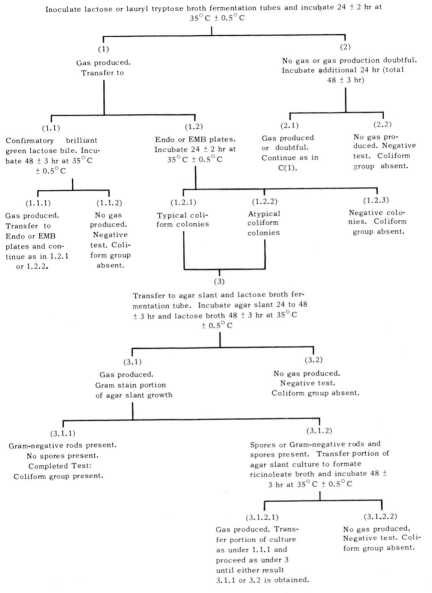

FIG. 7-6. Schematic outline of the completed test.

were used of which four were positive; one 1-ml tube was used and it was negative; and one 0.1-ml tube was used and it was positive?

Solution: From Eq. 7-10, $N_1 = 10$, $N_2 = 1$, $N_3 = 0.1$, $p = 4$, $r = 0$, $t = 1$, $q = 1$, $s = 1$, and $u = 0$.

The MPN of this series is at the mode of the curve. The modal value is determined by selecting the value of λ that will make Y a maximum. The value of a is a constant for any particular set of observations and may be omitted in computation of λ.

In the analytical result cited, let the following trial values be assumed: $\lambda = 0.19, 0.20,$ and 0.21, respectively. Then the detailed solution is as follows:

$$Y = \frac{1}{a}(1 - e^{-10\lambda})^4 (e^{-10\lambda})(1 - e^{-\lambda})^0 (e^{-\lambda})(1 - e^{-0.1\lambda})(e^{-0.1\lambda})^0$$

Terms	Values of λ		
	0.19	0.20	0.21
$(1 - e^{-10\lambda})^4 =$	0.522	0.560	0.594
$e^{-10\lambda} =$	0.150	0.135	0.122
$e^{-\lambda} =$	0.827	0.819	0.811
$1 - e^{-0.1\lambda} =$	0.019	0.020	0.021
$aY =$ products $=$	0.00123	0.00124	0.00123

The value of aY is maximum where $\lambda = 0.20$ and the MPN per milliliter is 0.20, or 20 per 100 ml.

Table 7-7 gives the MPN and 95 percent confidence limits for various combinations of positive results in fermentation-tube tests. More complete tables listing all combination of results expected to occur more than 1 percent of the time are given in *Standard Methods*.

7-17. THE MEMBRANE FILTER

In 1960 the eleventh edition of *Standard Methods* assigned official status to the membrane-filter method for determining coliform bacteria. The use of this method was qualified in that adequate parallel testing had to be run to demonstrate that the use of the membrane filter method would yield information equal to that from the multiple-tube fermentation procedure.

The membrane filters are flat, highly porous, flexible plastic disks usually 47 to 50 mm in diameter. The pore structure occupies most of the volume of a filter pad and permits rapid filtration of aqueous suspensions. With some common filters, 67 ml of distilled water will pass through each square centimeter per minute with a differential pressure of 70 cm Hg at 25°C.

A sample is filtered through a membrane filter and the filter is placed in a culture container on a medium or paper pad impregnated with moist cultural medium. The inoculated filter is incubated under prescribed conditions of time, temperature, and humidity. After incubation, the resulting culture is examined and the necessary interpretations made. With variations in such factors as culture media, incubation time, and in

TABLE 7-7
MPN AND 95 PERCENT CONFIDENCE LIMITS FOR SELECTED
COMBINATIONS OF POSITIVE RESULTS IN FERMENTATION-TUBE TESTS

Number of Positive Tubes Out of:			MPN	Limits of MPN	
Five 10-ml Tubes	Five 1-ml Tubes	Five 0.1-ml Tubes		Lower	Upper
0	0	1	2	0.5	7
0	1	0	2	0.5	7
1	0	0	2	0.5	7
1	0	1	4	0.5	11
1	1	1	6	0.5	15
2	1	1	9	2	21
2	2	2	14	4	34
3	0	0	8	1	19
3	2	2	20	6	60
4	0	0	13	3	31
4	3	2	39	13	106
5	0	0	23	7	70
5	1	1	46	16	120
5	2	0	49	17	126
5	3	3	175	44	503
5	4	4	345	117	999

Five 10-ml Tubes	One 1-ml Tube	One 0.1-ml Tube	MPN	Limits of MPN	
				Lower	Upper
0	0	0	0	0	5.9
1	0	0	2.2	0.05	13
2	0	0	5	0.54	19
2	1	0	7.6	1.5	19
3	0	0	8.8	1.6	29
3	1	0	12	3.1	30
4	0	0	15	3.3	46
4	0	1	20	5.9	48
4	1	0	21	6.0	53
5	0	0	38	6.4	330
5	0	1	96	12	370
5	1	0	240	12	3700
5	1	1	—	88	—

combinations with other cultural and biochemical procedures, many different kinds of tests are available.

In testing for coliform organisms, results are obtained in approximately 24 hr as compared to 48 to 96 hr required for the fermentation-tube tests. Larger volumes of water sample are used with the membrane-filter method and, therefore, a more representative sample is tested. The precision of the membrane-filter method is better than the fermentation-tube procedure. The method has some limitations in that high numbers of noncoliform bacteria capable of growing on the media complicate the procedure and suspended solids interfere with interpretation of the test.

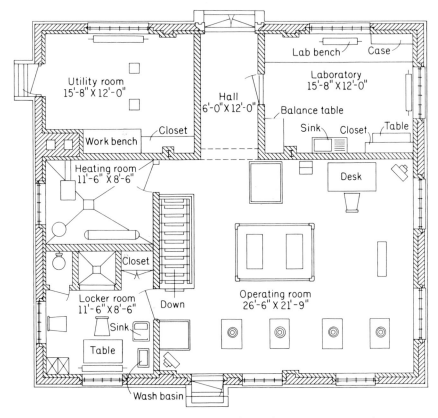

Fig. 7-7. Laboratory as part of the control room in a waste-treatment plant.

Most water and waste treatment plants have some laboratory facilities for limited examination. Figure 7-7 shows the laboratory of a small waste treatment plant located in the control building.

7-18. VIRUS IN WATER

During the past 15 years more than 70 new enteric viruses have been recognized, all of which can be found in human feces. Many of these can be recovered from domestic sewage.[21] Some strains of viruses have been found to be more resistant to chlorination than the common bacteria. Kelly and Sanderson[22] have reported this for the polio virus and Clarke and Kabler[23] for the Coxsackie virus in water. The density of enteroviruses in sewage is low in comparison with that of coliform bacteria. The low densities do not appear to be the result of inactivation of viruses en route to the plant since detention by primary treatment does not affect the density. The presence of minimum densities of virus in the winter months indicates that there is a small reservoir of enterovirus infection in the population at all seasons.[24]

The density of plague-forming enteroviruses in sewage, shown in the study by Kelly and Sanderson,[24] estimated from the density in swab expressions, was 2 to 44/100 ml. The highest densities were found in August and early September in samples of raw sewage. The enteroviruses isolated were identified as strains of Coxsackie, ECHO, and polio viruses.

The mechanism for the removal of enteroviruses from sewage by activated sludge is not fully understood. Removal of polio virus by activated sludge experiments in the laboratory has been shown to involve at least two steps: (1) aeration with sludge floc and nutrient and (2) the settling of the floc.[25] Removal by Step 2 depended on the metabolic state of the floc. Aeration with sludge floc was essential and was affected by respiratory metabolites and the absence of air. Aeration itself appeared to have no effect nor was there any correlation with the oxidation-reduction potential. Viruses were inactivated during the removal process, and the isolation of at least four strains of bacteria with antiviral activity indicates that biological antagonism is a possible third step.[25] The percentage of virus isolations indicated that there was a progressive decrease in virus content of the sewage as it passed through the plant.[26] This has not been borne out in some other experiments.

Small-scale water-treatment pilot plants have been used to study the removal of polio virus Type I as water was passed through sand under groundwater conditions along with a flocculation-filtration process at rapid rates.[26] Groundwater flow conditions through 2 ft of well-packed sand removed polio virus from water (velocities less than 4 ft/day). Some virus passed through the rapid sand filters but 99 percent removal was possible with increased alum and conventional flocculators and settling. The results were erratic, and more testing is necessary to resolve design and operating problems with rapid sand filters.

There is a need for improved methods of quantitative estimation of virus concentrations and easier methods of identification. It should be remembered that a possibility always exists that a water may be classified as potable by any of the official bacterial tests and still contain dangerous concentrations of virus.

REFERENCES

1. American Public Health Association, American Water Works Association, and Water Pollution Control Federation, *Standard Methods for the Examination of Water and Wastewater*, 11th ed. (New York: American Public Health Association, American Water Works Association, and Water Pollution Control Federation, 1960).

2. "Public Health Service Drinking Water Standards," U.S. Public Health Service, Washington, D.C., 1962.

3. Gerald E. Arnold, "Thermal Pollution of Surface Supplies," *J. Am. Water Works Assoc.*, vol. 54, no. 4 (November 1962), pp. 1332–1336.

4. Jesse M. Cohen, "Taste and Odor of ABS in Water," *J. Am. Water Works Assoc.*, vol. 55, no. 5 (May 1963), pp. 587–591.

5. Robert A. Baker, "Threshold Odors of Organic Chemicals," *J. Am. Water Works Assoc.*, vol. 55, no. 7 (July 1963), pp. 913–916.

6. A. H. Romano and S. S. Safferman, "Studies of Actinomycetes and Their Odors," *J. Am. Water Works Assoc.*, vol. 55, no. 2 (February 1963), pp. 169–176.

7. Thomas E. Maloney, "Research on Algal Odor," *J. Am. Water Works Assoc.*, vol. 55, no. 4 (April 1963), pp. 481–486.

8. James E. Foxworthy and Harley K. Gray, "Removal of Hydrogen Sulfide in High Concentrations from Water," *J. Am. Water Works Assoc.*, vol. 50, no. 7 (July 1958), pp. 872–878.

9. I. W. Santry, Jr., "Hydrogen Sulfide in Sewers," *J. Water Pollution Control Federation*, vol. 55, no. 12 (December 1963), pp. 1580–1588.

10. "Evaluation of Legislation to Control Synthetic Detergents," *J. Am. Water Works Assoc.*, vol. 55 (October 1963), pp. 1229–1237.

11. Bernard J. Conway, "Legal Aspects of Municipal Fluoridation," *J. Am. Water Works Assoc.*, vol. 50, no. 10 (October 1958), pp. 1330–1336.

12. Averill J. Wiley, B. F. Lueck, Ralph H. Scott, and T. F. Wisniewske, "Commercial-Scale Stream Reaeration," *J. Water Pollution Control Federation*, vol. 34, no. 4 (April 1962), pp. 401–411.

13. F. E. Budd and G. F. Lambeth, "High-Purity Oxygen in Biological Sewage Treatment," *J. Water Pollution Control Federation*, vol. 29, no. 3 (March 1957).

14. Herbert A. Bevis, "Significance of Radioactivity in Water Supply and Treatment," *J. Am. Water Works Assoc.*, vol. 52, no. 7 (July 1960), pp. 841–846.

15. E. O. Jordan, "The Kinds of Bacteria Found in River Water," *J. Hyg.*, vol. 3 (1903), p. 1.

16. L. A. Allen, M. A. F. Pierce, and H. M. Smith, "Enumeration of Streptococcus Faecalis with Particular Reference to Polluted Waters," *J. Hyg.*, vol. 51 (1953), p. 458.

17. L. D. S. Smith and M. V. Gardner, "Vegetative Cells of Clostridium Perfringens in Soil," *J. Bacteriol.*, vol. 58 (1949), p. 407.

18. F. W. Kittrell and S. A. Furfari, "Observations of Coliform Bacteria in Streams," *J. Water Pollution Control Federation*, vol. 35, no. 11 (November 1963), pp. 1361–1385.

19. M. Greenwood and G. U. Yule, "On the Statistical Interpretation of Some Bacteriological Methods Employed in Water Analysis," *J. Hyg.* (1917), p. 1636.

20. J. K. Hoskins, "Most Probable Numbers for Evaluation of Coliaerogenes Tests by Fermentation Tube Method," *U.S. Public Health Report*, vol. 49, reprint 1621 (1934), p. 393.

21. N. A. Clarke, G. Berg, P. W. Kabler, and S. L. Chang, "Human Enteric Viruses: Source, Survival, and Removability in Waste-water, London Program, Section II," *Intern. Conf. Water Pollution Research* (1962).

22. Sally Kelly and Wallace W. Sanderson, "The Effect of Chlorine in Water on Enteric Viruses," *Am. J. Public Health*, vol. 48 (1958), p. 1323.

23. N. A. Clarke and P. W. Kabler, "The Inactivation of Purified Coxsackie Virus in Water by Chlorine," *Am. J. of Hyg.*, vol. 59 (1954), p. 119.

24. Sally Kelly and Wallace W. Sanderson, "Density of Enteroviruses in Sewage," *J. Water Pollution Control Federation*, vol. 32, no. 12 (December 1960), pp. 1269–1275.

25. Sally Kelly, Wallace W. Sanderson, and Carol Neial, "Removal of Enteroviruses from Sewage by Activated Sludge," *J. Water Pollution Control Federation*, vol. 33, no. 10 (October 1961), pp. 1056–1062.

26. W. N. Mack, J. R. Frey, B. J. Riegle, and W. L. Mallmann, "Enterovirus Removal by Activated Sludge Treatment," *J. Water Pollution Control Federation*, vol. 34, no. 11 (November 1962), pp. 1133–1139.

27. Gordon G. Robeck, Norman A. Clarke, and Kenneth A. Dostal, "Effectiveness of Water Treatment Processes in Virus Removal," *J. Am. Water Works Assoc.*, vol. 54, no. 10 (October 1962), pp. 1275–1292.

PROBLEMS

7-1. Using the waste flows as shown in Fig. 3-8, compute the volume of sample to be taken each hour, for the full 24-hr period, to make up a composite sample. The minimum sample size is 120 ml.

7-2. Biochemical oxygen demand values run on the individual samples taken in Prob. 7-1 were as follows:

Hour	BOD, mg/l	Hour	BOD, mg/l
1 a.m.	194	1 p.m.	270
2 a.m.	198	2 p.m.	260
3 a.m.	214	3 p.m.	254
4 a.m.	200	4 p.m.	262
5 a.m.	195	5 p.m.	240
6 a.m.	184	6 p.m.	273
7 a.m.	190	7 p.m.	258
8 a.m.	225	8 p.m.	240
9 a.m.	260	9 p.m.	225
10 a.m.	221	10 p.m.	211
11 a.m.	211	11 p.m.	200
12 a.m.	255	12 p.m.	196

What is the approximate composite BOD?

7-3. Using the waste flows as shown in Fig. 3-8 and a 200-ml volume of grab sample, at what times should samples be taken over the 24-hr period to make up a composite?

7-4. A city of 200,000 population produces sewage at the rate of 150 gpcd and the sewage plant effluent has a 5-day BOD of 22 mg/l. The temperature of the sewage is 27°C and there is 1.6 mg/l of dissolved oxygen in the plant effluent. The waste effluent is discharged into a stream which has a flow of 225 cfs and the temperature of the water is 21°C before the sewage is mixed with the stream. The stream is 84 percent saturated with oxygen and it has a 5-day BOD of 3 mg/l. What is (a) the sewage flow in cfs, (b) the DO of the mixture of stream water and sewage plant effluent, and (c) the temperature of the mixture of water and sewage plant effluent?

7-5. If the scale of a map is 500 ft/in. and the density of population is 200 persons per acre, with an average waste flow of 120 gpcd, what will be the maximum rate of sewage flow, in cfs, from 10 sq in. and 100 sq in. of map area, respectively, if the ratio of maximum to average flow is taken as $Q = 5q/p^{0.2}$, where Q = maximum flow, q = average flow, and p = population in thousands?

7-6. An industrial waste flow of 3.1 mgpd has a 5-day BOD of 24,000 lb daily. This waste is added to the domestic sewage flow of 7.8 mgpd. The BOD of the domestic sewage is 205 mg/l: (a) what is the concentration of BOD in the industrial waste? (b) What is the BOD in the combined sewage? (c) What is the population equivalent based upon the BOD load of the combined sewage?

7-7. Calculate the total hardness (as $CaCO_3$) of water having the following analysis:

Free CO_2 .... 12 mg/l as CO_2
Calcium .... 90 mg/l as Ca^{++}
Magnesium............................. 21 mg/l as Mg^{++}
Bicarbonate alkalinity .... 180 mg/l as $CaCo_3$

7-8. The total alkalinity of a sample of water with pH 6.5 and temperature of 25°C is 4.0 mg/l. Find the concentration of CO_2 in milligrams per liter. Neglect the effect of salinity.

7-9. The total alkalinity of a sample of water with a pH of 10.5 is 180 mg/l. Find the distribution of the alkalinity as (a) carbonate, (b) bicarbonate, and (c) hydroxide alkalinity in mg/l as $CaCO_3$. The water temperature is 25°C and the effects of salinity can be neglected.

7-10. Determine the carbonate and noncarbonate hardness of a water sample with the following analysis:

Total hardness....................................... 175 mg/l
Bicarbonate alkalinity.............................. 130 mg/l
Carbonate alkalinity .... 45 mg/l

7-11. Calculate the temporary and permanent (noncarbonate) hardness of water with the following analysis:

Free CO^2 .... 15 mg/l as CO_2
Calcium .... 70 mg/l as Ca^{++}
Magnesium............................. 25 mg/l as Mg^{++}
Bicarbonate alkalinity .... 200 mg/l as $CaCO_3$

7-12. Using the water analysis given in Prob. 7-11, calculate the SO_4 content of the water assuming the noncarbonate hardness is entirely due to calcium sulfate.

7-13. In a molar solution of a strong base the concentration of OH^- ions is 0.004. What is the pH of this solution? What is the pOH of this solution?

7-14. Two electrolytic solutions are to be mixed in equal parts. The first solution is at pH 5 while the other is at pH 9. What is the average pH of the solution after mixing?

7-15. Determine the *p*H of a molar solution of ammonium hydroxide that has a dissociation constant of 0.000018. This is a weak base and is practically undissociated.

7-16. In a community of 70,000 population, what is the minimum number of samples of water for bacteriological tests that should be collected monthly?

7-17. One milliliter of a $1:10^4$ dilution of a water sample was found to contain 35 microorganisms. What was the probable concentration of microorganisms in the original sample?

7-18. What is the most probable number of coliform organisms per 100 ml as determined by the following series of observations: five 10-ml tubes were used of which three were positive; five 1-ml tubes were used of which three were positive; and five 0.1-ml tubes were used of which one was positive?

7-19. What is the most probable number of coliform organisms per 100 ml as determined by the following series of observations: Three 10-ml tubes were used of which three were positive; three 1-ml tubes were used of which one was positive; and three 0.1-ml tubes were used of which none were positive.

7-20. A test for coliform organisms produced the following results: five of five 100-ml portions were positive, three of five 10-ml portions were positive, and none of five 1-ml portions were positive. Find the MPN per 100 ml.

chapter 8

Physical-Treatment Processes

The first seven chapters of this book were concerned primarily with problems related to water-supply development, the transportation of fluids, and the examination of water and wastes. This and the following four chapters will be concerned largely with methods of processing various quality waters to produce a specific desired result.

Traditionally, the approach to processing has been one of considering separately the operation of a water-treatment plant, a sewage-treatment plant, or an industrial waste-treatment plant. The approach used in this book is to consider independently a number of individual unit operations or processes which might be found in any or all of the traditional "treatment plants." For example, sedimentation is employed in both water and waste treatment operations. If the engineer understands the basic principles of sedimentation he should be able to design a sedimentation basin for most purposes. This approach eliminates the need for teaching independently the theory of sedimentation as related to water supply and then teaching it again for sewage treatment, etc. It also avoids the pitfall of having the student think in terms of some "standard" water-treatment or sewage-treatment plant.

The approach followed in this book is one of presenting a series of unit operations which will be broadly categorized as physical, chemical, or biological. It is hoped that this organization of material will instill in the student the concept that there are numerous treatment processes possible and that these may be assembled in an infinite variety of ways to produce a desired result. Considering the current emphasis on water reuse and the need for developing our water resources to an extent previously unknown, it is becoming more apparent that waters of poorer quality will have to be processed for use. Under such circumstances many operations previously considered to be used in "sewage treatment" may in fact be used as part of a "water-treatment process." The modern sanitary engineer must, therefore, move away from some of the present concepts of "special-treatment sequences." In designing a treatment plant the primary concept should be to: (1) evaluate the quality of the water to be treated, (2) establish a quality standard for the final effluent of the processing operation (this will depend entirely upon the use to which the water is to be put), and (3) select a sequence of unit operations which will yield the desired degree of treatment in the most efficient and economical manner. This basic approach permits the designer the greatest latitude in developing an effective processing operation without being guided into a sterotyped format which may or may not produce optimum results.

With these concepts in mind, the student should consider the operations discussed in the following pages not as isolated procedures but as tools to effectively accomplish specific objectives. The manner in which these processes should be assembled for use in any one plant must be determined on the basis of the applicability of a particular operation in producing the required effluent quality. A so-called "water-treatment plant" for example, might take many forms depending on the quality of the source of the process water and the standards established for the effluent.

SCREENING DEVICES

A common operation in the treatment of water or wastes is screening. The source waters for many processes contain large suspended or floating materials varying in size from logs to small bits of paper and rags. This kind of material is extremely objectionable in any water-handling process because of its potential for damaging plant equipment, fouling pumps, etc. The first operation encountered in many treatment plants is screening.

8-1. INTAKE SCREENS

Where water supplies are drawn from rivers or lakes, the intakes are usually screened. These screens are built of corrosion resistant materials and should present an unobstructed cross-sectional area of approximately 150 to 200 percent of the area of the conduit being serviced. Flow velocities should generally be less than 2 fps through the screen to permit optimum removal. In northern regions it is sometimes necessary to protect screens from icing during the winter months. Heat, compressed air, and periodic flow-reversal are some of the measures taken to overcome this problem.

8-2. COARSE SCREENS

Coarse screens or racks are commonly used to remove larger solids such as sticks, rags, and paper. Typical racks are constructed as a series of metal bars spaced 1 or 2 in. apart and often inclined about 45 degrees to the horizontal. Coarse screens are usually constructed of a heavy wire fabric with openings about 1 in. square.

8-3. MEDIUM AND FINE SCREENS

Medium and fine screens have openings which range in size from 1 in. or more down to $1/32$ in. Screens having very small openings are often not square-meshed. The minimum or controlling dimension might be $1/32$ in. while the maximum dimension would normally be considerably larger than this. Fine screens with openings of $1/16$ to $1/8$ in. are common. They are usually constructed of wire mesh or slotted metal plates.

Medium screens may be expected to remove from 5 to 15 cu ft of solids per million gallons of average domestic sewage. Fine screens have been found to remove from 5 to 20 percent of the suspended matter for the same type of flows.

Where fine screens are employed, they should usually be preceded by a coarse screen to remove the larger materials.

All screens must be cleaned. This may be accomplished either manually or mechanically. Fine screens should be cleaned continually and are therefore always mechanically operated. Coarse screens and racks are sometimes cleaned by hand, especially in small plants, but mechanical cleaning provides greater efficiency of operation.

Screenings are usually high in water content and cannot be burned without drying or dewatering. The usual means of disposal are incineration, burial, or digestion with other solid materials.

8-4. COMMINUTORS

Comminutors or cutting screens are often employed which chop the sewage solids to about $1/4$ to $3/8$ in. in size. The use of these devices eliminates the need for screenings disposal as the particles coming out of the comminutor do not tend to float or clog pumping equipment. Various types of comminutors are available but basically they all make use of a vertical or horizontal screen with cutting teeth. In some designs the screen rotates while in others it is fixed. Normally the comminutor is located in a split channel which has a bypass through a coarse screen. This permits removal of the large solids when the comminutor is out of service for maintenance or repair.

8-5. HYDRAULIC CONSIDERATIONS

In designing a screening system, care must be taken to see that the approach velocity is great enough to preclude sedimentation of suspended materials in the screening channel while at the same time preventing the dislodgment of materials trapped by the screen. In addition, head losses resulting from the screening operation must be controlled so that backwater will not cause the entrant sewer to operate under pressure. Normally head losses in excess of about 2.5 ft for clogged screens are not tolerated. Since racks or screens behave hydraulically as orifices, the hydraulic losses through them are a function of the velocity head. For racks built of various shaped bars, Kirschmer has proposed the follow-equation for head loss:[2]

$$h = \beta \left(\frac{w}{b}\right)^{4/3} h_v \sin \theta \qquad (8\text{-}1)$$

where h = head loss in feet
β = a bar-shape factor
w = maximum cross-sectional width of the bars facing the direction of the flow
b = minimum clear spacing of the bars
h_v = velocity head of the flow approaching the rack in feet
θ = angle of the rack with the horizontal

The effective velocity is considered to be the geometric mean of the horizontal approach velocity and the component of this velocity normal to the rack. Table 8-1 indicates Kirschmer's values of β for several shapes of bars.

TABLE 8-1
KIRSCHMER'S VALUES OF β

Bar Type	β
Sharp-edged rectangular	2.42
Rectangular with semicircular upstream face	1.83
Circular bars	1.79
Rectangular with semicircular upstream and downstream faces	1.67

MIXING AND AGITATION

Mixing and agitation are operations of considerable significance to the sanitary engineer. Mixing may be defined as the blending of constituents to some desired state of uniformity. Agitation is an operation whose major function is to promote fluid turbulence. A primary example of the application of agitation is the promotion of floc growth in suspensions (flocculation). Mixing processes are employed to disperse a variety of chemicals and gases in fluids.

8-6. CONTINUOUS MIXING

Continuous-flow systems are employed almost exclusively in water-processing operations. The mixing characteristics of these systems are of particular importance to the sanitary engineer. Unfortunately the nature of these systems is often quite complex and thus they cannot usually be described in exact mathematical terms. Simplified mixing models are therefore employed as aids in approximating their characteristics. An understanding of the three basic mixing models is important if the student is to approach the design of continuous reactors in a rational manner.[4,5]

Plug Flow. Plug flow may be defined as that flow in which the individual particles of feed pass through the reaction vessel in the same sequence in which they entered. In addition, there is no intermixing or interaction between the particles. Each particle is retained in the reaction vessel for a time equal to the theoretical retention time:

$$t_0 - \frac{V}{Q} \qquad (8\text{-}2)$$

where t_0 = theoretical retention time
    V = volume of the reactor
    Q = flow rate

Reaction vessels which are long and narrow (tubular reactors for example) are often designed on the basis of the plug-flow model. In this case the conversion (degree of completion of the reaction) can be estimated from batch data provided such factors as temperature change or volume changes are known. For any reactor, the maximum conversion will be indicated if the plug-flow model is used. This is because it is assumed that all feed particles are retained for exactly the theoretical retention time. In reality, flow increments are usually retained for variable amounts of time—some for less than the theoretical time and some for a greater amount of time.

Complete Mixing. A second basic model is complete mixing. This may be defined as a flow in which the feed particles become completely intermixed in the reactor and thereby lose their identity. The effluent and the content of the reaction vessel are exactly alike and are uniform in this case. This condition is approximately equivalent to that encountered in a rapid mixing tank. Since the contents of the tank are uniform, the reaction can proceed at only one rate, the rate corresponding to the concentration.

A mathematical statement describing complete mixing may be derived by considering a mixing reactor having an influent Q containing a reactant A at concentration c_0, an effluent Q containing the reactant at final concentration c_t, and a holding volume equal to V. For this steady continuous-flow system, the quantity of material converted per unit time is

$$Q(c_0 - c_t) \qquad (8\text{-}3)$$

If a single, first-order, homogeneous reaction of the type $A \rightarrow$ products, is considered, an expression for rate takes the form

$$\frac{dc_A}{dt} = Kc_A \qquad (8\text{-}4)$$

where c_A = concentration of the reactant
    K = rate constant.

For complete mixing, the concentration is uniform and equal to c_t.

Therefore, the amount of material converted per unit time must equal

and

$$VKc_A$$

$$Q(c_0 - c_t) = V\left(\frac{dc}{dt}\right)_{c_t}$$

The theoretical retention time is therefore

$$t_0 = \frac{V}{Q} = \frac{c_0 - c_t}{(dc/dt)_{c_t}} \tag{8-5}$$

Equation 8-5 is the basic equation for the complete mixing model. The term (dc/dt) can be evaluated by taking the slope of the batch curve at a point which corresponds to c_t. Figure 8-1 illustrates a typical batch curve.

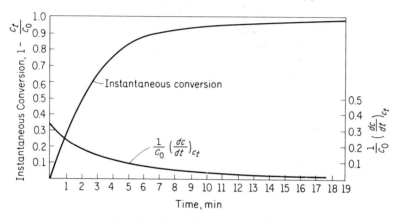

FIG. 8-1. Typical batch reaction data.

The theoretical retention time t_0 can be found by substituting for c_t in Eq. 8-5, c_t as a fraction of c_0 and then substituting for dc/dt the value of $1/c_0(dc/dt)$ found from Fig. 8-1 multiplied by c_0. Considerable information may be found in the literature on graphical and analytical methods applicable to problems in complete mixing.[11,12] An example will illustrate the determination of retention time for this model.

EXAMPLE 8-1. For an instantaneous conversion of 80 percent with a reaction whose rate is indicated by Fig. 8-1, find the required holding time.

Solution:

(1) For $\left(1 - \frac{c_t}{c_0}\right) = 0.80$, $\frac{c_t}{c_0} = 0.2$ and $c_t = 0.2c_0$

(2) From Fig. 8-1, $\frac{1}{c_0}\left(\frac{dc}{dt}\right) = 0.11$

(3) $t_0 = \frac{c_0(1 - 0.2)}{0.11c_0} = 7.3 \text{ min}$

Complete Mixing with Zero Intermixing. The complete mixing with zero intermixing model is essentially a combination of the two previous models. In this case the feed particles are immediately and uniformly displaced in the reactor but they do not intermix or interact. The feed particles leave the reactor vessel in a purely random fashion.

Because the particles do not interact, they each behave similar to an individual batch reactor. The difference between this condition and ideal plug flow is that each particle remains in the reactor for a different period of time. The result is that each batch reaction reaches a different degree of completion before leaving the vessel. The effluent is then composed of a series of increments having varied degrees of reaction completion.

The relative probability P that one feed particle will remain in the reactor longer than another if the particles are uniformly distributed is a known mathematical function. Figure 8-2 indicates the probability that a portion of the inflow will be retained in the system at time t and leave before time $t + dt$ for various values of t/t_0 and for various numbers of vessels in series. The area under the curves represents the feed slug.

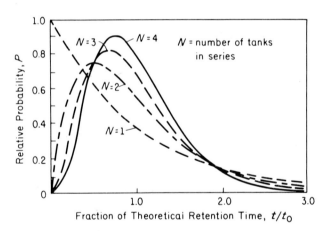

FIG. 8-2. Probability curves for zero intermixing model. (Adapted from Fig. 2, T. R. Camp, "Flocculation," *Trans. ASCE*, vol. 120, 1955, p. 8.)

Considering that each feed element acts as an individual batch reactor, the conversion of each element depends on its residence time. Gilliland and Mason have shown that the average conversion of the effluent is equal to the sum of the conversions in each increment of feed.[11] Mathematically, this may be stated as

$$\text{Average conversion} = \left(1 - \frac{c_t}{c_0}\right) = \frac{1}{t_0} \int_0^\infty P\left(1 - \frac{c_t}{c_0}\right) dt \qquad (8\text{-}6)$$

where the terms are as previously defined. The average conversion may be calculated by integrating the batch-conversion data with the relative probability function.[5] An approximate solution may be had by determining values of $P(1 - c_t/c_0)\Delta t$ at various intervals of time and then summing. In doing this, values of P and $(1 - c_t/c_0)$ are obtained from data such as presented on Figs. 8-1 and 8-2.

When data are available on flow rates and the residence-time distribution of the feed particles is known or may be assumed, upper and lower limits of conversion may be predicted. For simple homogeneous reactions, individual tanks which are well stirred will yield conversions that are in close agreement with those predicted by the complete mixing model. In long tubular reactors, conversions will approach those indicated by the plug-flow model. The zero-intermixing model is theoretically limited in application to zero-order reactions and to first order single homogeneous reactions.[4]

8-7. RAPID MIXING DEVICES

Various devices have been employed in rapid-mixing operations. Common equipment includes pumps, venturi flumes, air jets, and rotating impellers (paddles, turbines, propellers). Of all the devices listed, the vertical shaft, turbine-type, impeller is the most widely used rapid-mixing device.[8] It is composed of a vertical shaft driven by a motor on which one or more straight or curved turbine blades are mounted. These turbines are designed to provide both horizontal and vertical mixing. Flow through the mixing tank is usually from bottom to top. Mixing-tank diameters commonly range from 3 to 10 ft. Detention periods are usually less than one minute, although longer periods have been used.

Baffles are commonly used in tanks with rotating impellers to reduce vortexing about the impeller shaft. This vortexing action hinders the mixing operation and complicates the calculation of impeller power consumption. Effective baffling can be accomplished by placing vertical strips along the periphery of the tank. Usually no more than four baffles are required. These strips tend to disrupt the rotational flow pattern by deflecting the liquid inward toward the impeller shaft. Considerable information on baffling may be found in several of the references at the end of the chapter.[8,12]

8-8. FLUID REGIMES AND MODEL-PROTOTYPE RELATIONSHIPS

The flow pattern established in a fluid by a particular impeller has an effect on the results of the mixing operation being performed. This flow pattern is a function of the size, shape, and speed of the impeller, baffling, and the nature of the mixing tank.[5] Viscous flows do not support mixing except through diffusion. Turbulent flows readily promote mixing through the erratic displacement of fluid particles. The turbulence produced in mixing vessels is principally derived from the contact between low- and high-velocity flow streams. Strong shearing stresses are developed within the fluid as a result of the transfer of momentum associated with this turbulent motion. In most cases, fluid shear is important in mixing operations.

The design of mixing processes should be based on a relationship between the fluid regime and the results expected from the operation. It is therefore necessary first to determine the fluid regime required and then to find a means for producing the regime in a mixing vessel. Fluid regimes may be defined in terms of the active forces involved or by some measure of the power required. A knowledge of the active forces implies complete identification of the regime and permits geometric, kinematic, and dynamic similarity (complete similarity) to be introduced in the scale-up operation. If some index, such as the power input per unit volume is used, only an incomplete similarity between a model and the prototype can be applied.

The primary forces generated in a mixing operation are inertial, viscous, and gravitational. Normally these are represented by the power number N_p, Reynold's number Re, and the Froude number Fr, respectively. A general relationship between these dimensionless numbers is indicated as[13]

$$N_p = K(\text{Re})^a (\text{Fr})^b \qquad (8\text{-}7)$$

where K is a constant depending upon the impeller size, shape, the number of baffles, and other factors, and a and b are exponents which are functions of the mixing conditions. A more detailed discussion of this can be found elsewhere.[5]

Unfortunately, there is not a great deal of information available which permits the prediction of process performance on the basis of specific operations. It has therefore been necessary to conduct model or pilot-plant studies of processes of interest to find the optimum conditions for carrying out these processes. Once this has been done, the large-scale or prototype operation can be designed using the principles of similitude.

The impeller-tank-diameter ratio is an important consideration in any model study as the process result for identical geometric conditions and equal power input is affected by changing this ratio. Experiments should be carried out to determine the ratio which gives the optimum process result.[5] Figure 8-3 illustrates this point.

8-9. FLOCCULATION

Flocculation is essentially an operation designed to promote agitation in the fluid for the purpose of inducing coagulation. In this manner, very

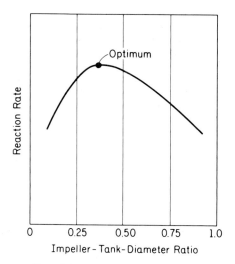

FIG. 8-3.   Impeller-tank-diameter
ratio vs. reaction rate for equal
power input.

small suspended particles are caused to collide and agglomerate into larger heavier particles or flocs, and settle out. Flocculation is a principal mechanism in the removal of turbidity from water. Floc growth depends on two factors—intermolecular chemical forces and the physical action induced by agitation. Chemical reactions are considered in Chap. 9.

Various processes have been employed to accomplish flocculation. The foremost of these are diffused air, baffles, transverse or parallel shaft mixers, vertical turbine mixers, and walking-beam type mixers. Diffused-air flocculators are costly to operate and do not produce results of equal quality to those obtained with mechanical devices. For this reason they are not extensively used today. Baffled flocculators were very common at one time but their use is decreasing because of their inflexibility, high head loss, and construction cost. The vertical-turbine mixer has been used successfully in water-softening operations but appears to have an adverse affect on the more fragile alum floc.

The most common type of flocculator used today is the paddle flocculator. Paddle wheels may be mounted on vertical or horizontal shafts although for a series of units, the vertically mounted paddle wheels have been found to be more expensive.[8] The horizontally mounted units may be located transverse to the flow or parallel to the flow. The orientation does not seem to have any appreciable effect on the results. The construction of the paddle flocculator consists essentially of a shaft with protruding steel arms on which are mounted a number of wooden or metal blades. The shaft slowly rotates (on the order of 60 to 100 revolu-

tions per hour) causing a gentle agitation of the fluid. This agitation
results in the collision of the floc particles with one another and with the
suspended matter in the raw water. The end result is the promotion of
floc growth so that finely divided suspended solids and colloidal particles
can be removed by sedimentation. Figure 8-4 illustrates a plant sequence
involving the rapid mixing of chemicals, the promotion of floc growth,
and the sedimentation of the flocculent particles.

As previously stated, flocculation is the formation of suspended flocs
which lend themselves to removal by sedimentation or filtration. Essentially the flocculation process begins with the dissolving of chemicals in a
rapid-mix operation such as indicated in Fig. 8-4. Initial collisions between colloidal particles will result from Brownian motion and contacts
brought about due to the differences in settling velocities of the heavier
and lighter particles. In a quiescent vessel floc growth would be extremely slow. A period of gentle agitation or turbulent mixing is therefore
a necessary adjunct to the promotion of rapid floc growth. This turbulent mixing phase is extremely important in the design of coagulation
basins (flocculation tanks).

Flocculation is directly proportional to the velocity gradients that
are established in the water being treated. The stirring action derived
from the flocculating mechanisms is responsible for establishing these
gradients and is therefore fundamental to the process. The number of
contacts between particles in a unit time has also been shown to vary with
the number and size of particles.[15] Mathematically this may be stated as

$$N = \frac{1}{6} n_1 n_2 \left(\frac{\overline{du}}{dy}\right)(d_1 + d_2)^3 \tag{8-8}$$

where N = the number of contacts per unit time

n_1, n_2 = number of particles per unit volume of diameters d_1 and d_2 respectively

(du/dy) = mean velocity gradient in the system

Obviously for a given velocity gradient, the rate of flocculation is greatest
for a high concentration of particles of large size.

The absolute velocity gradient at a point in a moving fluid du/dy is
equal to the square root of the power loss through fluid shear per unit
volume of fluid divided by the dynamic viscosity of the fluid. The mean
velocity gradient $du/dy = G$ is given by[15]

$$G = \sqrt{\frac{W}{\mu}} \tag{8-9}$$

where μ = dynamic viscosity

W = dissipation function or the rate of power dissipation per unit of volume P/V

Here P is the power input and V is the volume of the tank. Considering

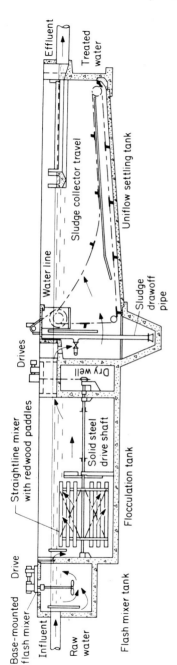

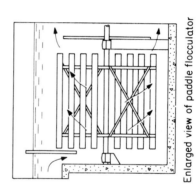

Enlarged view of paddle flocculator

FIG. 8-4. Rapid mixing, flocculation, and sedimentation. (Courtesy of the Link-Belt Company.)

that the rate of floc formation is directly proportional to the mean velocity gradient, the time of floc formation should decrease with increasing values of G. There is however, a maximum size of floc particle associated with each velocity gradient and the velocity gradient should therefore be selected with this in mind. In other words, the desired floc size should determine the velocity gradient to be used.

At a given point within a fluid, the shearing stress τ is equal to the velocity gradient G multiplied by the dynamic viscosity μ, or

$$\tau = \mu G \qquad (8\text{-}10)$$

It is obvious, therefore, that as the velocity gradient increases the shear stress also increases. As the floc particles increase in size they become weaker and are subject to being torn apart. One can therefore state in general that if small floc particles are desired, high-velocity gradients should be used, whereas to form large floc particles, lower-velocity gradients are required. Values of G between 10 fps/ft and 75 fps/ft have been found to promote floc growth without destruction of the floc particle. Detention periods should exceed 10 minutes and for lower values of G, 30-min or longer periods are indicated. Practice has shown that optimum conditions obtain for G values ranging from 30 to 60 fps/ft. Fair and Geyer have stated that the dimensionless product Gt may range within the limits 10^4 to 10^5 for satisfactory performance.[3]

A problem inherent in the design of flocculation basins, reaction tanks, and other vessels designed to hold a fluid for a specified theoretical retention time is that of short-circuiting. Short-circuiting occurs wherever a part of the influent is passed through a given system without remaining for a satisfactory period of time. (See also Sec. 8-14.)

Short-circuiting may be measured with the use of tracers such as dyes salts, or radioactive materials. The tracer can be injected at the entrance and measured at the exit at different time intervals. If the mixing is assumed to be such that the tracer is dispersed instantaneously, the concentration of the tracer at the outlet may be computed as[10]

$$\frac{C}{C_0} = e^{-t/T} \qquad (8\text{-}11)$$

where C = concentration of tracer at the outlet at time t
C_0 = initial concentration of the tracer if it is instantaneously dispersed
T = retention period of the tank
e = base of Napierian logarithms

Figure 8-5 shows a plot of Eq. 8-11 and the plot of an experimental curve from a model of a cubical tank with a moderate degree of mixing. In the case of the theoretical curve, 40 percent of the tracer slug leaves the tank in less than one-half the retention time, and 22 percent in less than one-fourth the retention time.

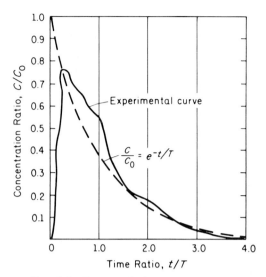

FIG. 8-5. Tracer solution concentration. (Adapted from Fig. 1, T. R. Camp, "Flocculation," *Trans. ASCE*, vol. 120, 1955, p. 7.)

To minimize the effects of short-circuiting, several tanks can be placed in series so that fluid which passes rapidly through the initial tank will be provided the opportunity to remain in the succeeding tank or tanks for a longer period. The following equation for the instantaneous dispersion curve for n tanks of equal size in series has been developed by Stein.

$$\frac{C}{C_0} = \frac{n^n}{(n-1)!} \left(\frac{t}{T}\right)^{n-1} e^{-nt/T} \tag{8-12}$$

where C_0 and T are based on the total volume of n tanks in series.[10]

When using diffused-air aeration, the work done by the rising air bubbles may be calculated by considering the expansion of the air in the bubbles or the drag forces between the fluid and the bubbles. The results obtained by considering either adiabatic or isothermal expansion are approximately the same and compare favorably with those obtained by computing the drag forces.

For the case of isothermal expansion, the work done is $\int p\,dv =$ constant, where p is the pressure and v is the volume of air. Since $pv =$ constant, the work may be written as

$$c\int \frac{dv}{v} \tag{8-13}$$

Integrating between the limits of p_1 and p_2, where p_1 is the pressure of the compressed air and p_2 is atmospheric pressure, the power input becomes

$$P = p_1 Q_1 \log_e\left(\frac{p_1}{p_2}\right) \tag{8-14}$$

where Q_1 is the volume of air at atmospheric pressure per unit time. Converting to base 10 logarithms, substituting units of cfm for Q_1, and expressing p in feet of water H, Eq. 8-14 becomes

$$P = 81.5 \, Q_1 \log [(H + 34)/34] \tag{8-15}$$

The mean velocity gradient can then be determined by substituting this expression for power in $G = \sqrt{P/V\mu}$. The expression for G using diffused-air aeration then becomes

$$G = 9.0 \sqrt{Q_1 \log [(H + 34)/34]/\mu V} \tag{8-16}$$

For optimum flocculation, the distribution of air bubbles should be uniform throughout the volume V. In addition, the bubbles should not be so large that they establish velocity gradients great enough to destroy the floc. Diffused-air aerators produce more regions of a high-velocity gradient than do comparable paddle flocculators. For this reason careful control of bubbles size is exceedingly important and has been a limiting factor in the use of diffused air as a flocculating mechanism. Future developments may alter this limitation, however.

Mechanical mixers are usually of the revolving-paddle type. When rotor paddles alone are used, the resistance to rotation of the water with the paddles is provided by the drag on the tank walls. Where stator blades are also used, these further resist the rotation of the fluid. In some instances, very wide paddles have been used with the result that the water is moved along with the paddle at a velocity approximately equal to that of the paddle. Mixing occurs only along the walls and outside edges of the paddles in such cases. Beam recommends that in basins where stator blades are not used, paddles should not exceed 15 to 20 percent of the cross-sectional area of the basin.[16] This is to prevent rolling of the water. At paddle areas equal to 25 percent of the cross-sectional area, significant rotation of the water is to be expected. Drobny indicates the manner in which paddle characteristics affect flocculation for a given input of power.[9]

In paddle flocculators, the useful power input is directly related to the drag of the paddles. The drag force may be stated in equation form as

$$F_d = \frac{C_D A \rho v^2}{2} \tag{8-17}$$

where F_d = drag force in pounds
C_D = drag coefficient for plates moving face-on to the fluid
A = the cross-sectional area of the paddles in square feet
v = relative velocity between the paddles and the fluid

The power input may. then be computed as the product of the drag force and the velocity. This may be stated as

$$P = F_d v = \frac{C_D A \rho v^3}{2} \qquad (8\text{-}18)$$

The mean velocity gradient G may be defined as [3]

$$G = \sqrt{\frac{C_D A \rho v^3}{2 V \mu}} \qquad (8\text{-}19)$$

where V is the volume of the flocculating basin in cubic feet. Common peripheral speeds of paddles are within the range of 3 to 0.3 fps. An example will serve to clarify the application of the foregoing principles.

EXAMPLE 8-2. A water-treatment plant is designed to process 25 mgpd. The flocculator is 100 ft long, 50 ft wide, and 16 ft deep. Revolving paddles are attached to four horizontal shafts which rotate at 1.5 rpm. Each shaft supports four paddles which are 8 in. wide and 48 ft long. These paddles are centered 6 ft from the shaft. Assume the mean velocity of the water is 30 percent of the paddle velocity and that C_D equals 1.9. Find (a) the difference in velocity between the paddles and the water, (b) the value of G, and (c) the time of flocculation.

Solution: (a) Rotational speed

$$V_p = \frac{2 \pi r n}{60}$$

where V_p = velocity of the paddle blades in feet per second
n = the number of revolutions per minute
r = distance from the shaft to the center of the paddle

$$V_p = \frac{2\pi \times 6 \times 1.5}{60} = 0.94 \text{ fps}$$

The velocity differential between the paddles and the fluid is therefore

$$0.70 \times 0.94 = 0.66 \text{ fps}$$

(b) The value of G may be found by using Eqs. 8-18 and 8-19. The total power input is first determined as

$$P = C_D A \frac{\gamma}{g} \frac{v^3}{2}$$

where C_D = 1.9
A = paddle area, $4 \times 4 \times 48 \times 8/12 = 512$ sq ft
v = velocity differential of 0.66 fps
Then

$$P = 1.9 \times 512 \times \frac{62.4}{64.4} \times (0.66)^3$$

$$= 271 \text{ ft lb/sec}$$

and

$$G = \sqrt{\frac{P}{V\mu}}$$

where V = tank volume, $100 \times 50 \times 16 = 80,000$ cu ft

μ = dynamic viscosity

For an assumed temperature of $50°F$, $\mu = 2.73 \times 10^{-5}$ (lb-force)(sec)/sq ft (see Table 8-2). Then

$$G = \sqrt{\frac{271 \times 10^5}{8 \times 10^4 \times 2.73}}$$

$$= 11.1 \text{ fps/ft}$$

(c) The time of flocculation is found by dividing the tank volume in gallons by the flow value;

$$t = \frac{80,000 \times 7.48 \times 24 \times 60}{25 \times 10^6}$$

$$= 34.5 \text{ min}$$

The dimensionless product Gt therefore $= 11.1 \times 34.5 \times 60 = 2.3 \times 10^4$, which is within the range of satisfactory performance.

TABLE 8-2
VALUES OF DYNAMIC AND KINEMATIC VISCOSITY OF WATER
(Based on data from Smithsonian tables)

Temperature, °F	μ, centipoises	μ, lb-sec/sq ft $\times 10^{-4}$	ν, sq ft/sec $\times 10^{-5}$	ν, sq cm/sec
32	1.792	0.374	1.93	0.0179
39.2	1.567	0.327	1.69	.0157
40	1.546	0.323	1.67	.0155
50	1.308	0.273	1.41	.0131
60	1.124	0.235	1.21	.0113
70	1.003	0.209	1.08	.0100
80	0.861	0.180	0.929	.00863
90	0.766	0.160	0.828	.00769
100	0.684	0.143	0.741	.00688
110	0.617	0.129	0.670	.00623
120	0.560	0.117	0.610	.00567
130	0.511	0.107	0.559	.00519
140	0.469	0.0979	0.513	.00477
150	0.432	0.0905	0.475	.00442
160	0.400	0.0835	0.440	.00409
170	0.372	0.0777	0.411	.00382
180	0.347	0.0725	0.385	.00358
190	0.325	0.0679	0.362	.00336
200	0.305	0.0637	0.341	.00317

SEDIMENTATION

Sedimentation as applied to sanitary-engineering processes may be defined as the removal of solid particles from a suspension through gravity settling. Other terms used to describe this process are *clarification* and *thickening*.

In water treatment, sedimentation is used to remove granular materials, flocculated impurities (usually color and turbidity), and precipitates which are formed in operations such as water softening or iron removal. In sewage and industrial water-treatment operations sedimentation is used to remove both inorganic and organic materials which are settleable or which have been converted to settleable solids. Most modern sedimentations basins are operated on a continuous flow basis.

Settling operations may be classified approximately as falling into four separate categories. These classifications are termed type I, type II, zone, and compression; are all dependent on the concentration of the suspension and the character of the particles.[5] Type I and type II clarifications both deal with dilute suspensions, the difference being that type I consists of essentially discrete particles while type II deals with flocculent materials. *Zone settling* describes a mass-settling process in intermediate-concentration suspensions of flocculent materials, and *compression* results when the concentration increases to the point where particles are in physical contact with one another and are supported partly by the compacting mass. The following section presents the theoretical aspects of the various types of sedimentation and indicates how this knowledge can be used to design sedimentation facilities.

8-10. TYPE I SEDIMENTATION

Type I sedimentation is concerned with the removal of nonflocculating discrete particles in a dilute suspension. Under such circumstances the settling may be said to be unhindered and is a function only of fluid properties and the characteristics of the particle. The settling of heavy inert materials would be an example of type I sedimentation.

A discrete particle (one which retains its individual characteristics) placed in a quiescent fluid will accelerate until fluid drag reaches equilibrium with the driving force acting on the particle. At the moment of equilibrium the particle will begin to settle at a uniform velocity. Since this condition of equilibrium is rapidly reached for the general conditions encountered in practice, the terminal settling velocity is of particular importance in sedimentation studies.

The driving force may be written as

$$F_i = (\gamma_s - \gamma) V \qquad (8\text{-}20)$$

where F_i = driving force
γ_s, γ = specific weights of the particle and fluid respectively
V = volume of the particle

The drag force acting on the particle is a function of the density and viscosity of the fluid, the settling velocity of the particle v_s, and a characteristic dimension of the particle d. A dimensionally derived relationship for fluid drag can be shown to take the form

$$F_D = \frac{C_D A \rho v_s^2}{2} \qquad (8\text{-}21)$$

where F_D = drag force

C_D = Newton's drag coefficient

A = projected area of the particle in the direction of motion[17]

The drag coefficient is a function of Reynolds number as shown in Fig. 8-6. For Reynolds numbers less than about 1, $C_D = 24/Re$, for Reynolds numbers between 1 and 10^4, C_D may be approximated by[3]

$$C_D = \frac{24}{Re} + \frac{3}{\sqrt{Re}} + 0.34 \qquad (8\text{-}22)$$

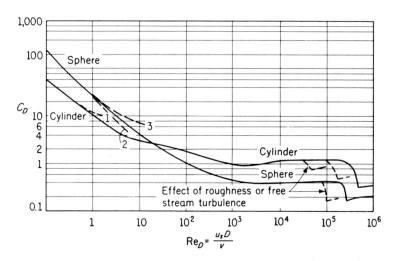

FIG. 8-6. Drag coefficients for spheres and infinite circular cylinders. Curve I: Lamb's solution for cylinder. Curve II: Stokes' solution for sphere. Curve III: Oseen's solution for sphere. From R. M. Olson, *Essentials of Engineering Fluid Mechanics*, (Scranton, Pa.: International Textbook Company, 1961), p. 261.

Equating the driving force and the drag force, which must be equivalent for equilibrium conditions, one obtains

$$(\gamma_s - \gamma) V = C_D A \rho v_s^2 / 2$$

A rearrangement of this equation yields

$$v_s = \sqrt{\frac{2(\gamma_s - \gamma) V}{C_D A \rho}} \qquad (8\text{-}23)$$

which is the expression for the settling velocity of a discrete particle. If the particles are assumed to be spherical in shape, $V = \pi d^3/6$ and $A = \pi d^2/4$. Making these substitutions and setting $\gamma = \rho g$ and $\gamma_s = \rho_s g$,

$$v_s = \sqrt{\frac{4}{3}\frac{g}{C_D}\frac{(\rho_s - \rho)}{\rho}d} \qquad (8\text{-}24)$$

where the Reynolds number is less than 1, substitution of 24/Re for C_D will transform Eq. 8-24 to the form

$$v_s = \frac{g}{18}\frac{(\rho_s - \rho)}{\mu}d^2 \qquad (8\text{-}25)$$

which is known as Stokes' law.

Discrete particles will settle at a constant velocity as indicated provided the fluid temperature does not change. A knowledge of this settling velocity is fundamental to the evaluation of the performance of a sedimentation basin. To illustrate this the operation of an ideal sedimentation basin will be discussed. Consider that Fig. 8-7 represents an idealized rectangular continuous horizontal-flow basin. This basin may be divided

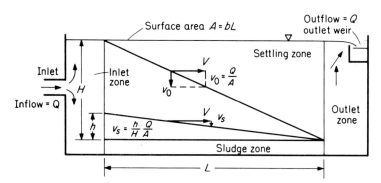

FIG. 8-7. Sketch of an ideal rectangular sedimentation basin, indicating the settling of discrete particles.

into four general zones[23]—the inlet zone, the settling zone, the outlet zone and the sludge zone. The *inlet zone* is a region in which it is assumed that the incoming flow is uniformly distributed over the cross section of the tank in such a manner that the flow through the settling zone will follow horizontal paths. In the *settling zone* it is considered that settling occurs in exactly the same manner as it would in an equivalent quiescent tank. It is assumed that flow through this region is steady and that the concentration of each size particle is uniform throughout the cross section normal to the flow direction. In the *outlet zone* the clarified effluent is collected and discharged through the outlet weir. The *sludge zone* is provided for the collection of sludge below the settling zone. It is assumed that particles reaching this zone are effectively removed from the suspension. Where mechanical equipment continually removes the sludge this zone may be neglected for all practical purposes.

Consider first a uniform dilute suspension of discrete particles which have settling velocities equal to v_s. The path taken by a particle originally at height h will be described by the vector sum of the flow velocity V and the settling velocity of the particle v_s. This is shown on Fig. 8-7. It is apparent that a particle initially at height h will just be removed by the time it traverses the settling zone. Particles initially at heights less than h will also be removed while those initially at a greater height will not reach the bottom before they reach the outlet zone. If we now consider a particle having a settling velocity v_0, it can be seen from the figure that 100 percent removal would be effected if all particles in the suspension had settling velocities at least equal to v_0. This velocity is of particular interest as a reference since it can be said that all particles in a suspension with settling velocities $\geq v_0$ will be removed while only part of those having settling velocities $< v_0$ will be removed.

From the geometry of Fig. 8-7 it can be seen that if the area of the triangle having legs H and L represents 100 percent removal of particles, then the removal ratio of particles having a settling velocity equal to v_s will be h/H. Since depth equals the product of settling velocity and retention time t_0,

$$h/H = \frac{v_s t_0}{v_0 t_0} = \frac{v_s}{v_0}$$

Thus the proportion of particles of a given size that are removed in a horizontal flow tank is[23]

$$\frac{v_s}{v_0} = \frac{v_s}{Q/A} \tag{8-26}$$

where Q = rate of flow
  A = surface area of the settling zone

Consider now the modification of the tank of Fig. 8-7 by the addition of a tray or false bottom at depth $H/2$ of the tank. The conditions of flow through the tank (Q and V remain as before) and other dimensions are unchanged. The settling velocities also remain the same but it can be seen that the removal ratio v_s/v_0 is now doubled. The maximum depth through which the particles must settle is reduced by one-half, while the effective floor area of the tank is doubled.

It can be demonstrated that this increased removal is not a function of the depth change but only of the change in floor area. Consider now a tank of depth $H/2$ with a flow of Q. For these conditions to prevail, the horizontal flow velocity must now be equal to $2V$. This will mean that the particle trajectories will be one-half those shown in Fig. 8-7, since the settling velocities are unchanged. The removal ratio for particles having a settling velocity v_s will still remain equal to v_s/v_0, however. This indicates that the rate of removal for a given discharge in an ideal sedimentation tank is entirely independent of depth but is directly related to the floor area of the tank. Therefore the depth of the tank may be varied with no effect on the removal ratio. Small depths are economically desirable. Other governing factors are space requirements for sludge-removal equipment, and the control of the horizontal flow velocity to avoid the scour of deposited sludge.

The *overflow rate* of a settling tank is defined as the settling velocity v_0 of particles which are just removed in an ideal basin if they enter at the surface. This may also be considered as the discharge per unit surface or floor area of the tank. Overflow rates ranging from 200 to 1,000 gpd/sq ft are common for the primary sedimentation of sewage.[23] Where sand, silt, and clay are to be removed by plain sedimentation, maximum surface loadings as low as 150 gpd/sq ft of tank surface are not unusual.

The efficiency of a sedimentation basin indicates the overall percentage removal of suspended matter for a given overflow rate v_0. For an ideal basin this may be formulated by making use of Eq. 8-26 and referring to Fig. 8-8. For a particular clarification rate v_0, it has already been shown that those particles having settling velocities $\geq v_0$ will be

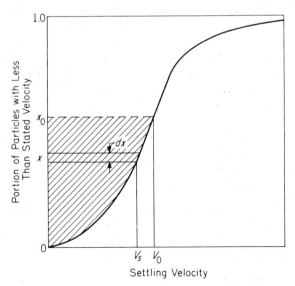

Fig. 8-8. Discrete particle velocity cumulative frequency distribution. (After Fig. 9, T. R. Camp, "Sedimentation and the Design of Settling Tanks," *Trans. ASCE*, vol. 111, 1946, p. 909.)

completely removed. Of the total number of particles in the suspension, the percentage that will be removed may then be stated as $1 - x_0$, where x_0 represents the portion of particles with a settling velocity $\leq v_0$. For each size particle with a settling velocity $v_s \leq v_0$ it has been indicated that the portion removed would be equal to v_s/v_0. Thus when considering various particle sizes in this category, the percentage removal of these particles will be given by

$$\int_0^{x_0} \frac{v_s}{v_0} dx \qquad (8\text{-}27)$$

and the overall removal will therefore be

$$R = (1 - x_0) + \frac{1}{v_0} \int_0^{x_0} v_s dx \qquad (8\text{-}28)$$

The second term in this equation can be determined by a graphical integration of a settling analysis curve such as given in Fig. 8-8. This involves the shaded portion of the figure.

8-11. TYPE II SEDIMENTATION

The settling properties of dilute suspensions of flocculating particles differ from those of nonflocculating particles in that the flocculating properties of the suspension must be considered along with the settling characteristics of the particles.[5,47] In this case, heavier particles having large settling velocites overtake and coalesce with smaller, lighter particles to form still larger particles with increased rates of subsidence. The opportunity for particle contact increases as the depth of the settling vessel increases. As a result, the removal of suspended matter depends not only on the clarification rate but on depth as well. This is the important difference between type I and type II clarification. The settling of raw sewage solids in the upper levels of a primary clarifier would be typical of type II sedimentation.

Unfortunately there is no adequate mathematical relationship which can be used to determine the effect of flocculation on sedimentation. Settling-column analyses are required to evaluate this effect.[5,47]

A standard method for performing a settling-column analysis is to place the suspension to be studied in a column which includes sampling ports at various depths. The suspension is allowed to settle in a quiescent manner. Samples are withdrawn at various selected time intervals from different depths. The concentration of particles is determined from this portion and the information used to compute the percentage of material removed or settled out. The actual value of the fraction removed is then plotted in the manner shown in Fig. 8-9. A particular value is plotted at the proper coordinates of depth and time. After sufficient data have

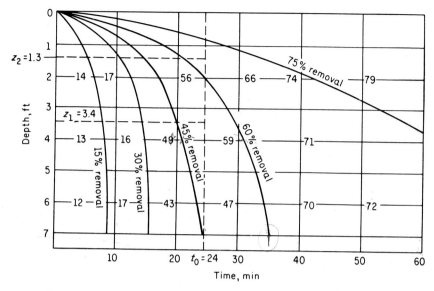

(Note: Numbers plotted represent fraction removed based on settling column analysis. Percentage removal curves are interpolated using this data.)

FIG. 8-9. Settling trajectories for a flocculent suspension.

been plotted, lines of equal concentration or isoconcentration lines may be drawn. These lines represent equal fractions of removal. They also trace the maximum trajectories of particle settling paths for specific concentrations in a flocculent suspension. For example, 45 percent of the particles in the suspension will have average velocities not greater than $4/21 = 0.19$ ft/min by the time the 4-ft depth has been reached.

To determine the overall removal in a specific basin, an approach similar to that outlined for discrete particles is used. An example will illustrate the procedure.

EXAMPLE 8-3. Using the settling trajectories determined by the settling column analysis shown in Fig. 8-9, find the overall removal for a settling basin 7 ft deep with an overflow rate v_0 of $7/24$ ft/min.

Solution:

1. From the figure, 45 percent of the particles will have settling velocities not greater than $7/24$ ft/min.

2. Using 15 percent increments, it can be seen that an additional $60 - 45 = 15$ percent of the particles will have an average settling velocity $v_s \geq 3.4/24$ ft/min and a second $75 - 60 = 15$ percent will have an average settling velocity $\geq 1.3/24$ ft/min. The next increment would have a negligible velocity and will therefore be neglected. (NOTE: These values are determined as shown on Fig. 8-9.)

3. The removal ratio of each percentage of particles considered to have a certain characteristic is v_s/v_0 as stated previously.

4. The overall removal in percent is therefore

$$R = 45 + \frac{v_{s1}}{v_0}(C_1) + \frac{v_{s2}}{v_0}(C_2) + \ldots \frac{v_{sn}}{v_0}(C_n) \qquad (8\text{-}29)$$

where in the example $C_1 = C_2 = C_3 = 15$ percent. Also since $v_{s1} = z_1/t_0$ and $v_0 = z_0/t_0$, $v_{s1}/v_0 = z_1/z_0$, etc., where $z_1, z_2 \ldots$ are measured down from the top of the tank and $z_0 = 7$ ft. Thus

$$R = 45 + \frac{3.4}{7}(60 - 45) + \frac{1.3}{7}(75 - 60) + \cdots$$

$$= 45 + 7.3 + 2.8 + \cdots$$

and the overall removal is approximately 55.1 percent.

8-12. ZONE SETTLING

Where concentrated suspensions are considered, there is an interference of the velocity fields of the closely spaced particles with the result that there is an upward displacement of the fluid and settling is hindered. In a dilute suspension particles settle freely at their terminal velocity until they approach the sludge zone at the bottom of the settling tank. In the vicinity of this region the particles deaccelerate and finally become a part of the sludge blanket. For more concentrated suspensions a zone will be formed in which the more rapidly settling particles act as a group with a reduction in the velocity of subsidence.[5] With further increases in concentration, the formation of this zone occurs at progressively earlier periods. Finally, complete collective settling will take place. When the particle concentration reaches this point, a definite interface will be formed between the settling particles and the clarified fluid. Figure 8-10 illustrates the manner in which the location of the interface will vary with respect to time. In the region from A to B there is a hindered settling of the particle-liquid interface. The region from B to C represents a deacceleration as the transition into the compression zone is accomplished. Settling in the region from C to D depends upon the compression of the sludge blanket.

The manner in which the settling of a thick flocculent suspension occurs may be further clarified by considering a batch process carried out in a cylindrical settling column. Initially the column will contain a suspension which is of a uniform concentration. After $t = 0$ an interface will be formed at some depth below the surface and there will result a zone of clarified fluid directly above the interface. Below the interface a constant uniform suspension having some specific settling velocity remains. The velocity of subsidence in this zone will be defined as

$$v_s = f(C) \qquad (8\text{-}30)$$

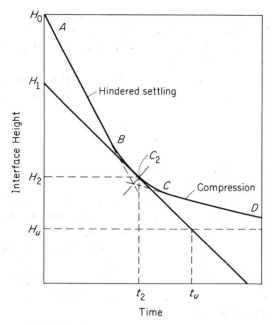

FIG. 8-10. Graphical representation of interface height vs. time for a batch settling test. (After W. P. Talmadge and E. B. Fitch, "Determining Thickener Unit Areas," *Ind. Engr. Chem.*, vol. 47, 1955.)

where v_s = settling velocity for conditions of hindered settling

C = initial concentration of particles in the suspension

Two other zones are also formed along with the zone of clarified liquid. One of these is directly below the zone of uniform suspension and it represents a transition region in which settling velocity is being reduced due to an increase in solids concentration. Below this zone, a compression zone develops in which the solids are supported mechanically by those beneath them. Thus there is an upper zone of clarified liquid, a second zone of hindered settling at uniform concentration, a transition zone, and a compression zone. As time passes, all zones except those containing the clarified liquid and the sludge will disappear as no new solids are introduced into the column. In a continuous-flow reactor, all of the zones would be maintained. Zone settling occurs for activated sludges in final clarifiers and for raw sewage wastes when the particles approach the bottom of the sedimentation tank.

The surface area required in a continuous-flow system designed to handle concentrated suspensions is based on the clarification and thickening capacities of the system. Batch-settling tests of the nature shown in Fig. 8-10 can be used to estimate both of these factors.

The initial rate at which interface subsidence takes place is used to estimate the clarification capacity of the system. Essentially, the design must be such that the surface area is large enough to preclude the rate of liquid rise exceeding the velocity of subsidence. The rate of liquid rise is based on the quantity of liquid overflow only (the portion passing out with the sludge is excluded). The area required for clarification may be stated as

$$A = \frac{Q_0}{v_s} \qquad (8\text{-}31)$$

where A = surface area of the settling zone
$\quad\quad Q_0$ = overflow rate
$\quad\quad v_s$ = subsidence rate in the zone of hindered settling
The value of v_s may be determined from batch data as shown in Fig. 8-10 by computing the slope of the hindered settling portion of the interface height-vs.-time curve. The clarification area found by using Eq. 8-31 must then be compared to that computed on the basis of thickening capacity and the larger of the two will yield the design surface area.

Thickening capacity is determined through a consideration of the batch-sedimentation characteristics of thick suspensions. The required cross-sectional area for adequate thickening is given by[5,18]

$$A = \frac{Qt_u}{H_0} \qquad (8\text{-}32)$$

where A = required surface area of the settling zone
$\quad\quad Q$ = volumetric rate of influent to the settling basin
$\quad\quad t_u$ = time it takes to reach a desired underflow or sludge concentration C_u
$\quad\quad H_0$ = depth of fluid in the settling column (the initial interface height)
In settling analyses of this type, there is a critical concentration layer which will yield the largest value for A. This is the concentration which must be used as the basis for design. Usually this concentration occurs in the transition zone at the inception of compression. An estimate of this critical concentration C_2 may be had by bisecting the tangents to the hindered settling and compression portions of the interface height-vs.-time curve. This procedure is illustrated on Fig. 8-10. The point at which the bisector intersects the curve is considered to be representative of the actual compression point.

The value of t_u can be determined from the batch settling curve also. This is done by first plotting a line parallel to the time axis which passes through the desired underflow concentration C_u. Next a tangent is constructed at C_2. The time-scale intercept of the tangent with the underflow-interface height line is the required time t_u (see Fig. 8-10).

The proper design of a final clarifier must satisfy three criteria: (1) the clarification capacity based on the hindered settling rate must be met; (2) the thickening capacity which is based on the removal of material in the transition and sludge zone must be satisfied; and (3) the detention period should not be excessive, otherwise the bottom sludge may become anaerobic.

Common practice is to express thickening capacity in terms of unit area. The units employed are square feet per ton of solids per day. An example will serve to illustrate the foregoing principles. A more detailed discussion may be found elsewhere.[5,18]

EXAMPLE 8-4. Use the batch-settling analysis given on Fig. 8-11 to find the minimum surface area of the sedimentation basin. The influent has a solids concentration of 0.175 lb/cu ft and is to be settled in a continuous flow unit

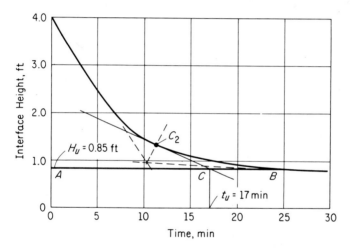

FIG. 8-11. Batch-settling data for Example 8-4.

operated at a rate of 1.3 cfs. An underflow concentration of 0.823 lb/cu ft is considered desirable.

Solution:

1. First the height of the particle-liquid interface must be determined for the underflow concentration C_u. Since the total weight of solids in the system must equal $C_0 H_0 A$ or $C_u H_u A$,

$$H_u = \frac{C_0 H_0}{C_u}$$

$$= \frac{0.175 \times 4.0}{0.823}$$

$$= 0.85 \text{ ft}$$

2. Construct a horizontal line AB through H_u. Then draw tangents to the hindered settling and compression portions of the curve given in the figure. Bisect the angle formed by these tangents and using the bisector locate the compression point C_2. Construct a tangent to the curve at C_2 and project this tangent to an intersection at C with line AB. Project C vertically downward to the time scale to find $t_u = 17$ min.

3. The thickening area requirement can then be determined by using Eq. 8-32:

$$A = \frac{Qt_u}{H_0}$$

$$= \frac{1.3 \times 17 \times 60}{4}$$

$$= 331 \text{ sq ft}$$

4. Determine the subsidence velocity v_s which obtains in the hindered settling portion of the curve.

$$v_s = \frac{4.0 - 2.25}{6 \times 60}$$

$$= 4.86 \times 10^{-3} \text{ ft/sec}$$

5. The area required for clarification is given by

$$A = \frac{Q_0}{v_s}$$

where Q_0 is the overflow rate and is proportional to the volume above the sludge zone.

$$Q_0 = 1.3 \times \frac{3.15}{4.0}$$

$$= 1.02 \text{ cfs}$$

and

$$A = \frac{Q_0}{v_s} = \frac{1.02}{4.86 \times 10^{-3}}$$

$$= 211 \text{ sq ft}$$

6. Therefore the controlling requirement is the thickening area of 331 sq ft, since it exceeds the area required for clarification.

8-13. COMPRESSION

The consolidation of the sediment at the bottom of the basin is extremely time-consuming, because the fluid which is displaced must flow through the ever-decreasing pore space between the particles. The rate of settlement decreases with time due to the increased resistance to the flow of the fluid. The porosity of the deposited sediment is a maximum in the lowest portion of the sludge blanket due to compression resulting from the weight of the supported particles above and because the consolidation time for this lowest portion is also greatest. The consolidation rate in the zone of compression is approximated by[20]

$$-\frac{dH}{dt} = i(H - H_\infty) \qquad (8\text{-}33)$$

where H = sludge line height at some time t

$\quad H_\infty$ = final sediment depth

$\quad i$ = a constant for a given suspension

The time required for the sludge line to drop from the critical height at the compression point H_c to a height H can be determined by integrating Eq. 8-33. The resulting expression is

$$i(t - t_c) = \ln(H_c - H_\infty) - \ln(H - H_\infty) \qquad (8\text{-}34)$$

where t_c = time at which the sludge line is at the compression point

$\quad H_c$ = interface height at the compression point

and the other variables are as previously defined. A plot of log $(H - H_\infty)$ vs. $(t - t_c)$ will yield a straight line having the slope $-i$. The final sludge height H_∞ is primarily determined by the liquid surface film which adheres to the particles. Gentle agitation will facilitate compaction.

8-14. SHORT-CIRCUITING

Short-circuiting can be defined as the deviation from plug flow which is exhibited by fluid particles passing through a reaction vessel. In the case of ideal plug flow, all of the fluid particles are retained for a theoretical time $t_0 = V/Q$, whereas if short-circuiting is apparent, part of a slug will be retained for a period less than t_0 and part for a time greater than t_0. Short-circuiting produces clarification efficiencies which are less than expected due to the nonuniform times of passage. Major causes of this phenomenon are influent velocity, density, thermal, wind induced, and effluent structure induced currents. In general, the relative importance of the various causes of short-circuiting is related to the characteristics of the suspended solids being settled.

The short-circuiting characteristics of tanks are usually measured by introducing a slug of dye, salt, or radioactive tracer into the inlet of a tank and then by measuring the concentration of the tracer as it appears at the outlet of the vessel at specific intervals of time. If the entire slug traversed the system at the nominal tank velocity, the slug would pass out of the system in its entirety at the nominal detention line $t_0 = V/Q$. In reality, however, parts of the tracer will remain for different periods of time, but the average will approach t_0. Typical concentration-time curves for different types of tanks are given in Fig. 8-12.[23]

The vertical scale of Fig. 8-12 is the ratio of the actual concentration to that which would be obtained if the slug of tracer material were mixed

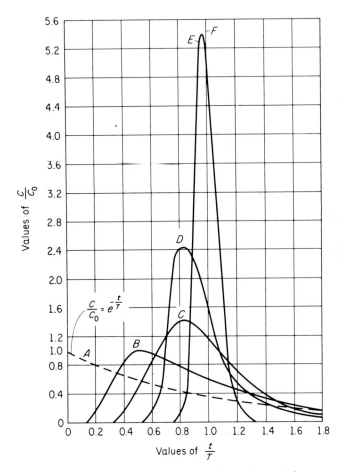

FIG. 8-12. Typical dispersion curves for tanks. (After
T. R. Camp, "Studies of Sedimentation Basin Design,"
Sewage and Industrial Wastes, January 1953.)

instantaneously with the entire tank contents. The horizontal scale is the
ratio of the actual time at which a certain concentration appears at the
outlet to the nominal retention time t_0.

Curve *A* in Fig. 8-12 represents conditions that would prevail in an
ideal dispersion tank in which the slug mixes immediately with the entire
contents of the tank. The characteristics of actual vessels designed for
violent mixing closely approximate curve *A*. With such vessels however,
a short time is recorded before the tracer first reaches the outlet. Curve *B*
is typical of stable flow conditions for radial-flow circular tanks. The
curve indicates that the largest concentration of suspended matter passes
the outlet in about 50 percent of the nominal detention period. Curve *C*

characterizes wide shallow rectangular tanks while curve D is typical of long narrow rectangular tanks. The largest concentrations of suspended matter for curve D are seen to be retained for about 80 percent of the detention period. Curve E represents round-the-end baffled mixing chambers and curve F represents the condition of ideal plug flow.

It has been shown that it is extremely difficult to reproduce the short-circuiting curves for square tanks and radial flow circular tanks. This is because the flow patterns in these basins are not stable and are readily affected by density and convection currents. Short-circuiting curves in long, narrow rectangular basins can be reproduced quite well, however, due to the particular stability of such basins.

On a qualitative basis it is generally considered that dye fronts which take long periods to arrive at the outlet and which are not greatly dispersed indicate the more nearly optimum settling conditions. This premise is not valid in all cases, however. The removal of particles which settle out in an unhindered manner is not affected by detention time but is solely a function of overflow rate. In this case, density currents and vertical short-circuiting do not affect the removal of the particles. Dye-test curves do not reflect the difference between density current short-circuiting and mixing effects or short-circuiting resulting from the nonuniform lateral distribution of flows. For this reason there may be no direct correspondence between the dye-front curve and the sedimentation efficiency in type I operations.

For type II particles, detention time may be of greater significance than overflow rate.[24] Under these circumstances, the detention characteristics of the basin are important and the dye test will serve as an indicator of removal efficiency. Thus all of the possible short-circuiting mechanisms must be considered in design.

Morrill has proposed that volumetric basin efficiency be related to the ratio of the times of occurrence of the 10 and 90 percentiles of the tracer-front curve.[25] Fiedler and Fitch have suggested the use of the standard detention efficiency as a functional measure of basin efficiency where detention time is required in a clarification basin. The standard detention efficiency (S.D.E.) is given by[21]

$$
\text{S.D.E.} = \frac{\displaystyle\sum_0^\infty (D - \tfrac{1}{2}\Delta D)\Delta t}{\displaystyle\sum_0^\infty \frac{(D - \tfrac{1}{2}\Delta D)\Delta t}{t - \tfrac{1}{2}\Delta t}} \Bigg/ \frac{V}{Q} \tag{8-35}
$$

where D = dye concentration
t = time
Q = influent rate of flow
V = tank volume

For a more complete discussion of this the reader is referred to the work of Fiedler and Fitch.[21]

On the basis of tracer studies it appears that, in general, long, narrow rectangular basins are superior to radial-flow circular tanks. This is based on the unstable, poorly shaped flow waves normally exhibited by the latter. It has been indicated however that the unstable flow wave associated with the radial-flow tank may not be a valid index of the efficiency of that type of sedimentation vessel.[22]

Short-circuiting effects in sedimentation basins may be minimized by covering the basin to eliminate effects related to the sun or wind. Large horizontal currents can be induced by the wind, whereas vertical convection currents can be induced by the sun. Influent and density current short-circuiting may be offset by the utilization of stream-deflecting baffles, feed-stream dividing mechanisms, impingement of opposed jets or streams, radial-type velocity dispersing feedwells, vertical-flow feedwells, and tangentially fed velocity-dispersing feedwells.[26] The short-circuiting due to effluent structures can be minimized by providing an effluent weir length which is as large as possible.

8-15. SEDIMENTATION TANK DESIGN

Sedimentation basins often occupy a position of considerable importance in the overall process of treating a specific water. Poor design or operation of these basins will result in the passage of inadequately conditioned water to the next unit process. Such a happening may adversely affect the outcome of the entire remaining treatment sequence.

The physical construction of a sedimentation basin may vary from an excavation in the ground (often for presedimentation of extremely turbid waters) to a structure of concrete or steel. Basins may be rectangular, square, or round. Some are deep, others shallow, and both may be covered or uncovered. Sludge-removal equipment may be provided or hand-cleaning methods may be employed. Most modern sedimentation basins are concrete and are not covered.

Several two-story installations are in evidence and it appears that some three-story basins will be constructed. These multistoried structures are gaining in popularity due to the area and cost-saving properties they exhibit.[19] Normally the larger installations combine flocculation and sedimentation in a single structure.

Size. There have been a considerable variety of sedimentation basin designs. Generally however, they vary in depth from about 7 to 15 ft, with 8- to 12-ft depths being the most common. Circular tanks range from about 35 to 200 ft in diameter, with most tanks being about 100 ft in diameter. Square tanks are usually smaller than circular ones. A common dimension for a square tank is about 70 ft. Rectangular tanks have been built as long as 300 ft but most are closer to 100 ft in length. The length-to-width ratio of rectangular tanks varies from about 3:1 to 5:1, with width being controlled in many instances by the size of the sludge-removal apparatus. Bottom slopes range from about 1 percent in rectangular tanks to about 8 percent for circular or square tanks. Some typical sedimentation tank designs are given in Fig. 8-13 to 8-15.

Inlets and Outlets. In order to minimize the effects of short-circuiting, considerable attention should be directed toward the effective hydraulic design of inlet and outlet structures.

Inlet structures are employed to uniformly distribute the influent over the cross section of the settling zone; to initiate parallel or radial flow; to minimize large-scale turbulence, and to preclude excessive velocities near the sludge zone. Generally, the influent is distributed across the width or around the periphery of the tank through entrance ports or pipes. Various methods of employing baffles or deflectors to dissipate the velocity of the influent jets have been devised.[26] Considerable large-scale turbulence is usually developed by the inlet structures, but by controlling the overall tank dimensions the inflow distribution can be confined to a relatively minor volume of the tank. Model studies of inlet structures have been found to be particularly useful.

Part of the volume in a sedimentation tank is ineffective for settling purposes because particles which enter this zone will become entrained in the effluent. To minimize this effect, a relatively long flow path is desirable. Long, narrow tanks are especially effective under such circumstances. Outflows are normally controlled by weirs which are placed along the sides of outlet troughs. These troughs may be located along the walls of rectangular tanks or may extend into the center of the tank as indicated in Fig. 8-13 and 8-14. In circular basins the weirs are usually located on the periphery of the tank. The various types of outlets are of little importance in comparison to inlet types for the control of dispersion characteristics.[27]

Detention Times and Loading. In practice, detention periods vary from less than one hour to several days. The most significant removals are accomplished early in the detention period however, so that normal designs are for periods considerably less than one day. Common holding periods range up to about 8 hr, but for mechanically cleaned basins the usual range is from 1.5 to 3 hr, with 2 hr being the most common. Except in the case of the settling of discrete particles of known characteristics, settling-velocity studies are necessary for the effective determination of overflow rates and detention times.

Recommended surface loadings range between 300 and 4,000 gal/sq ft/day for granular solids, 800 to 2,000 gal/sq ft/day for slow settling solids; and 1,000 to 2,000 gal/sq ft/day for flocculent particles. Generally it is considered that a surface loading of about 900 gal/sq ft/day for coag-

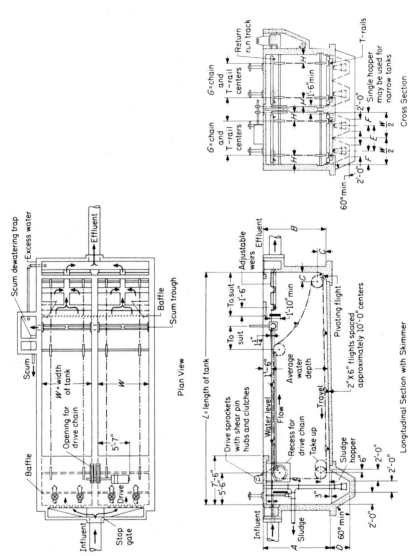

FIG. 8-13. Typical horizontal-flow sedimentation basin. (Courtesy of the Link-Belt Company.)

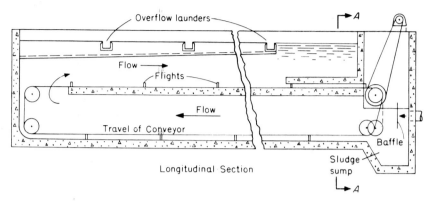

Overflow launders

Flow

Flights

Flow

Travel of Conveyor

Baffle

Sludge sump

Longitudinal Section

FIG. 8-14. A two-story sedimentation basin. (From S. L. Tolman, "Sedimentation Basin Design and Operation," *Public Works*, June 1963.)

ulated water or sewage which is to be settled in a tank about 10 ft deep is representative. A corresponding detention period of about 2 hr would be obtained.

Sludge Removal. Sludge may be removed from sedimentation tanks either manually or mechanically. For small installations dealing with waters of low turbidity, hand methods are often employed since the volume of sludge is small and relatively stable. For water-softening opera-

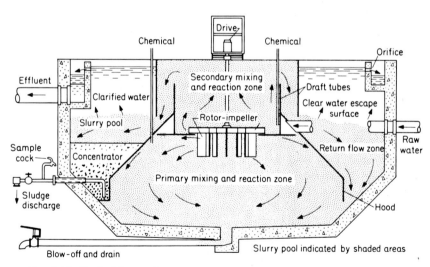

Drive

Chemical   Chemical

Orifice

Effluent

Clarified water

Secondary mixing and reaction zone

Draft tubes

Clear water escape surface

Slurry pool

Rotor-impeller

Sample cock

Concentrator

Return flow zone

Raw water

Primary mixing and reaction zone

Sludge discharge

Hood

Blow-off and drain

Slurry pool indicated by shaded areas

FIG. 8-15. Vertical-flow sedimentation basin. The "Accelator" unit includes a basin in which is contained a raw water inlet and distribution duct; a primary mixing and reaction zone; two concentric draft tubes which form the secondary mixing and reaction zone; a rotor-impeller for mixing and pumping, driven by a motorized reducer; and effluent launder system; concentrators to accumulate and remove excess slurry. (Courtesy of Infilco, Inc.)

tions or where sewage or industrial wastes must be processed, the volumes of sludge are usually quite large and highly putrescible. Under these circumstances, continuous mechanical removal of the sludge is desirable. Various types of sludge collectors are employed in practice. Chain-driven collectors like those shown in Fig. 8-13 are widely used in rectangular tanks. These devices move quite slowly, usually about 1 to 2 ft/min. They have exceptionally large conveying capacity and move the solids toward sumps located at the ends of the tanks. Another common design which is used principally in circular or square tanks employs rotating trusses to the bottom of which are attached scraper blades. These blades move the sludge toward a sump located at the center of the basin. In small-diameter basins peripheral speeds are about 3 ft/min. For large basins, speeds up to 20 ft/min are not uncommon. Other types of rotating collectors and reciprocating collectors have also been used.[19]

FILTRATION

Filtration is an operation in which water and suspended matter are separated by passing the water through a porous material. This media may be sand, anthracite, diatomaceous earth, a finely woven fabric, or similar material.

8-16. GRANULAR FILTERS

The most common types of granular filters used in sanitary-engineering processes employ sand as the filter media. Trickling filters which employ large rock (3 in.) are used in the secondary treatment of sewage and are covered in Chap. 10, since their mode of operation is of a different nature than that of the filters discussed here.

There are two basic types of sand filters in use today—the rapid filter and the slow filter. The slow sand filter is usually about $\frac{1}{2}$ acre in size and consists of a bed of unstratified sand resting on a gravel bed. Rates of operation of these filters range from about 2 to 10 mgad. Solids which accumulate at the surface must be removed periodically (about every 30 days) to preclude the clogging of the filter. Today slow sand filtration is normally prescribed only for the secondary or tertiary treatment of sewage. Reasons for the declining use of these filters in drinking-water treatment include their high cost of construction combined with the need for considerable land area and the difficulties encountered in cleaning.

Rapid sand filters may be either of the free-surface type or the pressure type. Most filtration of water supplies is accomplished today by the use of such filters. In a free-surface filter the water is passed downward through the filter media by gravitational action. Filtration rates are usually about 2 to 3 gpm/sq ft although more recent trends are toward higher rates (4 to 5 gpm/sq ft) depending upon the nature of the process water. Pretreatment by coagulation is essentially a necessary requirement where rapid filters are used. This is so that much of the suspended matter will be removed by sedimentation. Rapid sand filters consist of beds of stratified sand and are ordinarily about 500 sq ft in size. Filter cleaning is accomplished by reversing the flow through the filter. This process is known as backwashing. Figure 8-16 illustrates a typical rapid sand filter.

Pressure filters are built into steel cylinders or tanks and are operated under pressure to produce flow rates of about 2 to 4 gpm/sq ft. These filters are also cleaned by reversing the flow. Because of size limitations, pressure filters are not generally employed in large-scale treatment works.

8-17. DIATOMACEOUS EARTH FILTERS

Diatomaceous-earth filters are pressure-operated filters which make use of a processed diatomaceous earth as the filter media. They were first used extensively during World War II to provide water to military units in the field within a short period of time after the occupancy of the water point. The filter medium is supported on a fine metal screen, a porous ceramic material, or a synthetic fabric known as a septum. There are three basic steps in the diatomite filtration cycle[35]—(1) the precoat, (2) The filtration and body-feed addition, and (3) the removal of the filter cake. During the precoat operation a thin layer of diatomite is deposited on the septum by a flow of filtered water. The filter is thus formed on the outside of the septum element. Once this has been completed, the raw water combined with a small amount of diatomaceous earth (body feed) is fed into the filter. The reason for the body feed is to continually build the filter itself so that clogging at the filter surface will be minimized. This permits significantly longer filter runs. When the pressure drop or filtration rate reaches an economic limit it becomes necessary to wash the filter. This is done by reversing the flow through the septum and discharging the dirty filter cake to wash. Once the septum has been cleaned of the original precoat, the added body feed and the particles removed by filtration, it is ready for a new precoat and continued use. Common rates of filtration range from about 1 to 5 gpm/sq ft, depending on the quality of the raw water and the results to be obtained. The use of diatomaceous-earth filters has been generally limited to swimming pools, military field units, and installations for small communities.

8-18. MICROSTRAINING

Microstraining is a form of filtration whose primary objective is the removal of microorganisms (various forms of phytoplankton, zooplank-

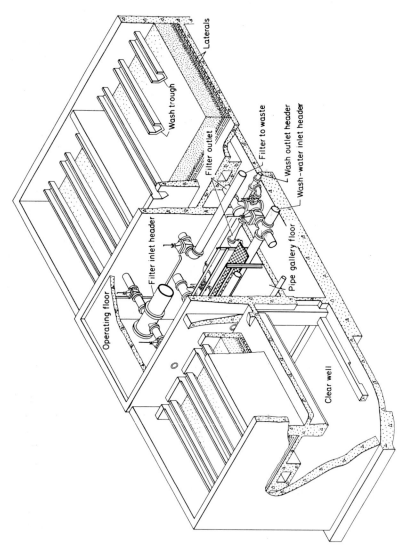

Fig. 8-16. Cross section of typical rapid sand filter. (Courtesy of the Permutit Company.)

ton, and other general microscopic debris) and other suspended solids. A filtering media consisting of a finely woven stainless steel fabric is normally used. This fabric supports a thin layer or mat of removed materials which further improves the ability of the filter to effect removals. Microstrainers usually have high flow ratings corresponding to low hydraulic resistance. Fabrics become matted rapidly and for this reason they must be backwashed almost continuously. Most microstrainers are of the rotating drum type where the fabric is mounted on the periphery of the drum and the raw water passes from the inside to the outside of the drum. Backwashing is usually accomplished through the utilization of wash-water jets.

Microstrainers have been successfully employed in the primary clarification of water preceding filtration, in the preparation of water prior to its use for groundwater recharge, in the final clarification of sewage effluents, in the treatment of industrial waters and wastes, and in other aplications.[36,37] It is expected that the future utilization of microstrainers by municipalities and industry will be widespread.

8-19. THE FILTRATION PROCESS

The effectiveness of the filtration process (when granular materials are used) is a function of several mechanisms. These are straining (the primary process), sedimentation, flocculation, and under certain conditions, biological activity.

The straining process occurs principally at the interface between the filter media and the water to be filtered. Initially, materials are strained out which exceed in size the pore openings at the interface. During the filtration process the amount of material deposited as a mat at the filter surface builds up. This mat further enhances the straining process and tends to further restrict the removal of impurities to the interface. When the raw water contains considerable organic matter (such as in the filtration of sewage) bacteria grow within the surface mat and utilize the accumulated deposits for food. As the organisms multiply, the mat becomes slimy. This improves the effectiveness of the mat in removing objectionable materials. Such biological activity is important, however, only where the mat is left intact for relatively long periods of time.

Hazen has stated that a filter medium acts in part in a manner similar to that of a sedimentation basin with a very large number of trays or false bottoms.[38] When particles smaller than the pore spaces are introduced into the filter they are given the opportunity to settle out on the surface of the filter material while they are passing through the filter bed. In this respect, each pore space acts as a tiny sedimentation basin. Based on spherical sand grains of 5×10^{-2} cm in diameter, Fair and Geyer indicate that the settling velocity of removable particles is approximately $1/400$ that of particles which can be removed effectively in a sedimentation basin of equal loading.[3]

As was pointed out earlier, floc growth is dependent upon the opportunity for particle contacts to be made. In the filtration process conditions are such that within the pores of the filter bed flocculation is promoted. Particles thus grow in size and as a result become trapped in the interstices and removal is further enhanced.

Biological metabolism may play a significant role in the slow sand-filtration process or where a filter is operated intermittantly as in the case of sewage disposal. Under these conditions the surface mat is retained for a sufficient period to permit the deposited matter to be utilized in the growth of biological organisms. The improvement in straining resulting from the formation of slimes has already been mentioned. In addition, the chemical composition of the deposited materials is altered through the utilization of these substances by the various organisms.

8-20. FILTERING MATERIALS

Broadly speaking, a filter media should possess the following qualities: (1) It should be fine enough to retain large quantities of floc; (2) it should not permit floc to pass through the filter; (3) it should allow relatively long filter runs; (4) it should be easily cleaned, and (5) it should be clean and free of foreign materials. These attributes are not all compatible. An obvious example is that very fine sand will retain floc but will tend to shorten the filter run, while for a coarse sand the opposite would be true. Recent trends are toward coarser sands so that higher rates of filtration can be obtained. Care must be exercised, however, because the efficiency of bacterial removal will be reduced if the sand is too coarse. In general, coarse filter beds should be of greater depth than fine ones.

In the past, filter sand has been classed primarily by its effective size and the uniformity coefficient. The effective size is the 10 percentile size, such that 10 percent of the filter sand by weight is less than this size. The uniformity coefficient is the ratio of the 60 percentile size to the 10 percentile. Common ranges in effective size and uniformity coefficient are from 0.4 to 0.55 mm and from 1.35 to 1.75 respectively.[39] Grain-size distributions for potential filter sands can be determined by using standard sieve analyses. From these the effective size and uniformity coefficient of the sand may be determined. Where these values lie outside the recommended range, a usable material may be prepared by screening out part of the coarse materials and washing out some of the fines.[33]

Experiments with high rates of filtration in Chicago have led to the conclusion that for Chicago filter sands the usual effective size data cannot be used successfully to correlate sand size with length of filter run.[40] Instead, a representative effective size is obtained by averaging a specific series of percent sizes. The percent size is the particle diameter which has the stated percent of material finer in size by weight. The *Chicago uniformity coefficient* is the weight percentage of material which has a diameter less than 1.5 times the one percent size. Additional information on the Chicago filter-sand specifications may be found in the literature.[40]

It is desirable to have a relatively uniform sand so that effective filtration will occur throughout the filter depth. In rapid sand filtration, once the filter has been backwashed the sand will stratify; if the size variation is great, effective filtering may be confined to the upper few inches of sand. In practice the depth of the sand bed varies from about 24 to 30 in. for rapid sand filters and from about 24 to 42 in. for slow sand filters. For optimum efficiency the depth of filter media should be as small as possible without sacrificing safe bacteriological removal.

In recent years there has been an increased usage of anthracite coal as a filter medium. In 1956 it was used in 23 states. Advantages claimed for anthracite include: (1) lower backwash velocities because of the low specific gravity, (2) higher rates of filtration, (3) lower terminal head losses, and (4) longer filter runs.[28,41] The effective size and uniformity coefficient are also used as parameters when anthracite is considered.

A detailed discussion of the properties of diatomaceous earth and woven fabrics may be found elsewhere.[35,36]

Below the sand beds in filter units there is a supporting layer of gravel. This coarse material does not contribute significantly to the purification of water but does function to distribute the wash water evenly. Gravel beds, which should be well graded, commonly have particles varying in size from about 0.10 to 3 in. The usual depth of the gravel layer is about 12 in in slow sand filters and about 18 in. in rapid-filter units. The arrangement of sand and gravel in a rapid sand filter is indicated in Fig. 8-17.

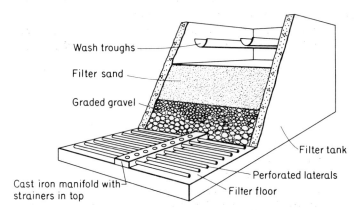

FIG. 8-17. Cross section of a typical rapid sand filter. (Courtesy of National Lime Association.)

8-21. FILTRATION HYDRAULICS

The hydraulics of granular filters is derived from the basic concepts of the flow of fluids through porous media. An analogy may be drawn to the flow of fluids through small pipes when filtration is the subject of interest. When backwashing or the expansion of the filter bed is of concern, an analogy may be drawn to the settling of particulate matter. Studies of the filtration process have indicated that the head lost through a filter media can be expressed by the following functional relationship:

$$H_f = F(e, L, d, v, \mu, \rho, g) \tag{8-36}$$

where H_f = head lost in a depth of filter L
  e = porosity of the bed
  d = diameter which characterizes the filter-media grains
  v = velocity of flow moving toward the filter media
  μ = dynamic visosity
  ρ = mass density of the fluid
  g = acceleration due to gravity

The practical evaluation of head loss is of great significance in the hydraulic design of a filter unit. In clean filters, initial head losses commonly range from about 1.5 to 2.5 ft. Terminal head losses of about 9 ft are common. These head losses have an important bearing on the overall design of a water treatment plant. This is so because it is common practice to have gravity flow from the filters to the next plant unit which is generally a clear well. The elevation of the clear well is thus controlled to a great extent by the loss of head through the filter and the connecting transportation system.

Two general equations, one proposed by Rose and one proposed by Carmen-Kozeny, are used to compute the head loss resulting from the passage of the water through the filter media.[30,33] The results obtained using either equation are essentially equivalent.

The Carmen-Kozeny Equation. The Carmen-Kozeny equation is obtained by first considering the fundamental Darcy-Weisbach relationship,

$$h_L = f \frac{L}{D} \frac{v^2}{2g} \tag{5-4}$$

where h_L = frictional head loss
  f = a dimensionless friction factor
  L = depth of filter
  D = pipe diameter
  v = mean pipe-flow velocity
  g = acceleration due to gravity.[5]

Since flow through the filter involves passage through channels whose cross sections are irregular, it is necessary to replace the term D in Eq. 5-4 with an equivalent term $4R$, where R is the hydraulic radius. This is equivalent to D for a circular pipe. The Darcy-Weisbach equation then becomes

$$h_L = f \frac{L}{4R} \frac{v^2}{2g} \tag{8-37}$$

If a unit volume of the filter medium is considered, it can be seen that the channel volume or volume available for flow is essentially equal to the porosity of the bed. For the entire filter bed, then, the channel volume is obtained by multiplying the porosity by the total volume occupied by the bed. Now for N particles of volume V_p, the volume of the solids is NV_p, and the total volume of the bed is $NV_p/(1 - e)$. Thus the total channel volume is given by

$$\text{Total channel volume} = \frac{e}{1 - e} NV_p \tag{8-38}$$

where e is the porosity of the bed. If the wetted surface area is considered to be the surface area of the particles, the following relationship is obtained:

$$\text{Total wetted surface area} = NA_p \tag{8-39}$$

where A_p is the surface area of an individual particle. From Eqs. 8-38 and 8-39 the hydraulic radius is computed as

$$R = \frac{e}{1 - e} \frac{V_p}{A_p} \tag{8-40}$$

For spherical particles of diameter d, $V_p = \pi d^3/6$ and $A_p = \pi d^2$. Substituting these values one obtains

$$\frac{V_p}{A_p} = \frac{d}{6} \tag{8-41}$$

Considering that the granular materials used in practice are usually not spherical, it is necessary to correct Eq. 8-41 by inserting a dimensionless particle shape factor ϕ. The general relationship then becomes

$$\frac{V_p}{A_p} = \phi \frac{d}{6} \tag{8-42}$$

where ϕ equals one for spherical particles. Carman has reported shape factors of 0.73 for pulverized coal, 0.95 for Ottawa sand, 0.82 for rounded sand, and 0.73 for angular sand.[42] These values can be used as a guide, but for reliable results, an analysis of the material to be used should be made. Settling velocity determinations afford one means for evaluating the particle-shape factor.

The velocity of flow downward just above the filter bed is given by Q/A, where A is the surface area of the filter. When the fluid enters the filter, the cross-sectional area is reduced due to the space occupied by the filter media. Consequently, the velocity through the interstices of the filter exceeds the face or approach velocity. The face velocity is thus

$$V_s = ev \tag{8-43}$$

where V_s = face or approach velocity
$\quad\quad v$ = mean velocity through the filter
$\quad\quad e$ = bed porosity

By substituting V_s/e for v, and $\phi ed/6(1 - e)$ for R in Eq. 8-37, the following relationship for head lost through the filter is obtained:

$$H_L = f_1 \left(\frac{L}{\phi d}\right)\left(\frac{1 - e}{e^3}\right)\left(\frac{V_s^2}{g}\right) \tag{8-44}$$

This is known as the Carmen-Kozeny relationship.[30, 31] The dimensionless friction factor f_1 can be determined in the following manner:[32]

$$f_1 = 150 \frac{1 - e}{\text{Re}} + 1.75 \tag{8-45}$$

where

$$\text{Re} = \phi \frac{\rho V_s d}{\mu} \tag{8-46}$$

Equation 8-44 is applicable to the determination of head loss in a filter bed consisting entirely of particles of some specific size. The equation can be used for beds of mixed particles and for stratified beds, however, by making a slight modification. By solving Eq. 8-42 for d, substituting this relationship for d in Eq. 8-44, and by substituting the total volume V and surface area A of all the particles in the bed for the volume V_p and surface area of an individual particle A_p, a relationship applicable to mixed beds can be obtained. This relationship is of the form

$$h_L = f_1 \frac{L}{6} \frac{1 - e}{e^3} \frac{V_s^2}{g} \frac{A}{V} \tag{8-47}$$

For particles having a uniform shape which are packed homogeneously, the average area-volume ratio for the bed, based on Eq. 8-42, is[3]

$$\left(\frac{A}{V}\right)_{avg} = \frac{6}{\phi} \int_{x=0}^{x=1} \frac{dx}{d} \tag{8-48}$$

where dx is the proportion of particles of a specific size d. The value of $(A/V)_{avg}$ is customarily determined on the basis of a sieve analysis by using

$$\left(\frac{A}{V}\right)_{avg} = \frac{6}{\phi} \sum \frac{x}{d} \tag{8-49}$$

where x represents the weight fraction of particles retained between adjacent sieve sizes and d is the geometric mean size of the adjacent sieve openings. Substitution of the value of $(A/V)_{avg}$ determined in this manner in Eq. 8-47 will permit computation of the head loss in a homogeneously packed bed of uniformly shaped particles. This type of packing is found in slow sand filters.

For stratified beds an additional consideration must be made. In the case of the homogeneous bed, one value of f_1 can be used to represent the entire bed. For a stratified bed, each layer will have a different value of the friction factor f_1 since the representative particle size in each layer will be different.

If the porosity of the stratified bed is uniform and the particles are of uniform shape, Eq. 8-47 can be written as

$$\frac{dh_L}{dL} = K f_1 \frac{1}{d} \tag{8-50}$$

for a particular stratum under some set of operating conditions. To obtain the total head lost through the filter depth L, Eq. 8-50 must be integrated:

$$h_L = \int_0^{h_L} dh_L = K \int_0^L \frac{f_1}{d} dL \tag{8-51}$$

Noting that $dL = L dx$, where dx represents the proportion of particles of a size d, Eq. 8-51 becomes

$$h_L = KL \int_{x=0}^{x=1} f_1 \frac{dx}{d} \tag{8-52}$$

If the particles between adjacent sieve sizes are considered uniform, Eq. 8-52 takes the form

$$h_L = LK \sum \frac{f_1 x}{d} \tag{8-53}$$

where

$$K = \frac{1}{\phi} \frac{1 - e}{e^3} \frac{V_s^2}{g} \tag{8-54}$$

Equation 8-53 can be used to compute the head loss in stratified filter beds. It is therefore applicable to conditions encountered in a rapid-sand-filter plant.

The Rose Equation. A second relationship for determining the head lost through filter beds was derived experimentally by Rose.[33] It is applicable to filters having uniform spherical or nearly spherical particles. This equation has been widely used in hydraulic computations for rapid sand filters. The equation is of the form

$$h_L = \frac{1.067}{\phi} \frac{C_D}{g} L \frac{V_s^2}{e^4} \frac{1}{d} \tag{8-55}$$

where C_D is a coefficient of drag, and the other variables are as defined previously. Figure 8-6 indicates a relationship between C_D and the Reynolds number for spherical particles. The following equation relating the two can also be used:

$$C_D = \frac{24}{Re} + \frac{3}{\sqrt{Re}} + 0.34 \tag{8-56}$$

where the upper limit for the Reynolds number[3] is 10^4.

By relating the particle diameter d to the area-volume ratio, Eq. 8-55 can be used for homogeneous or stratified beds in a manner similar to that indicated for the Carmen-Kozemy equation.[3] For homogeneous mixed beds the equation takes the form

$$h_L = \frac{1.067}{\phi} \frac{C_D}{g} L \frac{V_s^2}{e^4} \sum \frac{x}{d} \tag{8-57}$$

For stratified beds with uniform porosity, the equation takes the form

$$h_L = \frac{1.067}{\phi} \frac{L}{g} \frac{V_s^2}{e^4} \sum \frac{C_D x}{d} \tag{8-58}$$

In both equations the summation terms can be evaluated by making use of a sieve analysis in a manner similar to that already indicated. An example will serve to illustrate the manner in which the equations for head loss can be used.

EXAMPLE 8-5. Determine the initial head loss in a rapid sand filter which is 24 in. deep and has a porosity of 0.40. Assume a water temperature of 50°F and and a filtration rate of 2.5 gal/sq ft/min. A sieve analysis of the sand is given in Table 8-3. Consider that the sand has a particle-shape factor ϕ of 0.95.

TABLE 8-3
SIEVE ANALYSIS AND COMPUTATION OF HEAD LOSS FOR
EXAMPLE 8-5

1	2	3	4	5	6
Sieve Number	Percentage of Sand Retained, $100 \times$	Geometric Mean Size, d, ft $\times 10^3$	Reynolds Number $\frac{\rho V_s d}{\mu}$	C_D	$C_D \frac{x}{d}$
14–20	1.10	3.28	1.30	18.5	62.0
20–28	6.60	2.29	0.91	26.4	761.0
28–32	15.94	1.77	0.70	34.3	3,090.0
32–35	18.60	1.51	0.60	40.0	4,930.0
35–42	19.10	1.25	0.49	49.0	7,480.0
42–48	17.60	1.05	0.42	57.2	9,600.0
48–60	14.30	0.88	0.35	68.6	11,150.0
60–65	5.10	0.75	0.30	80.0	5,450.0
65–100	1.66	0.59	0.23	104.4	2,940.0
Summations	100.00			$\sum \frac{C_D x}{d} =$	45,463.0

Solution:

1. Columns 1, 2, and 3 are given data related to the sieve analysis and standard sieve sizes.

2. Column 4, the Reynolds number, is determined from

$$\text{Re} = \frac{\rho V_s d}{\mu}$$

where μ = 8.78 × 10^{-4} lb-mass/ft-sec for water at 50°F

V_s = face velocity of the water in ft/sec = 2.5 gpm/sq ft × 2.228 × 10^{-3} ft/sec

ρ = mass density of water = 62.4 lb-mass/cu ft

d = geometric mean particle size from column 3

3. For Reynolds numbers less than about 1.9, C_D = 24/Re.[5]

4. The head loss h_L is computed by using Eq. 8-58 with ϕ = 0.95, L = 2 ft, and e = 0.40.

$$h_L = \frac{1.067}{\phi} \frac{L}{g} \frac{V_s^2}{e^4} \sum \frac{C_D x}{d}$$

$$= \frac{1.067}{0.95} \times \frac{2.0}{32.2} \times \frac{(5.57 \times 10^{-3})^2}{(0.40)^4} \times 45,463.0$$

$$= 3.84 \text{ ft}$$

8-22. THE HYDRAULICS OF EXPANDED BEDS

After a filter has been in operation for a period of time, the operating head loss increases due to the suspended matter which has been collected. When the head loss has reached the point (usually 8 to 10 ft) where the flow controller from the filter to the clear well is wide open, an additional loss of head would produce a reduction in flow. To prevent this, it becomes necessary to remove the particles which have been trapped in the filter bed. This removal may be accomplished by scraping off the clogged portion of the bed, or by reversing the flow through the bed so that it is expanded and the trapped particles can be washed out. This latter procedure, known as *backwashing*, is the method used to cleanse rapid sand filters.

The backwashing process is carried out by reversing the flow in the underdrainage system so that it moves upward through the filter bed. For very low upflow velocities the bed remains fixed, but as the velocity is increased the lighter particles begin to be moved upward. The velocity at which a given size particle is suspended or "fluidized" is known as the critical velocity. As the velocity is further increased, the particles become more widely separated and behave in an unhindered manner. The lighter soiled materials which have been previously trapped are then freed and pass to waste with the wash water. During the expansion of the bed the trapped particles are dislodged by the shearing action of the water or by the abrasive action resulting from contacts made between the rising bed particles. This scouring action is an important phase of the cleansing operation and it can be enhanced by agitating the expanded filter bed. Hydraulic jets are used primarily to accomplish this, although mechanical rakes and compressed air have also been employed.

Uniform Beds. When a bed of uniform particles is subjected to back-washing, the bed will just begin to open up when the backwash velocity equals the critical velocity of the particles. At this time the effective weight of the particles in the water will be exactly balanced by the upward drag on the particles resulting from the upflow velocity. If the velocity is increased above the critical value, the bed will be further opened. This will not improve the cleansing action of the upflow but may be important in allowing sufficient open space for the trapped suspended matter to be washed away. A study of Fig. 8-18 will help to understand the mechanism of filter-bed expansion which follows.

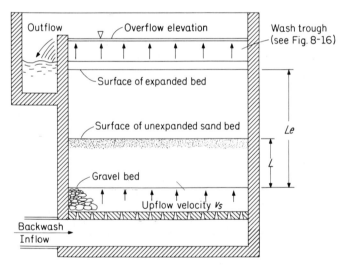

FIG. 8-18. Diagram illustrating the expansion of a filter bed during backwashing.

Consider now a filter bed composed of uniform particles of sand. During normal filter operation, these particles will occupy the depth L in Fig. 8-18. During backwash the bed will be expanded to depth L_e. As the critical velocity V_c is reached, there will be a balance between the frictional resistance of the particles and the head loss of the fluid in ex-panding the bed.[3,5] Stated mathematically,

$$h_L \rho g = (\rho_s - \rho) g (1 - e_e) L_e \qquad (8\text{-}59)$$

where h_L = head loss incurred in expanding the filter
    ρ_s, ρ = mass density of the particles and fluid respectively
    L_e = expanded depth
    e_e = porosity of the expanded bed

The frictional pressure drop $h_L \rho g$ is just balanced by the weight of the particles in the fluid. Rearranging,

$$h_L = L_e \frac{\rho_s - \rho}{\rho} (1 - e_e) \tag{8-60}$$

The solution of this equation depends upon a knowledge of the porosity of the expanded bed e_e. For a bed of uniform sand grains, Fair and Geyer have indicated that e_e can be determined by using

$$e_e = \left(\frac{V_s}{v_s}\right)^{0.22} \tag{8-61}$$

where v_s = terminal settling velocity of the particles
    V_s = face or upflow velocity of the fluid [3]
Thus a uniform bed of particles will expand when

$$V_s = v_s e_e^{4.5} \tag{8-62}$$

    The relative expansion of a bed of uniform sand grains can be determined by considering that the volume of sand in the unexpanded bed is exactly equal to that of the expanded bed. Thus it can be written that

$$L(1 - e)A_b = L_e(1 - e_e)A_b \tag{8-63}$$

where A_b equals the surface area of the bed. Therefore

$$L_e = L \left(\frac{1 - e}{1 - e_e}\right) \tag{8-64}$$

or

$$L_e = \frac{L(1 - e)}{1 - (V_s/v_s)^{0.22}} \tag{8-65}$$

From this it can be seen that the required flow rate of the wash water to obtain a given expansion will depend upon the settling velocity of the particles at the operating temperature.

    Stratified Beds. For stratified beds, expansion takes place successively for the different layers. The upper strata will be expanded at lower rates of backwash than the lower ones. The bed will be fully expanded when Eq. 8-62 is satisfied for the largest particles.

    The relative expansion of the bed can be determined by

$$L_e = L(1 - e) \sum \frac{x}{1 - e_e} \tag{8-66}$$

where x is the fraction by weight of particles having a particular expanded porosity e_e. The value of e_e is obtained by using Eq. 8-61.

EXAMPLE 8-6. Using the data given in Example 8-5, find (a) the backwash rate required to expand the bed, (b) the head loss, and (c) the depth of the expanded bed. For this filter, $e = 0.40$, $L = 24$ in., and $T = 50°F$. A sieve analysis of the sand is given in Table 8-4. Assume the specific gravity of the sand grains is 2.65.

TABLE 8-4
SIEVE ANALYSIS AND COMPUTATIONS FOR EXAMPLE 8-6

1	2	3	4	5	6
Sieve Number	Percentage of Sand Retained, $100 \times$	Geometric Mean Size, d, ft $\times 10^3$	Settling Velocity v_s, ft/sec $\times 10^2$	Porosity of Expanded Bed, e_e	$\dfrac{x}{1 - e_e}$
14–20	1.10	3.28	46.3	0.378	0.0177
20–28	6.60	2.29	30.6	0.414	0.1125
28–32	15.94	1.77	22.7	0.443	0.287
32–35	18.60	1.51	18.9	0.460	0.344
35–42	19.10	1.25	15.3	0.483	0.370
42–48	17.60	1.05	12.8	0.502	0.353
48–60	14.30	0.88	10.2	0.521	0.299
60–65	5.10	0.75	8.1	0.555	0.1145
65–100	1.66	0.59	6.4	0.585	0.040

$$\sum \frac{x}{1 - e_e} = 1.9377$$

Solution:

1. Columns 1 to 3 are data provided on the sand filter.

2. To determine the backwash rate, it is necessary to first compute the settling velocity of the largest particle. This is accomplished by using the equation

$$v_s = \left(\frac{4}{3} \frac{g}{C_D} \frac{\rho_s - \rho}{\rho} d \right)^{1/2} \qquad [8\text{-}24]$$

and a relationship between C_D and Re for Reynolds numbers between 1.9 and 500 (the normal range for this type of problem). The relationship is[5]

$$C_D = \frac{18.5}{Re^{0.6}} \qquad (8\text{-}67)$$

By setting $(\rho_s - \rho)/\rho = S_g - 1$, where S_g is the specific gravity of the particles, and by substituting Eq. 8-67 in Eq. 8-24, the following relationship between v_s and d is obtained:

$$v_s = 313 d^{1.14}$$

For the maximum-size particle this yields

$$v_s = 313(3.28 \times 10^{-3})^{1.14} \qquad \text{and} \qquad v_s = 46.3 \times 10^{-2} \text{ ft/sec}$$

The backwash rate is then obtained by using

$$V_s = v_s e^{4.5} \qquad [8\text{-}62]$$

for the largest particle. Thus

$$V_s = 0.463(0.40)^{4.5}$$
$$= 7.42 \times 10^{-3} \text{ ft/sec}$$
$$= 0.45 \text{ ft/min}$$

3. The head loss is computed using Eq. 8-60 after substituting $(1 - e)L$ for $(1 - e_e)L_e$, an equivalent expression as shown in Eq. 8-64.

$$h_L = L \frac{\rho_s - \rho}{\rho} (1 - e) \qquad \text{[8-60]}$$
$$= L(S_g - 1)(1 - e)$$
$$= 2.0(1.65)(1 - 0.40)$$
$$= 1.98 \text{ ft}$$

4. Column 4 values are computed using the expression $v_s = 313d^{1.14}$.
5. Compute column 5 values using Eq. 8-61.
6. The depth of the expanded bed is found by using

$$L_e = L(1 - e) \sum \frac{x}{1 - e_e} \qquad \text{[8-66]}$$
$$= 2.0(1 - 0.4) \times 1.9377$$
$$= 2.32 \text{ ft}$$

8-23. DESIGN OF FILTER UNITS

In designing a filter unit it is necessary that consideration be given to the capacity of the filter unit, the volumetric dimensions of the unit, the placement of wash-water troughs, the depth of filter medium and gravel layer, the underdrainage system, and various associated equipment or filter appartenances.

The Filter Capacity. Operating rates for rapid-sand-filter plants have been essentially duplicated from plant to plant in the last fifty years. This has been due largely to a lack of knowledge of the performance of filters operated over a wider range of loads. In addition, where the public health is concerned there is a hesitancy to break with proven tradition. Normally, gravity filters are designed to operate at some multiple or fraction of 1 mgpd so that accessories (meters, flow controllers, etc.), which are generally standardized for these rates, can be used. Past practice has been to design rapid sand filters to operate at a load of about 2 gpm/sq ft. More recent trends have been toward higher rates however, and Chicago has reported rates up to 5 gpm/sq ft.[40] It is expected that future designs will follow this trend.

Length, Width, and Depth of the Filter Unit. Rapid filter units are usually rectangular in shape with an average length-to-width ratio of about 1.25. The surface area of a filter unit commonly ranges from about 450 to 4,500 sq ft. The choice of a rectangular section is based primarily on the optimum utilization of space and on the most efficient system of piping between filter units. These criteria must be evaluated individually for each specific design and thus only a general guide can be given. In the final analysis, economic considerations (dependent largely on piping) will dictate the choice.

The depth of the filter unit should be as small as possible for maximum economy. Essentially, depth is controlled by the minimum permissible distance from the filter bottom to the freeboard required above the wash-water trough or by the maximum operating head of the filter. Usually the overall depth of a filter unit will be in excess of 8 ft.

Depth of Filter Medium. Theoretically, the thickness of the filter medium should be based on the depth to which impurities will penetrate the filter during a prescribed mode of operation. This depth is generally a function of the characteristics of the materials which are to be removed by filtration and the manner in which these materials react to removal by filtration. Rate of filtration, grain size and manner of stratification, porosity of the filter medium, water temperature, and final head loss all affect the removal reaction.

Usually water which is applied to rapid sand filters has been coagulated and settled previously. Under these circumstances the load applied to the filter can be expressed reasonably in terms of the percentage of iron or aluminum present in the water. Without pretreatment, an adequate quantitative measure of the load usually can not be made.

Hudson, Stanley, and others have developed empirical relationships for determining the depth of penetration of various flocs for several conditions of operation.[43,44] These relationships are limited in applicability, however, and additional studies are required. This paucity of information on the reaction of filters to various load conditions explains to a large extent why depths of filter materials have not varied significantly in past years. Common depths of filter sand and gravel have already been presented in Sec. 8-20.

Wash-Water Troughs. Wash-water troughs are placed above the filter sand to remove the soiled water released from the filter during the backwash operation. These troughs are constructed in a variety of cross sections. Materials commonly used include concrete, steel, cast iron, aluminum, and asbestos cement.

The arrangement of the wash-water gutters varies but it is considered good practice to restrict the horizontal flow distance to 3 ft or less for any one gutter. Edge-to-edge distances of parallel gutters should therefore not exceed 6 ft. An important consideration is that the overflow weirs along the gutter edges be level and that all troughs be set at the same elevation. The weir along the edge of the trough should be set far enough above the sand to preclude loss of fine sand during the backwash operation. At the same time, it should not be set so high that a considerable quantity of dirty water is left in the filter after washing. Normally the weir should be slightly above the maximum expanded depth of the sand as determined by test or application of Eq. 8-65 or Eq. 8-66. The bottom of the wash-water trough should be at least 2 in. above the unexpanded bed. An approximate method for setting the wash-water trough is to set the weir above the surface of the unexpanded bed a distance equal to the rise of the wash water in 1 min.

The cross-sectional area of the gutter is determined by considering the weirs along the edges of the troughs to act as side-channel spillways. Theoretical and empirical approaches to this problem are available in the literature.[3,5,34] Figs. 8-16, 8-17, and 8-18 illustrate some typical gutter cross sections and settings for wash-water troughs.

Filter Underdrainage. Underdrainage systems serve the dual purpose of furnishing an outlet for the filtered water and providing a means for distributing wash water during cleaning operations. It is very important that the rate of removal of filtered water be uniform over the entire filter bottom and that the backwash water be distributed uniformly as well. Since backwash rates are considerably greater than filtration rates, they govern the design of underdrainage systems. Several types of underdrainage systems are in use today. They may be categorized generally as perforated-pipe, pipe and strainer, vitrified-tile block with orifices, porous plates, and precast concrete underdrains. Detailed information on the various types of underdrainage systems may be found in the manufacturer's literature and elsewhere.[34] Figure 8-17 illustrates a typical layout of a system of perforated-pipe laterals. Fair and Geyer discuss the determination of head loss in a perforated-pipe underdrainage system.[3]

The uniform distribution of wash water may be had by maintaining high head losses in orifices or by using porous plates or clay blocks to form a double bottom. If pipe lateral systems are used, about 15 psi pressure should be maintained at the orifices or strainers and flow velocities should not exceed about 8 or 10 fps. In general, 6- to 12-in. spacings of laterals will yield satisfactory results. Laterals should not be longer than about 60 diameters if uniform pressure and equal distribution of flows are to be maintained. Normally, the total orifice area should be approximately 0.2 to 0.3 percent of the filter surface area. Orifices in perforated pipes are commonly $\frac{1}{4}$ to $\frac{1}{2}$ in. in diameter and are spaced from about 3 to 8 in. apart. For $\frac{1}{4}$-in. orifices the lateral cross-sectional area should total about twice the total orifice area. For $\frac{1}{2}$-in. orifices the lateral cross-sectional area should be approximately 4 times the orifice area.

Headers supplying the underdrainage system should deliver the required wash-water flow at a velocity of about 6 to 8 fps. The cross-sectional area of the header is usually about $1\frac{1}{2}$ times the total orifice area.

Other Equipment.   Other equipment associated with the filtration of water includes gate valves, metering devices, flow-rate controllers, surface washing equipment, loss-of-head gages, and wash-water controllers. Figure 8-16 indicates a typical rapid-sand-filter unit showing the piping layout and placement of some of the filter appurtenances. Information on most of the items is readily available from numerous manufacturers.

8-24.   OPERATION OF A RAPID SAND FILTER

As previously indicated, a rapid sand filter is operated at some prescribed rate until the head loss developed becomes excessive.   Usually this is about 8 or 9 ft.   At maximum operating head it is normal for the lower portion of the filter to be under a partial vacuum.   When this occurs, the piezometric level in the underdrainage system is below the bottom of the sand layer.   This negative head permits the release of dissolved gases which tend to fill the pores of the filter bed.   This condition, known as *air binding*, reduces filter capacity.   Once a negative head has been established it becomes undesirable to operate the filter and backwashing is prescribed.   Under average operating conditions, most rapid sand filters are backwashed about once in 24 hr.   About 5 to 10 min are usually required to backwash the filter.   An additional run to waste of about 3 to 5 min is common.   The amount of water used in backwashing varies but is usually about 4 percent of the filtered water.

Figure 8-19 can be used to illustrate the normal operating procedure for a rapid-sand-filter-plant.   Initially valves 1 and 4 are opened and valves 2, 3, and 5 are closed. This permits filtration to proceed. Water flows from the sedimentation tank to the filter and passes through the filter to storage in the clear well.   From the clear well, water is distributed to the consumer. After the operating-head loss becomes excessive, valves 1, 3, and 4 are closed and valves 2 and 5 are opened to permit backwashing.   Water then flows from the wash-water storage tank to the underdrainage system of the filter where it is distributed upward through the filter medium. The dirty wash water is collected by the wash-water troughs and then passes out of the filter to the drain. If a portion of the water at the beginning of filtration is to be wasted, valves 1 and 3 are opened and the remaining valves are kept closed. This sequence is then repeated for every cycle of the operation.

8-25.   FILTRATION EFFICIENCY

Suspended matter, color, and bacteria can be removed by filtration, although the actual degree of removal often depends on the processes

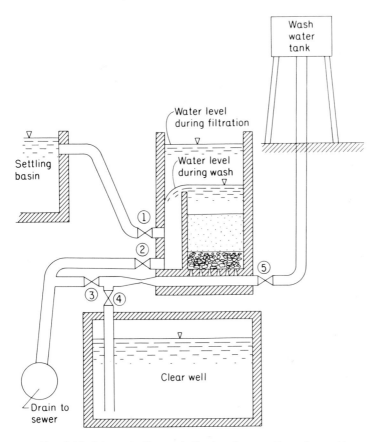

Fig. 8-19. Schematic diagram indicating the operation of a rapid sand filter.

which precede the filtration unit. For example, slow sand filtration alone will usually remove about 30 percent of the natural color in water, whereas a colorless water can be produced if adequate flocculation and sedimentation are also employed. The removal of turbidity is effectively accomplished by sand filters provided proper attention is given to coagulation and sedimentation. Large microorganisms such as algae and diatoms are effectively removed by filtration. The tastes and odor associated with these are in general not removed unless special taste- and odor-control operations are employed (see Chap. 12). Amoebic cysts are of sufficient size to be retained in the filter media under normal conditions. The *cercariae* of the blood flukes, on the other hand, have been found to be capable of moving themselves through sand filters of standard depth.

The efficiency of a sand filter for removing bacteria is dependent on a variety of factors. These include the degree of flocculation and sedimenta-

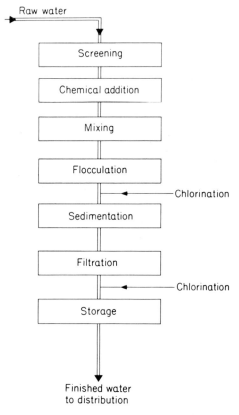

Raw water

Screening

Chemical addition

Mixing

Flocculation

Chlorination

Sedimentation

Filtration

Chlorination

Storage

Finished water
to distribution

Fɪɢ. 8-20. Water-treatment plant flow diagram.

tion, prechlorination, presedimentation, and the concentration of the organisms in the water to be treated. If the raw water is subjected to flocculation, sedimentation, and chlorination (Chap. 12), average most probable number (MPN) coliform counts of about 5,000 per 100 ml can be adequately handled. Where MPN counts range from 5,000 to 20,000 per 100 ml, prechlorination, presettling, and postchlorination are commonly required. If the MPN count exceeds about 20,000 per 100 ml, protracted storage and other measures will be needed. For the lower ranges of bacterial loading, rapid sand filters have been found to have a high removal efficiency (about 90 to 99 percent).[45] Adequate chlorination should follow filtration under all conditions of operation.

The bacterial content of effluent waters as related to the bacterial content of influent waters has been determined by the U. S. Public Service as

$$Y = CX^n \qquad (8\text{-}68)$$

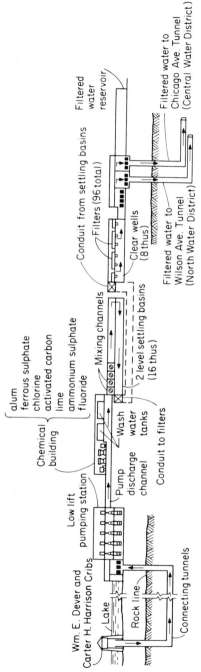

FIG. 8-21. The Chicago Water Filtration Plant. (*Civil Engineering*, March 1958.)

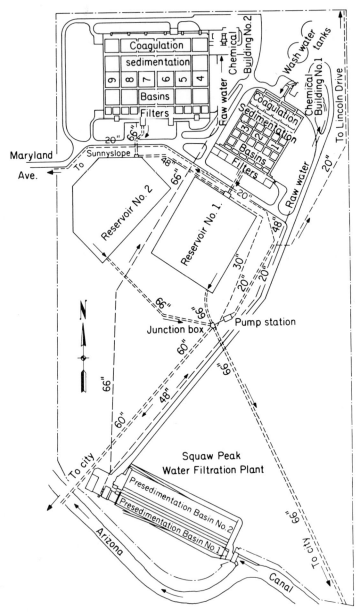

Fig. 8-22. Layout of Squaw Peak filtration plant showing canal and treatment units. (*Public Works*, December, 1961.)

where Y = bacterial quality of the effluent water
      X = quality of the influent water
C and n = constants[46]

Tables showing the removal of bacteria by various water-treatment-unit operations are available in the literature.[3,34]

SOME UNIT PROCESS SEQUENCES

To give the student a feeling for the manner in which some of the unit processes previously discussed might be related or coordinated in practice, several illustrations (Figs. 8-20 to 8-22) showing unit-process sequences are presented here. It should be clearly understood that these are not to be construed as "typical" plant sequences which should be studied as model packages. They represent, rather, the manner in which certain operations might be combined to provide a particular service. Many possible combinations of the foregoing unit processes are possible and the designer must select the optimum combination for a given set of circumstances.

REFERENCES

1. Harold E. Babbitt and R. E. Baumann, *Sewerage and Sewage Treatment*, 8th ed. (New York: John Wiley and Sons, Inc., 1958).
2. O. Kirschmer, "Untersuchungen uber den Gefallsverlust an Rechen" (translated by R. Oldenbourg), *Trans. Hydraulic Inst.*, vol. 21 (1926).
3. G. M. Fair and J. C. Geyer, *Water Supply and Waste-Water Disposal* (New York: John Wiley and Sons, Inc., 1961).
4. R. E. Greenhalgh, Ronald L. Johnson, and Howard D. Nott, "Mixing in Continuous Reactors," *Chem. Eng. Progr.*, vol. 55 (February 1959), pp. 44–48.
5. Linvil G. Rich, *Unit Operations of Sanitary Engineering* (New York: John Wiley and Sons, Inc., 1961).
6. Harold A. Thomas and Ralph S. Archibald, "Longitudinal Mixing Measured by Radioactive Tracers," *Trans. Am. Soc. Civil Engrs.*, vol. 117 (1952), pp. 839–856.
7. "Mixers and Mixing," Infilco Inc., Bull. 730-5430.
8. S. L. Tolman, "The Mechanics of Mixing and Flocculation," *Public Works* (December 1962).
9. Neill Drobny, "Effect of Paddle Design on Flocculation," *J. Sanit. Eng., Div., Proc. Am. Soc. Civil Engrs.*, vol. 89, no. SA2, Part I (1963).
10. T. R. Camp, "Flocculation and Flocculation Basins," *Trans. Am. Soc. Civil Engrs.*, vol. 120 (1955).
11. E. R. Gilliland and E. A. Mason, "Gas Mixing in Beds of Fluidized Solids," *Ind. Eng. Chem.*, vol. 44 (1952).
12. J. H. Rushton and J. Y. Oldshue, "Mixing of Liquids," *Chem. Eng. Progr. Symp. Series*, vol. 55, no. 25 (1959).
13. J. H. Rushton, E. W. Costich, and H. J. Evert, "Power Characteristics of Mixing Impellers, Part I," *Chem. Eng. Progr.*, vol. 46 (1950).
14. H. L. Langhaar, *Dimensional Analysis and Theory of Models* (New York: John Wiley and Sons, Inc., 1960).

15. T. R. Camp and P. C. Stein, "Velocity Gradients and Internal Work in Fluid Motion," *J. Boston Soc. Civil Engrs.*, vol. 30 (1943).

16. Elwood L. Beam, "Study of Physical Factors Affecting Flocculation," *Water Works Eng.* (January 1953).

17. Reuben M. Olson, *Essentials of Engineering Fluid Mechanics* (Scranton, Pa.: International Textbook Co., 1961).

18. W. P. Talmadge and E. B. Fitch, "Determining Thickener Unit Areas," *Ind. Eng. Chem.*, vol. 47 (January 1955).

19. S. L. Tolman, "Sedimentation Basin Design and Operation," *Public Works* (June 1963).

20. J. M. Coulson and J. F. Richardson, *Chemical Engineering*, Vol. II (New York: McGraw-Hill Book Co., Inc., 1955).

21. R. A. Fiedler and E. B. Fitch, "Appraising Basin Performance from Dye Test Results," *Sewage Ind. Wastes*, vol. 31, no. 9 (1959).

22. E. B. Fitch, "Flow Path Effect on Sedimentation," *Sewage Ind. Wastes*, vol. 28, no. 1 (January 1956).

23. T. R. Camp, "Studies of Sedimentation Basin Design," *Sewage Ind. Wastes*, vol. 25, no. 1 (January 1953).

24. E. B. Fitch, "The Significance of Detention in Sedimentation," *Sewage Ind. Wastes*, vol. 29, no. 10 (1957).

25. Arthur B. Morrill, "Sedimentation Basin Research and Design," *J. Am. Water Works Assoc.*, vol. 24 (1932).

26. E. B. Fitch and W. A. Lutz, "Feedwells for Density Stabilization," *J. Water Pollution Control Federation*, vol. 32, no. 2 (1960).

27. A. C. Ingersoll, J. E. McKee, and N. H. Brooks, "Fundamental Concepts of Rectangular Settling Tanks," *Trans. Am. Soc. Civil Engrs.*, vol. 121 (1956).

28. A. C. Ingersoll, J. E. McKee, and N. H. Brooks, "Filtration," *Water Quality and Treatment*, 2d ed. (New York: American Water Works Association, 1950), Chap. 11.

29. T. R. Camp, "Theory of Water Filtration," *J. Sanit. Engr. Div., Am. Soc. Civil Engrs.*, vol. 90, no. SA4, Part I (August 1964).

30. G. Kozeny, *Sitzber. Akad. Wiss. Wien, Math-Naturw. Kl. Abt.* IIa, vol. 136 (1927).

31. P. C. Carman, *Trans. Inst. Chem. Engrs.* (*London*), vol. 15 (1937).

32. Sabri Ergun, *Chem. Eng. Progr.*, vol. 48 (1952).

33. H. E. Rose, "On the Resistance Coefficient-Reynolds Number Relationship for Fluid Flow Through a Bed of Granular Material," *Proc. Inst. Mech. Engrs.* (*London*) (1945), p. 153 and (1949), pp. 154, 160.

34. Harold E. Babbitt, James J. Doland, and John L. Cleasby, *Water Supply Engineering*, 6th ed. (New York: McGraw-Hill Book Co., Inc., 1962).

35. Anonymous, "The Filtration of Water," Johns-Manville Co., New York, Publ. FA-74A 11-61 (1961).

36. Anonymous, *Microstraining* (New York: Glenfield and Kennedy, Inc., 1956).

37. P. L. Boucher and G. R. Evans, "Microstraining Description and Application," *Water Sewage Works* (November 1962).

38. Allen Hazen, "On Sedimentation," *Trans. Am. Soc. Civil Engrs.*, vol. 53 (1904).

39. Committee Report, "Filter Sand for Water Purification Practice," *J. Am. Water Works Assoc.* (August 1953).

40. Anonymous, "High-Rate Water Filtration Meeting Practical Tests at Chicago," *Eng. News-Record* (July 1947).

41. R. Mounsey, "Sand and Fine Coal Compared for Water Filtering," *American City* (May 1953).

42. P. C. Carman, "Fluid Flow Through Granular Beds," *Trans. Inst. Chem. Engrs.* (*London*), vol. 15 (1937).

43. H. E. Hudson, "Factors Affecting Filtration Rates," *J. Am. Water Works Assoc.*, vol. 48 (1956).

44. D. R. Stanley, "Penetration of Floc into Sand Filters," thesis (Harvard University, Cambridge, Mass., 1952).

45. W. A. Hardenbergh and E. R. Rodie, *Water Supply and Waste Disposal* (Scranton, Pa.: International Textbook Co., 1961).

46. *U.S. Public Health Service*, Bull. 172 (1927), Bull. 193 (1929).

47. D. J. O'Connor and W. W. Eckenfelder, Jr., "Solid-Liquid Separation and Anaerobic Digestion," in Joseph McCabe and W. W. Eckenfelder, Jr. (eds.), *Biological Treatment of Sewage and Industrial Waste*, vol. 2 (New York: Reinhold Publishing Corp., 1958).

PROBLEMS

8-1. A bank of medium screens are to be used to aid in the removal of solids from a municipal sewage flow. If the discharge is 25 mgpd, approximately how many cubic feet of solids will be removed?

8-2. Make a sketch of (a) a hand-cleaned inclined rack, (b) a mechanically cleaned movable screen, and (c) a mechanically cleaned rack.

8-3. Find the head lost through a rack inclined at 45 degrees to the horizontal. The bars are sharp-edged rectangular, $1/4$ in. wide, and are clear-spaced 2 in. apart. The channel approach velocity is 2.5 fps.

8-4. For an instantaneous conversion of 85 percent, find the required holding time if Fig. 8-1 applies.

8-5. A diffused air system is used to accomplish flocculation in a water treatment plant. If 1,000 cfs of free air is supplied at the bottom of the tanks at a pressure of 8 psi, what will be the power input?

8-6. A flocculator is designed to handle 5 mgpd of water. The reactor is 10 ft deep and has a volume of 9,000 cu ft. The water temperature is 50°F and 500 cfm of free air are provided. Find (a) the theoretical retention time, (b) the mean velocity gradient G, and (c) the power input. Does this flocculator fall within the prescribed limits for satisfactory performance?

8-7. A water-treatment plant is designed to process 20 mgpd of water. The flocculator must be 15 ft deep to accommodate mechanical equipment. There are to be four horizontal-shaft paddle flocculators installed. Assume the mean flow velocity is 28 percent of the paddle velocity and $C_D = 1.9$. Design the flocculation tank and paddles. Also determine the value of *G* and evaluate the performance of the flocculator system. Water temperature is 50°F.

8-8. A fine sand particle 0.10 mm in diameter settles 1 ft in 38 sec at a water temperature of 50°F. Compute the Reynolds number and find out if Stokes' law is applicable.

8-9. A fine sand particle has a diameter of 0.08 mm. If the water temperature is 50°F, the specific gravity of the sand is 2.65, and Stokes' law applies, find the settling velocity of the particle.

8-10. A settling-column analysis is performed on a dilute suspension of discrete particles. Data collected from samples taken at the 5-ft depth are as follows:

Time required to settle 5 ft, minutes	0.7	1.2	2.3	4.6	6.3	8.8
Portion of particles with velocities less than those indicated	0.58	0.49	0.34	0.16	0.07	0.03

Find the overall removal if the overflow or clarification rate of the basin is 0.09 ft/sec.

8-11. Discuss how you would go about designing a rectangular sedimentation basin. What information would you need? How would you use this information?

8-12. If a rectangular sedimentation basin is modified by adding two trays or false bottoms at one-third and two-thirds of the total depth, and if the rate of flow through the tank remains unchanged, what will be the new removal ratio?

8-13. Use the data below on interface height vs. time to find the minimum acceptable surface area of the clarifier. The influent solids concentration is 0.168 lb/cu ft and is settled in a continuous flow unit operated at a rate of 1.2 cfs. The desired underflow concentration is 0.80 lb/cu ft.

Interface height, feet	5.0	4.0	3.0	2.3	1.8	1.4	1.15	1.0	.95
Time, minutes	0	2.6	5.0	5.4	10.0	15.0	20.0	25.0	30.0

8-14. A rectangular sedimentation basin or basins is to be used to treat 5 mgpd of a waste containing granular solids. The basin depth must be 10 ft and the recommended surface loading is not to exceed 1500 gpd/sq ft. What will be the basin dimensions and theoretical retention time?

8-15. A sedimentation basin outflow of 1.5 mgpd is to be discharged over a sharp-crested weir into a horizontal rectangular outlet trough 16 in. wide. How deep must the trough be so that the weir discharge will be free? Assume the outflow from the trough drops to a lower elevation so there is no backwater effect.

8-16. A water-treatment plant is to process approximately 23 mgpd. About how many slow sand filters would be required? How many rapid sand filters? What would be the size of each unit and the surface loading?

8-17. Water is to be filtered through 18 in. of uniform sand having a porosity of 0.42 and a grain diameter of 0.9×10^{-3} ft. Assume spherical particles and a water temperature of 55°F. The surfaee loading is 2.5 gpm/sq ft. Find the head loss using the Carmen-Kozeny equation.

8-18. Solve Prob. 8-17 using the Rose equation.

8-19. What will be the head loss in Prob. 8-17 if a particle shape factor of 0.82 is introduced?

8-20. Find the initial head loss in a rapid sand filter which is 20 in. deep and has a porosity of 0.42. Assume a water temperature of 55°F and a filtration rate of 2 gpm/sq ft. Consider spherical particles. The sieve analysis is given below. Use the Carmen-Kozeny equation.

SIEVE ANALYSIS FOR PROB. 8-20

Sieve Number	Percentage of Sand Retained	Geometric Mean Size, d, ft × 10^3
14–20	1.05	3.28
20–28	6.65	2.29
28–32	15.70	1.77
32–35	18.84	1.51
35–42	18.98	1.25
42–48	17.72	1.05
48–60	14.25	0.88
60–65	5.15	0.75
65–100	1.66	0.59
	100.00	

8-21. Solve Prob. 8-20 using the Rose equation.

8-22. Solve Prob. 8-20 if the water temperature is 45°F and ϕ = 0.95.

8-23. Solve Prob. 8-20 if the water temperature is 60°F and ϕ = 0.95.

8-24. Consider the expansion of a bed of uniform particles 20 in. thick. The porosity of the bed is 0.40 and the water temperature is 50°F. The specific gravity of the particles is 2.65. Find (a) the upflow velocity need to just open the bed and (b) the head lost in expanding the bed.

8-25. Use the sieve analysis given in Prob. 8-20 and find (a) the backwash rate required to expand the bed, (b) the head loss, and (c) the depth of the expanded bed. Assume porosity = 0.43, L = 24 in., and T = 50°F. Specific gravity of the particles = 2.65.

8-26. Solve Prob. 8-25 if the depth of the unexpanded bed is 20 in. and T = 55°F.

8-27. For a rapid sand filter which is 20 × 25 ft, design a perforated-pipe-lateral underdrainage system. Use a sketch and indicate pipe sizes, spacing, orifice sizes, and orifice spacing.

8-28. By consulting the literature, wirte a brief paper discussing the application of screening devices in some existing treatment plant.

8-29. By consulting the literature, write a paper discussing the application of settling basins in some existing treatment plant.

8-30. Write a paper describing a modern water-filtration plant. Sketch the flow sequence and unit processes. Label all operations.

8-31. Discuss the factors that should be considered before selecting any of the unit operations in this chapter for inclusion in a treatment plant design.

chapter 9

Chemical-Treatment Processes

The preceding chapter covered treatment systems that involved physical and mechanical properties. The present chapter is concerned with chemical reactions common to water and waste-treatment processes. The treatment of water and wastes is a synthesis of a number of different operations. Many chemical-treatment techniques are not ends in themselves but ancillary to other treatment methods. Coagulation prepares water or waste for sedimentation. Precipitation must be followed by sedimentation and sometimes also by coagulation and filtration. Adjustment of pH is necessary for chemical reactions, disinfection, and for optimizing biological activity. Each water or waste must be carefully analyzed and a series of unit processes engineered to produce economically the desired end result.

WATER STABILIZATION

9-1. CHEMICAL EQUILIBRIA

The quality of a water or waste depends to a considerable extent upon its content of dissolved substances. An understanding of the chemical equilibria and reaction velocities involved in aqueous solutions is essential for a rational attack on water- and waste-treatment problems.

There are many points of similarity between chemical and physical equilibria, although in the latter no chemical changes take place. The physical equilibrium between ice and water is familiar. Ice and water can exist in contact with each other at 0°C. If the container could be completely insulated so that no heat entered or escaped, the solid and liquid forms of water could be kept together indefinitely. Ice melts and water freezes at 0°C and it is apparent that both processes can occur simultaneously within the insulated system.

$$\text{Ice} \rightleftharpoons \text{water} \qquad (9\text{-}1)$$

Molecules of water are transferred from the solid to the liquid state and from the liquid to the solid state at the same rate. Any spontaneously reversible chemical reaction can reach a state of equilibrium in which the forward and reverse reactions proceed at equal speeds. The principles which govern the behavior of molecules engaged in physical or chemical equilibria apply equally to those equilibria in which ions participate. Ionic equilibria, like molecular equilibria, are subject to shifting under the influence of certain stress. An equation indicating the low concentration of ions in pure water has been given in Chap. 7.

$$H_2O \rightleftharpoons H^+ + OH^- \tag{9-2}$$

At room temperature approximately one water molecule in 300 million is withdrawn from the molecular state by the ionization reaction. The scarcity of the ions suggests that the forward reaction is a less probable reaction than the reverse reaction, between ions. It so happens that the collisions between the ions, which occur much less often than collisions between water molecules, are much more fruitful of reaction. It is useful to know the rates of these reactions.

$$\text{Rate of reaction} = k[H^+] \times [OH^-] \tag{9-3}$$

where k is a proportionality constant which takes into account the possibility that not every collision between ions or molecules is fruitful of reaction.

Several simultaneous equilibria can exist in a solution. In the system outlined below, gaseous carbon dioxide is in equilibrium with carbon dioxide dissolved in the water. A portion of the dissolved gas reacts with water to form carbonic acid, H_2CO_3, which in turn ionizes.

$$CO_2 \text{ (gas)} \rightleftharpoons CO_2 \text{ (solution)} \tag{9-4}$$

$$CO_2 \text{ (solution)} + H_2O \rightleftharpoons H_2CO_3 \tag{9-5}$$

$$H_2CO_3 \rightleftharpoons H^+ + HCO_3^- \tag{9-6}$$

$$HCO_3^- \rightleftharpoons H^+ + CO_3^{--} \tag{9-7}$$

The equilibrium of Eq. 9-4 is physical since the solubility of the gas in water is determined by the pressure under which the gas is contained. The other three equilibria involve reversible chemical reactions which do not proceed very far toward completion. The equilibria can be disturbed in several ways. If the pressure on the carbon dioxide above the solution is increased, the concentration of carbon dioxide in solution is increased and all of the reactions shift to the right. The end result is a higher concentration of carbonate ions.

The equilibria can also be disturbed by introducing a number of hydrogen ions into the solution. A few milliliters of any strong acid will suffice. The equilibria in both Eq. 9-7 and Eq. 9-6 will then shift to the left and more H_2CO_3 will be formed. This will cause the equilibrium in Eq. 9-5 to shift to the left, with the formation of more dissolved CO_2. The solubility of CO_2 will be exceeded and the end result will be the evolution of carbon dioxide from solution. This can be demonstrated by noting the strong effervescence which results from the addition of a few drops of hydrochloric acid to carbonated water.

It is often useful to remove one product of a reversible reaction. The removal can be effected by forcing the desirable reaction to completion with the formation of an insoluble solid, a relatively insoluble gas, or a nonionized product.

The law of mass action indicates that for a reversible reaction at equilibrium at a fixed temperature.

$$aA + bB \rightleftharpoons cC + dD \tag{9-8}$$

the product of the concentrations of the reaction products divided by the product of the concentrations of the reactants (each concentration being raised to a power equal to the coefficient of the substance in the balanced equation for the reversible reaction) is a constant:

$$\frac{[C]^c [D]^d}{[A]^a [B]^b} = K \tag{9-9}$$

Here A and B are molecular or ionic species called the reactants, and C and D are molecular or ionic species called the products of the reaction. The small letters, a, b, c, and d, are coefficients in the balanced equation for the reaction, and K is the equilibrium constant of the reversible reaction. The brackets indicate activities of the enclosed substances.

In dilute nonelectrolyte solutions as normally experienced in water and waste treatment, the activities in Eq. 9-9 may be replaced by the molar concentrations. In more precise work and with most electrolyte solutions, activities must be used. The activity of an ionic solution is related to the concentration by

$$a = fc \tag{9-10}$$

where c = the concentration in gram-mole/liter
f = activity coefficient

An approximate value of the activity coefficient for ionic concentrations normally encountered in environmental engineering may be obtained from the equation[1]

$$-\log f = 0.5Z^2 \frac{\sqrt{N}}{1 + \sqrt{N}} \tag{9-11}$$

where Z = the magnitude of the ion's charge
N = the ionic strength
Equation 9-11 is useful for all types of ions up to about 0.1 ionic strength. This corresponds to 6,000 mg/l of sodium chloride.

The effective concentration of each ion is generally less than its molar concentration because of the presence of other ions. The effective ionic strength N of a solution is defined as

$$N = 0.5 \sum_{1}^{i} C_i Z_i^2 \tag{9-12}$$

where C_i = the concentration of the ith species of the ion expressed in gram moles/liter

Z_i = the magnitude of the charge on the specific ion

Figure 9-1 gives values of f calculated from Eq. 9-11 for ions with charges of 1, 2, and 3. Table 9-1 lists some of the solubility products common to water and waste treatment.

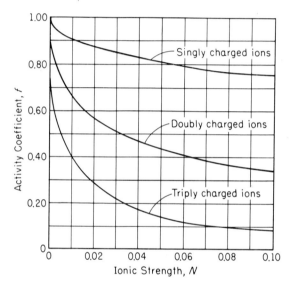

FIG. 9-1. Activity coefficients as a function of ionic strength.

EXAMPLE 9-1. Compute the solubility of $CaSO_4$ in water at 25°C if the composition of the solution is such that the activity coefficient f is unity and (a) if the hardness of the water is zero and (b) if the water contains 200 mg/l of calcium hardness.

Solution: (a) From Table 9-1, $K_s = 2.4 \times 10^{-5}$

$$[Ca^{++}][SO_4^{=}] = K_s = 2.4 \times 10^{-5}$$

In the zero-hardness water, $[Ca^{++}] = [SO_4^{=}]$; therefore

$$[Ca^{++}] = \sqrt{2.4 \times 10^{-5}} = 4.9 \times 10^{-3}\,\text{mole/1}$$

$$4.9 \times 10^{-3} \times \frac{136}{10^{-3}} = 666\,\text{mg/1 as } CaSO_4$$

TABLE 9-1
SOLUBILITY OF SOME SLIGHTLY SOLUBLE SUBSTANCES AT 25°C

Substance	Ion Product	K_s
$Al(OH)_3$	$[Al^{+++}][OH^-]^3$	1.9×10^{-33}
$Fe(OH)_2$	$[Fe^{++}][OH^-]^2$	1.65×10^{-15}
$Fe(OH)_3$	$[Fe^{+++}][OH^-]^3$	4×10^{-38}
$FeCO_3$	$[Fe^{++}][CO_3^=]$	2.11×10^{-11}
FeS	$[Fe^{++}][S^=]$	1.0×10^{-19}
$Ca(OH)_2$	$[Ca^{++}][OH^-]^2$	7.9×10^{-6}
$CaCO_3$	$[Ca^{++}][CO_3^=]$	4.82×10^{-9}
$CaSO_4$	$[Ca^{++}][SO_4^=]$	2.4×10^{-5}
$MgCO_3$	$[Mg^{++}][CO_3^=]$	1×10^{-5}
CaF_2	$[Ca^{++}][F^-]^2$	3.9×10^{-11}

SOME OTHER EQUILIBRIUM EXPRESSIONS AT 25°C

Substance	Ion Product	Equilibrium Constant
H_2O	$[H^+][OH^-]$	$K_w = 1.0 \times 10^{-14}$
H_2S	$\dfrac{[H^+][HS^-]}{[H_2S]}$	$K_1 = 1.1 \times 10^{-7}$
HS^-	$\dfrac{[H^+][S^=]}{[HS^-]}$	$K_2 = 1 \times 10^{-14}$
$CO_2 + H_2O$	$\dfrac{[H^+][HCO_3^-]}{[H_2CO_3]}$	$K_1 = 4.45 \times 10^{-7}$
HCO_3^-	$\dfrac{[H^+][CO_2^=]}{[HCO_3^-]}$	$K_2 = 4.69 \times 10^{-11}$

(b) In addition to the Ca^{++} from the $CaSO_4$, the 200 mg/l or 2×10^{-3} molar Ca^{++} hardness in the water must be taken into account, so that

$$[2 \times 10^{-3} + (Ca^{++})][SO_4^=] = 2.4 \times 10^{-5}$$

Substituting X for $[Ca^{++}]$ and $[SO_4]$,

$$X^2 + (2X) \times 10^{-3} - 2.4 \times 10^{-5} = 0$$
$$X = 4 \times 10^{-3}$$
$$[Ca^{++}] = 4 \times 10^{-3} \, mole/l$$

or the solubility is equal to

$$4 \times 10^{-3} \times \frac{136}{10^{-3}} = 544 \, mg/l \text{ as } CaSO_4$$

9-2. CARBONATE EQUILIBRIA

Water is considered to be stable when it will neither dissolve nor deposit calcium carbonate. Calcium carbonate must be in equilibrium with the hydrogen-ion concentration in water if deposits of calcium carbonate on the walls of pipes are not to be dissolved or increased. If the pH is raised, the water will dissolve calcium carbonate. When the pH is lowered from the equilibrium point, water will deposit calcium carbonate. A thin coating of calcium carbonate protects metal surfaces from corrosion. Excessive deposition affects the hydraulic efficiency of pipes. Deposits also affect heat transfer in hot-water heaters and boilers. Solid masses of calcium carbonate cemented material can occur in sand filters with adverse effects on operation. The point of the carbonate balance varies with pH, temperature, and chemical characteristics of the water. The equilibrium point can be determined by laboratory test.

Langelier devised an expression to indicate the pH at which water would be in equilibrium with calcium carbonate.[2] The equations developed by Langelier form a basis for the calculation of pH at carbonate saturation (pH_s).

$$pH_s = \log \frac{K_s'}{K_2'} - \log[Ca^{++}] - \log[A] + 6.301 + \log\left(\frac{1 + 2K_2'}{[H^+]}\right) \quad (9\text{-}13)$$

The last term in the equation can be omitted when the pH_s is less than about 9. At values above a pH_s of 9, the last term should be included. If the water contains significant amounts of dissolved solids, the concentration equilibrium constant K_s' must allow for the effective concentrations of the ions (see Eqs. 9-10, 9-11, and 9-12). In Eq. 9-13, $[Ca^{++}]$ and $[A]$ are expressed in gram millequivalents per liter, while $[H^+]$ is expressed in gram-moles per liter. Where the activity equilibrium constants are used, Eq. 9-13 becomes

$$pH_s = 6.301 + \log \frac{K_s}{K_2} - \log[A] - \log[Ca^{++}] + S \quad (9\text{-}14)$$

where

$$S = \frac{2\sqrt{N}}{1 + \sqrt{N}} \quad (9\text{-}15)$$

This is called the *salinity term* and can be evaluated with the use of Eq. 9-12. Where the dissolved solids concentration is known and is less than 500 mg/1, the ionic strength N can be estimated from the following empirical relationship:[1]

$$N = 2.5 \times 10^{-5} C_s \quad (9\text{-}16)$$

where C_s is the dissolved solids concentration in mg/1.

Equations 9-15 and 9-16 were used to establish the relationship pre-

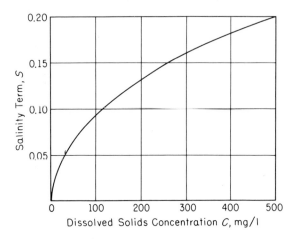

FIG. 9-2. Salinity term as a function of the dissolved solids concentration.

sented in Fig. 9-2. This curve can be used for the estimation of S where the dissolved solids concentration is less than 500 mg/l.

Langelier devised a *saturation index* by substracting the pH_s from the pH of the water and called this index I.[2]

$$I = pH - pH_s \qquad (9\text{-}17)$$

where pH = measured pH of the water

  pH_s = calculated or observed pH at equilibrium

When $I = 0$, the water is in equilibrium. A positive value of I indicates that the water is oversaturated with $CaCO_3$ (or lacking CO_2) and will tend to deposit $CaCO_3$; a negative value indicates that the water is undersaturated with $CaCO_3$ (excess CO_2) and will tend to dissolve existing deposits of $CaCO_3$.

Figure 9-3 shows the variation of equilibrium constants with temperature.

EXAMPLE 9-2. A laboratory analysis of water gives the following information:

Total dissolved solids	210 mg/l
Calcium-ion concentration	1.7 me/l
Total carbonate alkalinity	0.6 me/l
Temperature	20°C
pH	7.4

Determine the condition of the water in relation to the calcium carbonate in solution.

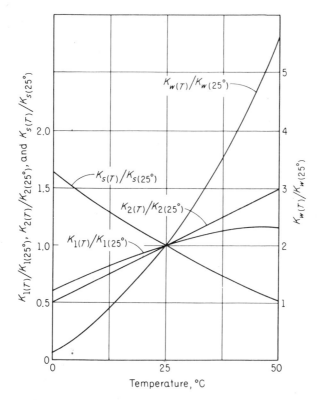

FIG. 9-3. Variation of equilibrium constants with temperature.

Solution:

1. From Table 9-1 and Fig. 9-3, K_s and K_2 at 20°C are

$$K_s = 4.82 \times 10^{-9}(1.10) = 5.30 \times 10^{-9}$$
$$K_2 = 4.69 \times 10^{-11}(0.90) = 4.21 \times 10^{-11}$$

2. From Fig. 9-2, for $C_s = 210$ mg/l, $S = 0.13$
3. Solving Eq. 9-15,

$$pH_s = 6.301 + \log \frac{5.30 \times 10^{-9}}{4.21 \times 10^{-11}} - \log(0.6) - \log(1.7) + 0.13 = 8.5$$

4. From Eq. 9-17,

$$I = pH - pH_s = 7.4 - 8.5 = -1.1$$

The index I has a negative value, therefore the water is undersaturated with respect to calcium carbonate.

The saturation index I may be used to determine the direction a water is out of carbonate balance and to estimate the amount of chemical adjustment necessary to produce equilibrium. This index is used more than any other corrosion index but is is not always dependable. It has not been possible to corroborate through field investigations many of the well-known concepts of corrosion control concerning pH and $CaCO_3$ saturation.[3]

Lime beds for water stabilization have been used for many years on soft waters but the lime chips tend to become dirty and have to be cleaned regularly. Soft waters have been treated with lime dust, acidified, and then stabilized with $Ca(OH)_2$.[4]

9-3. CORROSION

All metal in contact with water is subject to chemical corrosion. The corrosion of metals is a complex and as yet a poorly understood process. In its simplest form corrosion occurs when positive ions enter a solution and combine with negative ions of the water to form a hydroxide.

Anodic reaction

$$4Fe + 2O_2 + 8H_2O \rightleftharpoons 4Fe(OH)_3 + 4H^+ + 4e^- \qquad (9\text{-}18)$$

Cathodic reaction

$$O_2 + 4H^+ + 4e^- \rightarrow 2H_2O \qquad (9\text{-}19)$$

There is a complex mutual interaction of corrosion stimulating and inhibiting factors such as pH, buffer capacity, $CaCO_3$ deposition, alkalinity, and the activity of electrolytic cells.

The mechanism of corrosion is primarily electrochemical in nature, with reactions occurring between metal surfaces and chemicals in the soil or water in contact with the metal surface. An elementary example of this theory is the "corrosion battery" which illustrates the principles involved (Fig. 9-4).

Corroding metal surfaces contain innumerable local galvanic cells or "corrosion batteries" wherein the corrosion takes place. These "batteries" result from areas of differing electrical potential over the metallic surface which form the anodes and cathodes while the water or soil in contact with the metal surface acts as an electrolyte. As the current flows from the anodic to the cathodic area, metallic ions are released into solution at the anode, resulting in rust and pitting. Figure 9-4 shows the cause, effect, and result.

Dissolved oxygen has a dual influence on the corrosion process. Metallic corrosion results primarily from electrolytic action. Hydrogen ions in solution are reduced by electrons to atomic hydrogen at the cathode. If left undisturbed, atomic hydrogen would form a protective film on the surface of the cathode and materially reduce the rate of corrosion. The accumulation of hydrogen is prevented by any dissolved oxygen present, and the oxygen and hydrogen react to form water. High concentra-

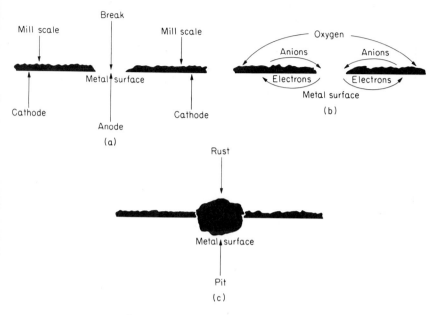

Fig. 9-4. One form of corrosion battery.

tions of dissolved oxygen lower the probability of corrosion by improving the anodic films. It is considered that dissolved oxygen is adsorbed on the surface of the iron and takes part in the formation of protective films.[3] Therefore, before the effects of dissolved oxygen can be fully evaluated on the corrosion process, it must be determined whether the chemical reaction is governed by cathodic or anodic control. It appears that cathodic reactions control the early stages of corrosion on water pipes but that the control over a period of years is largely anodic.[3] In the absence of dissolved oxygen or some other oxidizing agent, such as chlorine, nitrate, nitrite, or dichromate, the corrosion process cannot proceed very far in the early stage.

Metallic corrosion may be retarded or prevented by (1) cathodic protection, (2) application of coatings or linings, (3) control of the outside pipe environment, (4) the addition of inhibitors to the water, and (5) production of films by chemical treatment of the water.

Corrosion of Sewers. If waste is retained in sewers for long periods, the metabolic activity of microorganisms will deplete the oxygen supply and anaerobic degradation will set in. This problem is accelerated during the warm summer months. Anaerobic digestion is accompanied by the production of hydrogen sulfide. The gaseous hydrogen sulfide is soluble in the moisture of condensation on the sewer walls. The sulfur-oxidizing bacteria *Thiobacillus* oxidize the hydrogen sulfide to sulfuric acid. In concrete sewers the sulfuric acid which has been formed reacts with the lime to form calcium sulfate. This material lacks the structural strength to support pipe loads.

The best way to control hydrogen sulfide corrosion is to prevent its formation. This is accomplished by proper sewer design so that retention time is not critical. Once a sewer is built, temperature and retention are somewhat fixed and under adverse conditions it is necessary to use some form of chemical treatment for control. The primary type of chemical treatment is to use a strong oxidizing agent, such as chlorine, which retards bacterial activity and allows the waste flow to reach the treatment plant with little production of hydrogen sulfide. Unfortunately, chlorine reacts chemically with some of the organic matter in the waste, with the result that it is not completely available for use in controlling the microorganisms. In addition, some chlorine compounds have been reported to be toxic to aquatic life. Nitrate salts have been used to supplement the oxygen supply in sewers to prevent anaerobic conditions from developing. In this way the production of hydrogen sulfide is controlled by accelerating the biological process without any known toxic effects.

Cathodic Protection. Forms of electrolytic corrosion can be controlled by cathodic protection. This type of protection is simply the original "corrosion battery" with an auxiliary anode acting as a substitute for the local anode on the metal surface to be protected.

The auxiliary anodes may be either electrolytic (energized by an external source of direct current) or galvanic (composed of a metal higher in the electromotive series than the metal to be protected). In either case, the electrical energy supplied by the auxiliary anodes forms a block to prevent the flow of current in the local cells on the protected surface. With the flow of current blocked, the escape of metallic ions from the local cell anodes also ceases and corrosion is prevented (see Figs. 9-5 and 9-6).

Where the current demand of the cathodes is satisfied by the local anodes on the metal surface to be protected in the "corrosion battery," the current in cathodic protection is furnished by a power supply and the corrosion processes are transferred to the auxiliary anode. These auxiliary anodes, which may be easily replaced, are thus eventually expended to protect the pipe or structure surface.

Coatings and Linings. Coatings and linings are used to prevent corrosion and to increase or maintain the smoothness of the pipe wall. Materials used for the protection of steel and concrete surfaces include asphaltics, resins, rubber bases, galvanizing, and plastics. Several types of plastic coatings appear to be the most promising since they resist corrosion and are chemically inert to acids and alkalies. Although plastic coatings are not very resistant to sunlight, this presents no problem in pipe-corrosion control.

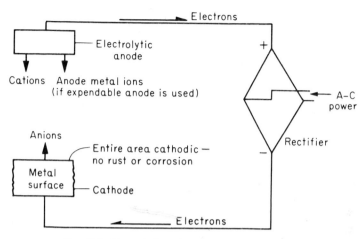

Fig. 9-5. Electrolytic cathodic-protection battery.

Control of the Outside Pipe Environment. Corrosion-control measures for the outside pipe environment are similar to those used on the inside. The galvanic anode principle is widely employed for pipelines and metal in contact with the ground. Outside coatings are sometimes necessary for the protection of metal and concrete pipes because of the chemical nature of the soil which they contact.

The Addition of Inhibitors to the Water. Certain compounds, when added to water in small amounts, will reduce the rate of corrosion. Such compounds include the polyphosphates, which are widely used in water treatment. They form soluble complexes with the iron in solution. These iron-phosphate complexes prevent the formation of insoluble iron hy-

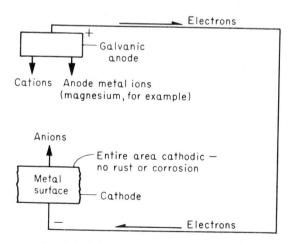

Fig. 9-6. Galvanic cathodic-protection battery.

droxide tubercules which reduce the hydraulic efficiency of pipes. "Red water" formation is also eliminated. The polyphosphates also function as sequestering agents which prevent the precipitation of calcium, magnesium, and iron. Sodium silicate apparently functions in a manner similar to the polyphosphates, but this compound is not widely used in municipal water treatment.

Films by Chemical Treatment. The deposition of coatings of calcium carbonate on pipes and metal tanks has been discussed in Sec. 9-2. Silicate films have also been reported as successful in protecting the walls of pipes. These films are dense, but slightly permeable, however, and corrosion can take place if the conditions are favorable once the film is deposited.

COAGULATION, PRECIPITATION, AND ION EXCHANGE

9-4. WATER SOFTENING

Hard water and *soft water* are relative terms. People who are accustomed to a 35-mg/l water hardness think that a 125-mg/l water is hard. In general, water having less than 150 mg/l of total hardness is still not sufficiently hard to interfere seriously with most domestic uses. Hardness above 150 mg/l is noticed by most consumers. If the hardness is above 175 mg/l, many homes will be provided with household softeners.

Figure 9-7 represents the annual cost of hardness reduction in municipal plants. The figure is based on waters of 200, 300, and 400 mg/l total hardness, with a reduction in hardness to 100 mg/l. The hardness is evenly divided between carbonate and sulfate hardness.

Figure 9-8 shows representative costs of water softening with household units. Municipal softening of water will cost the average consumer about one-sixth the cost with household softeners.[5]

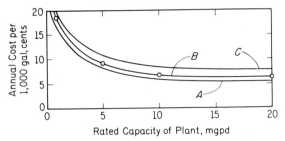

FIG. 9-7. Annual cost of hardness reduction in municipal plants. *A* represents hardness reduction of 100 ppm; *B*, 200 ppm; *C*, 300 ppm. (From Louis R. Howson, "Economics of Water Softening," *J. Am. Water Works Assoc.*, vol. 54, no. 2, 1962, p. 163.)

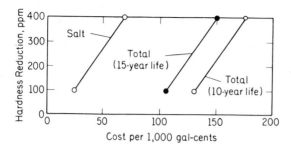

FIG. 9-8. Annual cost of hardness reduction with household softeners. (From Louis R. Howson, "Economics of Water Softening," *J. Am. Water Works Assoc.*, vol. 54, no. 2, 1962, p. 164.)

Hardness in water is caused by the ions of calcium, magnesium, iron, manganese, strontium, and aluminum. Most of these hardness-producing elements can be found in natural waters in some concentrations. However, in most waters only the ions of calcium and magnesium are present in objectionable quantities.

There are various methods for reducing the hardness of water for home and industry. The water may be centrally softened at the treatment plant prior to being introduced into the distribution system, or it may be softened at the point of use. Softening at the treatment plant is usually by one of the two following methods:

1. Softening with lime and soda ash
2. Softening with ion-exchange resins

Softening at the point of use at the home or industry is usually by one of the three following methods:

1. Softening with ion-exchange resins
2. Softening with lime and soda ash
3. Softening with detergent additives

9-5. LIME-SODA-ASH PROCESS

In the lime-soda-ash process, lime, $Ca(OH)_2$, and soda ash, Na_2CO_3, are added to the water. The equations expressing the reactions occurring when lime is added to remove the calcium and magnesium bicarbonates are

$$Ca(HCO_3)_2 + Ca(OH)_2 \rightarrow 2CaCO_3 + 2H_2O \qquad (9\text{-}20)$$

$$Mg(HCO_3)_2 + Ca(OH)_2 \rightarrow MgCO_3 + CaCO_3 + 2H_2O \qquad (9\text{-}21)$$

$$MgCO_3 + Ca(OH)_2 \rightarrow Mg(OH)_2 + CaCO_3 \qquad (9\text{-}22)$$

In Eq. 9-20, lime reacts with bicarbonate, resulting in the precipitation of the normal carbonate, $CaCO_3$. This removal is not complete, as

$CaCO_3$ is soluble to the extent of about 15 mg/l at normal temperatures. Equations 9-21 and 9-22 show the precipitation of magnesium as magnesium hydroxide. This precipitation results because the solubility of magnesium hydroxide is quite low. It will be noticed that two molecules of lime are necessary to react with one molecule of $Mg(HCO_3)_2$. If insufficient lime is added, a soluble compound, magnesium carbonate, $MgCO_3$, is formed that still produces hardness.

Lime also reacts with the carbon dioxide in solution as follows:

$$CO_2 + Ca(OH)_2 \rightarrow CaCO_3 + H_2O \qquad (9\text{-}23)$$

The demand exerted by the dissolved carbon dioxide must be taken into account when computing quantities of lime to be added.

The removal of the calcium noncarbonate hardness is usually done with soda ash, Na_2CO_3. The removal of the magnesium noncarbonate hardness requires the addition of both lime and soda ash. The following equations generalize the reactions involved:

$$CaSO_4 + Na_2CO_3 \rightarrow CaCO_3 + Na_2SO_4 \qquad (9\text{-}24)$$

Here most of the $CaCO_3$ is precipitated out and the nonhardness-producing sodium sulfate remains in solution.

$$MgSO_4 + Ca(OH)_2 \rightarrow Mg(OH)_2 + CaSO_4 \qquad (9\text{-}25)$$

The $Mg(OH)_2$ is precipitated out in Eq. 9-25 but again the $CaSO_4$ must be reacted with Na_2CO_3 as shown in Eq. 9-24.

In order to determine the amount of lime and soda ash required to soften a water, it is necessary to have information concerning:

1. Dissolved carbon dioxide
2. Alkalinity
3. Noncarbonate hardness
4. Magnesium

The following calculations show the amount of lime, $Ca(OH)_2$ (mol. wt. 74.1) and soda ash, Na_2CO_3 (mol. wt. 106.0) needed for precipitation of carbonate hardness:

1. By Eq. 9-23, 74.1/44 = 1.68 mg/l, or 1.68 × 8.34 = 14.0 lb of lime per million gallon of water are required to react with 1 mg/l of CO_2. This reaction produces no hardness removal but the CO_2 must be taken care of before other reactions can proceed.

2. By Eq. 9-22, the amount of lime required to precipitate 1 mg/l of magnesium (at. wt. 24.3) is $^{74.1}/_{24.3}$ = 3.04 mg/l, or 3.04 × 8.34 = 25.4 lb/mg. An equivalent amount of calcium is added with the lime and the hardness remains the same except that it is now all calcium.

3. By Eq. 9-20, the amount of lime required to precipitate 1 mg/l of bicarbonate hardness equivalent to the alkalinity as $CaCO_3$ (mol. wt. 100) is $^{74.1}/_{100}$ = 0.74 mg/l, or 0.74 × 8.34 = 6.2 lb/mg.

4. The amount of soda ash, Na_2CO_3 (mol. wt. 106.0), needed for

precipitation of the noncarbonate hardness is given by Eq. 9-24. For 1 mg/l of noncarbonate hardness, $106.0/100 = 1.06$ mg/l, or $1.06 \times 8.34 = 8.84$ lb/mg.

The reactions are assumed to go to completion when computing quantities of lime and soda ash for this process. In some softening processes, coagulating agents are used to hasten the sedimentation of the precipitates resulting. Excess lime beyond that calculated as necessary is normally used. This aids the precipitation of magnesium hydroxide and elevates the *p*H. The maximum insolubility of magnesium hydroxide is at a *p*H of about 10.4. Commercial grades of lime and soda ash must be adjusted in weight for purity.

The addition of lime to water reduces the carbonate saturation index and increases the tendency of the water to deposit calcium carbonate. This creates a serious problem with sand filters as the calcium tends to deposit on the sand and cements the grains together, forming large lumps which decrease filter efficiency. The carbonate balance may be restored by diffusing carbon dioxide gas through the water. Carbon dioxide may be obtained from the exhaust of internal combustion engines or from boiler flues or underwater combustion burners. The amount of CO_2 added should be controlled so that the resulting water is noncorrosive. The *p*H should normally not be lowered below 9.2.

The lime-soda-ash process can be varied in numerous ways to meet local requirements. Some plants operate using a split-treatment method, wherein a portion of the water is softened and then remixed with the rest of the water. Recarbonation is usually not necessary in this process. The lime-soda-ash process is also used in conjunction with ion-exchange processes to produce high-quality waters. Where a high quality of water is necessary, such as for boiler feedwater, the temperature of the water is raised to accelerate the chemical reactions and decrease solubilities.

EXAMPLE 9-3. Determine the amounts of lime as $Ca(OH)_2$ and soda ash theoretically required to remove all of the hardness from a water showing the following analysis:

Dissolved CO_2	$= 30$ mg/l as CO_2
Alkalinity with	
phenolphthalein	$= 0$
Total	$- 270$ mg/l as $CaCO_3$
Magnesium	$= 40$ mg/l as Mg
Noncarbonate hardness	$= 60$ mg/l as $CaCO_3$

Solution: (Using factors calculated from Eq. 9-20–9-25)

1. Carbon dioxide

$$30 \times 14.0 = 420 \text{ lb } Ca(OH)_2 \text{ per mg of water}$$

2. Alkalinity

$$270 \times 6.2 = 1,670 \text{ lb } Ca(OH)_2 \text{ per mg of water}$$

3. Magnesium

$$40 \times 25.4 = 1{,}020 \text{ lb } Ca(OH)_2 \text{ per mg of water}$$

Total lime $= 420 + 1{,}670 + 1{,}020 = 3{,}110$ lb of $Ca(OH)_2$ per mg of water.

4. Noncarbonate hardness

$$60 \times 8.84 = 520 \text{ lb } Na_2CO_3 \text{ per mg of water}$$

Total lime as $Ca(OH)_2 = 3{,}110$ lb/mg. Total soda ash as $Na_2CO_3 = 520$ lb/mg. These values would have to be adjusted to allow for the impurity of commercial chemicals. Some excess lime is usually necessary to adjust the pH upward to about 10.4.

9-6. ION EXCHANGE

Ion exchangers are used in water and waste treatment to soften water, to selectively remove specific impurities, and to recover valuable chemicals lost in industrial waste discharges. Ion exchangers are also used to demineralize water completely for laboratory and industrial purposes. In very dilute ionized solutions, such as natural waters, the ion-exchange process is an economic method of producing water free of all ions. It is also useful in removing the hardness-producing elements of calcium and magnesium.

A cation resin operating on the sodium cycle is normally used in the softening process. Ion-exchange reactions for softening, may be written as

$$Na_2R + \left.\begin{matrix} Ca \\ Mg \end{matrix}\right\} \begin{matrix} (HCO_3)_2 \\ SO_4 \\ Cl_2 \end{matrix} \rightarrow \left.\begin{matrix} Ca \\ Mg \end{matrix}\right\} R + \left\{\begin{matrix} 2\ NaHCO_3 \\ Na_2SO_4 \\ 2\ Na\ Cl \end{matrix}\right. \qquad (9\text{-}26)$$

where R represents the exchange resin. These reactions show that when a water containing calcium and magnesium is passed through an ion exchanger, these metals are taken up by the resin, which simultaneously gives up sodium in exchange.

After the ability of the bed to produce soft water has been exhausted, the unit is removed from service and backwashed with a solution of sodium chloride. This removes the calcium and magnesium in the form of their soluble chlorides and at the same time restores the resin to its original sodium condition. The bed is rinsed free of the undesirable salts and returned to service. The governing reaction may be written as follows:

$$\left.\begin{matrix} Ca \\ Mg \end{matrix}\right\} R + 2\ NaCl \rightarrow Na_2R + \left.\begin{matrix} Ca \\ Mg \end{matrix}\right\} Cl_2 \qquad (9\text{-}27)$$

The vast majority of ion-exchange softeners are of the pressure type, with either manual or automatic controls. They normally operate at rates of 6 to 8 gpm/sq ft of surface of filter area.[6] A water meter is usually employed on the inlet or outlet side. For manual type operations, this meter can be set to turn on a light or sound an alarm at the end of the softening run.

About 8.5 lb of salt are required to regenerate 1 cu ft of resin and remove approximately 410 g of hardness in a commercial unit. The reduction in hardness is directly related to the amount of cations present in the raw water and the amount of salt used to regenerate the resin bed.

9-7. ION EXCHANGE IN WASTE TREATMENT

The ion-exchange process can be used to concentrate and recover valuable or harmful chemicals for reuse or disposal in industrial waste operations. Metal-finishing wastes containing chromic acid are a good example. The finished parts in a chrome-plating operation must be rinsed free of chromic acid in order to avoid staining and postchemical action. The process requires an acid regenerated cation exchange, followed by a highly basic anion exchange. The chemical reaction for the cation-exchange reaction, with R representing the resin, is:

$$H_2Cr_2O_7 + FeCr_2O_7 + 2HR \rightarrow 2H_2Cr_2O_7 + FeR_2 \qquad (9\text{-}28)$$

This metal-free rinse water passes on to the anion exchanger for removal of the chromate radical. The reaction may be expressed as

$$H_2Cr_2O_7 + ROH \rightarrow RCrO_3 + H_2O \qquad (9\text{-}29)$$

The resulting water may be reused for rinsing, since it is free of metal and chromic acid, or it may be discharged to waste. Chromic acid may be recovered when the anion-exchange unit is regenerated with caustic. This reaction proceeds as follows:

$$RCrO_3 + 2NaOH \rightarrow ROH + Na_2Cr_2O_7 \qquad (9\text{-}30)$$

Sodium chromate, $Na_2Cr_2O_7$, can be reformed to chromic acid by passing the solution through the first cation exchanger. Here H^+ is exchanged for Na^+, which may be expressed as:

$$Na_2Cr_2O_7 + 2HR \rightarrow 2NaR + H_2Cr_2O_7 \qquad (9\text{-}31)$$

The chromic acid recovered in this process can again be used in the chrome-plating baths. This method affords considerable reuse of both the water and the toxic waste material.

Mixed-bed-ion-exchange units (cation and anion) have been used for the removal of radioactivity.[7] The resins are buried or disposed of in the ocean after use.

9-8. IRON AND MANGANESE REMOVAL

Iron and manganese are highly objectionable constituents in water supplies for either domestic or industrial use. Iron compounds are generously distributed in nature and impart a brown color to laundry goods and containers and appreciably affect the taste of beverages. Much the same thing can be said for manganese except that this metal is less common. Water should be free of manganese. The U.S. Public Health Service limit of 0.05 mg/l is the least amount that can be detected with common equipment however. The recommended limit for iron is 0.3 mg/l.

Iron and manganese impart the same characteristics to water and have approximately the same chemical behavior. They are normally removed from water by the same processes. Iron is more prevalent in water supplies than manganese, but iron is usually much easier to remove. At normal pH values, iron in the ferrous (Fe^{++}) state is quite soluble, as compared to the ferric (Fe^{+++}) state. The solubility constants at 25°C are

$$Fe(OH)_2, K_s = 1.65 \times 10^{-15}$$
$$Fe(OH)_3, K_s = 4 \times 10^{-38}$$

Ferrous iron can be removed by aeration, precipitation, or filtration:

$$4Fe^{++} + 3O_2 + 6H_2O \rightarrow 4 Fe(OH)_3 \qquad (9\text{-}32)$$

The precipitation of ferric hydroxide is impeded when the pH of the water is less than 7.8. Aeration washes out CO_2 with a resultant rise in pH. If the pH is below 7.8 after the CO_2 is removed, lime or soda ash can be added to raise the pH. This aeration method has been found effective for oxidation of iron in waters that contain principally bicarbonate salts and little or no organic matter.

Iron and manganese can also be removed by ion exchange during softening. This process must be used with care to avoid the oxidation of ferrous to ferric iron within the ion-exchange bed. In many waters containing iron, pretreatment to remove the iron has been necessary prior to ion-exchange softening.

Municipal and industrial treatment plants have accomplished satisfactory iron removal with the lime-soda-ash process. This process has not been as successful for the removal of manganese.[8]

Iron and manganese can be removed from water with the use of potassium permanganate and manganese dioxide-greensand. Greensands are naturally occurring sodium-aluminum silicates. Water containing iron and manganese is passed through a filter containing manganese dioxide affixed to greensand. The manganese dioxide oxidizes the iron and manganese compounds to trivalent forms which precipitate out on the filter. When the manganese dioxide sand has been depleted, it is regenerated with potassium permanganate. A continuous process has been developed in which the potassium permanganate is fed continuously to the water prior to entering the filter. The potassium permanganate oxidizes the iron and manganese and is precipitated out on the filter. If too little potassium permaganate, is used, the manganese dioxide on the filter sand will oxidize the iron and manganese, and if too much potassium permanganate is used, it will regenerate the greensand. Alling reports a cost of $3\frac{1}{2}$ cents per 1,000 gal for potassium permangate for treating a water that contains 13 mg/l of iron-manganese.[9]

Various combinations of the aforementioned processes are used in the economic removal of hardness, taste, and odor, and specific pollutants.

9-9. COAGULATION

In water and waste treatment, coagulation involves the formation of chemical flocs that adsorb, entrap, or otherwise bring together suspended matter. This material may vary in size from 10^{-7} to 0.1 mm, a range of 1 to 1,000,000. Particle sizes of 10^{-4} mm and larger produce turbidity, whereas smaller particles (primarily colloids) impart color, tastes, and odors.

The colloidal state is defined as a heterogeneous system in which one phase of matter is finely scattered throughout a second, continuous phase. The continuous phase is water. The actual boundaries of the colloidal state are indefinite. If the dispersed phase is divided finely enough, the properties of a colloidal dispersion merge gradually into those of a true solution. This occurs at a particle size of about 10^{-6} mm. If the particles of the dispersed phase increase in size, the colloidal dispersion takes on the properties of an impermanent suspension. This occurs at a particle size of about 10^{-3} mm. Not all particles of this approximate size form stable colloidal systems, since factors other than size must be taken into account. Figure 9-9 gives approximate settling velocities of silica particles in water based on Stokes' law.

In order to bring about the coagulation of a colloidal suspension it is necessary to offset the various factors which account for its stability. Much of the behavior of colloidal particles is associated with surface phenomena. The increase in surface area brought about by the reduction in particle size is shown in Fig. 9-10. This may be further illustrated by considering the subdivision of a cube of side length 1 mm and surface area of 6 sq mm. If this cube is subdivided into smaller cubes of side length 10^{-6} mm, a total of 6 sq m of surface area will be exposed. This represents a millionfold increase in surface area.

Colloidal systems dispersed in water are termed *hydrophilic* where the solid particles strongly attract and hold molecules of water. If this attraction is weak, the colloidal system is termed *hydrophobic*. Normally organic colloids are hydrophilic and inorganic colloids are hydrophobic.

9-10. ZETA POTENTIAL

Colloidal particles are normally charged with respect to the surrounding liquid. This can be demonstrated by placing the electrodes from a d-c source in the colloidal system. The colloidal particles will move toward the electrode of unlike charge. Ferric hydroxide can be used to demon-

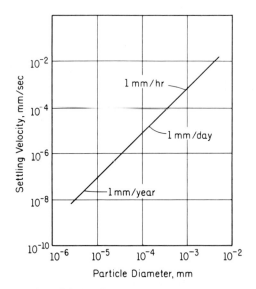

FIG. 9-9. Settling velocities of spherical silica particles (specific gravity = 2.65) in still water at 15°C as computed from Stokes' law.

strate this principle. The colloidal particles of ferric hydroxide impart a color to the water. After the current has been on for a while, the intensity of color will increase at the negative electrode and decrease at the positive electrode. The charge on ferric hydroxide particles is positive.

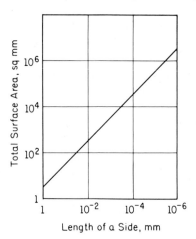

FIG. 9-10. Surface area exposed when a cube with side lengths of 1 mm is subdivided into smaller cubes.

The presence of electric charges on the surface of colloidal particles is largely responsible for their stability. These like charges cause the particles to repel each other. This stability is a function of the zeta potential which is dependent upon the relative charge on the particle, thickness of the layer around the particle, and the dielectric constant of the liquid. Bound water that envelops many organic colloids also affects their stability. The colloidal and suspended particles found in natural surface waters are predominantly of a hydrophobic nature and are negatively charged. If the negative charge can be reduced by decreasing the zeta potential, the colloidal system loses some of its stability. The zera potential can be reduced by adjustment of the pH and by the addition of ions or colloids of opposite charge.

9-11. COAGULATION OF COLLOIDS

The destabilization of colloids is, as yet, poorly understood. A simplified version of the physical theory is as follows: "Foreign" ions are adsorbed on the surfaces of the colloidal particles. Therefore, the dispersed particles are electrically charged. Upon the addition of electrolytes, flocculation is brought about by counter-ion adsorption and compaction of the double layer as shown by Fig. 9-11. The colloidal particle is thus neutralized.[10]

Coagulation results when ions of a charge opposite to the charge of the colloidal system are added to the solution. The diffused layer surrounding each particle is reduced as the added ion is increased. This diffused layer is reduced until a point is reached when the Van der Waals attractive forces are stronger than the repulsive forces of the zeta potential and coagulation results. The valence of the ion of opposite charge is important and the observed effects, in general, follow the Schulze-Hardy rule.[11] This rule states that a bivalent ion is 50 to 60 times more effective than a monovalent ion and that a trivalent ion is 700 to 1,000 times more effective than a monovalent ion.

The two coagulants most used in sanitary engineering are aluminum sulfate, $Al_2(SO_4)_3$, and ferric sulfate, $Fe_2(SO_4)_3$. These both possess positive zeta potentials and have the ability to precipitate negatively charged color or turbidity by mutual coagulation. Alum reacts with the natural alkalinity of the water or, if the alkalinity is insufficient, with the added alkalinity in the form of lime or soda ash. The precipitate is usually considered to be aluminum hydroxide. When there is natural alkalinity in the water to react with the coagulant, the reaction is as follows:

$$Al_2(SO_4)_3 \cdot XH_2O + 3Ca(HCO_3)_2$$
$$\rightarrow 2Al(OH)_3 + 3CaSO_4 + XH_2O + 6CO_2 \qquad (9\text{-}33)$$

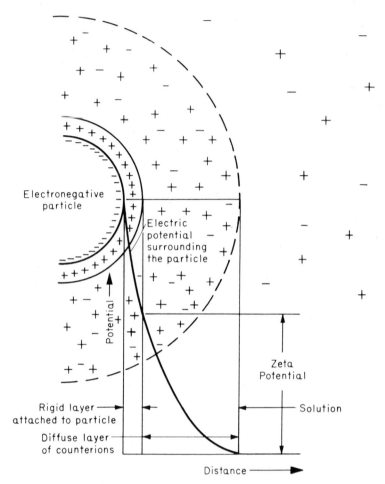

Fig. 9-11. Colloid particle showing the double layer and potentials through the electrostatic field surrounding the particle.

When natural alkalinity is not present in sufficient quantities, lime is added and the reaction is as follows:

$$Al_2(SO_4)_3 \cdot XH_2O + 3Ca(OH)_2$$
$$\to 2Al(OH)_3 + 3CaSO_4 + H_2O \qquad (9\text{-}34)$$

EXAMPLE 9-4. Calculate in pounds per million gallons the theoretical weight of alum, $Al_2(SO_4)_3$, required to give a dose of 7 mg/l. The water contains 2.5 mg/l of natural bicarbonate alkalinity as HCO_3^-. How much lime as $Ca(OH)_2$ must be added to complete the reaction with the alum?

Solution:

1. Alum as $Al_2(SO_4)_3$

$$1 \text{ mg/l} = 8.34 \text{ lb per million gallons}$$
$$7 \times 8.34 = 58.4 \text{ lb/mg of alum as } Al_2(SO_4)_3$$

2. 2.5 mg/l of HCO_3^-. By Eq. 9-33, for each mole of $Al_2(SO_4)_3$ there are 6 equivalents of HCO_3^- required.

$$Al_2(SO_4)_3 \text{ required} = \frac{2.5(342)}{6(61)} = 2.33 \text{ mg/l}$$

3. Alum remaining after natural alkalinity.

$$7 - 2.3 = 4.7 \text{ mg/l } Al_2(SO_4)_3$$

4. Required $Ca(OH)_2$ to react with this alum. By Eq. 9-34, 1 mole of $Al_2(SO_4)_3$ requires 3 moles of $Ca(OH)_2$

$$Ca(OH)_2 = \frac{4.7(3)(74)}{342} = 3.05 \text{ mg/l}$$

$$3.05 \times 8.34 = 25.4 \text{ lb of } Ca(OH)_2 \text{ per million gallons}$$

The quantity of alum would have to be adjusted for the water of hydration and $Ca(OH)_2$ would have to be adjusted for purity.

Waters vary widely in quality and chemical makeup, which is subject to change from time to time. The chemical reactions are complex and not subject to exact calculation. The optimum dosage must be determined in practice by trial. These trial determinations, called Jar tests, are made in a laboratory stirring device. Measurement of the zeta potential is also used in laboratory testing to formulate the coagulant dosage.

Alum is by far the most generally used coagulant.[12] It is effective over a wide pH range in waters of different chemical makeup. Normally the practical pH range is considered to be between 6.5 and 7.5. Ferrous sulfate has the advantage of being more efficient in plankton removal by settling, thereby increasing filter runs. Alum and ferrous sulfate are successfully used together. Because of their economy and effectiveness, activated silica sols are finding increasing use in water and waste treatment. The term "activated silica sol" refers to a negatively charged hydrophilic colloid formed by neutralizing the alkali in a dilute solution of sodium silicate. Silica sols have been used to floc very small particles and make alum or other types of coagulation more complete. They have been particularly effective in color reduction.

Coagulation in water treatment is normally carried out prior to sedimentation and filtration. The coagulant is applied in a fast mixing operation to disperse the chemicals evenly throughout the water. After a flash mix, the water is gently agitated for a longer period of time to build up the floc particles. The water is then passed through a settling basin and filtered.

9-12. COAGULATION IN WASTE TREATMENT

The principles of coagulation for waste treatment are generally the same as for water treatment. Nevertheless, because wastes are highly variable in variety and concentration, individual consideration is required. Paper-mill wastes have been treated with alum and silica sol. Oil and grease wastes have been similarly treated. Digested and undigested domestic sewage sludges are coagulated to improve their filtering and de-watering properties. Ferric chloride is commonly used as a coagulant in these sludge-dewatering processes.

SALINE-WATER CONVERSION

9-13. INTRODUCTION

There are approximately 32×10^7 cubic miles of seawater and large amounts of inland saline water on the earth. Seawater is available in almost unlimited quantities. Figure 9-12 shows the distribution of known inland brackish water resources of the United States. The conversion of saline water to fresh water is not a new idea. Man has known how to accomplish this for centuries by boiling water and condensing the result-ing vapors. In Julius Caesar's time his legionnaires devised a means of desalting sea water by using solar heat to supply fresh water for drinking

FIG. 9-12. Preliminary survey of the brackish water resources of the United States. (From *Saline Water Conversion*, Office of Saline Water, U.S. Govern-ment Printing Office, Washington, D.C., 1962.)

in order to survive the siege of Alexandria.[15] The first widespread practical application of seawater conversion units came with the advent of the steamship and its requirement of fresh water for boilers. At present, water is rapidly becoming a limiting factor on economic growth in many areas of the United States and the world.

Water quality is usually referred to as fresh, brackish, seawater, or brine.

1. Fresh water normally contains less than 1,000 mg/l of dissolved salts.

2. Brackish water ranges from 1,000 mg/l to 35,000 mg/l of dissolved salts.

3. Seawater generally contains 35,000 mg/l of dissolved salts.

4. Brine is water containing more dissolved salts than seawater, such as the Great Salt Lake or the Dead Sea.

The problem of obtaining fresh water from brackish water or seawater is essentially one of engineering economics. If costs were of no concern, then we could boil the ocean and condense the steam. Costs very definitely are of concern, however, and this gives rise to the technological problems of seawater conversion. Conversion costs result directly from land and materials, labor, and energy. The engineering problem is to design combinations of these resources that result in a minimum cost of fresh water for each given locality.

9-14. ENERGY REQUIREMENTS

Energy is an important consideration in saline-water conversion. The minimum energy requirement can be calculated as the lowest possible energy level at which conversion can take place without violating the second law of thermodynamics. The minimum work required for a completely reversible process is given by the relation

$$W_{min} = \Delta H - T_0 \Delta S \tag{9-35}$$

where W_{min} = minimum work
H = enthalpy
S = entropy
T_0 = absolute temperature

The value of work W_{min} does not depend on how the process is carried out but only on the initial state and the final state achieved. Equation 9-35 can be stated in a more convenient way for an isothermal process:

$$-W_{min} = \int_{n_1}^{n_2} RT \ln \frac{P}{P_0} \, dn \tag{9-36}$$

where P = vapor pressure of the salt solution
P_0 = vapor pressure of pure water

T = absolute temperature
R = gas constant
n = number of moles of water removed

For the case where an infinitely small amount of water is reclaimed from a very large amount of saline water (zero recovery), a special case can be developed. The process is assumed to be carried out in three infinitesimally slow steps. In this way reversibility can be achieved.

1. One mole of water is evaporated from a large volume of the salt solution (seawater), isothermally:

$$W_1 = P(V_{vapor} - V_{liquid}) \tag{9-37}$$

where W = work
P = pressure
V = volume

For practical purposes, V_{liquid} can be neglected, in comparison with V_{vapor}. Also, the vapor can be approximated closely as an ideal gas, for which $pv = RT$. Therefore,

$$W_1 = P\frac{RT}{P} = RT \tag{9-38}$$

2. The vapor is compressed reversibly and isothermally from P to P_0.

$$W_2 = \int_P^{P_0} P\,dv = -RT \int_P^{P_0} \frac{dP}{P} = -RT \ln\frac{P_0}{P} \tag{9-39}$$

3. The vapor at pressure P_0 is condensed isothermally

$$W_3 = P_0(V_{liquid} - V_{vapor}) = -P_0 V_{vapor}$$

$$= -P_0 \frac{RT}{P_0} = -RT \tag{9-40}$$

The total work is the sum of the individual work terms in 1, 2, and 3:

$$W_{min} = W_{total} = RT - RT \ln\frac{P_0}{P} - RT = -RT \ln\frac{P_0}{P} \tag{9-41}$$

The negative sign indicates that work is done on the system.

This analysis does not consider specifically the heat absorbed in vaporizing the liquid or the approximately equivalent heat given up in condensation. Infinite-heat reservoirs may be assumed for this purpose.

Compression distillation is based on the above principle of solvent transfer. Good heat contact is provided between the boiler and condenser, so that basically no heat of vaporization needs to be supplied from an external source, and no heat needs to be removed.

EXAMPLE 9-5. What is the minimum energy required to recover 1,000 gal of fresh water from the ocean? Assume that the temperature is 25°C and that the salt concentration is 35,000 mg/l as sodium chloride.

Solution: Using Eq. 9-41,

1. Absolute temperature $T = 25 + 273 = 298°K$. The gas constant = 1.987 cal/deg/mole. The vapor pressure for pure water is = 23.76 mm H_g. The vapor pressure for water with 35,000 mg/l as NaCl = 23.51 mm H_g.

2. The number of moles of water in 1,000 gal is

$$\frac{1,000 \times 8.34 \times 453.6}{18} = 21 \times 10^4 \text{ moles}/1,000 \text{ gal}$$

3. Therefore

$$-W_{min} = 1.987 \text{ cal/deg/mole} \times 298°K \times \ln \frac{23.76}{23.51} \times 21 \times 10^4 \text{ moles}/1,000 \text{ gal}$$

$$= 2.98 \text{ kwh}/1,000 \text{ gal}$$

This figure (2.98 kwh/1,000 gal) is normally cited as the minimum possible work, and the thermodynamic efficiency of an actual process is often based on it. Actual processes must have larger energy requirements than this for two reasons: (1) zero recovery is wholly impractical, as it would require infinite work to pump the infinite supply of saline water necessary for the process; and (2) the equation is based upon a reversible process which is an ideal with zero driving forces. The driving forces, which must have finite values for any real process, are temperature difference across heat exchangers, pressure difference for fluid flow, concentration differences, and electromotive-force (emf) differences.

The minimum work for a reversible process for various percentage yields of pure water using Eq. 9-36 is plotted on Fig. 9-13. The work required for pumping the feedwater is based upon a 50-ft head and 70 percent pump efficiency and the total of the two is also plotted on the same graph. The minimum separation work increases with increased recovery and pumping work normally decreases, resulting in a minimum total work at about 40 percent recovery. If Eq. 9-35 is used to calculate the minimum work, higher values will be obtained for all values except zero recovery. This is because the equation represents ideal work for a single stage process which is not completely reversible.[16]

The minimum work is considerably less for lower salt contents. For a 50 percent recovery from a feed of 5,000 mg/l of salt, the minimum reversible work is 0.71 kwh/1,000 gals of water produced, as compared to 4.15 kwh for seawater. All practical processes have a relatively low thermodynamic efficiency based upon the minimum work for zero recovery. These efficiencies are of the order of 2 to 5 percent. Some improvements are being made and the best efficiency to be achieved in the foreseeable future, according to Dodge, is in the area of 10 percent.[16] This corresponds to about 30 kwh/1,000 gal with seawater.

The reason for this low efficiency is that any decrease in the driving force of an operation such as heat transfer or gas compression results in an increase in the size and cost of the equipment. In the case of a heat

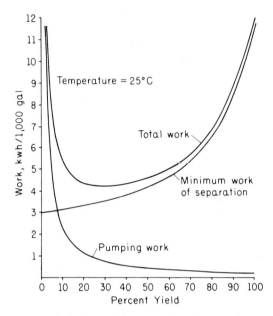

FIG. 9-13. The minimum work of separation
and pumping work as a function of percent
yield of fresh water from seawater.

exchanger, if the temperature difference is halved, the required surface
area will be twice as great for the same conditions.

9-15. COSTS

The "optimum-energy" technique has been used to design plants.
This technique employs thermodynamics, information theory, and economics. It has been shown that thermodynamic considerations alone
can fix the minimum energy requirements. Figure 9-14 shows the relationship between minimum and optimum energy. The optimum-energy requirement is the amount of energy consumption that results in the minimum total cost of fresh-water production. The cost of fresh water
from saline water is the amount the consumer must be charged in order
to pay for the total cost of producing and distributing the fresh water.

The economics of saline-water conversion have been widely discussed. Many of the conclusions drawn indicate that conversion costs
are decreasing while other water costs are increasing and that the conversion of saline water will soon be cheaper than methods of supply
currently in use. This is not supported by fact. Many conversion costs
made public by the Federal government and others do not include the
cost of delivery to the consumer or administrative costs involved in the

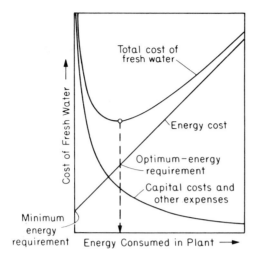

Fig. 9-14. Minimum and optimum-
energy requirements.

sale. Another cost associated with inland saline-water conversion is the
disposal of the waste brine. Viessman points out that consideration of
the enormous volumes of waste which might be produced by future saline
water conversion plants is cause for concern (Fig. 9-15).[18] These disposal
costs may amount to more than the cost of conversion. The in-plant
cost of producing fresh water by conventional methods approximates 5
cents per 1,000 gal. This is the figure with which the present $1.00
or more for saline-water conversion must be compared. Many municipal
water supplies are used as a means of additional taxation by the municipal government and private water companies must make a profit.

The current role of saline-water conversion in supplementing national
water resources may be considered as insignificant and it is not anticipated
that saline-water conversion will contribute significant quantities of fresh
water in the near future.[17] It should not, however, be concluded that
saline-water conversion has no role in water supply. It will be important
in isolated areas of critical water shortage. The processes developed in
saline-water research may have their greatest potential in the area of
waste-water reuse, as is discussed at greater length in Chap. 14.

On the basis of available operating data and current estimates, it is
impossible to predict the future cost of saline-water conversion with any
degree of accuracy. The new and constantly changing technology in this
field is improving rapidly with different processes. It is probable that
there will be some future reduction in the present costs for fresh water
from saline sources but the increasing costs for labor may level out these
figures when compared to conventional processes.

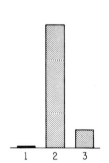

LEGEND

1. Solid waste produced by sewage treatment (sludge digestion
and dewatering are assumed).

2. Saline-water conversion waste
estimated on the premise that
total community water supply is
derived in this manner.

3. Saline-water conversion waste
estimated on the assumption that
only 15 percent of the community
water supply is derived in this
manner, with 85 percent furnished by other means.

FIG. 9-15. Relative annual per capita volumes of
solid wastes produced by sewage treatment and
saline water conversion operations of an inland
city with 40,000 population. These values are
estimated on the basis of brine waste composition
and saline water conversion capabilities at Roswell,
New Mexico, as of July, 1963. Changes in technology may alter these figures but it is considered
that the diagram is indicative of the general order
of magnitude of wastes produced by these operations. (*Public Works*, December, 1963.)

A report of the 1962–64 advanced seminar group at the Johns Hopkins University estimated that a redistribution cost of $0.10/1,000 gal
would be reasonable for a transportation system looping and interlooping
the United States.[19] The California Water Plan may someday become one
leg in an overall fresh-water distribution system. From this brief analysis,
it can be concluded that large-scale interregional distribution of fresh-
water merits further consideration.

9-16. CONVERSION PROCESSES

There have been many processes proposed but only a few are in
actual use and only a few potential processes will probably reach the
stage of practical application. Proposed projects have ranged from towing
icebergs from the arctic regions and melting them in dry docks in tem-
perate zones to the adsorption of salt on solids. Table 9-2 lists some
actual and potential processes for the separation of fresh water from
saline waters (some of the processes in Table 9-2 will be discussed later
on in more detail).

The possible key to the development of low-cost demineralization
processes might lie in the use and reduction of energy required in a

TABLE 9-2
ACTUAL AND POTENTIAL PROCESSES FOR SEPARATION OF WATER FROM SALINE WATERS

I. Processes that separate water from a brine
  A. Evaporation or distillation. There are many variations depending on conditions, type of equipment, and energy source.
    1. Single and multistage flash evaporation
    2. Vapor compression
    3. Combinations of vapor-compression and multiple-effect evaporation
    4. Solar energy
    5. Nuclear energy
    6. Ocean temperature difference
    7. Critical pressure
    8. Underwater combustion-distillation
    9. Electrolysis
  B. Freezing processes
    1. Direct refrigeration
    2. Zone freezing
    3. Indirect refrigeration
  C. Solvent extraction
  D. Osmosis
II. Processes that separate salt from a brine
  A. Ion exchange
  B. Electrodialysis
  C. Osmionic process
  D. Sublimation of salt
  E. Adsorption of salt on solids
  F. Selective solvent for salt
  G. Hydrate formation

separation process. This may require the development of new or little used sources of energy. Table 9-3 lists some presently used and possible energy sources.

TABLE 9-3
POTENTIAL ENERGY SOURCES FOR DEMINERALIZATION

  I. Combustion of fuels
  II. Hydropower
  III. Utilization of waste heat
    A. Waste heat from conventional industrial processes
    B. Waste heat from nuclear fission
  IV. Nuclear Fission
  V. Solar energy
  VI. Marine energy
    A. Thermal
    B. Waves
    C. Tides
  VII. Wind power
  VIII. Chemical energy
  IX. Atmospheric heat
  X. Geothermal energy

9-17.   EVAPORATION

Distillation is the oldest demineralization process. It consists of evaporating a part or all of the water from a saline solution and subsequent condensation of the mineral-free vapor. The products of distillation are pure water and either a concentrated salt solution or a mixture of crystalline salts. This is a process in which water is removed from the salts. The heat and power requirements are relatively independent of the amount of salt in solution. At present, most of the fresh water produced from the sea is by one of the evaporation methods.

A modification of the distillation process called *vapor compression* is used where the salt water is evaporated at atmospheric pressure. The vapor is compressed to raise the pressure of the steam to about 3 psig and the corresponding temperature to about 222°F. The compressed steam is returned to the heating side of the evaporator to heat more of the brine from which the original vapor was formed (Fig. 9-16). There is a temperature difference of about 9°F between the compressed steam and the boiling brine, which permits heat transfer back to the brine. Substantially all of the latent heat of the compressed steam is used in maintaining evaporation of the saline solution. The condensation of the compressed steam occurs directly in the steam chest forming the distilled water product. Therefore, no separate condenser or cooling water is required. From an engineering viewpoint the fact that no cooling water is required with the vapor-compression unit is an important difference between it and multiple-effect evaporators. One pound of fuel oil will evaporate about 250 lb of water in a clean vapor-compression unit. Scale formation is a major problem, as it decreases the efficiency of brine evaporators and periodic shutdowns are required for its removal.

In multiple-effect evaporation, water is evaporated at a given pressure in the first stage. The vapor is then fed to a second compartment, where additional water is evaporated at a lower temperature under a small vacuum produced by the condensed steam from the the first effect. The evaporation of water is carried out in successive stages (Fig. 9-17). This method has been under extensive commercial development for many years. Costs for this process for triple-effect evaporation have been estimated at $1.20 to $1.60/1,000 gal.[20]

Solar distillation has the advantage of "free" energy. There are vast quantities of solar energy, particularly in areas of the United States and other countries where other fuels and energy sources are not available. Since there is little energy cost, the cost of water produced by solar evaporation depends almost entirely upon capital cost and maintenance. These costs are approximately $1.60/1,000 gal with present equipment.

The quantity of solar energy striking the earth per year is approximately 25×10^{20} Btu. Of this total, about 5.5×10^{20} Btu are absorbed

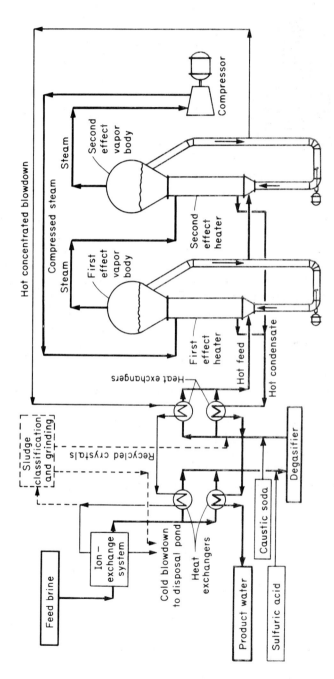

FIG. 9-16. Forced circulation vapor-compression distillation.

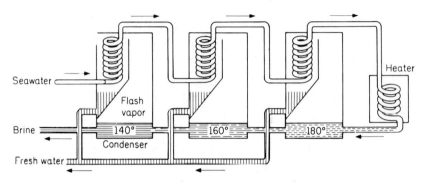

FIG. 9-17. Flash distillation.

by the oceans with the resulting evaporation of seawater. About two hundred billion acre-feet of water return to the land annually. Another additional forty billion acre-feet evaporate from land and plant life. The solar energy striking the earth's surface is many times the present energy consumption in all other forms from fuels and hydropower. The average solar energy in the continental United States is about 40 billion Btu per square mile on an average day. This is equivalent to 5 million gallons of water per day when compared to natural evaporation processes.

Although the figures concerning solar energy are large, the concentration in comparison with conventional energy transfer rates used industrially is low. Average solar energies are equivalent to approximately 1,500 Btu/sq ft/day. This figure may be compared to common industrial heat-transfer rates, as used in steam boilers, ranging from 100,000 to 3 million Btu/sq ft/day. It is apparent that the utilization of solar energy will involve large collectors in relation to the energy delivered. This requirement results in a relatively large capital cost per unit of energy developed.

The simplest solar-evaporation process is the evaporation of water

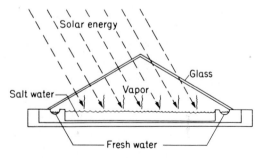

FIG. 9-18. Simple solar still.

from a shallow blackened pan exposed to the sun and covered with sloping glass sheets (Fig. 9-18). The evaporated water condenses on the sloping glass sheets and runs down to collecting channels at the base of the covers. About 0.63 lb of water can be produced per day per square foot of evaporator pan. This is operating with an efficiency of approximately 35 percent, which has been achieved in practice with large units.

9-18. DESIGN PROBLEMS OF A VAPOR-COMPRESSION PLANT

The saline-water conversion plant located at Roswell, New Mexico, is based on the vapor-compression principle. This plant is designed to produce one million gallons of fresh water per day and is the fourth of the demonstration plants authorized by the Office of Saline Water. The forced circulation vapor compression process is used. The plant was completed in 1963.

The Roswell plant was designed for a difficult brackish-water feed in which calcium sulfate concentrations can reach very high levels. Table 9-4 gives an analysis of the brine. The water is drawn from a well at the plant site. Sodium chloride is the major constituent of the dissolved salts, accounting for about 80 percent of the total salinity. The bulk of the remainder of the solids consists of calcium and magnesium sulfates. There are also some calcium and magnesium bicarbonates present. Bicarbonates decompose thermally to form a scale of calcium carbonate and magnesium hydroxide on heat exchanger surfaces. The Roswell water has only one-half the salinity of seawater but is richer in scale-formers. The water is saturated with respect to calcium sulfate and scaling can take place upon evaporation of only a small amount of water. This type of water is more difficult to process that seawater and it occurs widely in the Southwest and in a broad belt extending up into the Dakotas.

TABLE 9-4
ANALYSIS OF ROSWEL BRINE

	mg/l
Total hardness as $CaCO_3$	2,145
Calcium as $CaCO_3$	1,370
Magnesium as $CaCO_3$	775
Alkalinity as $CaCO_3$	202
Chlorides as Cl	8,064
Sulfate as SO_4	1,528
Iron as Fe	Trace
Silica as SiO_2	Trace
Calcium as Ca	549
Magnesium as Mg	303
Sodium as Na	5,000
Total dissolved solids	15,860
pH	7.4

A sea-water plant has available an unlimited supply of cooling water, while an inland plant normally has only its feedwater. The design must be based upon an efficient exchange of heat between the hot products and the cold feed. With a brine feed rich in salts, an upper limit on concentration is imposed by the boiling-point elevation. This represents a thermodynamic inefficiency which decreases the percent of recoverable energy supplied to the process. The maximum concentration of feed brine is also controlled by scaling considerations.

In the first step of the forced-circulation vapor-compression process, Fig. 9-16, the feedwater exchanges a major portion of its calcium for sodium in a conventional ion-exchange unit. The feed water is then heated to about 145°F by heat exchange with the product water and waste. This is followed by acidification to break down bicarbonates. The carbon dioxide and dissolved gases are then removed under vacuum in the degasifier. This water is then neutralized and further heated by exchange with product water and waste.

The heated water is introduced into the evaporator system. The flow is from the vapor body down to the pump and then up through the tubes of the evaporator heat exchanger at the rate of 90,000 gpm. The water emerges again in the vapor body where a high water level is maintained. This water level develops a sufficient hydrostatic head so that boiling cannot occur in the tubes. Boiling occurs as the heated water rises up in the vapor body (Fig. 9-16). About 250 lb of water is recirculated for every pound vaporized. The water temperature is raised 4°F as it passes through the heater tubes. After leaving the tubes, the heat represented by the 4°F temperature rise is used in the heat of vaporization. The remaining liquid is cooled to the original temperature by the vaporization process before starting upon another recirculation through the pump and heater. Therefore, the heat required to vaporize 1 lb of water is supplied by cooling 250 lb of water 4°F. The 250 lb of water is then reheated 4°F and pumped through the evaporator again. The heat taken up by the water is obtained from the condensation of steam on the outside of the tubes of the evaporator heater. The heating and boiling operation in the second-effect vapor body is identical to that in the first effect except that the temperatures and pressures are lower.

In order to recover the major portion of the heat energy of the steam generated in the second effect, the steam pressure and temperature are raised by the compressor. This operation compresses 75,000 cfm of steam from 2 psi to 8.5 psi. This higher-temperature steam is then condensed in the heat exchanger of the first evaporator heater which furnishes the heat of evaporation for the first effect.

A portion of the brine feed is withdrawn at a regulated rate from the recirculating water. Much of the heat is recovered from the waste water by heat exchangers. The waste water concentrated brine is termed *blow-*

down. The cooled blowdown water is used to regenerate the ion-exchange resin in the initial softening system. The condensed and cooled steam is the product water.

If the evaporators were rated as boilers, the rating would be about 1,320,000 hp. The power consumption of the vapor compressor is of the order of 2,300 hp or about 2 percent of the work accomplished in the evaporation system. The compressor represents 75 percent of the total power consumption of the plant. These values are based on clean heat-exchange surfaces. A longer period of operation is necessary to determine efficiencies under operating conditions. The Roswell plant represents a synthesis of a number of operations into a design having a capacity never before achieved.

9-19. FREEZING PROCESS

A salt solution, upon cooling, will eventually deposit ice crystals unless the brine concentration is very high in which case the dissolved salt will crystallize out of solution. Seawater freezes with the formation of ice and a higher concentration brine solution (Fig. 9-19). The residual brine solution is of a concentration greater than the initial brine solution because the ice crystals are pure water.

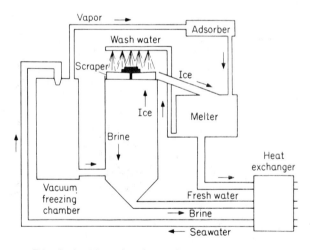

Fig. 9-19. Direct-freezing saline-water conversion process.

The temperature at which ice crystals begin to form is a function of the salt concentration of the brine. A lower temperature is required as the brine concentration is increased.

A curve showing the relationship between the freezing temperature and salt concentration is given in Fig. 9-20. Upon cooling, the first solid

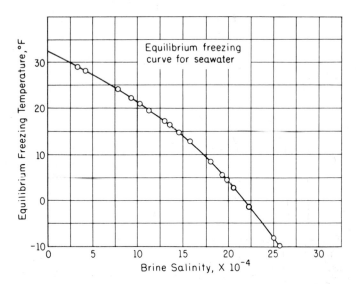

FIG. 9-20. Equilibrium freezing curve for seawater. (From "Research and Development of Processes for Desalting Water by Freezing," Office of Saline Water Report No. 10, U.S. Government Printing Office, Washington, D.C., 1956, p. 9.)

phase to separate from seawater is ice crystals. Continued cooling will result in additional ice being formed and the remaining brine being concentrated. The next solid phase to separate upon continued cooling is sodium sulphate decahydrade at a temperature below 17°F. The second salt to separate is sodium chloride dihydrate at a temperature of about −9°F. Therefore, the freezing process should stay above 17°F for the formation of pure ice from seawater. Even though the temperature is maintained above 17°F, the ice crystals are coated with the brine solution and must be washed with high quality water to remove this salt. At the higher freezing temperatures, a small variation in the equilibrium freezing temperature corresponds to a large change in the brine concentration. The ice particles formed by freezing salt water consist of practically pure water. Even if the freezing process is carried out above the temperature at which the first solid salt phase is separated out, it is not simple to separate the brine from the ice. A bed of ice particles, when drained by gravity of adhering liquid, contains about equal weights of ice and brine held to the ice by capillary and viscous forces. New processes are being investigated that might provide more efficient ice brine separation.

9-20. REVERSE OSMOSIS

The reverse osmosis process offers promise in the conversion of saline to fresh water. No phase change is involved and energy costs may be held to an extremely low value. Pressure in excess of the osmotic pressure (approximately 350 psi for seawater) is used to force fresh water at ambient temperature through a selective membrane. The membrane must be capable of allowing the water to filter through while rejecting the dissolved salts. The process derives its name from the fact that the flow of water under the applied driving force is in a direction opposite to that normally observed in osmotic processes. The success of the process depends upon the development of suitable membranes (Fig. 9-21).

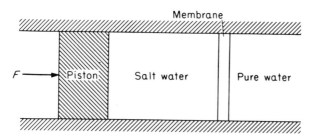

Fig. 9-21. Principle of the reverse-osmosis process.

The process membranes consist of a surface layer which contains bound water but practically no capillary water. The bulk of the membrane contains bound water and large quantities of capillary water. The surface layer rejects salt because the solution capability of bound water is nil. A "perfect" surface layer would reject all salt and yield a relatively pure water product. Thus far surface layers have contained some capillary water and possess structurals flaws. This has allowed some salt in the product water.

The salt-free water that passes through the surface layer of bound water is forced through the bulk of the membrane by passages formed by the capillary water. The rate of transport through the surface layer of bound water has been the limiting parameter. The principal pressure drop is believed to take place across this thin surface layer. The economic potential of the process has not been demonstrated.[21]

9-21. THE OSMIONIC PROCESS

This process is actually one of electrodialysis using ion-selective membranes but the driving force comes from the dilution of a salt solution more concentrated than the one to be separated rather than from an applied emf. The way in which the principle is applied is illustrated by the diagram in Fig. 9-22. At the beginning, compartments I, II, and III are filled with a brine of concentration C_1. Compartment IV, which sur-

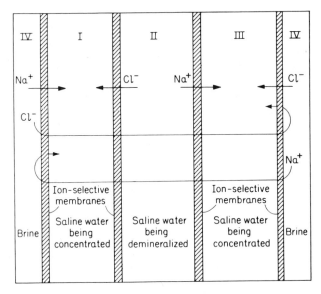

Fig. 9-22. Cross section of a unit illustrating the osmionic process.

rounds compartments I, II, and III, is filled with a brine at concentration C_2 which is greater than the concentration of C_1. Because of the concentration gradient, Cl^- and Na^+ ions from compartment IV diffuse into compartments I and III. In order for electrical neutrality to occur in compartments I and III, another process must take place simultaneously, Cl^- ions move from II to I and Na^+ ions from II to III. The net result is a decrease in the salt concentration in compartment II.

The process at present is limited to experimental work on brackish waters but with improvement in the permaselective membranes, the process might be used on seawater. Solar evaporation might be used to maintain the concentrated brine supply, or waste brines from other processes might be used. No other source of energy is required for this process other than pumping.

9-22. ELECTRODIALYSIS

The electrodialysis process is one of the most practical and widely used methods to treat brackish waters. At the present it is not very suitable for the treatment of sea water because of the high energy requirements. The energy requirement is directly proportional to the salt concentration of the water being treated.

The ingenious principle of this process is illustrated in Fig. 9-23. Plastic membranes are used that will not pass water but are ion-selective.

Some membranes will pass cations while others will permit only anions to go through. An electrodialysis cell consists of alternate cation and anion permeable membranes arranged in a stack with alternately charged electrodes on each side. In Fig. 9-23 the cation-premeable membranes *C* contain negatively charged ionic groups as in anion-exchange resins and therefore tend to repel the anions but allow the cations to permeate through. The anion-permeable membranes *A* have positively charged ionic groups that repel the cations but permit the anions to go through. An electromotive force is imposed across the assembly by electrodes *E* and all positive ions move toward the anode while all negative ions move toward the cathode. This movement is effected by the membranes in the

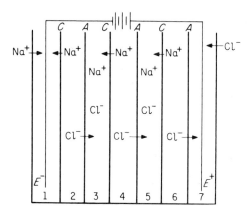

FIG. 9-23. Schematic cross section of the electrodialysis process. *C* = cation-permeable membrane; *A* = anion-permeable membrane; *E* = electrode.

following way. Na^+ ions can move out of compartment 2 through membrane *C* into compartment 1 but those in section 3 cannot move out of this compartment because they cannot penetrate an *A* membrane. In a similar manner, Cl^- ions can move from 2 to 3 but those in 3 are prevented from moving out by the *C* membrane. The net result is the depletion of ions in the even-numbered compartments and concentration of ions in the odd-numbered compartments. The even-number sections produce relatively pure water and the odd numbers a concentrated waste brine.

The energy requirements for this process are made up of the electrical energy to provide the emf across the electrodes and the mechanical energy required to move the liquid through the cells. The total energy is affected by the nature of the membrane, the number of membranes in a stack, the spacing, the fluid velocity in the cells, the salt concentration, and the current density. The electrical energy may be calculated from the formula

$$E = \frac{KiAqRFuN}{ne} \qquad (9\text{-}42)$$

where E = kwh/1,000 gal
  i = current density
  A = transfer area per cell pair
  R = resistance of unit
  q = total rate of flow through unit
  N = normality of feed solution
  u = fractional removal efficiency
  F = Faraday constant
  n = number of cell pairs
  e = current efficiency
  K = constant (dependent on units)

Equation 9-42 shows that the electrical energy required for a unit is directly proportional to current density and salt concentration. The electrical energy can be reduced by operating at lower current densities but the capacity is directly proportional to the current used. Accordingly, a balance must be designed between cost of energy and fixed charges for minimun cost. Equation 9-42 also shows that the electrical energy required is proportional to the salt concentration of the water being treated. In addition to the electrical-energy requirement, there is need for considerable pumping energy. For brackish waters of concentration less than 10,000 ppm, the energy requirement in an actual installation is of the order of 10 to 30 kwh/1,000 gal of product water.[16] This may be less than the energy required for distillation processes. The energy requirement for seawater for the electrodialysis process is on the order of 125 to 150 kwh/1,000 gal. This is much higher than for several vaporization processes.

EXAMPLE 9-6. An electrodialysis stack is made up of 400 membranes each 20 × 24 in. This unit will be used to partially demineralize 100,000 gal of saline water per day. The water contains dissolved solids of 2,500 mg/l as sodium chloride. The resistance through the unit has been determined to be 7 ohms and the current efficiency, 92 percent. The maximum current density-normality ratio that may be used without serious polarization is 500. Estimate the removal efficiency and the power consumption per 1,000 gal of product water.

Solution:
1. Normality of the feedwater:

$$N = \frac{2,500 \text{ mg/l}}{58,500 \text{ mg/l/mole}} = 0.0427 \text{ mole}$$

2. Maximum current density allowable:

$$CD = 500N = 500 \times 0.0427 = 21.3 \text{ ma/sq cm}$$

3. Current required:

$$I = \frac{21.3 \text{ ma/sq cm} \times 20 \text{ in.} \times 24 \text{ in.} \times (2.54)^2}{1000 \text{ ma/amp}} = 66.2 \text{ amp}$$

4. Power consumption:

$$P = I^2 R = (66.2 \text{ amp})^2 (7 \text{ ohms}) = 30,600 \text{ watts}$$

$$E = \frac{30,600 \text{ watts} \times 24 \text{ hr/day} \times 1,000}{1,000 \text{ watts/kw} \times 100,000 \text{ gal/day}} = 7.34 \text{ kwh/1,000 gal}$$

5. The removal efficiency from Eq. 9-42:

$$u = \frac{Ene}{kiA RqNF}$$

$$= \frac{7.34 \times 400/2 \times 0.92}{0.001 \times 21.3 \times 20 \times 24 \times 2.54^2 \times 7 \times 100,000/22,800 \times 0.0427 \times 96,500}$$

$$= 0.674 \text{ or } 67.4 \text{ percent}$$

The total energy requirement is the electrical energy E plus the mechanical energy necessary to pump the water through the system. The mechanical energy of pumping must pass the water uniformly between the closely packed membranes. This energy requirement is independent of the dissolved solids and is a constant for a particular flow rate. The pressure drop across a stack handling 100,000 gpd would be in the range of 15–40 psi.

9-23. MINERAL BY-PRODUCTS FROM THE SEA

Seawater contains appreciable quantities of salts beside sodium chloride. These include magnesium, potassium sulfates, chlorides, sulfur, and calcium, along with many other elements in lesser amounts (Table 9-5). The values listed in Table 9-5 are on a per ton basis, and there are approximately 14.25×10^{17} tons of seawater on the earth. The sea forms a storehouse of minerals, provided that man can find out how to recover them individually at costs competitive with present sources.

TABLE 9-5
MATERIAL CONTAINED IN A TON OF SEAWATER[23]

Material	Weight, lb	Material	Weight, lb
Sodium chloride	55	Iodine	9×10^{-5}
Magnesium	2.54	Iron	4×10^{-5}
Sulfur	1.75	Copper	2×10^{-5}
Calcium	0.8	Lead	1×10^{-5}
Potassium	0.75	Zinc	1×10^{-5}
Bromine	0.125	Uranium	3×10^{-6}
Strontium	0.025	Silver	6×10^{-7}
Boron	0.008	Gold	12×10^{-9}
Fluorine	0.0025	Radium	1×10^{-12}

Potash is probably the mineral of greatest economic potential present in seawater. It is used in large tonnage quantities in this country and throughout the world for agriculture as a fertilizer. In 1959 the United States produced about 2.3 million tons of potash, K_2O, and this market is expected to increase substantially. If all of the potash this country uses were obtained from seawater, it would be necessary to process about 300 billion gallons of seawater per day. Each 1,000 gallons of seawater contains approximately 4 lb of potash with a value ranging from 10 to 20 cents per pound.

Potassium can be recovered from seawater by precipitation with sodium phosphate:

$$Na_3PO_4 + KCl + MgCl_2 \rightarrow MgKPO_4 + 3NaCl \qquad (9\text{-}43)$$

The potassium is precipitated as magnesium potassium phosphate mixed with other magnesium and calcium phosphates. Magnesium potassium phosphate is chemically similar to magnesium ammonium phosphate and is an efficient source of phosphate for growing plants.

Bromine has been used in photography, drugs, and dyestuffs in quantities measured in pounds rather than in tons. With the development of the use of ethylene bromide as an antiknock compound in gasoline, however, large quantities have been required. About 4,000 gal of seawater are required to yield 1 lb of bromine. Many thousands of tons are now produced annually from the sea at a reasonable cost and the supply is assured for all time. Calculations indicate that there are nearly one billion tons of bromine in the Dead Sea.

The success with recovery of bromine from seawater prepared the way for the recovery of magnesium. The first commercial ingot made in America from seawater was produced on January 21, 1941, at the Dow Chemical Company plant. The demand for magnesium for aircraft parts has suddenly reached vast proportions, for as much as 1,000 lb may be used in the manufacture of a single airplane. Magnesium is the lightest of all metals, and today thousands of tons are required annually and most of these come from the sea.

Gold is present in the sea in trace amounts and has been extracted on a trial basis, although the cost of extraction is several times more than its value. It appears, therefore, that it will be cheaper to mine gold than to obtain it from seawater. Gold can be obtained from bottom sludges as it is removed from seawater by adsorption onto the surface of organisms and thereby deposited on the ocean floor.

These are but a few of the many possible elements from the sea which is a vast potential source of raw materials. Many of the elements considered uneconomic to obtain from seawater at present may become economic in the near future as a by-product of saline water treatment.

RADIOACTIVITY IN WATER AND WASTE TREATMENT

9-24. RADIOACTIVITY

The classical picture of an atom consists of a central nucleus about which rotate a number of electrons in orbit. The nucleus is made up of relatively massive protons and neutrons. The proton carries a positive electrostatic charge, whereas the neutron has no charge.

Certain atoms are radioactive—that is, they have nuclei which are unstable. These nuclei emit an energetic particle, a pulse of energy, or both. This process is radioactive decay. The radiations are known as α (alpha) and β (beta) particles, and γ (gamma) rays. Particles and rays are readily distinguished by their behavior in a magnetic field. The alpha and beta particles are deflected by the field in such a way as to indicate that the former carries a positive and the latter a negative electrical charge. The gamma rays are undeflected and therefore presumably uncharged. A strong magnetic field will separate a mixed beam of radioactive emanations into the three types.

The penetrating powers of the α and β particles and γ rays increase in the order listed. Alpha particles are stopped by a few centimeters of air or a sheet of paper. Beta particles have about 100 times this penetrating power, while gamma rays exceed ordinary X-rays in their ability to penetrate materials. The γ rays from 30 mg of radium can conveniently be detected through 30 cm of iron.

An alpha particle is a nucleus of a helium atom. In alpha decay the parent nucleus loses two protons and two neutrons. The resulting daughter nucleus, therefore, is reduced by four mass units, and its positive charge is lowered by two units. For example, radium (atomic number 88, mass number 226) decays by alpha emission to radon (atomic number 86, mass number 222). The alpha particle picks up two electrons from the environment and becomes an atom of helium gas.

With beta decay, an electron is given off by the nucleus. Because electrons have very little mass, the mass number of the daughter nucleus is unchanged but its atomic number is increased by one unit, since the electron carries one negative unit of charge. Radiophosphorus (atomic number 15, mass number 32) decays to sulfur (atomic number 16, mass number 32) by giving off an electron.

Gamma decay is the emission of energy and no new nucleus is formed but the nucleus is left in a lower energy state.

The scheme of decay is specific for each radioactive isotoype. This scheme consists of the type of radiation, its energy level, and its half-life. The half-life is the period of time during which 50 percent of the number of radioactive atoms initially present will decay. This decay scheme is the basis for many analytical methods by which specific radio-isotopes can be identified.

The quantity of radioactivity is measured by the number of emissions that take place in a unit of time. The standard unit, called a *curie*, is 3.7×10^{10} emissions per second. This is the rate of disintegration of 1 g of radium.

9-25. RADIOACTIVE POLLUTANTS

Radioactive materials may contaminate a water naturally or may come from such sources as tests of nuclear weapons, wastes from industrial use of atomic energy, or from the use of radioactive substances in research or medicine.

The nature and amount of radioactive fallout from a weapons test depends on the type and energy yield of the nuclear device and the conditions under which it was exploded. Fallout from tests taking place above the ground is readily carried into the atmosphere. There is the possibility that certain volatile products may be vented to the atmosphere from underground tests. From high-yield explosions, a substantial portion of the fallout penetrates the stratosphere. This fallout is dispersed to every part of the world by upper-air currents. Much of this radioactive debris reaches the earth by precipitation.

The refining of uranium ores is an important source of radioactive waste. Raw ore from the mine is processed at the mill to concentrate the uranium. The processing steps include crushing and grinding, washing, and several chemical treatments. The product from the mill is fused uranium salts. These salts are shipped to other installations for further processing, refining, and final use. Wastes from the mill include wash waters, process liquors, and solids. These liquid wastes are normally stored in ponds where the volume is reduced by evaporation and seepage.

Uranium is the mother of a chain of naturally occurring radio-isotopes. It decays to thorium, which in turn reduces to isotopes of radium, bismuth, etc. The end product is a stable form of lead. Uranium is normally the only isotope recovered from the ore, and the process wastes include all of the radioactive daughters in varying amounts. Radium is the most significant waste product. It is considered to be a hazard in drinking water. It is a bone-seeking alpha emitter having a half-life of 1,620 years.

Nuclear reactors for various industrial and research purposes represent a potential source of radioactive waste. The operation of reactors induces radiation in structural elements and coolants. The production of radioactivity in the materials discharged to the environment is minimized by design but there is always the possibility of rupture or failure.

The disposal of excessive quantities of radioactive material to streams would interfere with other uses of the water. The maximum allowable concentrations of radioactivity in drinking water are specified in the U.S. Public Health Drinking Water Standards (see Chap. 7). The control of radioactive-waste discharges to water is a problem no different in principle than the control of any other industrial waste. It involves a very direct public health hazard and must be rigidly controlled.

9-26. REMOVAL OF RADIOACTIVITY FROM WATER

The effects of normal water-treatment processes on radioactive liquids have been studied by the U.S. Public Health Service and others. These processes have been found to remove some radioactivity but not significant amounts of cesium and strontium. Filtration will normally remove only those wastes associated with suspended solids. The lime-soda-ash process of softening has been found effective in removing most radioactive wastes including strontium, but not cesium. Ion-exchange resins have been found effective for removing certain radionuclides. Distillation is the most effective method of radioactive waste removal from water but it is expensive.

These processes result in a concentrated sludge which must be disposed of by some form of isolation. The disposal of concentrated wastes includes disposal in wells, placement in salt mines, and solids fixation.

Each source of radioactive water pollution represents an individual problem to be solved in terms of a specific location. In each case, the type and quantity of waste involved, environmental factors, and planned water uses must be taken into consideration. All radiation exposure should be reduced and minimized to whatever extent is reasonable.

REFERENCES

1. G. M. Fair and J. C. Geyer, *Water Supply and Waste-Water Disposal* (New York: John Wiley and Sons, Inc., 1954), p. 468.
2. W. F. Langelier, "The Analytical Control of Anticorrosion Water Treatment," *J. Am. Water Works Assoc.*, vol. 28 (1936), p. 1500.
3. Werner Stumm, "Investigation on the Corrosive Behavior of Waters," *Trans. Am. Soc. Civil Engrs.*, vol. 127, part III (1962), p. 31.
4. S. P. Lawson and R. Snyders, "Lime Acid Reaction for Water Stabilization," *J. Am. Water Works Assoc.*, vol. 54 (February 1962), pp. 176–180.
5. Lours R. Howson, "Economics of Water Softening," *J. Am. Water Works Assoc.*, vol. 54 (February 1962), pp. 161–166.
6. Harry A. Alsentzer, "Ion Exchange in Water Treatment," *J. Am. Water Works Assoc.*, vol. 55 (June 1963), pp. 742–748.
7. H. Gladys Swope, "Mixed Bed Ion Exchange for the Removal of Radioactivity," *J. Am. Water Works Assoc.*, vol. 49 (August 1957), pp. 1085–1102.
8. Benjamin F. Willey and Harry Jennings, "Iron and Manganese Removal

with Potassium Permanganate," *J. Am. Water Works Assoc.*, vol. 55 (June 1963), pp. 729–734.

9. Sereno F. Alling, "Continuously Regenerated Greensand for Iron and Manganese Removal," *J. Am. Water Works Assoc.*, vol. 55 (June 1963), pp. 749–752.

10. Werner Stumm and James J. Morgan, "Chemical Aspects of Coagulation," *J. Am. Water Works Assoc.*, vol. 54 (August 1962), pp. 971–994.

11. A. P. Black, "Theory of Coagulation," *Water Sewage Works*, Reference Number (1961), p. R192–199.

12. James C. Vaughn, "Common Chemicals Used in Coagulation," *Water Sewage Works*, no. 108 (1961), pp. R207–210.

13. A. B. Middleton, "Activated Solica Sol Applications," *Water Sewage Works*, vol. 110 (July 1963).

14. "Saline Water Conversion Program," *U.S. Office Saline Water* (Washington, D.C.: U.S. Government Printing Office, 1962), pamphlet 649411 0-69-2.

15. York Sampson, "The Nation's Water Crisis," *Am. Engr.* (October 1963), p. 29.

16. Barnett F. Dodge, "Fresh Water from Saline Waters," *Am. Scientist*, vol. 48, no. 4 (December 1960), pp. 476–513.

17. James C. Lamb, III, "Economic Aspects of Saline-Water Conversion," *J. Am. Water Works Assoc.*, vol. 54 (July 1962), pp. 781–788.

18. Warren Viessman, Jr., "Desalination Brine Waste Disposal," *Public Works*, vol. 94, no. 12 (December 1963), pp. 117–118.

19. John E. Edinger et al., "The Future Uses of Saline and Fresh Water Resources of the United States," Report of 1962–1964 Advanced Seminar Sanitary Engineering and Water Resources, The Johns Hopkins University, Baltimore, Md., June 1964.

20. O. G. George, "Demineralization of Saline Water with Solar Energy," in *U.S. Office Saline Water, Saline Water Research and Development Progress Report No. 4* (Washington, D.C.: U.S. Government Printing Office, 1954).

21. Aerojet-General Corporation, "The Mechanism of Desalination by Reverse Osmosis," in *U.S. Office Saline Water, Saline Water Research and Development Progress Report No. 84* (Washington, D.C.: U.S. Government Printing Office, November 1963).

22. George W. Murphy, "The Osmionic Process," in *U.S. Office Saline Water, Saline Water Research and Development Progress Report No. 14* (Washington, D.C.: U.S. Government Printing Office, 1957).

23. Stewart J. Lloyd, "The World's Greatest Mine," *J. Chem. Educ.*, vol. 24, no. 6 (1947), p. 273.

PROBLEMS

9-1. A laboratory analysis of water gives the following information:

Total dissolved solids	230 mg/l
Calcium ion concentration	2.1 me/l
Total carbonate alkalinity	0.9 me/l
Temperature	20°C
*p*H	7.2

Determine the conditions of the water in relation to the calcium carbonate in solution.

9-2. Compute the ionic strength of a water at 25°C with the following analysis:

Substance	Molar Concentration
Ca^{++}	2.5×10^{-3}
Na^+	1.2×10^{-3}
HCO_3^-	3×10^{-3}
Cl^-	1.8×10^{-3}

9-3. Compute the solubility of $Ca(OH)_2$ in water at 25°C if the composition of the solution is such that the activity coefficient f is unity and (a) if the hardness of the water is zero and (b) if the water contains 250 mg/l of calcium hardness.

9-4. Determine the amounts of lime as $Ca(OH)_2$ and soda ash theoretically required to remove all of the hardness from the following water:

Dissolved CO_2.................................... 40 mg/l as CO_2
Alkalinity with phenolphthalein.................. 0
Total alkalinity.................................. 300 mg/l as $CaCO_3$
Magnesium.. 50 mg/l as Mg^{++}
Noncarbonate hardness............................ 75 mg/l as $CaCO_3$

This result will be theoretical, since it is not possible to soften water completely with lime and soda ash.

9-5. Calculate the quantities of lime as CaO and soda ash required to completely soften the following water:

Carbon dioxide	0.5 g me/l as CO_2
Total alkalinity	3.1 g me/l as $CaCO_3$
Total hardness	4.5 g me/l as $CaCO_3$
Magnesium hardness	1.8 g me/l as Mg^{++}

9-6. Calculate the weight of quicklime (90 percent CaO) and soda ash (97 percent Na_2CO_3) necessary to theoretically soften a water having the following analysis. Express the results in pounds per 1,000 gals.

CO_2.. 10 mg/l
HCO_3^- .... 160 mg/l
Mg^{++}... 30 mg/l
Total hardness .... 300 mg/l as $CaCO_3$

9-7. A water with a total hardness of 260 mg/l contains 150 mg/l of carbonate hardness. It is desired to soften this water to a total carbonate hardness of 75 mg/l with no sulfate hardness. How many pounds of hydrated lime and of soda ash will be required per million gallons to theoretically soften this water?

9-8. A zeolite exchanger is 4 ft deep and is operated at a rate of 8 gpm/sq ft. The zeolite will remove 15 gram-equivalents per cubic foot. A water is to be softened which contains 170 mg/l of Ca^{++}, 60 mg/l of Mg^{++}, and 10 mg/l of Fe^{++}. Sodium chloride is to be used for regeneration and the observed requirements are 3 equivalents of salt per equivalent exchanged. Determine the length of time during which the bed of zeolite will operate and the amount of salt required for regeneration.

9-9. A softening unit contains 1,000 cu ft of resin that has a $CaCO_3$ removal efficiency of 7,000 g/cu ft. It requires 0.5 lb of salt per 1,000 gr of hardness removed. The salt is stored as a 25 percent solution and diluted to a 7 percent solution for use. How many gallons of concentrated salt brine is used for regeneration? How much dilution water is used with this concentrated brine?

9-10. A zeolite exchanger is to be operated at the rate of 8 gpm/sq ft and is 3.5 ft deep. The zeolite will remove 12,000 gr/cu ft and is to be used to soften a water with a total hardness of 400 mg/l as $CaCO_3$. The water is to be softened to 100 mg/l of $CaCO_3$. What volume of resin is required to treat 70,000 gals of water without regeneration?

9-11. A water containing 200 mg/l total hardness as $CaCO_3$ is to be softened to 100 mg/l by base exchange with a resin with a removal efficiency of 10,000 gr/cu ft. Exchange equipment costs $75/cu ft installed. What should be the initial cost of a plant to soften 5 mgpd if the unit is to be regenerated hourly and requires 15 min? Provide no standby equipment.

9-12. A city of 150,000 population uses water of 300 mg/l total hardness as $CaCO_3$. It is estimated that the water can be softened to 100 mg/l at a cost of $1.50 per million gallons for each graim per gallon of hardness removed. It is ·estimated that the savings in soap will amount to 3 cents per person per day. Should the city soften the water by the proposed method?

9-13. It requires 0.5 lb of salt per 1,000 gr of hardness removed for the unit in Prob. 9-12. How many pounds of salt are required per month? A minimum of three-months' supply is maintained at all times and salt is delivered monthly. What salt-storage capacity is required?

9-14. A water-treatment plant is treating 15 mgpd of water. It requires 1.5 gpg of alum. How many milligrams per liter of natural alkalinity will be required to react with this alum? If no natural alkalinity is present, what is the theoretical dosage of lime as CaO in pounds per day?

9-15. A water requires 6.5 mg/l of alum. The water contains 2.8 mg/l of natural bicarbonate alkalinity as HCO_3^-. How much lime as CaO must be added to complete the reaction with the alum?

9-16. Ferrous sulfate, $FeSO_4 \cdot 7H_2O$, is used as a coagulant with a water containing 3 mg/l of dissolved oxygen and 4 mg/l of HCO_3^-. The pH is 6.5 and the flow is 11 mgpd. How much ferrous sulfate is theoretically required per day to treat this water?

9-17. What is the minimum energy required to recover 1,000 gallons of fresh water from a brackish water containing 4,500 mg/l as sodium chloride? The temperature is 25°C. What would be the probable energy requirements with a present process?

9-18. What is the theoretical minimum work required in a saline-water conversion process where the feedwater is pumped against a 110 ft head and 35 percent of the water is recovered as fresh water? Give the answer in horsepower per 1,000 gals.

9-19. With energy costing 0.1 cents per kwh and with the use of Fig. 9-13, what would be the necessary efficiency of a separation process in order to compete with the 5 cents per 1,000 gals for in-plant conventional water treatment?

9-20. An inland city of 300,000 population using water at the rate of 150 gpd plans to use a brackish raw-water supply. The brackish water contains

35,000 mg/l as sodium chloride. The proposed process will result in a 35 percent fresh water recovery. What is the annual volume of waste brine? What is the weight of the sodium chloride in this annual volume of waste brine?

9-21. The waste brine in Prob. 9-20 has an average annual evaporation rate in excess of rainfall of 11 in./year for the particular location. Solar evaporation is being studied as a means of disposal of the liquid brine waste. What is the surface area of the evaporation pond necessary to dispose of this waste?

9-22. An electrodialysis stack is made up of 500 membranes 48 × 48 in. This unit will be used to partially demineralize 300,000 gals of brackish water per day. The water contains 3,500 mg/l of dissolved solids as sodium chloride. The resistance through the unit has been determined to be 8 ohms and the current efficiency, 89 percent. The maximum current density-normality ratio that may be used without serious polarization is 600 ohms. Estimate the removal efficiency and the power consumption per 1,000 gals of product water.

9-23. Using the data in example Prob. 9-6, calculate the conversion cost per 1,000 gals based on the following assumptions:

1. Energy cost is equal to 0.1 cents per kwh.
2. Pumping head is 60 ft at 70 percent efficiency.
3. Operation, capital recovery, and maintenance costs are equal to 3 times the total energy cost.

9-24. How many pounds of seawater must be treated to produce 1 ton of magnesium if the process is 35 percent efficient?

9-25. Discuss the various treatment processes that would be encountered when using Missouri River water above Kansas City, Missouri, for a municipal supply. Use library references for water-quality information.

9-26. Discuss the various treatment processes that would be encountered when using Mississippi River water above St. Louis, Missouri, for a municipal supply. Use library references for water-quality information.

9-27. Discuss the various treatment processes that would be encountered when using Pecos River water above Carlsbad, New Mexico, for a municipal supply. Use library references for water-quality information.

chapter 10

Biological-Treatment Processes

Engineers are concerned with the reactions that characterize decomposition of organic wastes, and particularly with the the rates at which these reactions proceed. Treatment facilities provide environments in which processes of decomposition can operate at maximal rates. Design of a treatment system is executed by properly combining certain unit processes. Efficient design requires that the engineer understand some of the microbiology of the processes involved.

BIOLOGICAL CONSIDERATIONS

One of the fundamental attributes of living organisms is their ability to utilize and convert energy. One gram of *Escherichia coli* bacteria develops energy at the rate of 0.6 watt, a not unusual rate for bacteria.[1] It is essential in water and waste treatment for the engineer to have some knowledge of the way in which energy is transferred from one form to another and from one place to another. The biochemical processes involved in these energy transfers are known collectively as *metabolism*. Those involved in the breakdown of complex matter to simpler forms are known as *katabolism*, and the reverse process of synthesis of complex matter from simpler substances is called *anabolism*.

The decomposition of organic matter in polluted water is directly linked to the presence of bacteria and other organisms. Although some bacteria are responsible for causing disease, most are beneficial in the decomposition of organic matter—for example, fertility of soil depends upon this decomposition. The filamentous fungi also are important members of the population of organisms occurring in polluted waters. Like many bacteria, most fungi have simple cells devoid of chlorophyll. Protozoa and other plankton are present in polluted waters, but their growth rates are much slower than those of bacteria. They are significant in the life cycle of polluted water because they use bacteria as food. A community of organisms having varying degrees of complexity extends through all forms of aquatic life. Bacteria are by far the most influential organisms in waste-water treatment processes. The remaining discussion will be concerned with them.

Chemical reactions involved in metabolism proceed at a much greater rate than that in a normal environment. These high reaction rates are made possible by the presence of numerous catalysts. Catalysts are substances that affect the rate of a chemical reaction but which remain unchanged themselves at the end of the reaction. Organic catalysts produced by bacteria are called *enzymes*. These enzymes are rather specific in the reactions they promote. One enzyme is generally capable of promoting one or, at most, a few reactions, hence numerous enzymes are required to promote the wide range of metabolic processes occurring within and outside the bacterial cell.

The growth and multiplication of bacteria in water is dependent upon the presence of compounds containing carbon and nitrogen in a form capable of being synthesized into new cells and used to furnish energy for the cells. Ingestion of food by bacteria is accomplished by the passage of compounds through the cell walls. Small bacterial cells require food that is in true solution; some of the larger bacteria are capable of ingesting more complex molecules. Organic wastes in true solution, or which are finely divided, are immediately available to the bacteria as food. Insoluble larger particles of organic matter must be chemically acted upon with the aid of enzymes to bring them into solution prior to their being available as bacterial food. This reaction takes place outside the cell wall.

10-1. CELL GROWTH

Growth curves for pure cultures of microorganisms have been studied by many investigators. For a given set of environmental conditions these curves generally follow a predictable and reproducible pattern (Fig. 10-1). First, a lag is exhibited during which the organisms become adjusted to the substrate and surrounding physical conditions. The microorganisms then enter a stage of progressive multiplication—the logarithmic phase. The rate of multiplication later decreases until a period of stationary

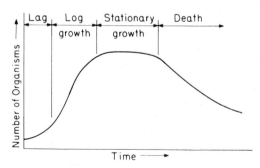

FIG. 10-1. An idealized curve representing growth of a bacterial culture.

growth is reached in which the number of organisms remains relatively constant. Finally, the culture enters a death phase during which the number of viable organisms surviving with each generation is fewer than the previous population.

Lag is characterized by little or no multiplication of cells and a rapid uptake of soluble substrate with extreme enlargement of the individual cells. For most cases this is not a lag in protoplasm formation but simply a delay in cellular division.

The maximum rate of oxygen uptake per cell closely follows the end of the lag phase and corresponds exactly to the time when the cells are largest. Total oxygen demand is a function of both protoplasm formation and growth rate. The lag period represents initially a period of expression of the energy which the bacterial cell retained from its previous environment. Until this stored energy is utilized and new enzymes are formed which can catalyze the new substrate, little or no growth will occur. Secondly, lag is a period of rapid assimilation of soluble substrate during which the soluble material is locked into the intracellular compartment, where it is later metabolized.

The nature of the inoculum (bacteria) transferred to the substrate has considerable influence on the length of the lag phase. Lag is inversely proportional to the initial number of viable cells added to the medium and is influenced by the period of growth prior to the time the organisms were transferred. Organisms when transferred from a logarithmic phase of growth usually have a shorter lag than when transferred from any other stage of development.

Organisms exhibiting rapid generation times commonly have short lag periods. Transfer to a medium different from that on which the culture was originally grown tends to induce longer lag periods as does treatment of the cells by washing. Toxic compounds, pH, concentration of the medium, carbon dioxide, and oxygen tensions all are physical factors that can influence lag. As these factors approach the optimum for growth, lag usually decreases.

The second well-defined stage known as the logarithmic microbial growth period follows the lag phase. It is characterized by a uniform division of the swollen cells from the lag phase according to a logarithmic progression. During this period, regular and maximum multiplication of cells takes place, the generation time is reduced to a minimum, the cell size decreases, and resistance to toxic materials and heat is a minimum.

The length of the logarithmic phase is controlled in part by the same physical factors affecting lag. The volume and concentration of the culture media ultimately control the maximum number of organisms that can be produced. Growth of *E. coli* in glucose increases up to a glucose concentration of about 40 mg/l, then is constant. A similar situation occurs for other nutrients such as tryptophan and phosphate.

During growth, biological space becomes critical and logarithmic reproduction can cease before the substrate is exhausted. A value of about 5×10^9 cells per milliliter has been reported in the literature as the concentration of cells at which all divisions cease for *E. coli*. At this maximum concentration, synthesis and respiration still go on although cellular division stops.

For mixed populations the rate of growth of one type organism may be controlled by the rate of production of certain by-products of other species. Simultaneous growth can occur, or dependent species may not grow well until the preceding species die off, yielding essential nutrients to the environment.

As each cell-division velocity decreases, the logarithmic phase changes to a stage of steady growth. This stationary condition is characterized by a rate of cellular production equal to the rate at which cells die. Steady-state conditions may be precipitated by depletion of the food supply, accumulation of toxic by-products, concentration of the substrate, exhaustion of an essential nutrient, or conditions which limit biological space. When two or more kinds of organisms are grown together, the type organism which can grow at higher cellular densities will usually predominate. The length of the stationary phase depends largely on the amount of substrate present.

The death phase represents metabolism of assimilated material and eventually results in a decrease of cell numbers. This declining growth phase is characterized by a minimal growth exhibited by the natural selection of resistant cells. The metabolic requirements of these cells are met at the expense of less resistant and dead cells. For mixed populations, a predominant species which can readily use proteinaceous material will prevail during the death phase.

In general the previous statements have been proven true from studies of pure cultures on pure substrates. The effect of changing environmental conditions for mixed populations has been mainly investigated, using soil microorganisms. The influence of variations in temperature, pH, substrate, nitrogen source, etc. normally produce shifts in the kinds of organisms which predominate. The predominant species of a mixed population are those which can grow more readily under the environmental conditions prevailing.

In practice it has been customary to translate data on pure cultures to mixed-culture systems. Parameters of many biological analyses, such as the BOD test used for designing sewage-treatment facilities, are measured by equations developed from such idealized situations and assumptions.

Cells, or bacteria, grow by taking material from outside the cell wall and converting it to build their own constituent material. The rate of chemical change and synthesis is very rapid; a growing bacterial cell will synthesize 40,000 amino acids of one kind per second. It will form 150,000 peptide bonds per second, and under certain conditions the bacteria will utilize the content of 50 times its own volume of material before division. Many bacteria multiply by binary fission, i.e., splitting of one cell to make two.

Bacteria in the proper environment follow the mathematical relation in terms of division shown by Eq. 10-1.

$$N = I(2)^{t/t_0}$$ (10-1)

where N = total number of cells present (the total population)
     I = initial number of cells
     t_0 = the time of one generation
     t = the total elapsed time

Behavior of an actual population of bacterial cells is somewhat more complex since the environment is normally not ideal (at least over a long period of time), and the population increase is certain to be limited at the upper end of the bacterial equivalent of overpopulation. The entire ecological system is always working toward a biological balance. Environmental factors affecting an organism and limiting its population may be considered under three loosely defined headings: (1) physical, (2) chemical, and (3) biotic. Physical factors include the physical nature of the habitat, temperature, light, and movement of the medium. Chemical factors include pH, oxygen content, salinity, and the presence of toxic substances. Biotic factors are those involving the interrelationship with other organisms. These include predator-prey relationships, competition for food, and the competition for oxygen and actual living space. The activity of a population may affect the chemical and physical environment (Fig. 10-2).

A change in environment may be unfavorable to the population, or be more suitable to another species which in time will take over as the dominant one. Repetition of this process produces a succession of dominant species. Evidence of such a sequence can be readily witnessed by following the variations in a typical five-day BOD (Fig. 10-3). In Fig. 10-3 the six peaks on the viable cell count represent different species of bacteria. Changes in the environment are shown by corresponding changes in turbidity, pH, and oxygen-uptake rates.

Energy for the respiration and synthesis of bacterial cells is supplied by wet combustion or oxidation of the chemical compounds. This combustion process can take place with or without molecular oxygen gas dissolved in the water. Oxidation accomplished by the use of molecular oxygen is called *aerobiosis;* without the use of molecular oxygen it is *anaerobiosis.* Bacteria requiring molecular oxygen for their respiration and synthesis are called *strict aerobes;* those whose growth requires the complete absence of dissolved oxygen are *strict anaerobes.* Most bacteria

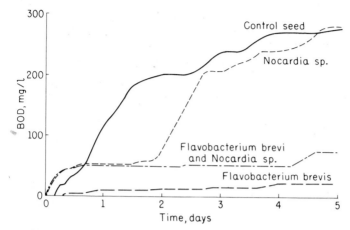

FIG. 10-2. Biochemical oxygen demand of a control mixed seed, *Nacardia* sp., *Flavobacterium brevis,* and a combination of *Nacardia* sp., and *Flavobacterium brevis* measured continuously over a five-day period. [2]

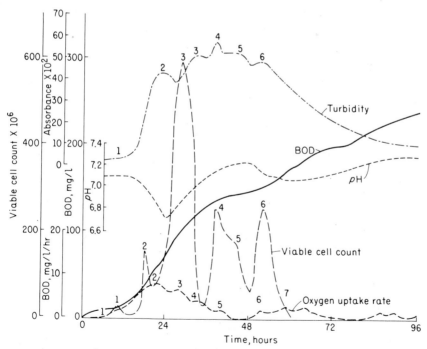

FIG. 10-3. The variation of dominant species in a five-day BOD, showing ecological succession.

concerned with waste treatment are *faculative anaerobes* and obtain their
energy for growth either aerobically or anaerobically, depending upon the
amount of dissolved oxygen available and the character of the organic
matter.

10-2. BIOLOGICAL OXIDATION

Biological oxidation, or aerobic digestion, describes those biochemical reactions in which materials combine with molecular oxygen to produce energy. The maximum amount of energy which can be obtained
from organic compounds results from their combustion in the presence
of oxygen at high temperatures. Hydrogen is oxidized to water and carbon to carbon dioxide and the energy is given off as heat. A reaction of
this type is of no use to the cell as the necessary temperatures are too
high. The cell uses enzyme-catalyzed reactions which take place in such
a way that not all of the energy is lost as heat. Some of the energy is
utilized by the cell and called *respiration*. Despite the different processes,
the final results of biological oxidation are similar to those of chemical
oxidation.

Oxidation of one substance results in the reduction of another and a
biological oxidation-reduction reaction may be regarded as the transfer
of electrons from the substance oxidized to the one being reduced. This
is the transfer of hydrogen atoms from the substance oxidized to oxygen,
the hydrogen acceptor.

$$\text{Organic H} + O_2 \xrightarrow{\text{bacteria}} H_2O - \Delta H \qquad (10\text{-}2)$$

The initial dehydrogenation of the organic matter is catalyzed by enzymes
and transfer of hydrogen takes place by one or more intermediate carriers.
These intermediate carriers are called coenzymes and form what is termed
a respiratory pathway. The respiratory pathway traps and stores chemical
energy which is released for subsequent use by the cell.

EXAMPLE 10-1.   What is the heat of reaction for forming one liter of water
from hydrogen and oxygen? The pressure is constant at one atmosphere and the
temperature is 25°C.

Solution:
1. $2H_2 + O_2 \rightarrow 2H_2O - \Delta H$
2. $-\Delta H = +68.3$ kcal/mole of water formed (from thermochemical tables
   for 25°C and one atmosphere)
3. One mole of water $= 18$ g
   One liter of water $= \dfrac{1,000}{18} = 55.6$ moles
4. $55.6 \times 68.3 = 3,790$ kcal or $3,790$ kcal of heat are given off by the reaction of hydrogen and oxygen to form one liter of water at 25°C and at
   a constant pressure of one atmosphere

10-3. NUTRITION

The nutritional requirements of microorganisms fall into four categories: (1) compounds that furnish carbon and nitrogen, (2) compounds used as a source of energy, (3) inorganics, and (4) trace substances. All naturally occurring organic substances, some inorganics, and many synthetic ones are attacked by at least one species of microorganism. The presence of specific substances in a waste is an important factor. Some organisms are able to utilize a wide range of organic substances as their primary food source, while others are more specific. All microorganisms require the basic elements carbon, nitrogen, phosphorus, and sulfur, together with certain trace elements such as potassium, calcium, zinc, magnesium, iron, manganese, copper, and cobalt. Carbon, nitrogen, and phosphorus are required in generally balanced amounts. In waste-treatment practice the carbon is usually represented by the five-day, 20°C BOD of the waste and other elements are given relative to the BOD. The following ratios have been suggested for adequate quantities of nitrogen and phosphorus.[4]

$$BOD \text{ to } N = 20 \text{ to } 1$$
$$BOD \text{ to } P = 100 \text{ to } 1$$

Domestic sewage normally provides a nutritionally balanced food with the necessary trace elements for bacterial activity. The presence of a large proportion of industrial waste mixed with domestic sewage may upset this balance. Some wastes such as those from milk processing may increase the nitrogen content, while others such as brewery wastes may create a nitrogen deficiency. Nitrogen and phosphorus deficiencies in industrial wastes may be overcome by the addition of agricultural chemicals.

A chemical analysis of the mixed aerobic bacterial population in waste treatment gave an approximate relationship for the principal elements.[5]

$$C_5H_7NO_2 \tag{10-3}$$

Other elements such as phosphorus and sulfur were present only in trace amounts. This empirical formula is useful in stoichiometric calculations. The nutritional balance of an aerobic system is based primarily upon satisfying the requirements of the cell structure produced by bacteria during BOD reduction.

OXYGEN REQUIREMENTS

10-4. THEORETICAL OXYGEN DEMANDS

Microorganisms are small chemical factories in which raw materials are processed. The raw materials can be almost anything in nature.

Finished products are cell material and energy. Most microorganisms are heterotrophic—that is, they use organic material for both food and energy. Autotrophic bacteria utilize inorganic compounds as their source of food and energy. Bacteria can exploit a single raw material as their sole source of energy and obtain necessary trace substances from the water environment. From a single raw-material source, bacteria produce the hundreds of different molecules that compose their cell structures.

In a BOD test using carbohydrate as the only carbon source, typical reactions may be shown as follows:

Carbohydrate Oxidation

$$C_x H_y O_z + O_2 \xrightarrow{\text{bacteria}} CO_2 + H_2O - \Delta H \qquad (10\text{-}4)$$

Cell Material Synthesis

$$C_x H_y O_z + NH_3 + O_2 \xrightarrow{\text{bacteria}}$$
$$CO_2 + H_2O + \text{bacteria cells} - \Delta H \qquad (10\text{-}5)$$

Cell Material Oxidation

$$\text{Bacteria Cells} + O_2 \xrightarrow{\text{bacteria}} CO_2 + H_2O + NH_3 - \Delta H \qquad (10\text{-}6)$$

All of these reactions are exothermic and ΔH represents the heat of reaction. The generalized equations must be modified to include trace elements such as phosphorus and sulfur.

Equation 10-4 is the typical equation of combustion. Where nitrogen, phosphorus, and sulfur are present in the organic material they will be oxidized in the following manner:

$$\text{Organic nitrogen} + O_2 \xrightarrow{\text{bacteria}} NO_3^- \qquad (10\text{-}7)$$

$$\text{Inorganic phosphate} \xrightarrow{\text{bacteria}} \text{Organic phosphate} \qquad (10\text{-}8)$$

$$\text{Organic sulfur} + O_2 \xrightarrow{\text{bacteria}} SO_4^- \qquad (10\text{-}9)$$

Equation 10-5 represents the synthesis of cell material from a carbohydrate using ammonia as the nitrogen source. The nitrogen may have been combined in the organic material along with other necessary elements.

Equation 10-6 represents the oxidation of cellular material. Here the nitrogen and other elements are available for reuse and energy is given off by the system.

Oxygen utilization in biological oxidation is intimately related to the growth and maintenance of living organisms. The relationship is shown in Fig. 10-4. Organic food sources not only furnish the elements out of which cell material is constructed but also provide the necessary energy. This energy is released through biological oxidation where hydrogen atoms are transferred from the substance being oxidized to oxygen, the hydrogen acceptor.

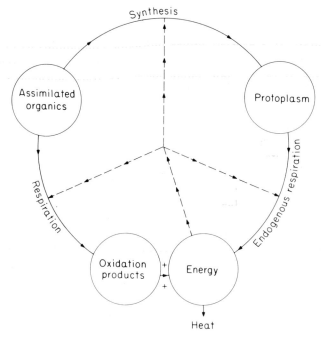

FIG. 10-4. Energy in metabolism.

EXAMPLE 10-2. How many pounds of ammonia gas are required in the synthesis of 1 lb of dextrose ($C_6H_{12}O_6$) to cell material?

Solution: The empirical formula for cell material given in Eq. 10-3 yields,

$$C_6H_{12}O_6 + NH_3 + O_2 \xrightarrow{\text{bacteria}} C_5H_7NO_2 + CO_2 + 4H_2O - \Delta H$$

From the equation, one molecule of ammonia is required for each molecule of dextrose and therefore, the amount of ammonia is given by

$$1 \times \frac{\text{mol. wt. } NH_3}{\text{mol. wt. } C_6H_{12}O_6} = 1 \times \frac{17}{180} = 0.09 \text{ lb}$$

10-5. BIOCHEMICAL OXYGEN DEMAND (BOD)

The biochemical oxygen demand (BOD) of sewage, industrial waste, or polluted water is the amount of molecular oxygen required to stabilize the decomposable matter present in a water by aerobic biochemical action. Oxygen demand is exerted by three classes of matter—carbonaceous material, oxidizable nitrogen, and certain chemical reducing compounds. The classes of matter present and the manner in which oxygen demand is exerted are a function of the type and history of the waste. The complete stabilization of a given waste may require too long a time for practical purposes; the five-day incubation period has been accepted as a standard.

The BOD test is among the most important made in sanitary analyses to determine the strength of sewage, industrial waste, or polluted water. It is used as a parameter in process design and loading and as a measure of plant efficiency and operation.

The presently accepted definition of biochemical oxygen demand is the fruition of over a century of research on a natural phenomenon that is relatively simple in principle yet exceedingly complex in evaluation and instrumentation.[6]

Frankland was the first to use a form of the BOD test in attempting to evaluate the pollutional load of the Thames River.[7] In 1868 he used an excess-oxygen technique involving the incubation of river-water samples in completely filled and tightly stoppered bottles. The dissolved oxygen remaining in the samples at 24-hr intervals was determined by boiling off the dissolved gases in vacuo and performing a gas analysis on the product. The seven-day curve produced in this experiment closely resembles present-day BOD curves.

The first chemical oxygen demand test (COD) using potassium permanganate was developed by Forchamer in 1849.[8] He did not recognize that the decomposition of organic matter is largely a biological process but did attempt to determine the oxidizable matter present in a water quantitatively. The possibility that microorganisms in water had the ability to consume the oxygen dissolved in water for their own metabolic processes was first proposed by Dupré in 1884.[9] He also made comparisons between the BOD and the COD tests, concluding that there was a difference between the amount of oxygen taken up by the microorganisms and by the amount of oxygen which the same water would take up from a solution of permanganate.

Investigators continued active interest in BOD related tests of various types but the most significant single contribution was reported by the Royal Commission in 1913.[10] The dilution-bottle method proposed by Adeney consisted essentially of the standard method used today. The determination of the biochemical oxygen demand by the standard dilution bottle method is accomplished by diluting suitable portions of the sample with water saturated with oxygen and measuring the dissolved oxygen both immediately and after a period of incubation, usually five days at 20°C. The acceptance of the dilution-bottle technique for determining BOD was not extended until the seventh edition of *Standard Methods,* published in 1933. One of the chief reasons for this acceptance was the research done by Theriault. His work was strongly in favor of the dilution method and his "Oxygen Demand of Polluted Waters," published as *Public Health Service Bulletin Number 173*, is one of the classics of the field.[11] The dilution method is based upon the following formulation:

$$\text{mg/l BOD} = \frac{D_1 - D_2}{p} \tag{10-10}$$

where D_1 = dissolved oxygen in the diluted sample after preaeration

$\quad\quad D_2$ = dissolved oxygen of the diluted sample after incubation

$\quad\quad p$ = decimal fraction of the waste sample used

A more complete description and procedure for the test will be found in *Standard Methods*.

Since its introduction, the dilution method has been the object of considerable research to improve its accuracy as an analytical tool. One of the chief areas of study has been toward the development of a satisfactory dilution water. As shown in Fig. 10-5, the progressive exertion of the

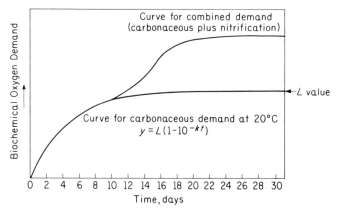

FIG. 10-5. Progress of biochemical oxygen demand.

BOD of freshly polluted water normally breaks down into two stages: a first stage in which the carbonaceous material is largely oxidized, and a second stage in which significant amounts of nitrification take place.

10-6. FORMULATION OF THE FIRST-STAGE BOD CURVE

During the first stage the rate of deoxidation at any time is normally assumed to be directly proportional to the amount of biologically degradeable matter present. This is a principle of physical chemistry which states that the velocity of a chemical reaction is some power of the concentration of the reacting substances. The actual progress of the BOD curve is more typical of processes having activation energy, as found in enzymatic reactions, but the generalization gives reasonable results, as shown by experiments. Assuming that the velocity of the bacterial reactions varies directly as the concentration of their food supply, the law may be expressed as

$$-\frac{dc}{dt} = K'C \tag{10-11}$$

In the BOD reaction, C is equal to the initial substrate concentration L, less the BOD (y), at any time t. Then;

$$\frac{d(L - y)}{dt} = -K'(L - y) \qquad \text{or} \qquad \frac{d(L - y)}{L - y} = k' dt$$

Integrating

$$\int_{y=0}^{y=y} \frac{d(L - y)}{L - y} = \int_{t=0}^{t=t} -K' dt$$

or

$$\ln \frac{L - y}{L} = k' dt$$

This equation is

$$\frac{L - y}{L} = e^{-k't} \qquad \text{or} \qquad y = L(1 - e^{-k't})$$

and since $e^{-k't} = 10^{-kt}$,

$$y = L(1 - 10^{-kt}) \qquad\qquad (10\text{-}12)$$

The evaluation of this equation is complicated by the fact that L and k are usually unknown. A number of methods for finding the magnitudes of L and k from a series of observations of y and t have been proposed. These include the use of tables as developed by Theriault[11], the "Method of Moments" developed by Moore, Thomas, and Snow[12] and graphic methods. The reader is referred to Nemerow[13] for a more complete analysis.

EXAMPLE 10-3.   The five-day BOD (y) of a waste is 200 mg/l. Assuming k to be 0.17, what is the ultimate demand L?

Solution: The data are

$$y = 200$$
$$t = 5$$
$$k = 0.17$$
$$y = L(1 - 10^{-kt}) \qquad\qquad [10\text{-}12]$$
$$200 = L(1 - 10^{-0.17 \times 5}) = L(1 - 10^{-0.85})$$
$$\text{Antilog of } (-0.85) = 0.141$$
$$200 = L(1 - 0.141) - L(0.859)$$
$$L = \frac{200}{0.859} = 233 \text{ mg/l BOD}$$

Percent BOD remaining $= (1 - 10^{-kt})(10^2)$
Log of percent remaining $= -kt + 2$
$$= 2 - (0.17 \times 5)$$
$$= 2 - 0.85$$
$$= 1.15$$

$$\text{Antilog of } 1.15 = 14.1$$
$$\text{Percent BOD oxidized} = 100 - 14.1 = 85.9$$
$$L \times 0.859 = 200$$
$$L = \frac{200}{0.859} = 233 \text{ mg/l}$$

EXAMPLE 10-4. The five-day BOD of a waste is 276 mg/l. The ultimate demand is reported to be 380 mg/l. At what rate is the waste being oxidized?

Solution:

$$\text{Percent BOD oxidized} = \frac{276}{380} \times 100 = 72.6\%$$
$$\text{Percent BOD remaining} = 100 - 72.6 = 27.4\%$$
$$\log 27.4 = 2 - kt = 2 - (k \times 5)$$
$$k \times 5 = 2 - \log 27.4 = 2 - 1.438 = 0.562$$
$$k = 0.11$$

EXAMPLE 10-5. Theriault tables[11] have been used to simplify calculations and eliminate the need for log tables. The function $1 - 10^{-kt}$ has been calculated by Theriault for a range of values of k and t. In use, the known values of k and t are used to find the fraction oxidized. The problems as stated in Examples 10-3 and 10-4 are used to illustrate this method.

Solution: As in Example 10-3,

$$y = 200$$
$$t = 5$$
$$k = 0.17$$

The value of $1 - 10^{-0.17 \times 5}$ is found in the table to be 0.859. Then

$$200 = L(0.859)$$
$$L = \frac{200}{0.859} = 233 \text{ mg/l}$$

As in Example 10-4,

$$\text{Fraction oxidized} = 1 - 10^{-kt} = \frac{276}{380} = 0.726$$

From the Theriault tables,

$$\text{Fraction oxidized} = 0.726 \quad (t = 5, k = 0.11^+)$$

A second-order chemical reaction is characterized by a rate reaction dependent upon the concentration of two reactants, or

$$\frac{-dc}{dt} = kC^2 \tag{10-13}$$

When applying this reaction to BOD data, C becomes the initial substrate concentration L, less the BOD (y), at any time t. Thus

$$\frac{d(L - y)}{dt} = -k(L - y)^2$$

Rearranging,

$$\frac{d(L - y)}{(L - y)^2} = -kdt$$

Integrating,

$$\int_{y=0}^{y=y} \frac{d(L - y)}{(L - y)^2} = \int_{t=0}^{t=t} -k\,dt$$

or

$$\frac{1}{L} - \frac{1}{L - y} = kt$$

Multiplying each side of the equation by L and rearranging,

$$y = \frac{kL^2 t}{kLt + 1}$$

Dividing both numerator and denominator by $1/kL^2$, the equation reads.

$$y = \frac{t}{\dfrac{1}{kL^2} + \dfrac{1}{L}\,t}$$

or

$$y = \frac{t}{a + bt} \tag{10-14}$$

where

$$a = \frac{1}{kL^2}$$

$$b = \frac{1}{L}$$

This second-order reaction equation is the equation of a rotated rectangular hyperbola. It can be solved by least-squares analysis when linearized in the form

$$\frac{t}{y} = a + bt \tag{10-15}$$

where $1/a$ = the initial and maximum velocity of reaction
$\quad\;\; 1/b$ = the ultimate BOD, L

The following simultaneous equations are found by least-squares treatment of Eq. 10-15.

$$\Sigma \left(a + bt - \frac{t}{y} \right) = 0 \qquad (10\text{-}16)$$

$$\Sigma \left(a + bt - \frac{t}{y} \right) t = 0 \qquad (10\text{-}17)$$

$$ta + b\Sigma t - \Sigma \frac{t}{y} = 0 \qquad (10\text{-}18)$$

$$a\Sigma t + b\Sigma t^2 - \Sigma \frac{t^2}{y} = 0 \qquad (10\text{-}19)$$

Solving,

$$b = 0.10 \left[\left(\Sigma \frac{t^2}{y} \right) - 3 \left(\Sigma \frac{t}{y} \right) \right] \qquad (10\text{-}20)$$

$$a = 1.10 \left(\Sigma \frac{t}{y} \right) - 0.30 \left(\Sigma \frac{t^2}{y} \right) \qquad (10\text{-}21)$$

Figure 10-6 shows a plot of t/y vs. t for hourly BOD values of a domestic sewage. The values plot in a straight line and a BOD curve can be developed along with considerable other information from the plotting of a minimum amount of data.

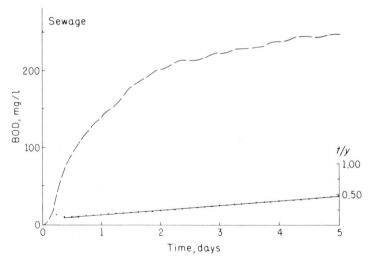

FIG. 10-6. A plot of t/y vs. t for hourly BOD values and a standard BOD curve, both of the same sewage sample.

EXAMPLE 10-6. The following daily BOD information was observed, using 307 mg/1 glucose-glutamic acid with 50 ml of settled sewage as seed. The temperature was 20°C. Calculate the maximum velocity of the reaction and the ultimate BOD.

Days	BOD mg/l
1	132.8
2	156.5
3	218.0
4	237.7
5	250.9

Solution:

t	y	t/y	t^2/y
1	132.8	0.00753	0.00753
2	156.5	0.01278	0.02556
3	218.0	0.01376	0.04129
4	237.7	0.01683	0.06731
5	250.9	0.01993	0.09964
Totals		0.07083	0.24133

From Eq. 10-21,

$$ a = 1.1\Sigma \left(\frac{t}{y}\right) - 0.3\Sigma \left(\frac{t^2}{y}\right) = 0.005514 $$

$$ k = \frac{1}{24a} = 7.55 \text{ mg/l/hr} $$

which is the maximum velocity for the reaction. From Eq. 10-20,

$$ b = 0.10 \left[\Sigma \left(\frac{t^2}{y}\right) - 3\Sigma \left(\frac{t}{y}\right) \right] = 0.002885 $$

$$ L = \frac{1}{b} = 346.7 \text{ mg/l} $$

the ultimate BOD.

10-7. BOD'S BY ELECTROLYSIS

The principle of measuring BOD's by electrolysis was developed by Clark in 1959.[17] The method involves using a flask into which a liter of undiluted waste is placed. An electrolysis cell and pressure switch are mounted on the flask (Fig. 10-7). The flask is then closed to the atmosphere. A magnetic stirrer is rotated inside the flask to renew continually the surface of the liquid. A vial containing potassium hydroxide is suspended from the top of the flask to take up the carbon dioxide.

Bacteria use the oxygen inside the flask to oxidize the organic matter present in the waste. The slight vacuum remaining in the flask actuates a pressure switch which turns on a d-c power supply. A small d-c current produces oxygen in the electrolysis cell and this oxygen is piped into the reaction vessel, replacing the oxygen used by the bacteria. The oxygen is produced until pressure equilibrium is established. The periods of oxygen demand are recorded electrically for later calculation of the shape of the BOD curve. The BOD at any point in time is read on a meter (Fig. 10-8).

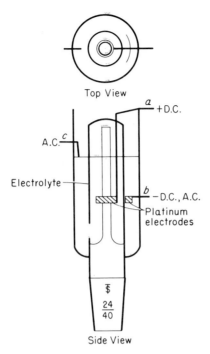

Top View

a +D.C.

A.C. *c*

Electrolyte

b −D.C., A.C.

Platinum
electrodes

$\frac{24}{40}$

Side View

FIG. 10-7. Electrolysis cell and
pressure switch combination.

Oxygen is produced from the electrolysis of water, according to Faraday's law. The faraday is that number of ampere-seconds required to decompose one equivalent weight of a substance. In the case of water, one faraday separates 8.00 g of oxygen per 96,519 amp-sec or coulombs. Then

$$\frac{96{,}519 \text{ amp-sec} \times 1 \text{ hr}/3{,}600 \text{ sec}}{8.00 \text{ mg oxygen}} = \frac{X \text{ amp-hr}}{30.0 \text{ mg oxygen}}$$

$$0.1007 \text{ amp-hr} = 30.0 \text{ mg of oxygen} \qquad (10\text{-}22)$$

or, 100.7 ma flowing for 1 hr will produce 30.0 mg of oxygen at the positive electrode of the electrolysis cell. Multiplying the number of hours recorded on the elapsed time meter of the power supply by 30.0 will yield the BOD in milligrams per liter. Larger currents may be used for strong industrial wastes.

The electrolysis method has the advantage over the standard dilution technique in that a short-term BOD is possible at elevated temperatures without loss of precision. The gaseous oxygen diffusion through the solution and the motility of the microorganisms may be factors which have contributed to variations in BOD data at elevated temperatures in tests by the dilution technique.

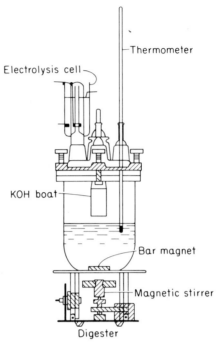

Constant Temperature Box

Fig. 10-8. Equipment for the measurement of BOD's by electrolysis.

Table 10-1 gives the relationship of 20°C, 30°C, and 35°C BOD data. The 35°C BOD has a higher rate of oxidation than the lower temperatures. The rate of biochemical oxidation k is approximately doubled by a temperature rise of 15° from 20° to 35°C. This reduces the time of testing by one half.

TABLE 10-1
THE RELATIONSHIP OF 20°C, 30°C AND 35°C BOD DATA.

Test Series	5-day, 20°C BOD	3-day, 35°C BOD	4-day, 30°C BOD	Percent of 5-day, 20°C BOD
1	199	—	183	92.0
2	110	—	104	94.6
3	408	411	—	100.8
4	113	116	—	102.6

The five-day 20°C BOD and the $2\frac{1}{2}$ day 35°C BOD are the same within the limits of experimental error when the tests are run by the electrolysis method.[3] Figure 10-9 shows typical BOD curves for glucose-glumatic acid at 35°C and at 20°C. The power supply was set at 0.1007 amp.

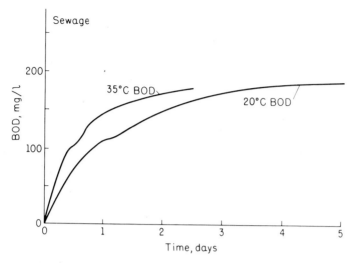

FIG. 10-9. Biochemical oxygen demand curves at 20°C and 35°C recorded continuously by the electrolysis method.

EXAMPLE 10-7. The following data were recorded from a 35°C BOD test by the electrolysis method.

Date	Time	Elapsed Time Meter Reading, hr
6-10-64	09:00 a.m.	0
	09:00 p.m.	4.6
6-11-64	09:00 a.m.	6.0
	09:00 p.m.	7.7
6-12-64	09:00 a.m.	8.3
	09:00 p.m.	8.6

Determine the five-day 20°C BOD, the ultimate BOD, and the maximum velocity of the reaction.

Solution: The five-day 20°C BOD is equal to the $2\frac{1}{2}$-day 35°C BOD. From Eq. 10-22, the five-day 20°C BOD = 8.6 × 30 = 258 mg/l.

The ultimate BOD and the maximum rate of reaction are found through the use of Eq. 10-15.

$$\frac{t}{y} = a + bt$$

In this case, t = 12 hr instead of 24 hrs as in the 20°C test.

t	y^*	t/y	t^2/y
1	138	0.007	0.007
2	180	0.011	0.022
3	231	0.013	0.039
4	249	0.016	0.064
5	258	0.02	0.10
		0.067	0.232

*y is computed by multiplying the elapsed time meter values by 30.0.

From Eq. 10-21,

$$a = 1.1\Sigma\left(\frac{t}{y}\right) - 0.3\Sigma\left(\frac{t^2}{y}\right) = 0.0041$$

$$k = \frac{1}{12a} = 20.3 \text{ mg/l/hr}$$

which is the maximum velocity for the reaction. From Eq. 10-20,

$$b = 0.10\left[\Sigma\left(\frac{t^2}{y}\right) - 3\Sigma\left(\frac{t}{y}\right)\right] = 0.003$$

$$L = \frac{1}{b} = 333 \text{ mg/l}$$

the ultimate BOD.

10-8. ORGANIC LOADS ON STREAMS

The discharge of sewage and industrial wastes into a body of water presents a problem of primary importance in the field of water-pollution control. The reduction of this organic matter by bacteria results in the utilization of dissolved oxygen. The primary replacement of this dissolved oxygen occurs through the water surface exposed to the atmosphere. An increase in the pollutional load stimulates the growth of bacteria, and oxidation proceeds at an accelerated rate. The concentration of the organic load can be so great that all of the dissolved oxygen in a receiving water is utilized by the bacteria. This lack of oxygen inhibits the higher forms of biological life, and conditions set in that are detrimental to man. The concentration of dissolved oxygen is one of the most significant criteria in stream sanitation.

Every stream is limited in its capacity to assimilate organic wastes. As long as this limit is not exceeded, the disposal of organic wastes in streams represents the most economical method of waste disposal. The evaluation of the natural purification capacity of a stream is of fundamental engineering value. Streams are used as natural treatment plants, and it is necessary to determine their capacity in order not to destroy their usage for other purposes.

The simultaneous action of deoxygenation and reaeration produces a pattern in the dissolved-oxygen concentration of river water. This pattern, known as "the dissolved-oxygen sag," was first described by Streeter and Phelps in 1925.[18] The equation describing the simultaneous action of deoxygenation and reaeration is

$$\frac{dD}{dt} = k_1'L - k_2'D \tag{10-23}$$

where D = dissolved oxygen deficit

L = concentration of the organic matter

k'_1 = coefficient of deoxygenation
k'_2 = coefficient of reaeration

The rate of change in the dissolved oxygen deficit D is the result of oxygen utilization in the oxidation of organic matter and the reaeration which replenishes oxygen from the atmosphere. The concentration of the organic matter L must be expressed in terms of the initial concentration L_0 at the point of waste discharge before integrating (Fig. 10-10).

$$L = L_0 e^{-k_1 t} \tag{10-24}$$

where L_0 = initial concentration of the organic matter in the stream (BOD in mg/l)

The substitution of Eq. 10-24 for the value L in Eq. 10-23 and integration gives

$$D = \frac{k'_1 L_0}{k'_2 - k'_1} (e^{-k'_1 t} - e^{-k'_2 t}) + D_0 e^{-k'_2 t} \tag{10-25}$$

where D = oxygen deficit in time t, mg/l
D_0 = initial oxygen deficit at the point of waste discharge, mg/l

Equation 10-25 is normally used with common logarithms.
Since $e^{-k't} = 10^{-kt}$, where $k = 0.434k'$,

$$D = \frac{k_1 L_0}{k_2 - k_1} (10^{-k_1 t} - 10^{-k_2 t}) + D_0(10^{-k_2 t}) \tag{10-26}$$

The proportionality factor k_1 is a temperature function. The proportionality factor k_2 is also a temperature function but, more important, it is a function of the turbulence of the stream.

A general approximate formula for the reaeration coefficient of natural rivers is given by O'Connor.[19]

$$k'_2 = \frac{(D_L U)^{1/2}}{H^{3/2}} \tag{10-27}$$

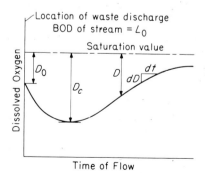

FIG. 10-10. The dissolved-oxygen sag curve.

where k_2' = reaeration coefficient (base e) per day

D_L = diffusivity of oxygen in water = 0.000081 ft/hr at 20°C

U = velocity of flow, ft/hr

H = depth of flow, ft

The effect of temperature on the reaeration coefficient k_2 is as follows:[19]

$$k_{2T} = k_{2\text{-}20} \times 1.047^{T\text{-}20} \qquad (10\text{-}28)$$

where k_{2T} = reaeration coefficient at the temperature T

$k_{2\text{-}20}$ = reaeration coefficient at 20°C

The value of k_2' ranges from 0.20 to 10.0 per day, the lower values representing deep slow-moving rivers and the higher values, shallow streams with steep slopes.

From an engineering design viewpoint, the dissolved-oxygen sag curve indicates the point of minimum DO. This critical point is the place in the stream where the rate of change of the deficit is zero and the demand rate equals the reaeration rate.

$$k_2' D_0 = k_1' L = k_1' L_0 e^{-k_1' t_c} \qquad (10\text{-}29)$$

Solving for the critical time t_c,

$$t_c = \frac{1}{k_2' - k_1'} \ln \left[\frac{k_2'}{k_1'} \left(1 - D_0 \frac{k_2' - k_1'}{k_1' L_0} \right) \right] \qquad (10\text{-}30)$$

These equations have constants which must be carefully evaluated. The k_1' term reflects the rate at which bacteria demand oxygen and is calculated from the BOD test by running BOD determinations. The k_2 term is the reaeration characteristic of the stream and varies from reach to reach in most streams. Constant k_1 can be evaluated in the laboratory while k_2 must be determined from field studies. In the development of these equations, it is assumed that k_1 and k_2 are constant and that only one source of pollution exists and that the only oxygen demand is the BOD. Variations from these assumptions may be taken into account in any practical case. Some of the following processes, in addition, may be taking place in any given river stretch:

1. Removal of BOD by adsorption or sedimentation.
2. The addition of BOD along the river stretch by tributary inflow.
3. The addition of BOD or the removal of oxygen from the water by the benthal layer.
4. The addition of oxygen by the photosynthetic action of plankton.
5. The removal of oxygen by plankton respiration.

EXAMPLE 10-8. A city of 200,000 population produces sewage at the rate of 120 gpcd and the sewage plant effluent has a BOD of 28 mg/l. The temperature of the sewage is 25.5°C, and there is 1.8 mg/l DO in the plant effluent. The stream flow is 250 cfs at 1.2 ft/sec and the average depth is 5 ft. The temperature of the water is 24°C before the sewage is mixed with the stream. The stream is 90 percent saturated with oxygen and has a BOD of 1 mg/l. The deoxygenation coefficient k_1' is equal to 0.50 at 20°C. Determine the following:

1. Sewage flow in cfs
2. The DO of the mixture of water and sewage plant effluent
3. The temperature of the mixture of water and sewage plant effluent
4. The value of the initial oxygen deficit for the river just below the plant discharge
5. The distance downstream to the point of minimum DO
6. The minimum DO in the stream below the sewage plant

Solution:

1. The sewage flow in cfs.

$$(120 \text{ gpcd})(2 \times 10^5) = 240 \times 10^5 \text{ gpd} = 24 \text{ mgpd}$$
$$1 \text{ mgpd} = 1.547 \text{ cfs}$$
$$\text{Sewage flow} = (24)(1.547) \text{ cfs} = 37.1 \text{ cfs}$$

2. The DO of the mixture of water and sewage plant effluent. Assuming a pressure of one atmosphere and a chloride concentration of zero, the solubility of oxygen in water at 24°C is 8.5 mg/l. The DO of the river water is (8.5 mg/l) (0.90) = 7.65 mg/l. The DO of the mixture is

$$\text{DO}_m = \frac{Q_r(\text{DO}_r) + Q_s(\text{DO}_s)}{Q_r + Q_s}$$

$$= \frac{(250 \text{ cfs})(7.65 \text{ mg/l}) + (37.1 \text{ cfs})(1.8 \text{ mg/l})}{287.1 \text{ cfs}}$$

$$= 6.89 \text{ mg/l}$$

3, Temperature of the mixture of water and sewage-plant effluent. As in (2),

$$T_m = \frac{(250 \text{ cfs})(24°C) + (37.1 \text{ cfs})(25.5°C)}{287.1 \text{ cfs}}$$

$$= 24.2°C$$

4. Value of the initial oxygen deficit. Assuming pure water at 24.2°C. The saturation value of O_2 is 8.48 mg/l but we have 6.89 mg/l.

$$\text{Deficit} = 8.48 - 6.89 = 1.59 \text{ mg/l}$$

5-6. The distance downstream to the minimum point of DO and the value of the minimum DO. Constant k_2' may be computed from Eq. 10-27.

$$k_{2\text{-}20}' = \frac{(D_L U)^{1/2}}{H^{3/2}}$$

$$= \frac{(81 \times 10^{-6} \text{ ft/hr} \times 1.2 \text{ ft/sec} \times 3,600 \text{ sec/hr})^{1/2}}{(5 \text{ ft})^{3/2}} \times 24 \text{ hr/day}$$

$$= 1.26$$

The value of k_2' and k_1' at 24.2°C are found by Eq. 10-28.

$$k_{2T} = k_{2\text{-}20} \times 1.047^{T\text{-}20}$$
$$k_{2\text{-}24.2}' = 1.26 \times 1.047^{24.2\text{-}20}$$
$$k_{2\text{-}24.2}' = 1.52$$

$$k'_{1\text{-}24.2} = 0.50 \times 1.047^{4.2}$$
$$k'_{1\text{-}24.2} = 0.608$$

The value of the initial BOD, L_0, of the mixture of river water and plant effluent is

$$L_0 = \frac{(250 \text{ cfs})(1 \text{ mg/l BOD}) + (37.1 \text{ cfs})(28 \text{ mg/l BOD})}{287.1 \text{ cfs}}$$

$$= 4.5 \text{ mg/l BOD}$$

The time t_c to the point of minimum DO is found by Eq. 10-30.

$$t_c = \frac{1}{k'_2 - k'_1} \ln \frac{k'_2}{k'_1} \left[1 - \frac{D_0(k'_2 - k'_1)}{k'_1 L_0} \right]$$

$$= 0.46 \text{ days}$$

The value of the minimum DO is found by Eq. 10-25 or Eq. 10-26.

$$D_c = \frac{k'_1 L_0}{k'_2 - k'_1} (e^{-k'_1 t_c} - e^{-k'_2 t_c}) + D_0 e^{-k'_2 t_c}$$

$$= 1.91 \text{ mg/l}$$

The distance downstream at which the critical DO occurs is calculated from the value of t_c and the velocity of flow.

$$\text{Distance} = 1.2 \text{ ft/sec} \times 3,600 \text{ sec/hr} \times 24 \text{ hr/day} \times t_c \text{ days}$$
$$= 47,600 \text{ ft}$$

Thus, under the given conditions the oxygen-sag curve takes the form shown in Fig. 10-11.

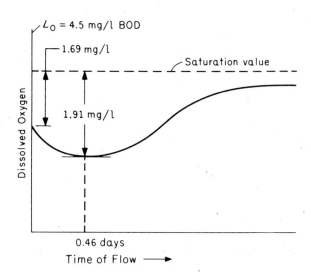

FIG. 10-11. Dissolved oxygen sag curve for Prob. 10-7.

SEWAGE-TREATMENT SYSTEMS

The water-carriage sewerage system provides an economical means for transporting waste materials away from their place of origin in household and industry. By so doing, it concentrates potential nuisances at the terminus of the collection system. These waste materials must be removed from the transporting water prior to its disposal or reuse.

The daily load of solids imposed upon domestic sewage amounts to about $\frac{1}{2}$ lb per day per person. This results in a mixture of water and waste of about 0.15 percent of solid matter by weight when the water consumption is 150 gpcd. Industrial wastes may be far more concentrated.

There are several different ways to treat sewage. Treatment processes are often classified as *primary*, *secondary*, or *tertiary* processes. The following outline describes sewage treatment and disposal methods.

METHODS OF LIQUID DISPOSAL
1. Disposal into a diluting body of water
2. Land disposal or irrigation
   (a) Surface application
   (b) Subsurface application
3. Reuse
4. Solar evaporation

METHODS OF SEWAGE TREATMENT
I. Primary Treatment
   A. Removal of coarse solids
      1. Screens
      2. Grit chambers
      3. Skimming tanks
      4. Sedimentation
      5. Raw-sewage lagoons
      6. Comminuters
   B. Removal of suspended solids
      1. Fine screens
      2. Sedimentation
         (a) Plain sedimentation
         (b) Chemical precipitation
      3. Lagoons
II. Secondary Treatment
   A. Biological oxidation
      1. Filters
         (a) Trickling filters
         (b) Intermittent filters

2. Activated sludge by several variations
3. Oxidation ponds
B. Chemical oxidation
1. Chlorination
2. Wet combustion
C. Disinfection
1. Chlorination
III. Tertiary Treatment
A. Oxidation ponds
B. Chemical precipitation
C. Ion exchange
D. Distillation
E. Electrodialysis
F. Freezing
G. Ultrafiltration

METHODS OF TREATING SEWAGE SOLIDS

I. Wet Sludges
A. Anaerobic digestion
B. Dumping at sea
C. Land disposal
D. Aerobic digestion
II. Dewatered Sludges
A. Composting
B. Land disposal
C. Incineration

Diagrammatic sketches of sewage-treatment plants are presented in Fig. 10-12. Various combinations of these and other methods are in use. The treatment of a waste is a synthesis of a number of different operations. Each waste must be carefully analyzed in light of its environment and a series of unit processes engineered to produce economically the desired end product.

ACTIVATED SLUDGE

10-9. THE PROCESS

The activated-sludge process may be defined as a system in which biologically active growths are continuously circulated and contacted with organic waste in the presence of oxygen. The oxygen is supplied to the system from compressed air injected into the sludge-liquid mass in the form of fine bubbles under turbulent conditions.

In the conventional activated-sludge process as normally operated (Fig. 10-13) the sewage is presettled and the effluent from the primary sedimentation tank is subjected to secondary treatment by activated-

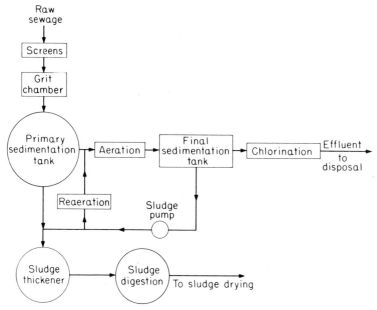

Flow Diagram for an Activated-Sludge Plant with a High Degree of Treatment

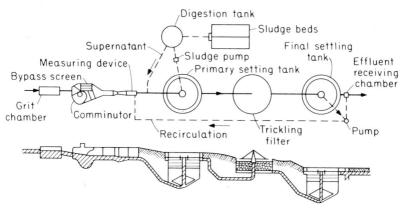

Plan and Profile of Typical Sewage-Treatment Plant

FIG. 10-12. Common types of sewage-treatment plants.

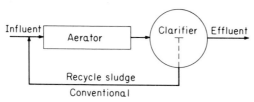

FIG. 10-13. Simplified flow diagram of conventional activated sludge process.

sludge organisms. This effluent, containing suspended and dissolved organic wastes, is aerated for a few hours in an aeration tank. During this period, adsorption, flocculation, and various oxidation reactions take place. The biochemical process is accelerated by the addition of a substantial volume of settled sludge from the secondary settling tank. This settled sludge is composed of microorganisms in an active state of growth and acclimated to the waste being treated. The effluent from this aeration tank is passed to the secondary sedimentation tank, where the flocculated microorganisms settle out. A portion of this sludge is again used for seed. The effluent from this secondary sedimentation tank is clear and low in BOD. Several modifications of this simplified flow pattern are used for both sewage and industrial-waste secondary treatment units.

The activated-sludge process consists of the following steps:

1. Mixing the activated sludge with the sewage to be treated.
2. Aeration and agitation of this mixed liquor for the required length of time.
3. Separation of the activated sludge from the mixed liquor.
4. Disposal of the excess activated sludge.

Before atmospheric oxygen becomes available to satisfy the BOD of the waste, it must be transferred to the heart of the floc—the respiratory enzymes within the cell wall. There are four general stages which must be considered in this transfer:

1. The transfer of atmospheric oxygen into solution in the mixed liquor.
2. The transfer of the oxygen dissolved in the waste water to the surface of the active cells.
3. The diffusion of the oxygen through the cell membranes into the cell itself.
4. The absorption by the appropriate respiratory enzyme in the cell.

In the design and operation of activated-sludge plants, we are concerned only with the first two steps, as the last two steps are governed by the cells themselves. It appears that the values of oxygen tension which affect metabolic rate lie below 0.5 mg/l of dissolved oxygen.[20] Slightly higher oxygenating capacities have been reported in the literature at higher dissolved oxygen concentrations, but these may be due to increased agitation of the mixture. Because the attainment of higher oxygen tension requires an increased agitation, the shearing force on the floc particles is increased. The breaking up of floc particles may enhance the opportunity for a greater number of cells to enter fully into reaction.

Oxygen is a sparingly soluble gas in pure water, having a saturation at 20°C of 8.9 mg/l in equilibrium with the standard atmosphere. The solubility is almost independent of the total pressure and the presence of other gases, but it is directly proportional to the partial pressure of oxygen in the gas phase. This is summarized by Henry's law, which states that the weight of any gas (or the number of its molecules) which dissolves in a definite volume of any liquid is directly proportional to the pressure which the gas exerts on the surface of the liquid, or

$$C_s = k_s P \qquad (10\text{-}31)$$

where C_s = saturation concentration of the gas in water, ml/l

P = partial pressure of the gas in the gas phase as a proportionality volume

k_s = proportionality constant, called the coefficient of adsorption, ml/l.

Rising temperatures decrease the saturation value, as do most common salts found in water. The oxygen saturation value for domestic sewage is about 95 percent of the calculated value for pure water.

Oxygen disperses itself through a liquid by the process of diffusion, which tends to produce a state of uniform concentration. This dispersion process is increased by turbulence. The magnitude of the diffusivity in the gas phase is much greater than in the liquid phase. The controlling resistance to oxygen transfer is in the liquid film at the air-liquid interface.

Oxygen is used for two basic purposes: (1) biochemical oxidation of organic matter to synthesize protoplasm and to supply the energy required for this synthesis, and (2) the oxidation of protoplasm. Oxygen-transfer capacity must be provided for the maximum BOD removal rates plus the concurrent related sludge-oxidation rates.

Activated sludge acts on organic material through two distinct mechanisms. The first is a clarification stage, in which most of the colloidal and suspended material is adsorbed on the surfaces of the floc particles. This stage takes place in less than one hour and extends only a short distance into the influent end of the basin. Slower, but equally important, is the oxidizing action of the sludge which occupies the rest of the basin. This continued oxidation covers a period of 4 to 6 hr and removes organic matter in solution and in colloidal, or suspended form, after adsorption. During this second stage the organics which are stored during the clarification stage are utilized in growth and oxidation. The adsorptive ability of activated sludge is attributed to the zoogleal bacteria in the sludge. Several species of bacteria have the property of forming a gel structure and these structures form a floc by agglomeration. The exact mechanisms of adsorption by gelled structures are not thoroughly understood, and are variously attributed to zeta potential, mechanical collision, chemical reaction of surface atoms, or to some property of the gel-forming organisms.

10-10. MODIFICATIONS OF THE ACTIVATED-SLUDGE PROCESS

Many modifications of the conventional activated-sludge process have been developed and find application in treating specific wastes or under special local conditions.

Step Aeration. A way to even out the oxygen demand in the mixed liquor of the aeration tank is to introduce the waste flow at intervals throughout the length of the tank (Fig. 10-14). The sewage flow is introduced at three or four points along the aeration basin. The waste load is distributed over the length of the basin. Accelerated growth and oxidation take place over most of the basin and are not confined to one end, as

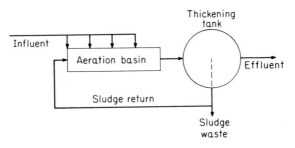

Fig. 10-14. Flow diagram of step aeration.

in the conventional process. This allows a volumetric loading in excess of 50 lb BOD/day/1,000 cu ft of aeration-tank capacity as compared to 35 lb BOD/day/1,000 cu ft of aeration-tank capacity with the conventional process. The BOD loading factors are approximately the same for both the conventional and step-aeration process, averaging about 0.2 to 0.5 lb BOD per pound of volatile suspended solids. The advantage with the step-aeration process is that the aeration tank is smaller than that employed in the conventional system. The difference between the oxygen-demand patterns of the conventional system and step aeration is illustrated in Fig. 10-15.

Contact Stabilization. Contact stabilization is yet another process which permits the use of the same loading factor as that employed in the conventional system. Its principal advantage is that it allows up to twice

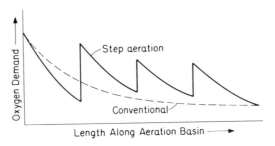

Fig. 10-15. The oxygen demands exerted in conventional and step aeration activated-sludge processes.

the volumetric loading of the conventional process. In contact stabilization, the volumetric loading of the system is on the order of 70 lb BOD/day/1,000 cu ft of aeration tank capacity. This system is shown in Fig. 10-16. The liquor from the primary sedimentation tank is mixed with return activated sludge in an aerated contact basin having a nominal retention time of less than 1 hr. During this period, waste materials are adsorbed by the sludge floc in what constitutes the clarification stage of the conventional process. Following the contact period, the sludge is settled in a sedimentation tank. A small portion of the sludge is wasted, while the remainder is transferred to the stabilization basin. Here the sludge is aerated for several hours, depending upon the strength of the waste. During the period in the stabilization basin, the stored and adsorbed wastes are utilized in growth and respiration. As a result, the sludge becomes stabilized and is returned to the contact basin to be mixed with the incoming waste.

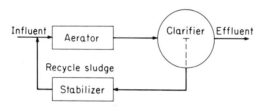

Fig. 10-16. Flow diagram of the contact stabilization process.

It is often possible to redesign an overloaded conventional activated-sludge plant without increasing or adding to the aeration-tank capacity. The redesigning may involve only changes in the plant piping and modification of the aeration-tank layout. The settling-tank capacity must be increased as the flows exceed the original design.

Modified Aeration Processes. There are several modifications of the aeration process that represent a combination of systems. They are able to provide a degree of treatment varying from that associated with the conventional system down to whatever is needed according to the dilution available. Loading factors on these systems go up to 5 lb BOD/day per pound of volatile suspended solids (VSS) and the volumetric loadings are on the order of 150 lb BOD/day/1,000 cu ft of aeration-tank capacity. These short-term aeration systems offer considerable economy of construction because of the very small aeration-tank capacities required. However, it will be noted that small aeration systems are able to contain only relatively low organism weights and that effluent quality will usually suffer.

10-11. EXTENDED AERATION

The extended aeration process consists of an aeration tank providing for a detention time much longer than conventional activated sludge. This is followed by a settling tank of several hours' detention. The supernatant liquor from this settling tank is discharged as plant effluent and all of the settled sludge is returned to the aeration unit. The design relies on the stabilization of waste material under aerobic conditions, with disposal of the end products through the air and plant effluent. In this process the conventional activated-sludge process is simplified by the elimination of the primary settling tank and the anaerobic sludge digester (Fig. 10-17).

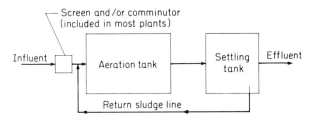

FIG. 10-17. Flow diagram of extended aeration process.

Extended aeration is characterized by loading factors that are much lower than those associated with the short-term aeration processes. Extended aeration typically operates at loading factors ranging from about 0.05 to 0.2 lb BOD/day/lb VSS. The volumetric loading is generally about 20 lb BOD/day/1,000 cu ft of aeration-tank capacity. Typical domestic sewage flows treated by extended aeration experience BOD removals on the order of 75 to 85 percent. The prime consideration in extended aeration is thorough mixing of the biological sludge and the raw waste. The oxygen requirements of the mixed liquor solids are very low, about 10 to 15 mg/l/hr. This is about 25 percent of the oxygen requirement at the head end of the conventional activated-sludge aeration tank. However, the air normally used is approximately double the air for the activated-sludge plant.

Extended aeration plants find wide applications in areas isolated from sewerage systems, such as shopping centers, housing developments, and certain industrial applications.

10-12. DESIGN CONSIDERATIONS

Most of the conventional activated-sludge plants designed in the past have been based on empirical criteria. The time required for aeration of mixed liquor depends on its organic nature and strength. With normal domestic sewage, the aeration period usually ranges from 4 to 8 hr with an air supply of 0.5 to 2.0 cu ft per gallon of sewage. A fair degree of treatment is obtained in 3 hr or less on some wastes. Some packing-house wastes require 16 hr of aeration. The aeration-tank loadings are usually limited to 25 to 50 lb BOD/day/1,000 cu ft of tank capacity. Much higher loadings have been used for varying degress of treatment in some process modifications.

The efficiency of the activated sludge process, as measured by the removal of BOD, is directly related to the weight of the volatile activated-sludge solids carried in the aeration tank. Experience has demonstrated a definite relationship between the sludge-volume index, the minimum percentage of return sludge, and the solids concentration in the mixed liquor. This relationship is as follows:

$$\text{Percentage of return sludge} = \frac{100}{100/ip - 1} \qquad (10\text{-}32)$$

where i = sludge volume index
P = percentage of solids in the mixed liquor

The sludge-volume index indicates the percentage of suspended matter in the mixed liquor, by volume, within acceptable limits of accuracy. It is obtained by allowing 1 liter of mixed liquor to stand quiescent for 30 min, in a graduated cylinder, and then measuring the volume of settled sludge. The dry-weight concentration of the suspended solids in the mixed liquor is then obtained. The ratio of the second result to the first is the sludge-volume index.

$$i = \frac{\text{volume of settleable sludge}}{\text{mg/l suspended solids}} \times 1,000 \qquad (10\text{-}33)$$

The solids content of the mixed liquor is basically that in the returned sludge, since the solids contribution of settled sewage is normally quite small.

The aeration-tank volume can be approximated if the mixed-liquor solids concentration, the BOD loading, and the ratio of the BOD loading to solids are established.

Aeration Tanks. In all but the smallest plants the total aeration-tank volume is generally divided amoung two or more units capable of operating independently. Most diffused-air aeration tanks have liquid depths of about 15 ft. The tanks are almost always constructed as long, relatively narrow, rectangular channels with a ratio of width to depth of not less than 1.5 and up to 2 times the depth. The tanks normally have 1 to 2 ft of freeboard above the liquid surface. They usually have some variation of the spiral type of flow, due to the placement of the air diffusers either along one side or in the middle near the bottom. The transverse velocity across the bottom of this type of tank should be at least 1 and preferably

1.5 fps in order to preclude any deposition of solids on the tank bottom. See Figs. 10-18 and 10-19 for typical cross section and arrangement of tanks.

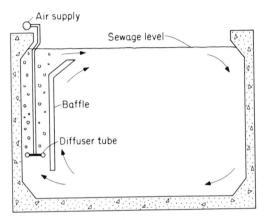

FIG. 10-18. Cross section of typical diffused-air aeration tank, showing placement of diffusers.

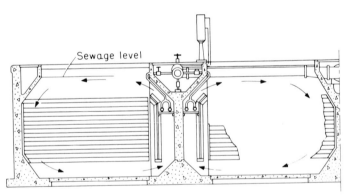

FIG. 10-19. Plan of typical aeration tank, showing tank arrangements and flow pattern.

EXAMPLE 10-9.   An aeration tank is to be designed, using diffused air, for a section of a city containing 30,000 population and no industrial waste. The mixed-liquor solids are assumed to be 2,500 mg/l, with a loading of 25 lb BOD/day/100 lb of aeration-tank solids. The sludge-volume index is to be maintained at 80. What are the tank dimensions?

Solution:

1. Percentage of return sludge, from Eq. 10-32:

$$\frac{100}{100/ip - 1} = \frac{100}{100/80(0.25) - 1} = 25 \text{ percent}$$

2. Total BOD loading on tank;

$$\text{Total BOD} = 30,000 \text{ population} \times 0.17 \text{ lb BOD/person/day}$$
$$= 5,100 \text{ lb BOD/day.}$$

Assume 30 percent BOD reduction in primary sedimentation tank.

Daily BOD load on aeration tank $= 5,100 \times 0.70$. 3,570 lb BOD/day

3. Allowing an additional 25 percent of return sludge, the total loading will be $3,570 \times 1.25 = 4,460$ lb BOD/day.

4. The corresponding amount of solids will be

$$4,460 \times \frac{100}{25} = 17,840 \text{ lb}$$

5. The amount of solids in 1 million gallons of the mixed liquor will be

$$2,500 \times 8.35 = 20,800 \text{ lb/mg}$$

6. For 17,840 lb of solids, the volume of aeration tank must be

$$\frac{17,850 \text{ lb} \times (10^6/7.48) \text{ cu ft/mg}}{20,800 \text{ lb/mg}} = 115,000 \text{ cu ft}$$

7. Assuming a tank depth of 14 ft, width of 21 ft, and two tanks,

$$\text{Tank length} = \frac{115,000 \text{ cu ft}}{14 \text{ ft} \times 21 \text{ ft} \times 2} = 196 \text{ ft}$$

EXAMPLE 10-10. Using the information from Example 10-9, design the aeration tank based on a 6-hr detention period.

Solution:

1. Assume a sewage flow of 100 gal/person/day based on inspection and knowledge of the area. The flow is 3 mgpd plus a 25 percent return for sludge, or a total flow of 3.75 mgpd.

2. The required tank capacity is

$$\text{Volume of tank} = 6 \text{ hr} \times 3.75 \text{ mg} \frac{1 \times 10^6 \text{ cu ft/mg}}{7.48} /24 \text{ hr} = 125,000 \text{ cu ft}$$

3. Assuming as before, a tank depth of 14 ft, width of 21 ft, and two tanks,

$$\text{Tank length} = \frac{125,000 \text{ cu ft}}{14 \text{ ft} \times 21 \text{ ft} \times 2} = 212 \text{ ft}$$

EXAMPLE 10-11. Using the information from Example 10-9, design the aeration tank based on the BOD per unit volume. Use 35 lb BOD/day/1,000 cu ft of tank capacity.

Solution:

1. The BOD load on the aeration tanks is

$$30,000 \times 0.17 \times 0.70 = 3,570 \text{ lb/day}$$

2. The tank capacity is given by

$$\text{Tank capacity} = \frac{1,000 \text{ cu ft} \times 3,570 \text{ lb/day}}{35 \text{ lb/day}}$$

$$= 102,000 \text{ cu ft}$$

3. Assuming as before, a tank depth of 14 ft, width 21 ft, and two tanks,

$$\text{Tank length} = \frac{102,000 \text{ cu ft}}{14 \text{ ft} \times 21 \text{ ft} \times 2} = 174 \text{ ft}$$

The computation in Example 10-9, using the solids under aeration, is preferable if all factors are known. If the assumed values are representative, the results do not depend on sewage or return sludge flows.

Aeration. A dissolved-oxygen concentration of at least 2 mg/l should be maintained in all parts of the aeration tank except possibly near the inlet. In order to maintain these concentrations it has been found necessary to apply from 0.2 to 1.5 cu ft of air per gallon of sewage treated, dependent upon the strength of the waste and the design of the plant. It is more logical to express the volume of air in terms of BOD removed. Normal requirements are about 1,000 cu ft of air per day per pound of BOD removed.

Two methods for mixing and aerating the sewage and activated sludge are in general use. One device involves diffused air, usually in connection with mechanical agitation (Fig. 10-20). In the other method, air is carried into the sewage by draft tubes, propellers, or other mechanical devices (Fig. 10-21). The object of aeration is to supply oxygen to all parts of the waste; the more efficient the oxygen transfer, the greater the treatment capacity of the system. In some designs both aeration methods are used.

It is desirable to diffuse the air into small bubbles to provide greatest surface area and increase the rate of oxygen transfer. The bubbles are made by blowing air through porous material in the form of tubes or plates made of aluminum oxide (Fig. 10-22). Figure 10-23 shows a typical installation using swing diffusers. A principal advantage is the ability to swing the diffusers out for cleaning and inspection while the aeration tank is in operation. The diffusers tend to clog on the air side from dirt in the air system and on the water side from sediment and aquatic growth.

Diffusers are classified by their ability to disperse air into the water under standard conditions. The standard permeability is defined as the volume of air, in cubic feet at 70°F, which will pass through an area of 1 sq ft of dry porous plate in a minute under an equivalent pressure of 2 in. of water. Diffuser plates normally have a permeability rating of 40 to

Fig. 10-20. Activated-sludge plant at Benton Harbor, Michigan, using compressed air.

Fig. 10-21. Activated-sludge plant at New Holstein, Wisconsin, using mechanical aeration. (Courtesy of Yeomans Brothers Company.)

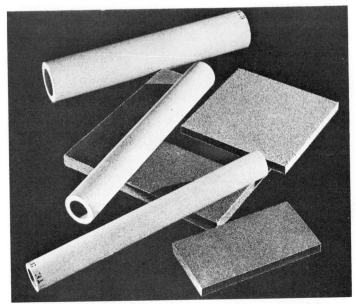

Fig. 10-22. Porous aluminum oxide plates and tubes used in air diffusion.

Fig. 10-23. Swing diffusers at the Hyperion sewage-treatment plant, Los Angeles, California. (Courtesy of Chicago Pump Co.)

60. The higher the permeability number the less clogging is experienced, but the bubbles are larger and have a lower oxygen-transfer rate.

Mechanical aerators are intended to produce aeration and turbulence in the liquid to maintain the floc in suspension. High-speed turbine mixers combined with an air sparger are used to develop higher oxygenation rates. These higher oxygenation rates will permit greater sludge concentrations and higher floc volume in a given tank capacity.

Air Piping. A satisfactory relation for the resistance of the flow of air in pipes can be based on the Darcy-Weisbach equation for the flow of incompressible fluids:

$$h_f = f \frac{LV^2}{d2\dot{g}} \tag{10-34}$$

where h_f = loss of head, feet
f = friction factor
L = length of pipe, feet
d = diameter of pipe, feet
V = velocity, ft/sec
g = 32.2 ft/sec^2

Conversion of Eq. 10-34 to a useful equation for the flow of air is had by making the following substitutions:

1. $\Delta p = h_f \gamma/144$, where Δp is the pressure difference in psi and γ is the specific weight of air. γ = 0.076 lb/cu ft at a pressure p_0 of 14.7 psia and a temperature T_0 of 60°F (519.6°R absolute).

2. γ varies directly with the absolute pressure and inversely with the absolute temperature:

$$\gamma = 0.076 \left(\frac{P}{P_0}\right)\left(\frac{T_0}{T}\right) = 2.71 \frac{P}{T}$$

3. The weight of air to be transported is constant but varies in volume with its density. The rate of flow of air in the pipe is 0.076 $Q/2.71$ $P/T = 0.028 (T/P)Q$, where Q is the rate of flow of free air in cubic feet per minute.

4. $Q = V \times 60 \times \pi D^2/(4 \times 144)$, where D is the diameter of the pipe in inches.

5. The pressure-volume relationship is $PV = RT$, where R is the gas constant (53.34 for air). PV^n = constant, the exponent n = 1.40 being the specific heat of the air at constant pressure and constant volume. Therefore, $T = 519.6 (P/14.7)^{0.283}$ for adiabatic compression of the air. Equation 10-34 becomes

$$\Delta P = \frac{fLTQ^2}{38,000 \, P D^5} \tag{10-35}$$

where ΔP = pressure drop due to friction, psi
f = friction factor.
L = length of pipe, ft

T = absolute temperature, degrees Rankine

Q = volume of free air, cubic feet per minute (cfm)

P = compressed air pressure, psi

D = diameter of pipe, in.

Friction factors f for various sizes and types of pipe are shown in Table 10-2.

TABLE 10-2

VALUES OF FRICTION FACTOR f FOR FLOW
OF AIR IN PIPES

Diameter, inches	Steel or Wrought Iron	Asphalted Cast Iron	Plain Cast Iron
1½	0.0206	0.027	0.0328
2	.0191	.025	.030
4	.0163	.021	.0252
6	.0153	.019	.0228
8	.0143	.0178	.0212
12	.0133	.0160	.0192
16	.0126	.0150	.0180
20	.0120	.0140	.0170
24	.0116	.0135	.0163
36	.0108	.0124	.0148
42	.0104	.0120	.0143

The foregoing data are based on the assumption that the free air temperature is 60°F and that sea-level conditions prevail. Any significant deviations for temperature or altitude must be taken into consideration.

EXAMPLE 10-12. Find the pressure drop in 1,000 ft of 16-in. asphalt-coated cast-iron pipe when transporting 20,000 cfs of air at an initial gage pressure of 8 psi. The temperature is 60°F and the plant is located at sea level.

Solution:

1. The friction factor from Table 10-2 is 0.015.
2. The absolute pressure is 8 + 14.7 = 22.7 psia.
3. The absolute temperature of the air T = 520 $(22.7/14.7)^{0.283}$ = 588R.
4. By Eq. 10-35,

$$\Delta P = \frac{0.015 \times 1,000 \times 588 \times 20,000^2}{38,000 \times 22.7 \times 16^5} = 3.9 \text{ psi}$$

TRICKLING FILTERS

10-13. THE PROCESS

Trickling filters are artificial beds of crushed stone or other porous media through which the liquid from settled organic waste is percolated. In the process the waste is brought into contact with air and with biologic growths. Trickling filters are widely employed for the biological treatment of wastes. Settled liquid waste is applied intermittently or continuously over the top surface of the filter by means of a distributor. The filtered liquid is collected and discharged at the bottom (Fig. 10-24).

The primary removal of organic material is not accomplished through a filtering or straining action. Removal is the result of an adsorption process similar to activated sludge which occurs at the surfaces of biological slimes covering the filter media. Subsequent to their adsorption, the waste materials are utilized by the slimes for growth and energy.

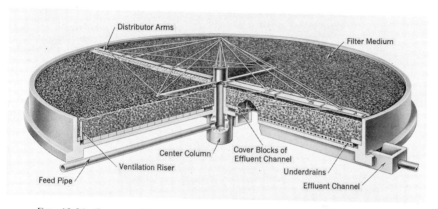

FIG. 10-24. Cutaway view of a trickling filter. (Courtesy of Dorr-Oliver, Inc.)

The composition of the biological slimes covering the filter media is very similar to the floc particles of the activated-sludge process. The strict nature of the bacterial flora is determined by the nature of the waste. Fungi are more important in trickling filters than in activated-sludge units. This is due to the more suitable physical environment and because of the constant supply of complex organic matter at or near the surface of the bed. A large population of various species of heterotrophic bacteria and fungi live on the waste. These organisms are in turn fed upon by a predator population consisting of protozoa and small metazoa. A zoogleal mass imparting a slimy consistency to the surfaces of the filter media is derived from the varied population of organisms.

As liquid waste passes around the filter media it is brought into contact with the biological slimes. Along with the adsorption of organic wastes by the slimes, end products resulting from previous oxidation are discharged to the liquid. Oxygen diffuses from the atmosphere into the outer layers of the slimes to support aerobic growth. The growth is most active at the outer layers of the slime where the concentration of organics and oxygen is the highest. As the slime layer increases in depth, the amount of diffused oxygen becomes limited and anaerobic activity is established. When the slimes become very thick, anaerobic activity predominates and the slimes lose their zoogleal properties near the supporting media. The slime layer then sloughs off under hydraulic loading. Sloughing is a function of both hydraulic loading and type of bacterial activity. Figure 10-25 shows a flow diagram of a trickling filter.

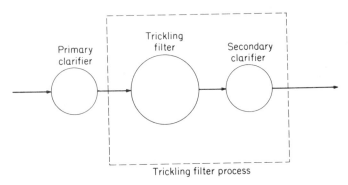

Trickling filter process

FIG. 10-25. Flow diagram of a single-stage trickling filter with no recirculation.

10-14. TRICKLING FILTER DESIGN

There are numerous variables which may affect the performance and, thus, the design of trickling filters. The designs have been based, for the most part, on empirical standards. A more rational approach appears possible in light of recent research. Some factors to be considered by the designing engineer are:

1. Composition and characteristics of the waste material
2. Hydraulic loading on the filter
3. Pretreatment by sedimentation or other processes
4. Organic loading to be applied to the filter
5. Recirculation ratio and system
6. Filter beds, their volume, area, and depth
7. Media to be used
8. Aeration
9. Temperature

Many of these factors are interelated and are considered jointly, due to lack of specific design information.[21]

Since the treatment of sewage with trickling filters is primarily a biochemical process, the five-day, 20°C, BOD determination is the principal yardstick used to measure both the characteristics of the applied organic load and the quality of the final effluent. Variations in concentration may be considerable and may vary hourly, daily, and seasonally in both volume and strength. Such variations are provided for in design by multiple pumping arrangements and recirculation facilities. Since the trickling filter is an aerobic process, it is essential that the waste applied to the filter be nonseptic for maximum efficiency. If the settled waste is septic, pretreatment may be necessary to improve conditions of the waste prior to the application to the filter. This may be accomplished by aeration or recirculation of the flow.

Hydraulic loading of the filter may be either continuous or intermittent. The BOD removal efficiency of the filter is not noticeably affected by the hydraulic dosage rate if the organic rate is constant with domestic wastes. Continuous loading at a constant rate helps prevent the heavy flushing of slime growth from the filter media which results from heavy instantaneous dosing. Intermittent dosing has some advantages if the filter is not dosed too heavily and the filter slime does not dry out. Rest periods are helpful in the control of filter flies and increase aeration efficiency under heavy organic loading.

Recirculation is an accepted method of increasing the BOD removal of trickling filters. Various systems of recirculation are shown in Fig. 10-26. Some methods of recirculation are:
1. At low flows only
2. A constant rate at all times
3. At a rate proportional to sewage flow
4. At two or more constant rates predetermined automatically or by manual control

Through recirculation, organic matter in the filter effluent is brought back into contact with the filter slime and increases the BOD removal. Passing the recirculation through the settling tank tends to average out the strength of the sewage. This helps to dilute strong sewage and supplement weak sewage.

The filter media is usually crushed stone, fieldstone, or blast-furnace slag. It serves to provide anchorage and space for the biological slime and assists in distributing the flow. Except for decreased efficiencies which have resulted from clogging due to too fine a medium, the types and sizes of media within ranges commonly used have little effect on filter efficiency.

The temperature of the sewage rather than that of the air is the controlling factor as long as the hydraulic loading is sufficient. The BOD removal in trickling filters is affected by climatic conditions in the same way that other biologic processes are affected by temperature. Howland has shown that the temperature effect on filter performance may be expressed by the relationship[21]

$$E = E_{20} 1.035^{(T-20)} \qquad (10\text{-}36)$$

where E = BOD removal efficiency at temperature T
E_{20} = BOD removal efficiency at 20°C

Single-stage filters

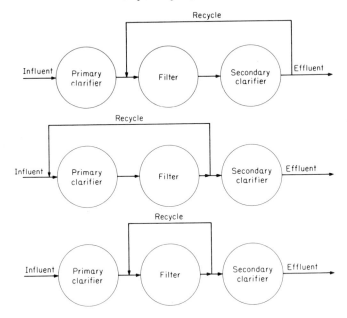

Two-stage filters

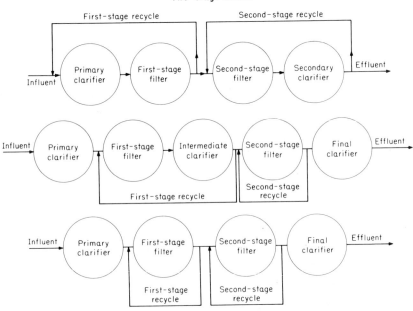

FIG. 10-26. Various systems of recirculation used with trickling filters.

Eckenfelder developed an efficiency formulation applicable to the design of rock filters treating domestic wastes.[21]

$$\frac{L_e}{L_0} = \frac{100}{1 + 2.5(D^{0.67}/Q^{0.50})} \qquad (10\text{-}37)$$

where L_e = BOD concentration in filter effluent
L_0 = BOD concentration applied to the filter
D = depth of the filter, ft
Q = hydraulic loading, million gallons per acre per day (mgad).

When recirculation is used, the influent BOD is diluted by the recirculated flow. The applied BOD including recirculation can be computed:

$$L_0 = \frac{L_a + NL_e}{N + 1} \qquad (10\text{-}38)$$

where L_a = influent sewage BOD
N = recirculation ratio
L_0 = BOD after admixture with recirculated flow, BOD concentration applied to the filter
L_e = BOD concentration in filter effluent

The filter performance of a recirculated flow can be estimated by combining Eqs. 10-37 and 10-38.

$$\frac{L_e}{L_a} = \frac{1}{(1 + N)[1 + 2.5\,(D^{0.67}/Q^{0.5})] - N} \qquad (10\text{-}39)$$

A filter has a limiting loading above which further removal and assimilation cannot occur. These equations are considered applicable only below the limiting loading.

EXAMPLE 10-13.   Compute the BOD removal from settled domestic sewage in a 6-ft-deep filter with a hydraulic loading of 15 mgad without recirculation.

Solution:
1. Using Eq. 10-37,

$$\frac{D^{0.67}}{Q^{0.5}} = \frac{(6)^{0.67}}{(15)^{0.5}} = 0.86$$

2. Substituting in Eq. 10-37,

$$\frac{L_e}{L_0} = \frac{100}{1 + 2.5\,(0.86)} = 31.8 \text{ percent}$$

3. Therefore, the BOD removal is $100 - 31.8 = 68.2$ percent.

EXAMPLE 10-14.   The BOD removal efficiency was found to be 71 percent at 20°C. What efficiency would be expected at 24°C?

Solution: Using Eq. 10-36,

$$E_{24} = 71(1.035)^4 = 81.5$$

Therefore, the BOD removal expected would be 81.5 percent.

EXAMPLE 10-15.   Compute the recirculation ratio to obtain 90 percent BOD removal, using a depth of 5 ft and a hydraulic loading of 15 mgad.

Solution:
1. Using Eq. 10-39,

$$\frac{L_e}{L_a} = 1.00 - 0.90 = 0.10$$

2.

$$\frac{D^{0.67}}{Q^{0.5}} = \frac{5^{0.67}}{15^{0.5}} = 0.74$$

$$\frac{L_e}{L_a} = 0.10 = \frac{1}{(1 + N)[1 + 2.5 (0.74)] - N}$$

Solving for N,

$$N = 3.87$$

which means that the ratio of recirculated flow to incoming waste flow is 3.87:1.

In order to remove treated liquid from the base of the trickling filter, and to provide adequate air supply to the filter slime, some system of underdrains is necessary. These are usually constructed as a false floor made of special tile pieces constructed for this purpose. Retaining walls around filter media are usually made of concrete.

General practice has been to use an empirical relationship for trickling-filter-process design. Several of these relationships have been developed from data collected at waste-treatment installations. The National Research Council developed one of the more popular relationships of this type. The NRC formula for a first-stage filter may be written as

$$E_1 = \frac{1}{1 + 0.0085 \sqrt{W/VF}} \tag{10-40}$$

where E_1 = fractional efficiency of the filter process
W = applied load, pounds of five-day, 20°C BOD/day of settled waste
V = volume of filter media, acre-ft
F = recirculation factor

The recirculation factor can be determined from

$$F = \frac{1 + r}{(1 + 0.1r)^2} \tag{10-41}$$

where r = ratio of recirculated flow to incoming waste flow

For a second-stage filter, this equation becomes,

$$E_2 = \frac{1}{1 + [0.0085/(1 - E_1)] \sqrt{W'/VF}} \qquad (10\text{-}42)$$

where E_2 = fractional efficiency of the second-stage filter
W' = applied load in pounds of five-day, 20°C BOD/day of settled waste to the second-stage filter

EXAMPLE 10-16. Find (a) the acre-feet of filter required to effect 85 percent removal of BOD from 10 mgpd of waste containing 180 mg/l of five-day BOD when it is applied to a single-stage trickling filter, (b) the BOD loading of the filter per acre-foot, and (c) the BOD loading and hydraulic loading if the filter is made 6 ft deep. Assume that the sewage is not to be recirculated.

Solution:
(a) By Eq. 10-40,

$$E_1 = \frac{1}{1 + 0.0085 \sqrt{W/VF}}$$

There is no recirculation; $F = 1$.

$$W = 10 \times 180 \times 8.34 = 1.5 \times 10^4$$

$$0.85 = \frac{1}{1 + 0.0085 \sqrt{1.5 \times 10^4/V}}$$

$$V = 34.6 \text{ acre-ft}$$

(b) $\dfrac{W}{V} = \dfrac{1.5 \times 10^4}{34.6} = 433.5 \text{ lb/acre-ft}$

(c) $433.5 \times 6 = 2{,}600 \text{ lb/acre}$

$$\frac{34.6}{6} = 5.76 \text{ acres}$$

and

$$\frac{10}{5.76} = 1.73 \text{ mgad}$$

The reaction-driven rotary distributor is used in most plants. The maximum hydraulic loadings are approximately 4 mgad for low-rate filters and 30 mgad for high-rate filters. Filters are constructed circular, although hexagonal filters have been used. The filter media is normally 4 to 8 ft deep and distributors are available up to 200 ft in diameter.

Filters are termed *standard-rate* and *high-rate* on the basis of recirculation and degree of hydraulic loading. A comparison of *standard-rate* and *high-rate* filters is shown in Table 10-3.

TABLE 10-3
COMPARISON OF STANDARD-RATE AND HIGH-RATE TRICKLING FILTERS

Feature	Standard Rate	High Rate
Depth of media	5–8 ft	3–6 ft
Hydraulic loading		
gallons/day/sq ft	25–100	200–1000
million gal/acre/day	Less than 4	10–40
Organic loading, BOD (lb)		
/acre-ft/day	600	3,000
/1,000 cu ft/day	Less than 15	Over 30

PHOTOSYNTHETIC PROCESSES

10-15. INTRODUCTION

Oxidation ponds are shallow basins used for the purpose of purifying sewage or other liquid waste by storage under climatic conditions that favor the growth of algae. The conversion of organics to inorganics or stabilization in such ponds results from the combined metabolic activity of bacteria and algae.

The ponds are usually 2 to 4 ft deep, although deeper ponds have been used. The minimum depth is controlled by weed growth. It has been found that a depth of 2 ft is sufficient to prevent most weed growth. The maximum depth is related to light penetration, mixing, and surface reaeration.

Oxidation ponds were originally used for secondary treatment, but in the past few years a large number of ponds have been constructed to treat raw sewage. Like other biological treatment processes, very little is known about the environment. Most oxidation ponds today are designed for complete treatment of raw sewage.

10-16. THEORY OF OPERATION

Oxidation ponds depend upon two primitive forms of life and the primary source of the earth's energy for their operation. The primitive life forms are algae and bacteria. The primary source of energy, other than the waste being treated, is the sun. Energy from the sun as converted by the photosynthetic properties of the algae makes it possible for the latter to use the metabolic end products of bacteria, primarily carbon dioxide, to produce more algal cells and free oxygen. This oxygen is then available to aerobic bacteria (Fig. 10-27). The bacteria utilize sewage organics for growth and energy, the latter being provided through oxidation of a portion of the organic carbon to carbon dioxide. Carbon dioxide along with other metabolic end products is utilized in algal growth through photosynthesis. Oxygen is produced in the process and is avail-

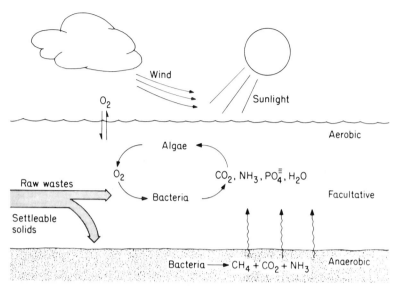

Fig. 10-27. Schematic diagram of oxidation pond symbiosis between bacteria and algae.

able for continued bacterial oxidation. This oxygen, along with the oxygen dissolved through surface aeration, keeps the process aerobic under ideal conditions.

Decomposition of the organic material by the bacteria is carried on in three distinct zones:

1. Aerobic bacteria in the zone of DO
2. Facultative anaerobes operating near the bottom or in the upper portions of the bottom sediments
3. Anaerobic bacteria in the interior of the bottom sediments in the absence of oxygen

It is desirable to maintain aerobic conditions because aerobic microorganisms bring about a more complete reduction of organic material. The zone of faculative anaerobes will be aerobic or anaerobic, dependent upon the presence or absence of molecular oxygen. Anaerobic biological activity will prevail under the surface of the bottom sediments. If the pond is not overloaded for the existing conditions, the anaerobic metabolic end products will be utilized and further reduced in the aerobic zone and never reach the liquid surface. Should the pond be overloaded for too long a period of time, the nuisance odors and effects of anaerobic digestion will be felt.

Sunlight having wavelengths falling between 4,000 and 7,000 angstrom units is available for photosynthesis. This light is mostly in the visible range and accounts for about 40 percent of the total energy from

solar radiation. The photosynthetic process can use only a small percentage of the sun's energy on a clear summer day. The process becomes
light-saturated at intensities above a value called the *saturation intensity*.
For algae, the saturation intensity is on the order of 600 ft-c (foot-
candles). The fraction of the light energy utilized in photosynthesis by a
homogeneous algal suspension is given by the equation[22]

$$f = \frac{I_s}{I_0} \left(\ln \frac{I_0}{I_s} + 1 \right)$$
(10-43)

where f = fraction of available light that may be utilized
   I_s = saturation light intensity
   I_0 = incident light intensity

At 30° north latitude, values of I_0 may range from 12,000 ft-c at noon on a
clear summer day to 800 ft-c on a rainy day.[22]   Using these values in
Eq. 10-43 and I_s of 600 ft-c, values of f range from 0.20 to 0.96.   This
means that only 15 to 35 percent of the visible spectrum of sunlight can be
used under the optimum conditions cited.   The light efficiencies under
field conditions with algae and higher plants run much lower than the
above optimum values.   Cultures in the logarithmic phase of cell growth
attain a higher value of I_s and utilize a greater fraction of available light
than do older cultures.   To support a population at the rapid rate of
growth requires a rich, well-balanced substrate.   This condition cannot be
maintained under field conditions with normal sewages.   Figure 10-28
shows isolines of average solar radiation received on a horizontal surface
in the United States during typical days in July and December.

10-17. DESIGN

The biochemical relationships existing in oxidation ponds are extremely complex and no completely rational method has been developed
for the design of ponds. However, a semirational method has been proposed in which the pond volume is related to the hydraulic loading, five-
day 20°C BOD loading, and temperature.[22] This method is based on a design temperature of the average of the pond during the coldest month at
the proposed geographic location.

$$V = 5.37 \times 10^{-8} Nqy \, 1.072^{(35-T)}$$
(10-44)

where V = volume of the pond, acre-ft
   N = number of people served
   q = daily per capita sewage flow, gpcd
   y = five-day 20°C BOD, mg/l
   T = Temperature, °C

An optimum depth of 3 ft is recommended.

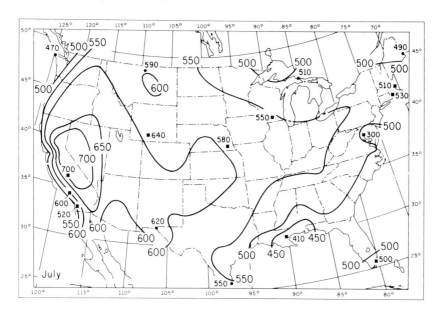

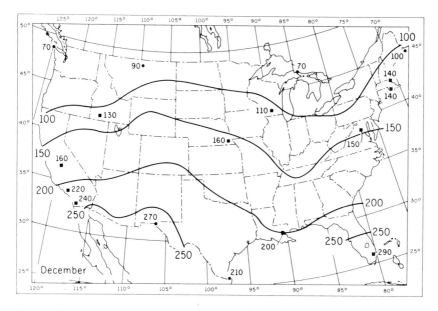

FIG. 10-28. Isolines of average solar radiation received on a horizontal surface in the United States during days with average cloudiness in July and December. Units are in calories per square centimeter per day.

The number of pond cells comprising a single installation should be at least two, and three are preferred for flexibility and control of operation. For a temperature difference of 20°C between winter and summer, the pond volume in summer would be only one-fourth as great as that needed in winter. The pond cells should be so connected that they could operate in parallel or in series. It has been recommended that the pumping capacity between cells be designed at 10 times the influent rate. If feasible, gravity flow should be provided through one operational pattern involving all cells.

EXAMPLE 10-17.   What is the volume of an oxidation pond required to serve a population of 3,000, where the per capita flow is 75 gpd and the five-day 20°C BOD is 200 mg/l? The design temperature is 10°C.

Solution: Using Eq. 10-44,

$$V = 5.37 \times 10^{-8} (3,000)(75)(200) 1.072^{(25)}$$
$$= 13.7 \text{ acre-ft}$$

ANAEROBIC DIGESTION

10-18. INTRODUCTION

The disposal of the concentrated organic solids removed from sewage in primary sedimentation and the excess sludges and slimes from the activated-sludge process and from trickling filters is often brought about by anaerobic biological action. This process is called *anaerobic digestion.* During the process, volatile organic matter is reduced through successive steps to gaseous end products. These end products are primarily methane, carbon dioxide, and water, along with lesser amounts of ammonia and hydrogen sulfide. A primary purpose of sludge digestion is to reduce the complex organic matter to a simpler, nonobjectionable state. This digested sludge is more amenable to dewatering without nuisance and is more readily disposable.

10-19. THEORY

The complex organic solids are unavailable to the bacteria as food in the solid state. Most of these complex organics are hydrolyzed to simpler soluble compounds by extracellular enzymes. This is referred to as the *liquefaction phase.* The cellulose and starches are hydrolyzed to simple sugars, while the proteins are broken down to amino acids. The end products of this first phase are primarily volatile organic acids which are produced by the acid formers, made up predominately of facultative anaerobes. The acids produced are primarily acetic, butyric, and propionic. This acid production leads to a drop in pH. This is one of the reasons for uniform feedings in digesters, so that the shock loadings will not lower the pH to the point of interference with other organisms and allow the volatile acids to accumulate.

At the end of the acid phase, the decomposition of organic acids and soluble nitrogenous compounds occurs. This results in the formation of ammonia, amines, acid carbonates, and some gases such as carbon dioxide, methane, hydrogen, and hydrogen sulfide. The pH rises to a level more favorable to bacterial growth. This rise in pH is due in part to the neutralizing effect of ammonia.

This phase in digestion is known as the *methane phase,* sometimes called the *alkaline fermentation phase.* At this point the pH is about neutral. The bacteria responsible for this stage are called the *methane bacteria.* They are strict anaerobes and have been difficult to study and little is known of the specific microorganisms.

The acid formers are resistant to high concentrations of volatile acids, while some of the methane formers are highly sensitive to such concentrations. The amount of volatile acid must not be allowed to reach an extreme level or digestion will be prolonged. Lime has been used to raise the pH of digesters during initial starting or in periods of overfeeding or shock loading. According to Pohland,[23] the alkalinity reacts with the organic acids as they are being produced during fermentation. They are stored in a neutralized state, thus precluding pH depression and allowing for a more rapid methane fermentation phase. During the methane phase, the acid salts are decomposed to methane and carbon dioxide and the alkalinity is then available for further neutralization. The reactions involved may be represented as follows:

Alkalinity Addition:

$$Ca(OH)_2 + 2\,CO_2 \longrightarrow Ca(HCO_3)_2 \qquad (10\text{-}45)$$

lime   carbon dioxide   bicarbonate alkalinity

Alkalinity-Acid Reaction:

$$Ca(HCO_3)_2 + 2\,CH_3COOH \longrightarrow (CH_3COO)_2Ca$$

bicarbonate alkalinity   organic acid   acid salt

$$+ \; H_2O + CO_2 \qquad (10\text{-}46)$$

water   carbon dioxide

Methane Fermentation:

$$(CH_3COO)_2Ca + 2\,H_2O \longrightarrow 2\,CH_4 + Ca(HCO_3)_2 \qquad (10\text{-}47)$$

acid salt   water   methane   bicarbonate

When shock loadings occur above the assimilation capacity of the bacterial population, alkalinity must be added to the system. A method has been developed by Pohland[23] for this control.

$$A = TA - 0.833\,TOA \qquad (10\text{-}48)$$

where A = alkalinity excess or deficit, in mg/l as $CaCO_3$
    TA = total alkalinity, in mg/l as $CaCO_3$
    TOA = total organic acids, in mg/l as CH_3COOH
    0.833 = equivalent weight of $CaCO_3$/equivalent weight of CH_3COOH

Where a positive value of A is obtained, an excess in alkalinity exists and pH depression should not occur. A negative value of A indicates the quantity of free acids present and the amount of alkalinity required to neutralize these acids. The amount of neutralizing chemical required is calculated as follows:

$$N = 8.34\, AEV \qquad\qquad (10\text{-}49)$$

where N = the amount of neutralizing chemical required, pounds
    A = the alkalinity deficit, mg/l as $CaCO_3$.
    E = equivalent weight of neutralizing chemical/equivalent weight of $CaCO_3$
    V = the digestion volume, millions of gallons
    8.34 = conversion factor, lb/gal

If hydrated lime is used, the respective value of E would be 0.74.

EXAMPLE 10-18. A digester with 30,000 gal of digestion volume is to be neutralized. The total alkalinity is 2,800 mg/l as $CaCO_3$ and the total organic acids are 3,700 mg/l as acetic acid. How many pounds of ammonium carbonate are required for this neutralization?

Solution:
1. Using Eq. 10-48,

$$A = 2800 - 0.833(3,700) = -280 \text{ mg/l as } CaCO_3$$

2. Using Eq. 10-49,

$$N = 8.34\,(280)(0.96)(0.030) = 67.2 \text{ lb ammonium carbonate}$$

where

$$E = \frac{\text{equivalent weight of } (NH)_2CO_3}{\text{equivalent weight of } CaCO_3} = \frac{48.04}{50.04} = 0.96$$

Therefore, 67.2 lb of ammonium carbonate should be added to the digestor.

The gas produced from the anaerobic digestion of sewage sludge is composed primarily of methane and carbon dioxide, with traces of hydrogen sulfide, ammonia, hydrogen, and nitrogen. The gas will contain approximately 70 percent methane and 30 percent carbon dioxide. The gas yield from a digesting sewage sludge will be about 16 to 18 cu ft/lb of volatile matter reduced.

Temperature exerts a material effect on anerobic digestion. Figure 10-29 shows the time required for digestion as a function of temperature. Time values have been omitted since the digestion period is affected by

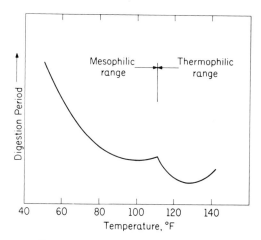

FIG. 10-29. Time required for anaerobic
digestion.

several other factors such as pH, bacterial population, mixing, rate of
feeding, and waste characteristics. As indicated in Fig. 10-29, there are
two distinct temperature ranges. The mesophilic range extends up to
110°F, with an optimum range of 95 to 100°F. The higher temperature, or
thermophilic range, is at an optimum at about 130°F. The digestion is
most rapid at the thermophilic range but digesters are normally operated
at 90 to 95°F in the mesophilic range. Additional heat is required for
thermophilic digestion and the process is more difficult to operate and
requires a high level of laboratory control for maximum results.

There are two basic types of digestion systems used, the conventional
and the high-rate processes. In the conventional system, fresh sludge is
introduced one or more times a day into the unit, usually near the center
of the digester. As decomposition proceeds, three more or less discrete
zones of activity can be identified (Fig. 10-30). These zones of separation
include the scum layer, the supernatant, and the sludge zone. The sludge
zone can be divided into actively digesting solids and to a relatively stable
sludge. Heating is generally provided with external heat exchangers, and
a temperature of 90 to 95°F is usually maintained unless thermophilic
digestion is employed.

In high-rate digestion the sludge is more or less continuously added
to the digester. Some type of agitation, or mixing, is provided in the
digester. Heating is similar to the conventional system (Fig. 10-31). Mixing provides thermal homogeneity to the process and brings the organisms
into contact with their food supply. The process then functions more
efficiently and higher loadings with shorter detention periods can be
achieved.

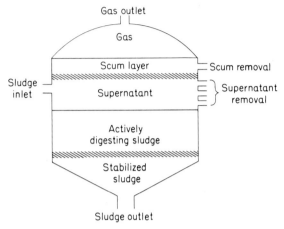

Conventional Digestion

1. Heated: 85° - 95° F
2. Detention time: 30 - 60 days
3. Loading: 30 - 100 lb volatile solids
    /1,000 cu ft /day
4. Intermittent feeding and withdrawal
5. Stratification

Fig. 10-30. Conventional digestion showing the zones of activity.

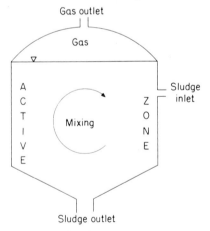

High-Rate Digestion

1. Heated: 85° - 95° F
2. Detention time: 15 days or less
3. Loading: 100 - 500 lb volatile solids
    /1,000 cu ft / day
4. Continuous or intermittent feeding
    and withdrawal
5. Homogeneity

Fig. 10-31. High-rate digester, showing mixing.

10-20. DIGESTER DESIGN

Conventional digesters are usually designed with a theoretical detention time of 30 to 60 days and a sludge loading between 30 to 50 lb of volatile solids per 1,000 cu ft of digester capacity per day. Heating requirements are normally provided by external heat exchangers and a temperature of 90 to 95°F is generally maintained unless thermophilic digestion is employed.

High-rate digesters are designed with a detention period of about 15 days with organic loadings in excess of 100 lb volatile solids per 1,000 cu ft of digester capacity per day. Heating requirements are similar to conventional digestion but some form of mixing of the digester contents must be provided.

Most digesters are circular and fairly deep. The depth normally ranges from 20 to 35 ft. The bottom is usually an inverted cone to facilitate sludge removal. The required capacity determines the diameter, which is adjusted to the manufacturer's standard sizes. Where two-stage digestion is employed, both tanks are usually the same size. The primary digester normally has a fixed cover and the secondary digester has a floating cover. This secondary tank serves as a gasholder (Fig. 10-32). State and regulatory agencies normally have requirements based on digester volume per contributing person at design loading. These values vary from south to north because of the ambient temperatures. Little engineering goes into the sizing of a digester for a particular location. Research is needed for a more rational approach to design.

Heat is required by digesters to raise the temperature of the sludge to the desired operating level and to compensate for heat losses through the walls, roof, and bottom of the digestion tank (Fig. 10-33). The formula for the heat required to raise the temperature of the sludge is:

$$Q = WC(T_2 - T_1) \tag{10-50}$$

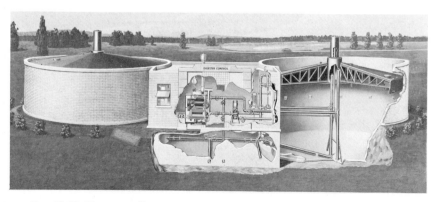

FIG. 10-32. Two-stage digester arrangement, showing piping in control room and external mixer and heater. (Courtesy Pacific Flush Tank Co.)

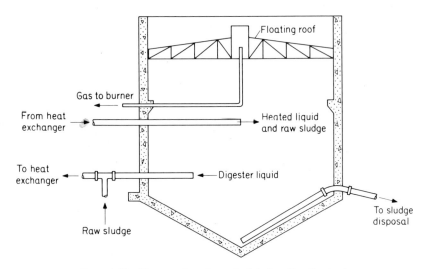

Fig. 10-33. Cross section of a typical sludge-digestion tank.

where Q = amount of heat, Btu/day
  W = pounds of raw sludge added to the digester per day
  C = mean specific heat of raw sludge, usually taken as 1.0
  T_1 = temperature of the raw sludge, °F
  T_2 = temperature of the digesting sludge, °F

The temperature of the raw sludge is usually taken as the temperature of the raw sewage during the coldest two-week period of the year. The heat required to raise the temperature of the sludge must be added to the heat required to compensate for that lost from the digester. The basic heat-flow equation is:

$$Q = \frac{k}{x} A(T_2 - T_1) \tag{10-51}$$

where Q = heat lost, Btu/hr
  k = thermal conductivity of the material, in Btu/hr/sq ft/°F/in. of thickness.
  x = thickness of the material, in.
  A = area of the tank, sq ft
  T_1 = outside boundary temperature, °F
  T_2 = digestion temperature, °F

The gas produced in the digester is normally used as fuel to heat the digesting sludge.

REFERENCES

1. Richard B. Setlow and Ernest C. Pollard, *Molecular Biophysics* (Reading, Mass.: Addison-Wesley Publishing Co., Inc., 1964), p. 42.

2. James C. Young, E. E. Staffeldt, and J. W. Clark, "BOD of Selected Organisms," *Water Sewage Works*, vol. 110, no. 8 (August 1964), pp. 358–359.

3. James C. Young, unpublished thesis (New Mexico State University, July 1964).

4. P. E. Gaffney and H. Heukelekian, "Oxygen Demand Measurement Errors in Pure Organic Compounds—Nitrification Studies," *Sewage Ind. Wastes*, vol. 30, no. 4 (April 1958), pp. 503–510.

5. Ross E. McKinney, *Microbiology for Sanitary Engineers* (McGraw-Hill Book Co., Inc., 1962), p. 32.

6. W. J. O'Brien and J. W. Clark, "The Historical Development of the Biochemical Oxygen Demand Test," New Mexico State University, Eng. Exptl. Sta., Bull. 20 (January 1962), p. 141.

7. E. Frankland, "First Report of the Rivers Pollution Commission of 1868," extracted in Royal Commission Fifth Report, Appendix VI (1908), p. 10.

8. J. B. Weems, "The Evolution of the Oxygen Absorption Test in Water Analysis," Thirteenth Annual Meeting Iowa Engineering Society, Davenport, Iowa, January 1901, abs., *Rev. Am. Chem. Res.*, vol. 8 (1902), p. 323.

9. A. Dupré, "Report on Changes in the Aeration of Water, As Indicating the Nature of the Impurities Present in It," Fourteenth Annual Report of the Local Government's Board, 1883–1884, Appendix B, no. 11 (1884), p. 304.

10. W. E. Adeney, "Studies in the Chemical Analysis of Salt and Fresh Waters, I. Applications of the Aeration Method of Analysis to the Study of River Water," Royal Commission, Fifth Report, Appendix VII (1908), p. 95.

11. E. J. Theriault, "The Oxygen Demand of Polluted Waters," U.S. Public Health Service, Washington, D.C., Bull. 173 (1927); *Chem. Abstrs.*, vol. 25 (1931), p. 4644.

12. E. W. Moore, H. A. Thomas, and W. B. Snow, "Simplified Method of Analysis of BOD Data," *Sewage Ind. Wastes*, vol. 22, no. 10 (1950), p. 1343.

13. Nelson L. Nemerow, *Theories and Practices of Industrial Waste Treatment* (Reading, Mass.: Addison-Wesley Publishing Co., Inc., 1963).

14. E. S. West and W. R. Todd, *Textbook of Biochemistry*, 3d ed. (New York: The Macmillan Co., 1963).

15. James C. Young, unpublished thesis (New Mexico State University, 1964).

16. R. L. Woodward, "Deoxygenation of Sewage—A Discussion," *Sewage Ind. Wastes*, vol. 25, no. 8 (1953), p. 918.

17. J. W. Clark, "New Method for Biochemical Oxygen Demand," Eng. Exptl. Sta., New Mexico State University, Bull. 11 (December 1959).

18. N. W. Streeter and E. B. Phelps, *U.S. Public Health Service, Bull.* 146 (1925).

19. J. D. O'Connor and W. E. Dobbins, "Mechanism of Reaeration in Natural Streams," *Trans. Am. Soc. Civil Engrs.*, vol. 123 (1958), p. 655.

20. A. F. Gaudy and B. G. Turner, "Effect of Air-flow Rate on Response of Activated Sludge to Quantitative Shock Loading," *J. Water Pollution Control Federation*, vol. 56, no. 6 (June 1964).

21. W. W. Eckenfelder, Jr., "Trickling Filtration Design and Performance," *Trans. Am. Soc. Civil Engrs.*, vol. 128, III (1963), p. 371.

22. E. R. Hermann and E. F. Gloyna, "Waste Stablilization Ponds, III.

Formulation of Design Equations," *Sewage Ind. Wastes*, vol. 30, no. 8 (August 1958), pp. 963–975.

23. F. G. Pohland, "High Rate Digestion," 46th Texas Water and Sewage Works Association's Short School, Texas A and M University, College Station, Texas, March 1–6, 1964.

PROBLEMS

10-1. What is the approximate horsepower being developed by the bacteria in an aeration tank 100 ft long, 25 ft wide, and 15 ft deep? Assume that the bacteria are all *E. Coli* under optimum conditions with a bacterial density of 600×10^6 per ml and that each bacteria is a rod $10\,\mu$ long and $4\,\mu$ in diameter with a specific weight of 1.3.

10-2. A single-cell microorganism is in the shape of a sphere and averages $5\,\mu$ in diameter with a density of 1.2. Assuming an asexual generation time of 20 min, optimum conditions, and that all organisms remain viable, how long will it take to produce 1 lb of cell material? One hundred pounds? The weight of the earth?

10-3. Assume that each organism in Prob. 10-2 remains alive for 12 hr, how long will it take to produce 100 lb of live cell material?

10-4. What is the heat of reaction for oxidizing one mole of glucose? The pressure is constant at one atmosphere and the temperature is 25°C.

10-5. How many grams of oxygen are required for the complete combustion of carbon when 700 kcal are liberated? The pressure is constant at one atmosphere and the temperature is 25°C.

10-6. What is the heat of reaction in Example 10-1 if the water is in the vapor state?

10-7. How many pounds of urea ($N_2 H_4 CO$) are required in the synthesis of 1 lb of dextrose ($C_6 H_{12} O_2$) to cell material?

10-8. In an oxidation tank experiment, glucose is being fed at the rate of 30 g/hr, how many grams of ammonia gas are required if it is assumed that 60 percent of the glucose is being converted to cell material?

10-9. One thousand grams of dead bacterial cell material is available in an oxidation system. If 55 percent of the dead cell material is synthesized to new cells and these new cells live for 7 days and the process is repeated, how long will it be before there is only 1 g of the original cell material remaining?

10-10. The five-day BOD of a waste is 250 mg/l. If K is equal to 0.15, what is the ultimate BOD of the waste?

10-11. The five-day BOD of a waste is 280 mg/l. The ultimate BOD is reported to be 410 mg/l. At what rate is the waste being oxidized?

10-12. The five-day, 20°C BOD of a waste is 250 mg/l and its temperature is 85°F. The five-day, 20°C BOD of the water in a stream is 5 mg/l and its temperature is 55°F. What will be the five-day, 20°C BOD of the stream below the point of waste discharge when the total flow is 150 cfs and the waste flow is 0.5 mgpd? Assume that the BOD rate is constant and that K at 20°C is 0.35 for both the stream and the waste.

10-13. The sewage flow from a city is 25×10^6 gpd. If the average five-day

20°C BOD is 265 mg/l, compute the total daily oxygen demand in pounds and the population equivalent of the sewage.

10-14. The following BOD information was taken from electrolysis equipment. The temperature was 20°C. What is the maximum velocity of the reaction and the ultimate BOD?

Time, days	BOD, mg/l
1	141
2	162
3	210
4	245
5	261

10-15. The following BOD information was obtained from electrolysis equipment. The temperature was 24°C. What was the maximum velocity of the reaction at 20°C and the ultimate BOD?

Time, days	Ampere-hours
1	0.31
2	0.42
3	0.58
4	0.71
5	0.75

10-16. The following information was recorded from a 35°C BOD test by electrolysis. What was the five-day 20°C BOD, the ultimate BOD, and the maximum velocity of the reaction?

Date	Time	BOD, mg/l
6-1-65	10:00 a.m.	0
	10:00 p.m.	130
6-2-65	10:00 a.m.	181
	10:00 p.m.	210
6-3-65	10:00 a.m.	241
	10:00 p.m.	269

10-17. A city of 150,000 population produces sewage at the rate of 150 gpcd and the waste-treatment-plant effluent has a BOD of 19 mg/l. The temperature of the waste is 26.1°C and there is 1.4 mg/l of DO in the plant effluent. The stream flow is 161 cfs at 1.3 fps and an average depth of 5 ft. The temperature of the stream before the waste flow is introduced is 21.2°C. The stream is 85 percent saturated with oxygen and has a BOD of 1.8 mg/l. The deoxygenation coefficient k_1 is equal to 0.45 at 20°C. Graph the oxygen-sag curve.

10-18. If all of the 7 mg/l of DO in a clean turbulent stream can be counted on for the oxidation of organic matter in a domestic waste (the reaeration is a factor of safety against nuisance), what should be the dilution factor in cfs per 1,000 population if the waste flow is 150 gpd and its BOD is 230 mg/l?

10-19. In a BOD determination 6 ml of sewage are mixed with 294 ml of diluting water containing 8.6 mg/l of dissolved oxygen. After incubation the dissolved oxygen content of the mixture is 5.4 mg/l. Calculate the BOD of the sewage. Assume the initial DO of the sewage is zero.

10-20. A city discharges 4 mgpd of 15°C sewage with a five-day, 20°C BOD of 250 mg/l into a stream whose discharge is 78 cfs and the water temperature is

17°C. If k_2 is equal to 0.28 at 20°C, what is the critical oxygen deficit and the time at which it occurs? Assume the stream is 100 percent saturated with oxygen before the sewage is added.

10-21. A stream with k_2 equal to 0.31, temperature of 28°C, and minimum flow of 800 cfs receives 10 mgd of sewage from a city. The river water is saturated with DO above the city. What is the maximum permissible BOD of the sewage if the dissolved oxygen content of the stream is never to be below 4.0 mg/l?

10-22. An aeration tank is to be designed, using diffused air, for a section of a city containing 70,000 population and no industrial waste. The mixed-liquor solids are assumed to be 2,300 mg/l, with a loading of 28 lb BOD/day/100 lb of aeration-tank solids based upon pilot-plant studies. The sludge-volume index is to be maintained at 85. What are the tank dimensions?

10-23. Using the information in Prob. 10-22, design the aeration tank based on an 8-hr detention period.

10-24. Using the information in Prob. 10-22, design the aeration basin on the BOD per unit volume. Use 30 lb BOD/day/1,000 cu ft of tank capacity.

10-25. Estimate the concentration of suspended solids needed in an activated sludge aeration tank to effect 75 percent BOD reduction of 3 mgpd of sewage with a BOD load of 4,900 lb/day when the aeration period is 6 hr.

10-26. Find the pressure drop in 2,000 ft of 4-in. steel pipe when transporting 1,500 cfs of air at an initial gage pressure of 10 psi. The temperature is 70°F and the plant is located at sea level.

10-27. The pressure drop in 3,000 ft of 6-in. cast-iron pipe is 11 psi. The initial gage pressure is 19 psi and the temperature is 72°F with an atmospheric pressure of 14.7 psi. How much air is being transported through this pipe?

10-28. Compute the BOD removal from settled domestic sewage in a filter 8 ft deep with a hydraulic loading of 16 mgad without recirculation.

10-29. The BOD removal efficiency of a trickling filter was found to be 78 percent at 20°C. What efficiency would be expected at 25°C?

10-30. Compute the recirculation ratio to obtain 94 percent BOD reduction in a trickling filter, using a depth of 6 ft and a hydraulic loading of 14 mgad.

10-31. Find (a) the acre-feet of filter required to effect 90 percent BOD removal from 15 mgpd of waste containing 140 mg/l of 5 day BOD when it is applied to a single-stage filter and (b) the BOD loading and hydraulic loading if the filter is made 6 ft deep. Assume that the sewage is not to be recirculated.

10-32. A flow of 1.5 mgpd of waste containing 260 mg/l of BOD is passed through a primary sedimentation tank, which removes 40 percent of the BOD before being applied to a trickling filter. If the filter surface is 0.4 acre and its depth is 6 ft, estimate the overall percentage of BOD reduction and the BOD remaining in the plant effluent without recirculation. Compute these values for a recirculation of 0.5 mgpd of plant effluent to the filter.

10-33. What is the volume of an oxidation pond required to serve a population of 4,000, where the per capita flow is 110 gpd and the five-day BOD is 240 mg/l? The design temperature is 12°C.

10-34. A 3-acre oxidation pond 2.5 ft deep is being used to serve a new residential area. The per capita flow is 90 gpd and the five-day BOD is 260 mg/l. The design temperature is 10°C. What population will this pond serve?

10-35. A digester with 50,000 gal of digestion volume is to be neutralized. The total alkalinity is 3,000 mg/l as $CaCO_3$ and the total organic acids is 3,800 mg/l as acetic acid. How many pounds of lime (CaO) are required for this neutralization?

10-36. A digester gives off 50,000 cu ft of gas daily. The gas is measured at a temperature of 80°F and at a pressure of 1.2 psig. Find the volume of gas at 20°C and 14.7 psia. If the gas contains 60 percent methane and is fed to a gas engine with a 30 percent efficiency, what is the available horsepower?

chapter 11

Processing of Sludges

The term *sludge* is used to designate the solid matter separated from water. Because of the various degrees and methods of treatment, more specific terms are used—*raw or primary sludge, activated sludge,* and *digested sludge.*

Raw or primary sludge is that solid material separated in the primary process of sewage treatment. This is usually accomplished by sedimentation and flotation, but various forms of screening or filtration have been used. Primary sludge is odoriferous, quickly putrescible, and generally difficult to handle mechanically. Activated sludge is the excess floc material not recycled through the aeration basin after secondary sedimentation. This sludge is normally collected in sedimentation basins but may be secured through screening or filtration. It is voluminous and at times difficult to dewater. A sludge with a relatively high solids content is desirable as there is less water to handle. Digested sludge is the final solids end product of digesters.

Sludge handling and disposal is a major part of the sewage-treatment process. About 25 to 40 percent of the total cost of a sewage-treatment plant is invested in sludge digestion and handling equipment, and much of the normal plant operation and maintenance is concerned with sludge disposal.

Sludge produced from primary and secondary treatment processes normally requires dewatering prior to disposal. Methods in use today include air drying, vacuum filtration, centrifugation, mechanical separation, and wet oxidation. In large plants, extensive mechanical equipment is used. The choice of method is materially affected by location and climate.

11-1. SLUDGE-DRYING BEDS

The most common method of dewatering digested sludge is by drying on open or covered sand beds. By using this procedure a sludge with about a 75 percent or less moisture content can be obtained in a few days. Such a sludge is conveniently handled with a shovel or garden fork and can be economically transported. The area required for sludge-drying beds is primarily determined by climatic conditions. Greenhouse structures are often placed over sludge-drying beds in northern areas.

The dewatering of sludge on sand beds occurs by filtration of the water through the sand and evaporation of the water from the sludge surface. Filtration is usually accomplished on digested sludge in 1 to 2 days. This is dependent upon the characteristics of the sludge and the depth to which the sludge is placed on the bed. After most of the water is filtered off, the sludge then dries to an equilibrium moisture content with the surrounding air. This final moisture content depends upon the temperature and relative humidity of the air and the nature of the water content. Bound water retained in capillaries and in cell walls will result in a high final moisture content. A high bound-water content is representative of raw or partially digested sludge. Well-digested sludge posesses a low bound-water content and is easily dewatered on sand beds.

EXAMPLE 11-1. Derive the square footage of drying beds needed per capita for primary digested sludge in the southwestern part of the United States. Assume the following data:
1. Suspended solids in raw sewage, 0.2 lb per capita per day
2. Suspended solids removal by primary sedimentation, 60 percent
3. Volatile content of raw sludge solids, 75 percent
4. Reduction in volatile matter by digestion, 55 percent
5. Solids content of digested sludge, 8 percent
6. Depth of sludge applied to beds, 8 in.
7. Number of bed applications per year, 11

Solution:
1. Per capita production of raw sludge.

$$365 \times 0.2 \times 0.60 = 43.80 \text{ lb per capita per year}$$

2. Volatile content of raw sludge.

$$43.80 \times 0.75 = 32.85 \text{ lb per capita per year}$$

3. Ash in sludge.

$$43.80 - 32.85 = 10.95 \text{ lb per capita per year}$$

4. Volatile solids in digested sludge.

$$32.85 \, (1-0.55) = 14.78 \text{ lb per capita per year}$$

5. Total solids in digested sludge.

$$10.95 + 14.78 = 25.73 \text{ lb per capita per year}$$

6. Volume of wet sludge.

$$\frac{25.73}{0.08 \times 62.5} = 5.15 \text{ cu ft per capita per year}$$

7. Bed area required:

$$\frac{5.15 \times 12}{8 \times 11} = 0.7 \text{ sq ft per capita per year}$$

This corresponds to a dry-solids bed loading of 25.73/0.7 or 36.7 lb of dry solids per square foot of drying bed annually.

Sludge-drying beds normally consist of 4 to 6 in. of sand over 8 to 12 in. of gravel or stone. The bed is drained by tile underdrains placed in the gravel about 6 to 12 ft apart. The spacing of the underdrains depends on the drainage characteristics of the subsoil. The underdrainage may be returned to the primary sedimentation tank. The side walls of the beds are made of concrete, wood, or earth embankments. The general type of construction is illustrated in Fig. 11-1. The side walls are normally about 12 in. high and the beds are filled to a depth of 8 to 10 in. Several smaller beds serve the purpose better than one large bed. The width of the drying bed is so chosen that the vehicle used for removing the dried sludge can be loaded conveniently. Common values for width are about 20 ft. The length is generally held below 100 ft. Sludge may be expected to flow approximately 100 ft from a single outlet when the bed slope away from the outlet is about 0.5 percent.

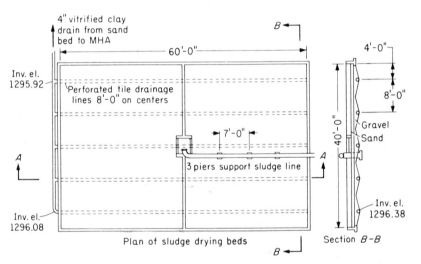

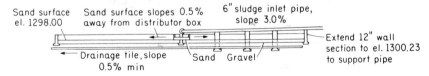

FIG. 11-1. Sludge-drying beds.

11-2. VACUUM FILTRATION

Vacuum filters are the most widely used type of mechanical sludge-dewatering device. Most large plants use some form of vacuum filter where dewatering processes are carried on. The filters are adaptable to various forms of raw or digested sludge. The filtration process is employed to separate the solids from the liquid by means of a porous media which retains the solids but allows the liquid to pass through. Media employed for this purpose include steel coils, metal mesh, and cloth. A vacuum filter system is shown in Fig. 11-2.

The filtration process is accomplished by means of a horizontal drum covered with the filter media. The drum is rotated in a tank with about one quarter of the drum submerged in wet sludge. Valves and piping are so arranged that as the drum rotates a vacuum applied on the inner side of the filter media draws out water from the sludge and holds a layer of sludge to the drum. The application of the vacuum is continued as the drum rotates out of the sludge into the atmosphere. This pulls additional water away from the sludge mat leaving a moist cake of sludge on the outer surface. This sludge mat is scraped, blown, or lifted away from the drum just before it enters the sludge tank again.

FIG. 11-2. Vacuum filter installation. (Courtesy of Eimco Corporation.)

The common measure of performance of vacuum filters is the rate at which dry solids are produced. This is usually measured in pounds per hour of dry solids filtered per square foot of filter surface. This rate will vary from 2.5 for activated sludge to 11 for well-digested primary sludges. The moisture content of this vacuum filtered sludge will vary from 60 to 85 percent, depending upon the quality of the conditioned sludge. Digested sludges are relatively easy to handle whereas activated and raw sludges become increasingly difficult to filter and handle.

Operating costs including conditioning of the sludge for vacuum filtration are normally higher than with drying beds. Vacuum filtration has the advantage of requiring much less area and not being affected by weather conditions. Vacuum filtration can be used on nondigested sludges and produces a sludge that can be handled for disposal by other means such as incineration. This eliminates the necessity for digestion.

11-3. CENTRIFUGATION

Continuous centrifuges have been widely used for separating solids from liquids in the chemical process and mining industries for many years. More recently they have been used for separating solids from liquid in waste-treatment plants. In general, the only requirement for this type of separation is that the suspended solids be of greater density than the transporting liquid. In most cases this rules out floating solids. However, material that floats because occluded gas bubbles tend to decrease its density is not necessarily excluded from this type of separation. The gas bubbles tend to be released as the feed sludge accelerates within the centrifuge and thus do not affect the separating effeciency.

Experience with centrifuges has been demonstrated in several areas of industrial waste. They have been used to dewater paper-mill wastes, packing-house wastes, foundry sludges, refinery wastes, and water-softening sludges. They are now being used to dewater various sewage sludges (Fig. 11-3).

The theoretical clarifying capacity of a centrifuge is limited by (1) the maximum settling rate of the smallest particle to be handled, (2) the retention time under centrifugal force available for settling these solids, and (3) the liquid depth through which the solid particles must settle. The terminal settling velocity for a given particle may be calculated by equating the centrifugal force which causes settling to the resisting force which results because fluid must be forced from the path of the settling material.

The terminal or equilibrium settling velocity of a particle at a given distance from the axis of rotation may be represented by the following formula for small particles subject to viscous resistance of the suspending medium.[1]

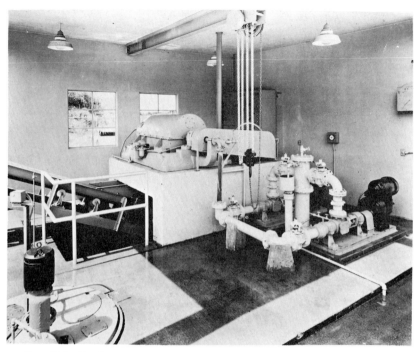

Fig. 11-3. Continuous centrifuge used for dewatering sludge. (Courtesy of Bird Machine Company.)

$$V_s = \frac{D^2(C_s - C_1)W^2r}{18M} \tag{11-1}$$

where V_s = terminal settling velocity

D = projected particle diameter

C_s = density of suspended solids

C_1 = density of suspending liquid

W = angular velocity

r = distance of the particle from the axis of rotation

M = liquid viscosity

The settling velocity of suspended matter and hence, the clarifying capacity of a given size of centrifuge operating at a specific speed will increase with larger particle size and increasing density of the solids. The greater the radial acceleration of the particles the better the clarifying capacity of a centrifuge. The acceleration can be increased by either increasing the speed or the size of the unit involved.

The physical action involved in separating solids from liquid by means of centrifuges varies with the character and particle-size distribution of the material being handled. Noncompressible solids, generally +200 mesh in size, dewater as liquid flows through the conveying cake. Extremely fine or compressible materials dewater primarily by explusion of liquid as the solids compact. Moisture contents less than 70 percent are obtainable on a continuous basis.[2]

11-4. WET OXIDATION

The wet oxidation process is a method of incineration that uses the principle of wet combustion to degrade the organic matter in sludges. Oxygen to support the combustion is supplied by the injection of compressed air into the system. The combustion temperatures in wet oxidation are considerably lower than the temperatures in normal dry combustion. This process has been used in the disposal of organic waste sludges.

The wet oxidation process as applied to the disposal of wastes is known as the *Zimmerman process* and is protected by patents held by the Sterling Drug Company.

This process is chemical oxidation, under pressure, and at elevated temperatures, of combustible material in water. Oxygen in air is the oxidant and the organic matter in waste is the combustible material. Oxidation will take place at 100°C and will be most active above 200°C and up to the critical temperature of water (374°C).[3]

The physical units of a wet oxidation process are:
1. An air compression unit
2. Sludge pump designed to pump against the desired pressure.
3. Reaction vessel to house the oxidation process
4. Heat exchangers to recover and recycle some of the heat

Figure 11-4 shows the change in reaction speed and percent of organic material oxidized with increasing temperature. Oxygen must be added to the wet oxidation process in stoichiometric proportions at a rate necessary to satisfy combustion requirements. Excess oxygen above that required for combustion will not accelerate the process.

The size of the sludge-pumping units are selected on the basis of the volume of sludge to be treated and the pressure at which the reactor will be operated. The pressures in such a flow system would normally range from 1,200 to 1,800 psi.

The air compressor is designed to deliver the calculated amount of oxygen necessary for the reaction. This amount of oxygen is based upon the COD of the waste. The utilization of oxygen has been found to follow very closely the utilization of oxygen from chromate as determined by the COD procedure.[3]

The size of the reactor vessel depends upon the volumetric load, the COD of the entering sludge, the temperature, and the reaction detention time. As shown in Fig. 11-4, the reaction time and percent COD removal

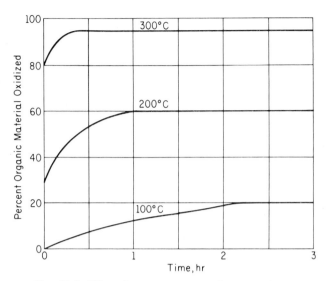

FIG. 11-4. Effect of temperature upon the rate and per-cent of oxidation in the wet oxidation process. (Adapted from E. Hurwitz and W. A. Dundas, "Ultimate Disposal of Sewage Sludge by Wet Oxidation," *Proceedings Four-teenth Industrial Waste Conference*, Purdue University, 1959, Fig. 2.)

are advantageously affected by increasing the temperature of the reaction. The size of the reactor will be reduced at higher operating temperatures. Figure 11-5 is a schematic flow sheet for the process.

The design of the heat exchanger is based upon volumetric load and the operating temperatures. The economy of the process depends on the

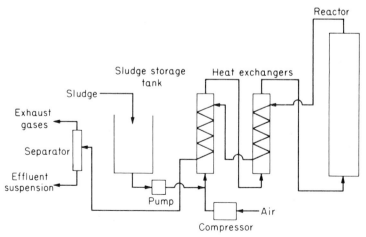

FIG. 11-5. Schematric flow sheet for the wet oxidation process.

recovery efficiency of the heat energy developed. Figure 11-6 shows the correlation of unit production costs at various loads. The unit production costs vary from about $1.40 per 1,000 gallon for a 10-mgpd plant to $36 per 1,000 gallons for a 1,000-gpd plant. These costs do not include plant costs, which will vary from $3 to $87 per 1,000 gpd for the same range.[4]

The reduction of the organic residuals resulting from this process may be accomplished by recycling the wet oxidation effluent to a conventional sewage-treatment process. The low-molecular-weight residual organics from wet oxidation are very amenable to biologic oxidation.

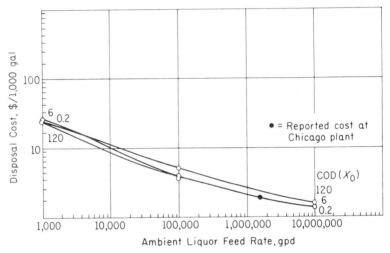

FIG. 11-6. Unit production disposal costs by wet oxidation.[4]

11-5. INCINERATION

Incineration of sewage sludge is a common method of sludge disposal. All types of sludges—primary, secondary, raw, or digested—may be dried and burned. Raw primary sludge with about 70 percent volatile solids contains about 7,800 Btu/lb of dry solids. This sludge will burn without supplementary fuel once combustion is started. Normally excess heat is available from the process and this extra heat is used in the sludge-drying process. Digested sludge may or may not require supplementary fuel, depending upon the moisture content and percent volatile solids in the sludge. Raw activated sludge normally requires supplementary fuel for drying and incineration. In all cases supplementary fuel is necessary to start the operation and to maintain it until combustion temperatures have been established.

Incineration is being used at many large plants where final disposal of the solid wastes is a problem. It has the advantage of freedom from many odors, independence of weather, and in the volume and weight of the end product to be disposed of. There is a minimum size of sewage-treatment plant below which incineration is not considered economical. There must be enough sludge to warrant resonable use of expensive equipment.

Sludge as delivered to an incinerator is generally in the form of filter cake normally produced by vacuum filtration of liquid sludge. This filter cake may contain 60 to 85 percent moisture. The sludge to be incinerated must be dried to a point where it will ignite and burn. The commonly used units for heat drying are:

1. Rotary kiln
2. Flash drier
3. Spray drier
4. Multiple-hearth furnace

The rotary-kiln drier is a cylinder set on an inclined plane with the length eight to ten times the diameter. The cylinder revolves 4 to 8 rpm. The sludge to be dried enters at the upper end and is carried to the discharge by gravity as the cylinder rotates. Heated gases are introduced to the cylinder with the hot gases coming into contact with the colder sludge. The drying temperature should be held below 700°F. The exhaust gases from the drier must be oxidized at a temperature of 1200 to 1400°F in order to reduce serious air pollution.

The flash drier is a cage-type mill where the sludge particles are dried almost instantly as they are dispersed and held in suspension in a stream of hot gases. These gas-borne sludge particles are blown to a separator where the dried sludge is trapped and removed from the moisture-laden gases. The exhaust gases must be treated in a similar manner to those from the rotary-kiln drier (Fig. 11-7).

The spray drier consists of a vertical tower down which a current of hot gases is flowing. Fine particles of wet sludge are sprayed into this tower. The water is quickly evaporated from the small sludge particles and passes off with the gases. As with the previous drying process, the moisture-laden exhaust gases must be treated.

The multiple-hearth furnace is a combination heat drying and incineration process. The furnace consists of a vertical cylinder containing a series of four or more hearths, one above the other. Partially dewatered sludge cake is fed to the upper hearth and dried by the hot gases from the lower hearths. This partially dried sludge is moved successively down to the next lower hearth mechanically until dried to a point where it will ignite and burn.

If a chemical analysis of a fuel is known, an approximate determination of the heat value can be made by use of the Dulong formula, which is[5]

$$Q = 14,600C + 62,000 \left(H - \frac{0}{8} \right) \qquad (11\text{-}2)$$

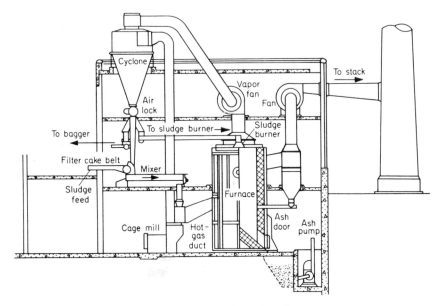

Fig. 11-7. System for flash drying.

where Q = heat value, Btu/lb
      C = percent of carbon in fuel
      H = percent of hydrogen in fuel
      O = percent of oxygen in fuel

This approximate formula works quite well with some coals but is not as applicable to sewage sludges. The best heating value for sludge is that determined experimentally in a calorimeter.

The thermal calculations required in an incenetration process are:

1. Heat taken up by
   (a) Latent heat in free moisture and moisture of combustion
   (b) Sensible heat in gases of combustion and excess air
   (c) Ash
   (d) Radiation
2. Heat evolved from combustibles in
   (a) Waste
   (b) Supplementary fuel

Figure 11-8 is a schematic diagram of the various processes in incinerator design.

11-6. COMPOSTING

The composting of sewage sludge and municipal refuse into a humus valuable as a soil conditioner and nutrient for plants is the alternative to landfill or incineration that is given most serious thought today. The

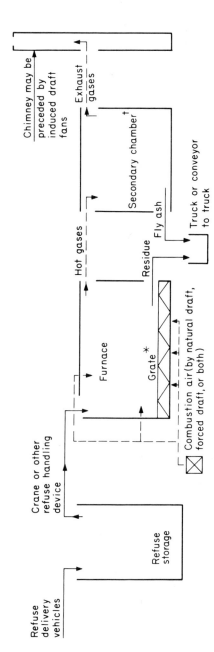

*Grate may be level, inclined, circular, rotating, fixed, movable, or any combinations of these.

†Secondary chamber may be one or more enclosures used for combustion, fly-ash settlement, gas cooling, fly-ash collection, or a combination of these functions.

Fig. 11-8. Incinerator schematic design.

principal deterrents to large-scale composting of organic wastes are the utilization of the finished compost and the American tradition of waste, which generates a vast public disinterest in the reclamation of organic matter.

At present, the atmosphere is the major region for disposal of the waste products of modern cities. Gaseous wastes are measured by weight as hydrocarbons, oxides of nitrogen and sulfur, carbon monoxide, organic gases, and aerosols. Carbon dioxide and water are not considered as gaseous wastes. For the air pollutants measured in Los Angeles County in 1964, the dry weight averaged 3.2 lb per capita per day. The dry weight of the total solids removed from the city by sewers amounted to 0.44 lb per capita per day. The solid wastes collected from households and commercial establishments averaged 1.98 lb per capita per day.[6] The atmosphere in many of our cities is already overburdened with waste and to convert solid wastes to gaseous wastes by incineration will only add to the problem. The composting of sludges has the added advantage that a high percentage of the solid wastes collected from households and commercial establishments can be added to the process. No satisfactory solution has been found to reduce materially the large volume of gaseous wastes from automobiles.

Composting may be defined as the biologic decomposition of organic solid wastes to a relatively stable end product. The moisture content is normally between 40 and 70 percent. The aerobic decomposition proceeds in the thermophilic range above 113°F and generally in excess of 140°F. The process is both oxidative and thermogenetic. The principal end products are humus substances, carbon dioxide, and water. Some anaerobic decomposition takes place but the end products are further reduced by aerobic digestion. The major breakdown of organic matter is brought about by facultative bacteria and fungi. Water is essential for biological degradation. If the refuse contains less than 60 percent moisture, it will be difficult for the bacteria actively to reduce the organic waste. Under these conditions the fungi will be predominant if sufficient moisture is available. The moisture and oxygen concentrations of compost are critical, because too much moisture will inhibit oxygen transfer and force the process anaerobic whereas too much ventilation will lower the moisture content and inhibit biological action.

Very little work has been done on the microorganisms of composting. The fungi which normally predominate in compost will be dependent upon the nature of the organic matter being decomposed. Various species of *Geothrichium, Penicillium, Rhizopus, Aspergillus,* and *Mucor* will usually be found in active compost. The bacteria usually associated with other biological processes of liquid-waste treatment will be found in compost with the thermophilic species predominating at the higher temperatures. The mesophilic bacteria are active in starting the compost and elevating the temperature to where the thermophilic species become active. A typical temperature curve for continuously mixed and aerated waste is shown in Fig. 11-9.

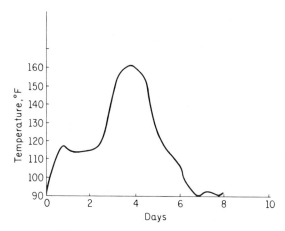

FIG. 11-9. Typical temperature curve for a continuously mixed and aerated waste.

The *p*H of a composting waste will be depressed in the early stages due to organic acid production by the bacteria. The process can be accelerated by the addition of a buffer. Lime has been added for *p*H control and the buffering action is similar to that in anaerobic digesters that have received shock loadings. The variation of *p*H with time in a continuously mixed and aerated composting sludge without buffering is shown in Fig. 11-10.

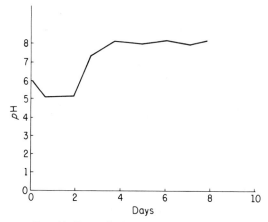

FIG. 11-10. Typical variation of *p*H in a continuously mixed and aerated compost.

A nutritional balance is required for maximum microbiological activity. Carbohydrates along with nitrogen, phosphorus, and other trace elements are necessary. There is often a deficiency of nitrogen and phosphorus in community solid wastes. The necessary carbon to nitrogen ratio is about 20 to 1 and carbon to phosphorus ratio is approximately 100 to 1. The addition of phosphorous and nitrogen accelerates the process and improves the fertilizer value of the end product.

In mechanical composting air is added to the composter continuously to satisfy the oxygen requirements. Normally excess air is supplied in order to ensure aerobic conditions. Too much excess air dries out the compost and lowers the temperature. The respiratory quotient (volume CO_2/volume O_2) has been reported to be of the order of about 0.9.[7,8] Schulze has shown that the oxygen requirements can be represented by the equation[8]

$$Y = 0.1 \times 10^{0.028T} \tag{11-3}$$

where Y = oxygen consumption rate, mg O_2/g vol. matter/hour
T = temperature, °C

This equation can be used to compute the oxygen consumption rate or the air-supply rate for a continuous composting process operating at temperatures between 20°C and 70°C.

Table 11-1 gives a stoichiometric balance for a batch of continuously mixed, ground refuse. The respiratory quotient for these average values in Table 11-1 was 0.91.

TABLE 11-1
COMPOST STOICHIOMETRIC BALANCE AVERAGE VALUES
(AFTER WILEY[7])

Constituent	Intake, lb	Output, lb
Volatile solids	14.64	10.03
Ash	1.25	1.43
Moisture	24.58	15.85
Total composting materials	40.47	27.31
Oxygen used	6.79	—
Water evaporated	—	8.73
Water produced	—	2.60
Carbon dioxide produced	—	8.52
Total	47.26	47.16

Very little has been reported to date on the survival of plant and animal pathogens in compost. Besides the physiothermic effect of killing pathogens, there are also antagonistic processes caused by antibiotic inhibitors which are present or produced in the composting process. Most pathogenic organisms are unable to survive temperatures of 60°C for longer than 30 min. The tubercle bacillus and anthrax bacilli are possible exceptions to this. The anthraox bacilli form spores which are very resistant to external influences and are capable of remaining virulent for decades.[9] There appears to be no problem in the spread of plant disease with properly prepared compost, although the causative agents may have been present in the original refuse.

Aside from the fertilizer value of compost, considerable improvement in soil characteristics have been noted.[10] In light soils the maintenance of soil moisture has been improved and the pore volume has been increased in heavy soils. The compost improved soils are of a relatively stable structure and are more effective against erosion.

There have been two general types of composting methods used, the open windrow and mechanical processes.

The windrow method of composting consists of placing the refuse in long row piles approximately 4 ft high and 8 ft wide. The moisture content is adjusted to approximately 60 percent and the composting process is allowed to begin. The pile is turned with an angle dozer or other mechanical equipment every few days. The temperature is sometimes used as an indicator as to when to turn the pile. This process is continued until the composting process is complete. Physical appearance is usually the best means of evaluating when the compost is finished. The process takes from 6 to 10 weeks.

Various types of mechanical systems have been developed to better control the composting process. They employ vertical and horizontal continuously mixed and aerated systems. The principal difference is that with the mechanical system the process is speeded up. Stable compost can be produced in 5 to 15 days. Figure 11-11 is typical of the many mechanical systems.

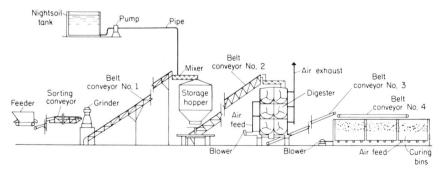

Fig. 11-11. High-rate composting plant.

11-7. SANITARY LANDFILL

Regardless of whether incineration, composting, or some other volume-reduction method is utilized on cities solid wastes, a sizable volume of material must be disposed of by dumping on land or in the sea. Grit and associated wastes from sewage plants and much nonorganic refuse from garbage collection is not amenable to reuse or volume reduction. Sanitary landfill operations are normally used for this purpose. There are four methods currently used to dispose of wastes on land:

1. Open dumping
2. Controlled burning dumping
3. Refuse filling
4. Sanitary landfilling

Open dumping is merely the use of a reasonably well-defined area for the disposal of all trash. The refuse is not covered and incidental burning takes place. This method of the final handling of waste constitutes a gross nuisance and health hazard. Controlled burning dumping is where refuse trucks are unloaded onto a prepared dirt bank. These banks are usually about 12 ft high with a slope of approximately 40 degrees. The slopes of waste are burned from the downwind side. Less smoke is produced and a greater volume reduction takes place than with open burning. Controlled burning dumping is common in the Southwest, even in metropolitan areas. Though better than open dumping, this type of operation has nuisance and health problems.

Refuse filling is a systematic dumping of waste into specially dug trenches. Operational techniques are the same as those conducted at sanitary landfills with the exception that the earth-covering operation is not conducted each day. This is a satisfactory type of fill operation in sparsely settled areas.

Sanitary landfilling is a method of disposing of waste material on land without creating nuisance or health hazards. This is accomplished by the systematic dumping of waste into specially dug trenches. These trenches are covered with a layer of earth at frequent intervals with a minimum of earth cover at the conclusion of each day's operation. Where compacted refuse is placed in the fill to a depth of 6 ft, 1 acre of land per year will be required per 10,000 population. This is estimated on the basis of handling all of the solid wastes normally collected by the governing authority. This does not include wastes from the construction industry. Figure 11-12 depicts a typical sanitary landfill operation.

11-8. WATER DISPOSAL

Sewage sludges and incinerator wastes are often disposed of at sea from our coastal cities. A number of large cities barge sludge 15 to 30 miles

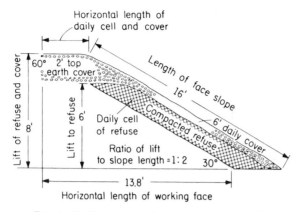

Fig. 11-12. The working face of a sanitary landfill.

at sea and discharge them into the ocean. These ocean dumping areas are designated by an agency of the federal government.

The city of Los Angeles operates a 21-in., 7-mile pipeline constructed out into the ocean for the disposal of 5 mgpd of digested sludge and plant effluent. This outfall line empties into 320 ft depth of water in Santa Monica Bay. The sludge field rises until it is in equilibrium with the surrounding water and then flows with the prevailing ocean currents. The waste does not normally rise to the water surface. Flotable materials of sewage origin have been observed in the bay waters.

11-9. OTHER REFUSE MATERIALS

Refuse other than sewage sludge originating in a community and requiring physical removal from the place of origin to a place of ultimate disposal includes the following:

1. *Ordinary Refuse*—the routine solid wastes produced in residences and commercial establishments, including waste resulting from the preparation and serving of foods and general dry rubbish.

2. *Trash*—all other kinds of solid waste originating in a community not collected on a regular schedule. This includes leaves, industrial wastes, used building materials, and house furnishings.

The final disposal of sewage sludge is sometimes incorporated with the disposal of refuse and trash. The collection of solid waste of a community is outlined in Fig. 11-13.

The refuse originating in a community has changed greatly during the past twenty years both in type and amount. The per capita production has steadily increased, while the refuse itself is less dense, dryer, bulkier, and contains more combustibles. The changes in characteristics have been brought about by improvements in the marketing and packaging of food-

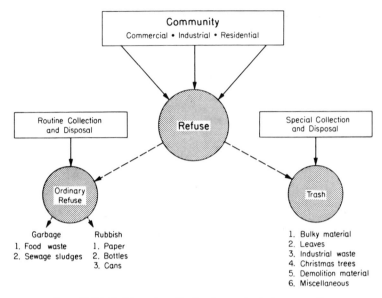

Fɪɢ. 11-13. Solid-waste collection from a typical community.

stuffs, the increasing use of paper, paper products, and plastics in packaging.

The characteristics of ordinary refuse of major concern in collection and disposal operations are weight, heating value, and stability. The unit weight of refuse varies from less than 200 lb/cu yd to more than 1,200 lb/cu yd. Uncompacted domestic refuse has a typical density of 200 to 300 lb/cu yd. The compacting equipment on collection trucks will increase this density to 400 to 500 lb/cu yd.

The heating value of ordinary refuse is largely plant fiber in some form. Calorimeter determinations indicate a value of about 9,500 Btu/lb of dry combustible solids. The actual heating value depends on the proportions of combustibles, noncombustibles, and moisture in the mix. A typical analysis of domestic refuse is shown in Table 11-2.

TABLE 11-2
ANALYSIS OF TYPICAL DOMESTIC REFUSE

Item	Percent by Weight
Combustible	45
Ash	25
Water	30
Btu per pound: 4,500	

The stability of a refuse is directly related to the proportion of its garbage and sludge content and to the type of sludge. Raw sludge is extremely unstable while digested sludge is very stable. The garbage and sludge will account for about 50 percent of the domestic solid wastes by weight.

Differences among communities for reasons of climate, geography, and living conditions have a bearing on the type and amount of refuse. The characteristics of the refuse and sludge in a community should be determined prior to undertaking or revising a disposal service.

The removal of solid waste materials from the place of origin or production and their transportation to a point of disposal constitutes refuse collection. This collection is properly a municipal function and should be under the direct supervision of the municipality. The operation of a refuse and sludge collection system may be by the municipality itself, by a private firm under contract, by arrangement between private collectors and the refuse producers, or by combinations of these three methods. There appears to be no fundamental reason for substantial differences in cost for equivalent service.

In planning the establishment of a municipal collection and disposal system for solid wastes, the most important elements are the scope of service, type of service, the individual community characteristics, and the type of sewage treatment. The community characteristics include population density, wage rates, prevalence of multiple dwelling units, commercial and industrial establishments, and degree of sewage treatment. Figure 11-14 indicates the reduction in volume of materials to be handled with and without incineration.

The engineering services for a solid-refuse collection and disposal system include many items. The principal services are as follows:

1. The development of a comprehensive study and report to provide in advance a clear picture of the scope and costs of the services and facilities.

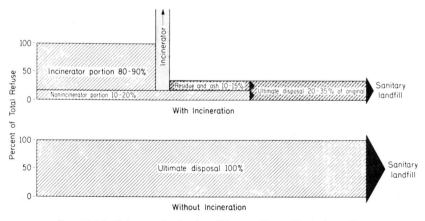

FIG. 11-14. Volume reduction in solid-waste disposal by incineration.

2. Project engineering, including preliminary plans and final preparation of detailed design, specifications, and contract documents.

3. Review and checking of shop drawings of materials and equipment to be built into the project; supervision of construction; and starting operation of the completed facilities.

All of these steps must be accomplished, and generally best results are obtained if these services are performed as part of the same engineering contract.

EXAMPLE 11-2. In order to illustrate the effect on cost of some of the variable and uncertain factors in solid-waste collection and disposal, a simplified outline of computations are shown. The computations are for a residential community of 50,000 people, with medium-size lots for single-family dwellings, and a population density of about 12 persons per acre. The figures are based on a disposal site near the collection area such as might be used for an incineration plant or land fill.

Item	Cost
1. Basic Data	
Population	
Present	50,000
For operating estimates	60,000
Basis of design for structures	75,000
Number of refuse collections per week	1
Point of pickup	Curb
Number of collection points	15,000
Average solid-waste quantities	
Refuse	
Pounds per capita per year	1,200
Total tons per year (60,000 population)	
Pounds per capita per week	23
Pounds per pickup	92
Total tons per week	
Operating estimates	690
Basis of design	860
Total tons per day (five day week)	
Operating estimate	138
Basis of design	172
Digested Sludge	
Pounds per capita per year	
Wet	321
Dry	25.7
Volatile solids	14.8
Ash	10.9
Cubic feet per capita per year	5.15
2. *Collection Costs*	
Refuse	
Total collection truck capacity, (cubic yards)	25
Number of men per crew	3

Average load, at 450 lb/yd, tons	5.6
Pickups per load	122
Pickups per truck-hour	60
Hours of collection time per load	2.03
Travel time to and from disposal	
Site, hours	0.67
Total time per load, hours	2.60
Average number of loads per 7-hour day per truck	
Trucks required	10
Labor Cost, including overhead, per man-year	$ 5,000
Cost of trucks, including fixed charges and	
allowance for spares, per truck-year	6,000
Annual cost of truck and crew	21,000
Total annual refuse collection cost	210,000
Cost per ton	5.80
Digested Sludge	
Truck capacity/cubic yards	6
Average load/cubic yards	7.13
Travel time to and from disposal site, hours	0.67
Loading time at waste treatment plant, hours	.11
Total time per load, hours	0.78
Average number of loads per 7-hour day	9
Trucks required	1
Number of men per crew	1
Labor cost, including overhead, per man-year	5,000
Cost of trucks, per truck-year	6,000
Total annual sludge hauling cost	11,000
Cost per ton	1.15
Total Collection Cost, year	$221,000

3. *Disposal Cost*
   A. Landfill

Compacted depth of fill excluding cover, feet	12
Unit weight of compacted refuse and	
sludge, pounds per cubic yard	888
Quantity of refuse per year, cubic yards	107,400
Area required per year, acres	5.56
Cover material per year, cubic yards	17,800
Land cost per acre	$200
Cover material cost per cubic yard	1.00
Annual cost	
land	$ 1,110
Cover material	17,800
Equipment	10,000
Labor	25,000
Miscellaneous	1,000
Total	$54,910
Cost per ton	1.20

B. Incineration and landfill

Plant capacity, tons per day	265
Construction cost per ton of capacity	$4,000
Total construction cost	$1,060,000
Annual cost of incineration	
(2 shift operation)	
Labor (16 men)	$ 80,000
Utilities	5,000
Maintenance and repair	10,000
Ash truck	6,000
Fixed charges, 7.5%	79,500
Total	$180,500
Annual cost of landfill	
Land	$ 1,000
Other	10,000
Total	$ 11,000
Annual cost of incineration and fill	$191,000
Cost per ton	$4.15

The choice in a specific community between landfill and incineration should reflect also the cost of refuse and sludge collection and haul. Landfill by itself is normally cheaper than incineration, the problem is to determine the length of haul to a landfill site, in excess of the haul distance to the assumed incinerator site, that will offset the higher cost of incineration. Then, too, there is the additional problem of air pollution with incineration.

REFERENCES

1. A. E. Flowers, "Centrifuges," *Chemical Engineers' Handbook,* 3d ed. (New York: McGraw-Hill Book Co., Inc., 1960).

2. W. F. White and T. E. Burnes, "Continuous Centrifugal Treatment of Sewage Sludge," *Water Sewage Works,* vol. 109, no. 10 (October 1962), pp. 384–86.

3. E. Hurwitz and W. A. Dundas, "Wet Oxidation of Sewage Sludge," *U.S. Dept. of Health, Education and Welfare, Public Health Service,* AWTR-3 (October 1963).

4. Louis Koenig, "Ultimate Disposal of Advanced-Treatment Waste," *U.S. Department of Health, Education and Welfare, Public Health Service,* AWTR-3 (October 1963).

5. Mark B. Owen, "Sludge Incineration," *J. Sanit. Eng. Div., Am. Soc. Civil Engrs.,* Paper 1172 (February 1957).

6. J. E. McKee, "Dimensions of the Solid Waste Problem," *Proc. Natl. Conf. Solid Waste Research* (New York: American Public Works Association, December 1963).

7. John S. Wiley, "Refuse and Refuse—Sludge Composting," *J. Boston Soc. Civil Engrs.,* Reprint (January 1962).

8. K. L. Schulze, Continuous Thermophilic Composting," *Compost Sci.,* vol. 3, no. 1 (Spring 1962), pp. 22–33.

9. G. Farkasdi, "Biological Processes in Composting Urban Refuse," *Intern. Res. Group Refuse Disposal,* Inform. Bull. 13 (December 1961), pp. 2–6.

10. H. J. Banse, "Influencing Physical Fertility of Soil Application of Compost," *Intern. Res. Group Refuse Disposal,* Inform. Bull. 13 (December 1961), pp. 34–40.

PROBLEMS

11-1. A waste-treatment plant produces 20,000 lb of sludge per day at a concentration of 4 percent solids. How many pounds of solids will there be when the sludge volume is reduced to a 65 percent moisture content?

11-2. A sludge containing 85 percent moisture is dried until it contains 60 percent moisture. Assuming a fundamental specific gravity of 1.05 for volatile matter and of 2.40 for fixed residue and that the sludge contains 75 percent volatile matter on a dry basis, estimate the specific gravity of the solids on a dry basis and the specific gravities of the wet sludges before and after thickening.

11-3. The volatile matter of a dried sludge has a fuel value of 6,800 Btu/lb. What is the fuel value of 100,000 lb of sludge solids containing 70 percent moisture if the dry solids contain 65 percent volatile matter?

11-4. The suspended solids in raw sewage is 0.22 lb per capita per day. The suspended solids removed by primary sedimentation is 55 percent and the volatile content of these raw sludge solids is 70 percent. If the reduction in volatile matter by digestion is 60 percent, what is the approximate daily volume of digested sludge containing 90 percent water from 100,000 population?

11-5. The digested sludge from Prob. 11-4 is to be applied to drying beds at the rate of 10 applications per year and to a depth of 9 in. at each application. What is the square footage of drying beds required for the 100,000 population? Approximately how many beds would be required?

11-6. A vacuum filter is 20 ft long and 10 ft in diameter. The filter operates 15 hr/day and produces 3 lb of dry sludge solids per hour per square foot of drum surface. How many pounds of 93 percent moisture sludge can be handled daily on this filter?

11-7. A vacuum filter 20 ft long and 12 ft in diameter is being used to process sludge at the rate of 3.6 lb of dry solids per hour per square foot of drum surface. How many hours per day must the filter be run to process 30,000 lb of 95 percent moisture sludge?

11-8. A 10-ft-diameter centrifuge is being used to settle out sludge particles averaging 4 μ in diameter. The density of the suspended solids is 1.2 and the centrifuge is being rotated at the rate of 1,600 rpm. What is the terminal settling velocity of the particles? Assume the suspending liquid has physical properties equivalent to water at 20°C.

11-9. A dry sludge is assumed to have a chemical makeup according to the formula $C_5H_7NO_2$. What is the approximate heat value of this sludge in Btu per pound?

11-10. A sludge has a moisture content of 80 percent and is assumed to have a chemical makeup on a dry basis as shown in Prob. 11-9. What is the approximate net heat value of this wet sludge? Assume the drying process is 100 percent efficient and that the initial sludge temperature is 20°C.

11-11. What is the weight of the oxygen required for theoretical combustion of the sludge in Prob. 11-9? What is the volume of air (sea level and 20°C) necessary to provide this oxygen?

11-12. What is the rate of oxygen supply necessary to support a composting process operating at 146°F and containing 3 tons of refuse? Assume that the refuse contains 68 percent volatile material.

11-13. One ton (dry weight) of refuse is being composted aerobically. Upon completion of the process, the organic material weighed only 520 lb (dry weight). If the empirical molecular weight of the initial refuse was $C_{31}H_{50}O_{26}N$ and that of the final compost $C_{11}H_{14}O_4N$, how many pounds of air (sea level and 20°C) is required by the process?

11-14. A community of 17,000 population produces solid wastes at the rate of 1,200 lb/year/capita. This material is compacted to a unit weight of 620 lb/cu yd and to a depth of 7 ft in a landfill. The fill is operated for 250 days per year. Assuming all other conditions as shown in Fig. 11-12, how many acres of land are required per year?

chapter 12

Disinfection, Taste, and Odor

The production of water of satisfactory quality is often dependent upon the elimination or destruction of two groups of living organisms: (1) the pathogenic microorganisms which may infect man through his use of contaminated water and (2) the algae and other aquatic growths which may render water aesthetically unfit for human consumption. Tastes and odors are, at times, associated with the destruction of these organisms. It is necessary to operate waste-treatment plants with a high degree of odor control.

DISINFECTION

12-1. THEORY

The purpose of disinfecting water supplies is to kill pathogenic organisms and thus prevent the spread of water-borne disease. Most pathogenic bacteria and many other microorganisms are destroyed or removed from water in varying degrees by most of the conventional treatment processes. The destruction and removal is brought about in several ways: (1) physical removal through coagulation, sedimentation, and filtration; (2) natural die-away of organisms in an unfavorable environment during storage; and (3) destruction by chemicals introduced for treatment purposes other than disinfection.

Although the number of microorganisms in polluted waters is reduced by treatment processes and natural purification, the term *disinfection* is used in practice to describe treatment processes that have as their sole objective the killing of pathogenic organisms. Strictly defined, disinfection is the destruction of all pathogenic organisms, while sterilization is the total destruction or removal of all microorganisms. These two terms are similar but quite different. Disinfection is usually brought about by heating, ultraviolet irradiation, chlorination, and the like. These methods and materials can be used to sterilize water, but it is usually impractical to do so from an economic point of view. Disinfection is far more practical.

With most disinfectants, the rate of kill is expressed by

$$\frac{dN}{dt} = -Nk \qquad (12\text{-}1)$$

where $\dfrac{dN}{dt}$ = time rate of kill

k = coefficient of proportionality

N = number of living organisms

Integrating Eq. 12-1 between the limits $t = 0$ and $t = t$, and N_1 and N_2,

$$\int_{N_1}^{N_2} \frac{dN}{N} = -k \int_{0}^{t} dt \qquad (12\text{-}2)$$

$$\ln \frac{N_2}{N_1} = -kt \qquad (12\text{-}3)$$

where N_1, N_2 = number of organisms living initially and at time t respectively

Changing to the log base 10 and rearranging,

$$t = \frac{2.3}{k} \log \frac{N_1}{N_2} \qquad (12\text{-}4)$$

The pattern of death will follow the typical curve shown in Fig. 12-1 when death is due to a single cause. There is an initial lag period before the disinfectant becomes effective. The shape and length of this lag period is a function of the type and concentration of disinfectant and the growth conditions of the organisms.

The rate constant k is a function of the disinfectant, temperature, growth phase of organisms, and other environmental conditions. The relationship between the concentration of disinfectant and the time required for destruction is expressed by the empirical equation[1]

$$t = \frac{K''}{C^n} \qquad (12\text{-}5)$$

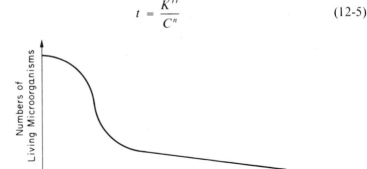

FIG. 12-1. Normal death curve resulting from disinfection.

where t = time required to kill a given percentage of organisms
C = concentration of disinfectant
n = coefficient of dilution
K'' = constant

For a given percentage destruction, Eq. 12-4 becomes

$$t = \frac{K'}{k} \tag{12-6}$$

where

$$K' = 2.3 \log \frac{100}{100 - \text{percentage kill}}$$

Equating Eqs. 12-5 and 12-6,

$$k = Kc^n \tag{12-7}$$

Values of $n > 1$ indicate that the effectiveness of the disinfectant decreases rapidly as it is diluted; values of $n < 1$ indicate that the period of contact is more important than the concentration.

Where the rate of diffusion through the cell wall or the rate of reaction with an enzyme determines the rate of kill, which is normal with most disinfectants, k increases with temperature. Disinfection may be accomplished through the use of heat, light, chemicals, and radioactivity.

12-2. CHLORINE

Chlorine and chlorine derivatives are the most common disinfectants used in environmental control. Chlorination of water supplies on an emergency basis has been used since about 1850. The continuous chlorination of a public supply was first attempted in England during 1904. The first use of chlorine on a continuous basis for a public supply in America was in 1908 when George A. Johnson and John L. Leal employed chloride of lime for the disinfection of the water supply of Jersey City, N.J.[2] This led to a celebrated court case in which the judge upheld the right of the city to chlorinate the water supply in the best interest of public health. From that time, chlorination of public water supplies has become routine practice. Figure 12-2 shows the estimated annual consumption of chlorine in water and waste treatment in the United States.

The practice of chlorinating public water supplies was limited in the early years because of the instability of the hypochlorites during storage. A process for feeding gaseous chlorine was developed about 1912. This greatly accelerated the use of chlorine.

12-3. CHEMISTRY OF CHLORINATION

One of the chief advantages of chlorination, when compared to most methods of disinfection, is that its concentration can be easily determined.

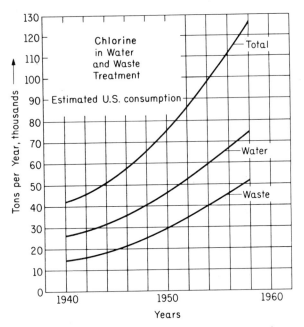

FIG. 12-2. (From E. J. Laubusch, "Chlorination of Water," in *Chlorination Guide*, Scranton Publishing Company, Chicago, Ill., 1959, p. 4.)

The addition to water of chlorine or its disinfecting compounds releases the following groups of substances: (1) hypochlorite ion (OCl^-), (2) hypochlorous acid (HOCl), (3) monochloramine (NH_2Cl), (4) dichloramine ($NHCl_2$), (5) nitrogen trichloride (NCl_3), (6) organic compounds containing chlorine, and (7) chlorine dioxide (ClO_2). Residuals consisting of the first two substances are called *free available chlorine residuals*. The next four substances are known collectively as *chloramines*. They are brought about principally by the reaction of hypochlorous acid with ammonia. This ammonia may be naturally present in or added to water. This is a stepwise process for which the successive reactions are

$$NH_3 + HOCl \rightarrow NH_2Cl + H_2O \qquad (12\text{-}8)$$
$$NH_2Cl + HOCl \rightarrow NHCl_2 + H_2O \qquad (12\text{-}9)$$
$$NHCl_2 + HOCl \rightarrow NCl_3 + H_2O \qquad (12\text{-}10)$$

The principal amines are mono- and dichloramine. Nitrogen trichloride is never formed in any appreciable amount during water treatment. The organic compounds containing chlorine are of little value in disinfection because of their low capacity for oxidation when compared with other forms of residual chlorine. Chlorine dioxide, produced by combining chlorine and sodium chlorite, is another chlorine compound that may be added to water in amounts sufficient to show a residual.

Chlorine gas is very soluble in water (7,160 mg/l at 20°C and 1 atm.). The gas hydrolizes rapidly to form hypochlorous acid.

$$Cl_2 + H_2O \rightleftharpoons HOCL + H^+ + Cl^- \qquad (12\text{-}11)$$

The hydrolysis goes virtually to completion at pH values and concentrations normally experienced in water- and waste-treatment operations.

The pH is a prime factor in the ionization of hypochlorites to hypochlorous acid. Figure 12-3 shows the relationship between HOCl and OCl$^-$ at various pH levels. Hypochlorous acid ionizes according to the following equation:

$$HOCl \rightleftharpoons H^+ + OCl^- \qquad (12\text{-}12)$$

$$\frac{(H^+)(OCl^-)}{HOCl} = K_i \qquad (12\text{-}13)$$

where K_i = ionization constant (1.5 × 10^{-8} mols/l at 0°C and 2.5 × 10^{-8} mols/l at 20°C)

The disassociation rate from hypochlorous acid to hypochlorite ion is sufficiently rapid so that equilibrium is maintained even though the former is being continuously consumed. If water containing 2 mg/l of free available chlorine has introduced into it a reducing agent that consumes 50 percent of the hypochlorous acid, the remaining residual will

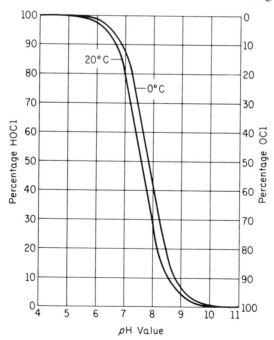

Fig. 12-3. Relationship between HOCl, OCl$^-$, and pH at 0 and 20°C.

ment, and on an emergency basis for water supply. The principal compound used is calcium hypochlorite, $Ca(OCl)_2$. This material has an
available chlorine content of 70 percent by weight and a good storage life.

12-4. DiSINFECTION WITH CHLORINE

The rate of kill with chlorine as a disinfectant does not follow Eq.
12-1. Instead the rate of kill, using chlorine, has been found to be expressed by the relationship[3]

$$\frac{dN}{dt} = -kNt \qquad (12\text{-}14)$$

where $\dfrac{dN}{dt}$ = time rate of kill

$\quad k$ = coefficient of proportionality
$\quad N$ = number of living organisms

Integrating Eq. 12-14 between the limits $t = 0$ and $t = t$, and N_1 and
N_2,

$$\int_{N_1}^{N_2} \frac{dN}{N} = -k \int_0^t t\,dt \qquad (12\text{-}15)$$

$$\ln \frac{N_2}{N_1} = \frac{-kt^2}{2} \qquad (12\text{-}16)$$

where N_1, N_2 = number of organisms living initially and at time t respectively

Changing to the log base 10 and rearranging,

$$t^2 = \frac{4.6}{k} \log \frac{N_1}{N_2} \qquad (12\text{-}17)$$

The rate constant k can be determined experimentally from a semilogarithmic plot of the percent surviving versus the square of the contact
time for a particular set of conditions or organisms. Limited information
is available on *E. coli*. The coefficient of dilution n in Eq. 12-7 is approximately equal to 1.3 for both free and combined chlorine. The value
of the constant K at a given temperature varies both with the type of available residual and the pH. At pH 8.5, the K value for free available
chlorine is approximately 2.4, while for chloramines it is around 1×10^{-4}
for a temperature of 3°C. These figures are calculated from limited data
and must be used with caution.

12-5. CHLORINE IN WASTE TREATMENT

The reactions that occur when chlorine is added to domestic or industrial wastes are essentially the same as those that occur when chlorine
is added to water. Free chlorine reacts with a variety of oxidizable ma-

terials found in wastes. While the use of chlorine as a disinfectant in water and waste treatment constitutes its most important application, its other usages include odor and corrosion control, BOD reduction, and as an adjunct to primary and secondary treatment.

Accomplishment of waste disinfection by chlorination is variable under waste-treatment plant conditions. The extent to which disinfection occurs depends upon such factors as the amount and form of available chlorine, contact time, temperature, and the composition of the waste being treated. Reducing substances common to all wastes in varying amounts may react with chlorine to form compounds having little or no bactericidal capacity. The formation of chloramines by the action of chlorine on nitrogenous constituents of wastes renders these materials unsuitable as food sources, but they possess definite disinfecting power.

Chlorine does not penetrate dense suspended solids and is ineffective in the destruction of bacteria and other organisms encased by these solids. Wastes containing substantial amounts of suspended solids that are discharged into receiving waters may contain large numbers of unaffected bacteria. These imbedded bacteria are released as the solids are broken down by turbulence and decay. Furthermore, some biological species that are relatively unaffected by chlorine dosages normally encountered may reproduce prolifically in the absence of large numbers of competitive organisms. Care must be exercised to select the points of application and dosages in such a manner as to accomplish the objective as efficiently as possible without interference with the action of saprophytic organisms essential to aerobic or anaerobic-treatment processes.

The use of chlorine for odor control is discussed in Sec. 12-9. It has been demonstrated that chlorine will reduce the BOD of a waste. The practice is not advocated as a substitute for properly designed and operated treatment processes. It has been recommended, however, for reducing the BOD load caused by unusual flows or during emergencies, but this treatment is impractical under normal circumstances.

The utility of chlorine as an adjunct to other treatment operations has been demonstrated. Up-sewer chlorination to retard the development of septic waste has been widely practiced. The psychoda fly nuisance associated with trickling-filter operation during warm weather is amenable to chlorine treatment. This so-called "filter" fly passes through window screens and is extremely troublesome. It does not bite but gets into the eyes, ears, nostrils, and mouths of plant personnel. Its radius of flight is short (a few hundred feet), but it may be carried farther by the wind. The life cycle varies from one to three weeks in the summer and the adult fly may be readily destroyed by DDT residuals on filter walls and other surfaces. The larvae of the psychoda fly may be destroyed by chlorination of the applied waste to the trickling filter. Trickling-filter ponding, due to the accumulation of excess solids that clog the interstices of the filter, may be alleviated by chlorine. This tends to loosen excess zoogleal material that can be flushed from the filter. Intermittent treatment of 5 to 10 mg/l residual at the filter nozzles has been effective for this treatment.

Chlorination has been employed to treat industrial wastes resulting from cleaning and electroplating, as well as those containing cyanide or phenols and other petrochemical wastes. These chemicals can be readily oxidized by chlorine.

It has been reported by Ingols and Gaffney that chlorinated organic compounds accumulate in the fatty tissue of fishes when these compounds are present in trace amounts.[4] Furthermore, from the large reduction in the BOD of waste by chlorination, a considerable portion of the added chlorine combines with organic compounds rather than merely oxidizing these materials. Ingols and Gaffney have suggested that a careful evaluation of each chlorine application to sewage should be made to reduce the quantity of chlorine used to the minimum.

Experiments by Blabaum and Nichols show that white mice can grow to adulthood from weanlings and thrive on water containing 200 mg/l of free available chlorine.[5] Two groups of white mice on standard dry diet drank nothing but water containing 200 mg/l of free available chlorine. Another group of mice drank nothing but water containing 100 mg/l of free available chlorine for 50 days. These mice at autopsy showed no pathology by either gross observation or by microscopic examination. There is little information in the literature on the effects on animals of high chlorine residuals in domestic water.

12-6. CHLORINE HANDLING AND CONTROL

Chlorine (at. wt. 35.5) is a poisonous, yellow-green gas at normal temperatures and pressures. It can be handled and stored safely when free from water and is amenable to proper measuring and dosing equipment. Relatively small amounts of chlorine can be detected in the atmosphere because of the characteristic, penetrating odor of the gas. Higher concentrations cause eye irritation, coughing, and labored breathing. High concentrations of chlorine gas have a corrosive, irritating action on the skin. There is little likelihood that anyone would freely choose to remain in an atmosphere seriously contaminated with chlorine.

The principal physiological effects of different concentrations of chlorine gas are shown in Table 12-1. Concentrations of one part of chlorine gas in one million parts of air (by volume) may produce slight symptoms after several hours of contact. The American Conference of Governmental Industrial Hygienists fixes as a guide, 1 ppm (by volume in air) for repeated 8-hr exposure. Since the gas is particularly irritating to persons afflicted with asthma and certain types of bronchitis, such persons

TABLE 12-1
PHYSIOLOGICAL EFFECTS OF VARIOUS CONCENTRATIONS OF CHLORINE GAS

Approximate ppm*	Concentration, mg/l	Effects on Unprotected Persons
3.5	0.010	Least detectable odor
15.1	0.044	Least amount required to cause irritation of throat
30.2	0.088	Least amount required to cause coughing
1.0	0.0029	Least amount required to produce slight symptoms (of poisoning) after several hours exposure
4.0	0.012	Maximum amount that can be breathed for 1 hr without serious disturbances
40–60	0.12–0.17	Amount dangerous in 30 min to 1 hr
1,000	2.9	Amount likely to be fatal after a few deep breaths

*Parts of chlorine gas per million parts of air, by volume. (From "Gas Masks for Gases Met in Fighting Fires," Bureau of Mines Technical Paper 248.)

should not be employed where exposure to chlorine is possible. Most other trained persons may be assigned to areas where chlorine is handled.

There are two basic types of chlorine dispensing equipment. The "direct-feed" equipment involves the metering of dry chlorine gas and conducting it under pressure to the water being chlorinated. The "solution-feed" apparatus involves the metering of chlorine gas under vacuum and dissolving this metered gas in a small amount of water to form a concentrated solution. This concentrated solution is then metered to the water being treated. At 20°C, one volume of water will dissolve 2.3 volumes of chlorine gas, or about 7,000 mg/l. When it dissolves in water, chlorine hydrolyzes immediately.

$$Cl_2 + H_2O \rightleftharpoons HOCl + H^+ + OCl^- \qquad [12\text{-}11]$$

At concentrations of total chlorine below 1,000 mg/l, no chlorine gas exists in solution as Cl_2, all of the chlorine is present as $HOCl$ or its dissociated ions.

The operation of direct or solution-feed equipment is based on the principle of orifice flow in the chlorine gas line. Some equipment is provided for controlling the feed rate by varying the size of a variable orifice. Other types of feeding apparatus control the feed rate by varying the pressure differential across a fixed orifice. Figure 12-5 shows a typical chlorine gas feeder as used in water and waste treatment.

Chlorine-equipment installations require adequate room for operation of equipment and handling of chlorine containers. The actual space requirements are based upon the number and types of units installed and the space necessary for containers and scales. In small installations feeding not more than 200 lb/day of chlorine, and not requiring more than

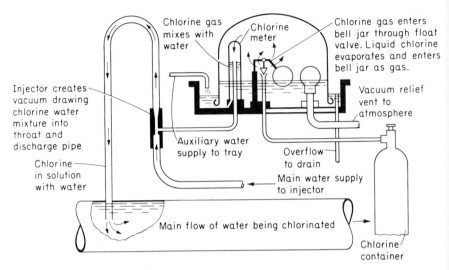

FIG. 12-5. Typical chlorine feeder.

one unit, an area 8 ft square is adequate. Larger installations require additional space. Ventilation is required for all chlorine-equipment rooms. The intake for ventilation must be located at floor level since chlorine gas is heavier than air. An air change every 3 min has been used as the basis for exhaust-fan design.

The chlorine-equipment room should be heated. For maximum safety, the chlorine room should be isolated from the rest of the building, with a separate outside entrance. Where possible, a fixed sash should be installed between the chlorine room and the operating building so that the equipment can be observed without entering the chlorine room.

Some regulatory agencies call for chlorinator capacities adequate to produce a residual of 2 mg/l in the final effluent for disinfection purposes. For domestic sewage, the dosing capacity listed in Table 12-2 will usually be sufficient.

TABLE 12-2

DOSING CAPACITY REQUIRED TO PRODUCE
A RESIDUAL OF 2 mg/l IN THE FINAL
EFFLUENT OF AVERAGE DOMESTIC WASTE[6]

Type of Waste	Dosing Capacity, mg/l
Raw waste	25
Primary plant effluent	20
Trickling-filter effluent	15
Activated-sludge effluent	8
Sand-filter effluent	6

The application of chlorine to water or waste must be controlled within definite limits to ensure satisfactory and economic attainment of the desired objective. Most methods for determination of free or combined available chlorine are based on reactions with reducing agents. The iodometric titration method was first used to measure chlorine residuals and is employed as a standard in *Standard Methods.* Iodometric titration is based on the principle that chlorine will liberate free iodine from potassium iodide solutions when the pH is 8 or less. The liberated iodine is titrated with a standard sodium thiosulfate solution, using starch as an indicator. The minimum detectable concentration of chlorine approximates 0.04 mg/l when 0.01N sodium thiosulfate is used with a 500-ml sample. Disadvantages of the test are that it is time-consuming, the titrating and indicator solutions are relatively unstable, and only total available chlorine residuals can be measured.

The orthotolidine method is widely used for routine measuring of residual chlorine control in plant and field. The orthotolidine procedure measures both free and combined available chlorine, and a modification of the method may be used to determine in which form the chlorine is available. The test is based on the principle that orthotolidine and chlorine will react to produce a color when the solution is at pH 1.3 or lower. Some interfering substances such as nitrite, ferric compounds, and possibly organic iron increase the apparent residual chlorine content of the sample. The orthotolidine-chlorine reaction is sensitive to residual chlorine concentrations as low as approximately 0.01 mg/l. The test is subject to certain errors such as color fading or false color production by the interfering substances.

For research work and for automatic recording, the amperometric titration method has been widely used. In this procedure, free available chlorine in water will produce a current between two electrodes. By titrating the chlorine with a reducing agent to the point where the current is zero, the end point is accurately detected. This is the most accurate method for determining chlorine residuals, and techniques have been developed to determine monochloramine, dichloramine, and free available chlorine. This method is adaptable to automatic recording and process control based upon chlorine residuals.

12-7. OTHER DISINFECTION METHODS

While chlorine is most commonly used as a disinfectant in water and waste treatment, other processes include heat, light, chemicals, and radioactivity.

Heat. Disinfection with heat, although too expensive to use in large-scale water and waste treatment, finds wide application in the food and beverage industry, in emergency water treatment, and the processing of waste sludges. The destruction of bacteria by heat is dependent upon the temperature and also upon the period of exposure to that temperature. While pathogenic organisms are more susceptible to heat than most of the harmless bacteria, the effectiveness of disinfection varies with the species. Bacterial spores have a very high thermal resistance. The relative resistance of microorganisms to moist heat is indicated in Table 12-3. Dry heat is much less effective than moist heat. For instance, dry heat at 300°F requires more than 3 times as long as boiling at 212°F to kill some bacteria.

TABLE 12-3
RELATIVE RESISTANCES OF MICROORGANISMS
TO STERILIZATION BY MOIST HEAT[7]

Organism	Relative Resistance
E. coli	1
Bacterial spores	3,000,000
Mold spores	2–10
Viruses and bacteriophages	1–5

Bacterial spores have approximately 3×10^6 times the relative resistance to moist heat as compared to *E. coli*. If sterilization is the objective, heat must be applied sufficient to kill bacterial spores. Because no important water-borne diseases are caused by spore-forming bacteria, the heat requirements found to be satisfactory for the pasteurization of milk should be equally useful for water. Diphtheria organisms are destroyed at a temperature of 130°F with an exposure time of 30 min, whereas it requires a temperature of 139°F to kill tubercle bacilli in the same time period. A 10-min exposure time requires about 3°F higher temperature. Still higher temperatures kill the pathogens in very short times. At 160°F, for example, the destruction of pathogens is obtained in 15 sec. The current temperature and time recommendations for milk pasteurization are 161°F for 15 sec or 145°F for 30 min.

A continuous-flow water pasteurizer for small supplies was developed and tested at the Robert A. Taft Sanitary Engineering Center.[8] This unit was designed to operate at 161°F for 15 sec, and the total cost was estimated to be approximately $1 per 1,000 gal on a household scale. No coliform organisms were found in any samples after the water passed through the pasteurizer.

Light. The exposure to sunlight for a period of time is a natural means of disinfection. Irradiation of water by ultraviolet light of suitable wavelength, for the proper period of time, will destroy bacteria, bacterial spores, molds, mold spores, viruses, and other microorganisms. The bactericidal waves extend from 2,000 to 2,950 A (angstrom units), with a maximum effect at about 2,540 A. The electromagnetic spectrum is shown in Fig. 12-6.

Death being due to a single cause, the rate of kill by ultraviolet radiation can be expressed by Eq. 12-4. The rate constant k is found by

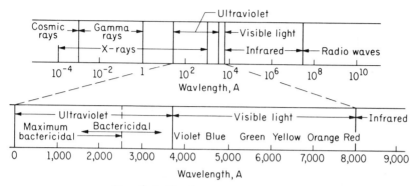

Fɪɢ. 12-6. The electromagnetic spectrum.

using Eq. 12-7, where the concentration of disinfectant is represented by the radiation intensity.

$$k = KI^n \qquad (12\text{-}18)$$

where K = constant

I = radiation intensity

n = coefficient of dilution

The value of n is found to be approximately equal to unity for most applications.[9]

The intensity of radiation I is reduced as it passes through matter. At any absorber depth x, the rate at which the energy decreases will be directly proportional to the absorption coefficient and to the initial intensity present.

$$\frac{dI}{dx} = -aI$$

Integrating (for a homogeneous absorber),

$$I = I_0 e^{-ax} \qquad (12\text{-}19)$$

where I = effective radiation intensity

I_0 = initial intensity

a = coefficient of absorption

x = distance between points where the intensities are I_0 and I

Ultraviolet radiation is applied to the water surface and the rate of kill varies throughout the depth. The average rate may be computed using an average-rate constant.

$$k_{\text{avg}} = \frac{\displaystyle\int_0^x k\,dx}{x} \qquad (12\text{-}20)$$

where x = depth of the water

k = rate constant at the surface

Substituting Eq. 12-18 for k, Eq. 12-19 for I, and assuming n to be unity,

$$k_{avg} = \frac{KI_0}{x} \int_0^x e^{-ax} dx$$

$$= \frac{KI_0}{x} \left[\frac{1}{a} - \frac{e^{-ax}}{a} \right] \tag{12-21}$$

The coefficient of absorption a varies with the wavelength of the light energy and the density of the absorbing medium. The presence of dissolved and suspended substances in water normally increases the coefficient. Values of the coefficient for ultraviolet light of wavelength 2,537 A (wavelength of maximum bactericidal effect) for some specific waters are listed in Table 12-4.

TABLE 12-4
COEFFICIENTS OF ABSORPTION[10] FOR
VARIOUS WATERS (λ = 2,537 A)

Source	a/cm
Distilled	0.008
Swimming pool	0.031
Cleveland tap	0.050
Drilled well	0.056
Fish pool	0.070
Lake Erie	0.083
Concrete cistern	0.297

When I and k have the units of calories per square centimeter per minute and per minute, respectively, the value of K is approximately 1,740. Additional information on the disinfection of water with ultraviolet light may be found elsewhere.[10]

EXAMPLE 12-2.   Lake Erie water containing 10,000 coliform organisms per milliliter is to be disinfected with ultraviolet light (wavelength 2,537 A) as it flows through a rectangular channel 8 ft long and 4 ft wide at a depth of 4 in. The ultraviolet lights are so arranged that the radiation intensity at the water surface over the channel is 800 μwatts/sq cm. At what rate can the water flow through the channel to attain a probable coliform density of 1 organism per liter.

Solution:
1. The radiation intensity at the surface is

$$800 \times 10^{-6} \text{ watts/sq cm} \times 0.239 \text{ cal/watt/sec} \times 60 \text{ sec/min}$$
$$= 11.47 \times 10^{-3} \text{ cal/sq cm/min}$$

2. The coefficient of absorption for Lake Erie water, as shown in Table 12-4, is 0.083/min.
3. The average rate constant as computed with Eq. 12-21 is

$$k_{avg} = \frac{1,740 \times 11.47 \times 10^{-3} \text{ cal/sq cm/min}}{4 \text{ in.} \times 2.54 \text{ cm/in.}} \left[\frac{1}{0.083} - \frac{e^{-0.083(10.16)}}{0.083} \right]$$

$$= 12.9/\text{min}$$

4. The exposure time is found by using Eq. 12-4.

$$t = \frac{2.3}{12.9} \log(10,000/1 \times 10^{-3}) = 1.25 \text{ min}$$

5. The maximum rate of flow is

$$q = \frac{\text{volume}}{\text{time}} = \frac{8 \text{ ft} \times 4 \text{ ft} \times 0.33 \text{ ft} \times 7.48 \text{ gal/cu ft}}{1.25 \text{ min}} = 63 \text{ gpm}$$

Chemicals Other Than Chlorine. Chlorination is recognized as the cheapest method for the disinfection of water and liquid waste. Other halogens cannot be expected to compete with chlorine generally, but special disinfection applications have been used.

Fluorine (at. wt. 19.0), the lightest and most electronegative halogen, is too reactive for use as a disinfectant. It attacks almost every material and is therefore difficult to store and apply. Although fluorine's extreme reactivity has discouraged its study as a disinfection agent, its germicidal power may be expected to be great.

Bromine (at. wt. 79.9) is a reddish-brown liquid. It is used for medicinal compounds and has been used for disinfection of swimming-pool water. Elemental bromine is relatively soluble in water. Like other halogens, it is an antiseptic and disinfectant. Bromine appears to become irretrievably bound up with organic matter or forms bromamines that break down rapidly. The residual bromine or bromamine is just as effective as chlorine but not much of the bromine dosage becomes a stable residue. McKee has shown that to achieve a 99.995 percent kill of coliforms, while working with Pasadena sewage, about 45 mg/l of bromine or iodine were required, whereas only 8 mg/l of chlorine were just as effective.[11]

Iodine (at. wt. 126.9), the heaviest halogen, is a violet-black solid at normal temperatures. It has been used extensively as a germicide in medicine, and more recently as a disinfectant for small quantities of drinking water. Elemental iodine is only slightly soluble in water, except in the presence of iodides, and it is not appreciably hydrolyzed in weak acid solutions. Its disinfecting power is not fully understood but is attributable not to the HOI molecule or to iodide but rather to molecular iodine. It has been used successfully for the disinfection of water in swimming pools with residual concentrations of free iodine in the range of 0.2 to 0.6 mg/l. It has been reported that 8 mg/l of iodine destroys all forms of water-borne pathogens and that no adverse effects were noted when personnel in the tropics used iodine at the rate of 12 to 19 mg/day for 26 weeks.[12] Chlorine is much less costly than other halogens. This cost tends to exclude bromine and iodine from any practical consideration on large volume disinfection. However, iodine offers considerable promise as a disinfectant for small volume use and for emergency water treatment.

Ozone predates chlorine for disinfection of municipal drinking water. Several of the over 200 municipal plants in Europe which use ozone as a disinfectant have been employing it continuously for more than 60 years. Ozone is relatively inexpensive but not as cheap as chlorine. Improvements in taste and odor resulting from ozone purification have been reported to offset the slight difference in cost. Organic matter in water has an ozone demand that must be met before the ozone becomes available for germicidal activity. Once this demand has been satisfied, the bactericidal action is very rapid. The higher the concentration of ozone the more rapid the disinfection. For ordinary drinking water, an ozone residual of 0.1 mg/l maintained for 5 min is adequate. Ozone will not persist as a residual germicide, but rapidly decomposes in water to ordinary oxygen.

Ozone is applied to water by mixing ozonized air with the water to be treated. The control of ozone is similar to the control of chlorine. The same orthotolidine reagent and comparators used to measure chlorine residuals can be employed to measure ozone residuals. This test is only semiquantitative but it is adequate for control purposes. Ozone is produced as used. When air is passed through an electrical discharge, a small percentage of the oxygen is converted to ozone. The reaction,

$$3O_2 \rightarrow 2O_3 \text{(ozone)} \tag{12-22}$$

is strongly endothermic, as might be surmised from the fact that it normally occurs only when high energies are available. The energy consumed when a mole of ozone is formed from molecular oxygen is 34.5 kcal/mole. The gas has a peculiar pungent odor which is noticeable even when the gas is present in small traces.

Ozone dosage requirements will depend upon the ozone demand, which is a function of water quality. The exact demand can be determined only by actual test but the data given in Table 12-5 may be used as a guide.

TABLE 12-5

OZONE DOSAGE REQUIREMENTS FOR VARIOUS
WATER QUALITIES[13]

Water Quality	Approximate Ozone Dosage, ppm
Clear, pure groundwater	$\frac{1}{2}$–1
Treated (filtered) surface water	2–3
Same as above, but from a heavily polluted source	2.5–5
Clear, colored water	3–6

For each pound of ozone produced and applied, 10 kwh of electrical energy are consumed in a large plant. Therefore the electrical energy cost might range from 0.75 to \$1.00 per million gallons per 1 mg/l of ozone applied, dependent upon the electrical energy cost. Although ozone plants require little operating supervision or maintenance, they do represent a substantial capital investment. Amortized over the life of the equipment (about 25 years), this fixed charge will approximately équal the operating cost.

Silver has been proposed as a disinfectant for many years but it has never been extensively used. The 1962 USPHS Drinking Water Standards contain a limit of 50 ppb for silver. This limit is not based upon toxicity because silver, although it is readily deposited in the body, is not particularly toxic. Under prolonged exposure to silver, the skin takes on a dark color which is cosmetically quite objectionable. Disinfection appears to be related to the concentration of the silver ions rather than the physical nature of the silver from which the ions were orginally derived.[14] Silver oxide has been used for water purification at Warsaw, Poland, and other cities and for swimming pools in the United States. Dosages of 1×10^{-6} to 0.5 mg/l of silver have been reported as sufficient to sterilize water.[15] There are many other chemicals that would serve as a disinfectant in water but the cost, difficulty of control, toxicity, and lack of residual effectiveness negate their use at the present. These possible disinfectants include, quarternary ammonium compounds, rosin amines, quinones, antibiotics, zinc, copper, and others.

Radioactivity. The increasing accessibility of radioactive materials has stimulated interest in the disinfection and sterilization of water by ionizing radiations. Radioactive decay involves the breakdown of atomic nuclei. This is accompanied by the conversion of mass to energy and the amount of energy released is governed by Einstein's equation

$$E = mc^2 \qquad (12\text{-}23)$$

where E = energy
m = mass
c = constant = velocity of light, cm/sec

The energy released in a nuclear reaction is enormous compared to that liberated in a chemical reaction involving the same amount of matter. For example, the complete fissioning of 1 kg (kilogram) (2.2 lb) of uranium would yield as much energy as the exploding of 20,000 tons of TNT. The total mass loss in the fissioning of the uranium would be approximately 1 g.

Ionizing radiations are those which interact with the electrons of an atom and eject one or more of them from their orbits. The remaining atom, which is charged in the process, is called an ion. The energy required to cause this ionization depends on two things: (1) the atom or molecule involved and (2) the orbit from which the electron is expelled. This ionizing radiation loses energy from knocking out the electron and by giving kinetic energy to both the electron and the ion produced.

Gamma radiation, because of its penetrating ability, is the most logical type of radiation for water disinfection. Gamma radiation is electromagnetic, as are radio waves and light waves, but of shorter wavelength and higher frequency. The energy of gamma radiation emitted by different radioisotopes varies considerably. The energy of gamma radiation is inversely proportional to its wavelength and directly proportional to its frequency:

$$E = \frac{hc}{\lambda} = \frac{0.012345}{\lambda} \qquad (12\text{-}24)$$

where λ = wavelength, angstroms

h = Planck's constant

c = velocity of light, cm/sec

The absorption of gamma radiation in any medium occurs almost entirely by interaction with free or bound electrons. There are three distinct processes of interaction between the gamma photon (a quantum of radiant energy) and the electron. These are the photoelectric effect, the Compton effect, and pair production. The importance of each process depends on the energy of the gamma radiation and the mass of the absorber.

Photoelectric effect is produced when a photon interacts with an orbital electron and in so doing transfers its energy to the electron. This electron may be ejected from the atom or raised to an unoccupied position in another shell. The photon of gamma radiation disappears, its energy being totally expended in overcoming the forces binding the electron to an atom. Any orbital electron can be ejected or shifted by this process as long as the energy relationship is overcome. See Fig. 12-7 for a schematic of the photoelectric effect.

The second possible interaction is Compton scattering. When the energy of the gamma radiation is increased until the energy required to remove an electron from its shell is negligible by comparison, the Compton effect becomes important. The primary photon has energy left after the electron has been displaced. This excess energy results in a scattered

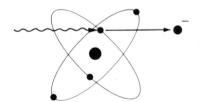

FIG. 12-7. Photon interacting with orbital electron ejects electron from one of the shells.

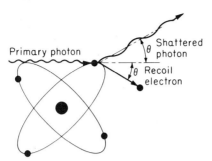

FIG. 12-8. Diagram indicating the
process of Compton scattering.

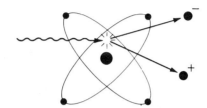

FIG. 12-9. Diagram of pair
production.

photon of somewhat lower energy level than the primary photon (Fig. 12-8). The mass of an electron has an energy of 0.51 mev (million electron volts). The energy of the scattered photon may be calculated from the formula

$$E = \frac{E_0}{1 + (E_0/0.51)(1 - \cos \theta)} \qquad (12\text{-}25)$$

where E_0 = energy of incident gamma photon, mev

E = energy of scattered photon, mev

θ = scattering angle (Fig. 12-8)

Pair production becomes important when the energy of the incident photon is increased to twice the mass of the electron (1.02 mev). This type of reaction is shown by Fig. 12-9. The incident proton disappears completely and a pair of particles is produced. Each particle of a pair has the mass of an electron but with equal and opposite charge. One is an ordinary electron while the other is called a *positron*. This process takes place in the vicinity of the nucleus. Figure 12-10 illustrates the apparent change in the nature of energy that takes place from pair production. The photon becomes matter, only to be changed back into radiation again by positron annihilation with an electron. Therefore, some wavelike properties must be ascribed to particles and some particulate properties to radiation.

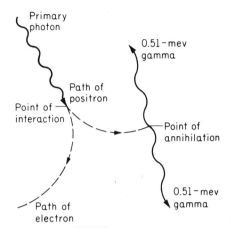

FIG. 12-10. Diagram of pair production and annihilation of positron.

At any absorber depth x (depth of water), the rate at which the number of photons decreases will be directly proportional to the absorption coefficient and to the number of photons present, or

$$\frac{dI}{dx} = -\mu I$$

Integrating (μ = a constant),

$$I = I_0 e^{-\mu x} \qquad (12\text{-}26)$$

where I_0 = intensity of gamma radiation at surface
I = intensity of gamma radiation at distance x
x = absorber thickness
μ = linear absorption coefficient

The radiation intensity at any point in an absorber (water) consists of the primary photons, the photons resulting from Compton scatter, and the radiation resulting from pair production.

For a primary radiation of a given energy passing through a homogeneous absorber, an equilibrium level of secondary radiation is reached. This buildup of intensity is greater than the original radiation intensity (Fig. 12-11). The calculated intensity I must be multiplied by the buildup factor B to account for this increased intensity.

$$I = B I_0 e^{-\mu x} \qquad (12\text{-}27)$$

Table 12-6 lists some buildup factors in water for various depths and energy levels.

The effect of gamma radiation upon molecules depends on the physical state of the molecules. Ionizing radiation ionizes gases to form ions,

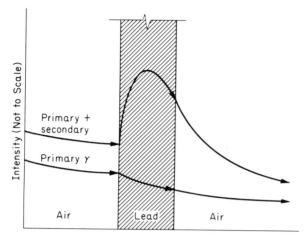

FIG. 12-11. Diagram showing a buildup of secondary radiation.

unstable atoms, free radicals, and reactive molecules. Gases may react chemically with other molecules, decompose, or interact by exchanging electrons. In the latter case, interaction between ions may form new compounds; for example, ozone is formed by the ionization of oxygen.

TABLE 12-6

DOSE BUILDUP FACTOR B IN WATER FOR POINT ISOTROPIC SOURCE[16]

(Relaxation Length μx)

E_0, Mev	1	2	4	7	10	15	20
0.256	3.09	7.14	23.0	72.9	166	456	932
0.5	2.52	5.14	14.3	38.8	77.6	178	334
1	2.13	3.71	7.68	16.2	27.1	50.4	82.2
2	1.83	2.77	4.88	8.46	12.4	19.5	27.7
3	1.69	2.42	3.91	6.23	8.63	12.8	17.0
4	1.58	2.17	3.34	5.13	6.94	9.97	12.9
6	1.46	1.91	2.76	3.99	5.18	7.09	8.85
8	1.38	1.74	2.40	3.34	4.25	5.66	6.95
10	1.33	1.63	2.19	2.97	3.72	4.90	5.98

Little decomposition occurs when pure water is exposed to gamma radiation. However, if the water contains dissolved impurities, appreciable decomposition of the water occurs. Inorganic solutes that are neither reducing nor oxidizing increase the concentrations of hydrogen and hydrogen peroxide in the water above that of pure water.

Organic materials under continued irradiation will eventually decompose. With most organic systems there are many intermediate products. In polluted water or waste there are many possible degradation pathways.

The effect of gamma radiation on biological materials may be divided into two mechanisms: "direct" and "indirect" actions. The direct action is produced by hits on the cell while indirect action is dependent on the interaction of the cell with surrounding radiation products. For example, amino acids in proteins may become ionized to form radicals and excited molecules, resulting in an infinitely great number of possible reactions. No organism ever tested has been found able to survive the more intense applications of gamma radiation. The simpler the organism the more resistant it is to radiation (Fig. 12-12). Tissues that grow rapidly are more sensitive to the effects of radiation than are the slower-growing cells. Microorganisms which are in a log state of growth are more easily killed than are bacterial spores.

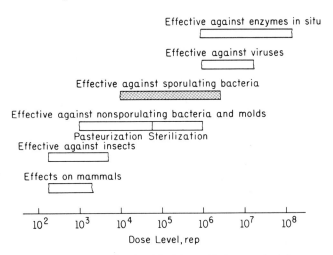

FIG. 12-12. Dose levels of ionizing radiation required for various biological effects.[16]

The effect of low doses of radiation may produce disinfection in a short period of time without killing the initial organisms. The initial daughter cells may not be able to redivide and the colony dies in a relatively brief period or changes take place in the cell that make it less capable of survival. Fischer and Kurtz considered direct action of radiation on microorganisms and indicated four possible methods of kill.[17] These four methods, indicated in Fig. 12-13, are: (a) a direct hit that takes place within the cell and within the target (vital area), resulting in an immediate biological effect; (b) a direct hit that takes place within the cell but out of the target area, resulting in an immediate biological effect but not necessarily killing the present cell; (c) an event that takes place outside the cell

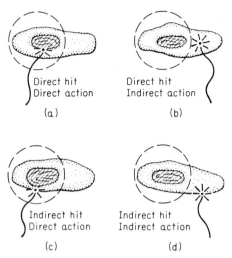

Direct hit
Direct action

(a)

Direct hit
Indirect action

(b)

Indirect hit
Direct action

(c)

Indirect hit
Indirect action

(d)

Fig. 12-13. Four possible methods of killing
microorganisms by ionized radiation.[17]

due to an indirect hit but within the target area, giving a direct biological
effect; and (d) a hit that takes place outside the cell and outside the target
area. Any biological effect will then be due to the reaction between the
cell and its environment.

Because the destruction of microorganisms by radiation is a statistical
phenomenon, no absolute value for dose exists. Equation 12-28 may be
used to calculate the approximate dose to obtain a reduction in bacterial
population:

$$D = D_d \log \frac{N_0}{N} + L \qquad (12\text{-}28)$$

where D = radiation dose given or required
N_0 = initial population
N = population after dose D
D_d = dose required to reduce population by a factor of 10 (10 percent survival)
L = dose required to overcome lag (this is zero for many organisms)

Figure 12-14 is a graphical representation of Eq. 12-28 and shows the
method for evaluating L. Selected values of D_d are shown in Table 12-7.
Radiation effects on *E. coli* are shown in Table 12-8.

EXAMPLE 12-3. Determine the dose in rads (the units of absorbed dose, which
is 100 ergs/g) if there are 10^6 *E. coli* per cc and it is desired to reduce the population to 1 *E. coli* per 1,000 cc when gamma radiation is to be used and $L = 100$
Krad?

Solution:
1. By Eq. 12-28,

$$D_d = 20 \text{ Krad from Table 12-7}$$
$$N_0 = 10^6 \qquad N = 10^{-3}$$

2.

$$D = 20 \log \frac{10^6}{10^{-3}} + 100$$

$$= 180 + 100 = 280 \qquad \text{Krad} = 0.28 \text{ Mrad}$$

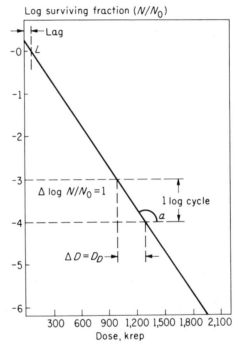

FIG. 12-14. Graphical illustration of Eq. 12-28.

Taste and Odor. Tastes and odors in water may result from any one or a combination of conditions such as the presence of microorganisms, dissolved gases, organic matter, and mineral substances. Reactions between these and added chemicals by treatment processes and from industrial wastes contribute to the problem. The consumer judges water quality by clarity, palatability, and freedom from objectionable taste and odor. These are subjective qualities that supplement the basic health requirements. If these water properties are not acceptable to the consumer,

TABLE 12-7
RESISTANCE OF SOME MICROORGANISMS[16]

Microorganisms	Type of Radiation	D_dK rad
E. coli	Beta	10–15
E. coli	Gamma	15–20
E. coli	X-ray	5
A. arogenes	X-ray	3
Ps. geniculata	Gamma	5
S. aureus	Gamma	20

TABLE 12-8
RADIATION EFFECTS ON *E. COLI* BY GAMMA RADIATION[16]

Radiation Dose, Mrep	Population Reduction, percent	E. coli Count
0	0	1,976,250,000
0.071	99.8	1,600,000
0.149	99.99	500
0.205	100	0

especially those of taste and odor, complaints are initiated to the water supplier.

12-8. ORIGIN AND NATURE OF TASTE AND ODOR

Odors in water are normally caused by volatile substances associated with organic matter, living organisms, and gases such as hydrogen sulfide. The chlorination of water may produce odors of its own or intensify odor-producing substances present. Heating of water generally intensifies odors. The nature of the odor often gives a clue to the material or organisms responsible for the odor. Observation of the odor of sewage provides a relative indication of its condition. It indicates whether the sewage is fresh, stale, or septic, and it may also indicate the presence of certain industrial wastes.

According to psychologists, there are only four true taste sensations: sour, sweet, salt, and bitter. All other tastelike sensations are actually odors, even though the sensation is not noticed until the material is taken into the mouth. The organs of taste and smell are quite sensitive detectors, but they are not precise. People vary widely as to sensitivity, and even the same person will not be consistent from day to day. Persons with extreme sensitivity are not required for taste and odor determinations but insensitive persons should not be used. Tests for odor are recorded according to the threshold number. The number of times the odor-bearing sample has to be diluted with odor-free water for the odor to be just detectable is the threshold odor number.

$$\text{Threshold number} = \frac{\text{volume of sample} + \text{odor free water}}{\text{volume of sample}} \qquad (12\text{-}29)$$

Table 12-9 shows the threshold odor numbers corresponding to various dilutions.

Suitable qualitative descriptions may be helpful in ascribing tastes and odors to the correct cause. Descriptions of taste and odor vary with the background and experience of the individual making the test. Table 12-10 from *Standard Methods* can serve as a guide for recording descriptions of odors. Its usefulness is limited, but no satisfactory substitute is

TABLE 12-9
THRESHOLD ODOR NUMBERS FOR
VARIOUS DILUTIONS

Sample Volume Diluted to 200 ml, ml	Threshold Odor Number	Sample Volume Diluted to 200 ml, ml	Threshold Odor Number
200	1	12	17
140	1.4	8.3	24
100	2	5.7	35
70	3	4	50
50	4	2.8	70
35	6	2	100
25	8	1.4	140
17	12	1.0	200

TABLE 12-10
QUALITATIVE DESCRIPTIONS OF ODORS [18]

Code	Nature of Odor	Description (Such as Odors of:)
A	Aromatic (spicy)	Camphor, cloves, lavender, lemon
Ac	Cucumber	*Synura*
B	Balsamic (flowery)	Geranium, violet, vanilla
Bg	Geranium	*Asterionella*
Bn	Nasturtium	*Aphanizomenon*
Bs	Sweetish	*Coelosphaerium*
Bv	Violet	*Mallomonas*
C	Chemical	Industrial wastes or treatment chemicals
Cc	Chlorinous	Free chlorine
Ch	Hydrocarbon	Oil refinery wastes
Cm	Medicinal	Phenol and iodoform
Cs	Sulfuretted	Hydrogen sulfide
D	Disagreeable	(pronounced, unpleasant)
Df	Fishy	*Uroglenopsis, Dinobryon*
Dp	Pigpen	*Anabaena*
Ds	Septic	Stale sewage
E	Earthy	Damp earth
Ep	Peaty	Peat
G	Grassy	Crushed grass
M	Musty	Decomposing straw
Mn	moldy	Damp cellar
V	Vegetable	Root vegetables

available. Consistence in naming odors is important if interpretations are to be made. The determinations for taste are made in a similar manner as odor measurements.

Tastes in water are normally due to the presence of chloride or sulfate ions associated with sodium, calcium, or magnesium. True tastes may also be produced by organic material, living or dead. Phenolic tastes are very disagreeable and are detectable in extremely small concentrations. Less than 10^{-3} mg/l or 1 ppb of phenol may produce an unsatisfactory odor.

12-9. CONTROL OF TASTE AND ODOR

In a water-treatment plant, consideration for the control of taste and odor should be incorporated into the design. Flexibility of operation is important, because tastes and odors vary widely at different times and normally only require concentrated treatment for relatively short periods. Complete control requires a wide range of chemical feeders.

Activated Carbon. The most common control measures in use are the application of activated carbon, free residual chlorination, combined residual chlorination, chlorine dioxide, ozone, and aeration. Activated carbon treatment has been widely used for taste and odor control. Activated carbon removes organic contaminants from water by adsorption. Adsorption is the attraction and accumulation of one substance on the surface of another. Adsorption is primarily a surface phenomenon—the greater the surface area of the adsorber the greater its adsorptive power. Carbon for water treatment is rated in terms of square meters of surface area per gram. It has been estimated that 1 lb of activated carbon has more than 100 acres of surface area. Excessive dosages of carbon do not harm the water as it is easily removed by filters. Besides controlling tastes and odors, carbon has been reported to stabilize sludge, improve floc formation, and reduce nonodor-causing organics.

Carbon is fed to water either as a dry powder or as a wet slurry. Special equipment is available for feeding carbon. Slurry feeding has the advantage of being cleaner to handle, and the slurry assures that the carbon is thoroughly wet which increases its effectiveness. The points of application of carbon will vary with local conditions and water problems. Carbon may be added to the water at any point ahead of the filters. The absorption is nearly instantaneous although a contact time is normally helpful. The amount of carbon needed will vary with the type of carbon used and water conditions. A few milligrams per liter of carbon is the usual dosage, but concentrations up to 100 mg/l may be needed at times.

The application of carbon is normally most effective at the lowest pH value of the raw water, and, if suitable mixing is available, the addition of the carbon to the raw-water intake is desirable. Carbon may also take up some of the materials that have a chlorine demand and hence a saving in chlorine is effected.

Oxidative Methods. The oxidative methods include chlorination, ozonation, and aeration for the control of taste and odor. Marginal chlorination consists of the application of enough chlorine to secure a residual without satisfying the potential demand (combined residual). It is common practice to maintain this residual through part or all of the treatment plant and distribution system. This treatment tends to develop tastes and odors with phenolic compounds and certain other pollutants. Some tastes and odors may, however, be removed by combined residual chlorination.

Free residual chlorination is the application of chlorine to water to produce, directly or through the destruction of ammonia or nitrogenous compounds, a free available chlorine residual. Tastes and odors from phenolic compounds are usually controlled by this treatment. Many other taste and odor materials are also destroyed or rendered less obnoxious. Complete reduction is not universal and free residual chlorination may have to be supplemented by other treatment, such as improved coagulation, algae control, and activated carbon.

Free residual chlorination followed by chlorine dioxide has been effective in difficult taste and odor control. The action of chlorine dioxide is very rapid and therefore does not initially show a residual. Further addition of chlorine dioxide should result in an increased residual. All of the chlorine practices have merits and can, under appropriate conditions, provide a means of control for taste and odor. Figure 12-15 is a schematic of the common chlorination practices. The graph is only descriptive, not quantitative.

Ozone has been widely used in Europe and to a limited extent for taste and odor control in the United States. There is a large installation at Philadelphia, Pennsylvania, and a smaller operation at Whiting, In-

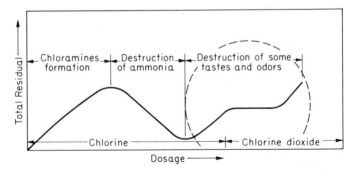

FIG. 12-15. Chlorination practices for taste and odor control. The area of free residual chlorine and chlorine dioxide represents the maximum destruction of taste and odor.

diana. Ozone does not form objectionable tastes and odors by reaction with phenolic compounds. The high capital investment required for generation equipment for ozone and the speed with which it dissipates from water have retarded its use.

Aeration has been successfully used for the control of tastes and odors. This method has been particularly effective in the removal of sulfides and volatile chemicals. It has been estimated that spray aeration with 110 psi pressure at the nozzles is equivalent in cost to treatment with 17 mg/l of activated carbon.

Raw-water storage tends to improve taste and odor qualities although few plants are in a position to provide it. The location or position of the intakes may be quite significant in procuring a good water quality. This is especially important where industrial wastes are concerned. The selection of intake locations may require considerable study.

REFERENCES

1. G. M. Fair and J. C. Geyer, *Water Supply and Waste-Water Disposal* (New York: John Wiley and Sons, Inc., 1954), p. 799.

2. J. L. Leal, "The Sterilization Plant of the Jersey City Water Supply Company at Boonton, N.J.," *Proc. Am. Water Works Assoc.*, vol. 100 (1909).

3. Linvil G. Rich, *Unit Processes of Sanitary Engineering* (New York: John Wiley and Sons, Inc., 1963), p. 160.

4. R. S. Ingols and P. E. Gaffney, "Biological Studies of Halophenols," Oklahoma Industrial Waste Conference, Oklahoma State University, November 17, 1964.

5. Carl J. Blabaum and M. Starr Nichols, "Effect of Highly Chlorinated Drinking Water on White Mice,: *J. Am. Water Works Assoc.* (December 1956), pp. 1503–6.

6. "Standards for Sewage Works," Upper Mississippi River Board of Public Health Engineers and Grant Lakes Board of Public Health Engineers, 1954.

7. O. Rahn, "Physical Methods of Sterilization of Microorganisms," *Bacteriol. Rev.*, vol. 9 (1945), pp. 1–47.

8. Melvin Goldstein, J. L. McCabe, and R. L. Woodward, "Continuous-Flow Water Pasteurizer for Small Supplies," *J. Am. Water Works Assoc.* (1960), pp. 247–254.

9. Linvil G. Rich, *Unit Processes of Sanitary Engineering* (New York: John Wiley and Sons, Inc., 1963), p. 154.

10. M. Luckiesh and L. L. Holladay, "Disinfecting Water by Means of Germicidal Lamps," *Gen. Elec. Rev.*, vol. 47 (1944), pp. 45–50.

11. Jack E. McKee, C. J. Brokaw, and R. T. McLaughlin, "Chemical and Colicidal Effects of Halogens in Sewage," *J. Water Pollution Control Federation*, vol. 32, no. 8 (1960), pp. 795–818.

12. D. P. Morgan and R. J. Karpen, "Test of Chronic Toxicity of Iodine as Related to the Purification of Water," *U.S. Armed Forces Med. J.*, vol. 4 (1953), p. 725.

13. Victor A. Hann, "Disinfection of Drinking Water with Ozone," *J. Am. Water Works Assoc.*, no. 10 (1956), pp. 1316–20.

14. C. W. Chambers, C. M. Proctor, and P. W. Kabler, "Bactericidal Effect of Low Concentrations of Silver," *J. Am. Water Works Assoc.*, no. 2 (1962), pp. 208–216.

15. J. E. McKee and H. W. Wolf, "Water Quality Criteria," State of California Water Quality Control Board, Sacramento, Calif., 1963, p. 257.

16. L. E. Brownell, "Radiation Uses in Industry and Science," *U.S. Atomic Energy Commission* (Washington, D.C.: U.S. Government Printing Office, 1961).

17. R. G. Fischer and G. W. Kurtz, "Mechanism of Action of Ionizing Radiation on Living Matter," U.S. Army Quartermaster Corps, U.S. Dept. Comm. Office of Technical Services, Washington, D.C., no. 178 (1957).

18. American Public Health Association, American Water Works Association, and Water Pollution Control Federation, *Standard Methods for the Examination of Water and Waste Water,* 11th ed. (New York: American Public Health Association, 1960), p. 255.

PROBLEMS

12-1. How many pounds of chlorine gas will be required to apply a dose of 0.3 mg/l to 5 million gal of water?

12-2. A water is to be chlorinated at a dosage of 0.35 mg/l. The chlorine is applied as a gas ahead of the pump. The flow is 800 gpm and the pump is operated 16 hr/day. At what rate in pounds of chlorine per 24 hr should the chlorinator be set?

12-3. An emergency water supply is to be chlorinated with a dosage of 10 mg/l. The water is to be treated daily in a clear well using calcium hypochlorite. The clear well holds 3 million gal. How many pounds of calcium hypochlorite are required each day?

12-4. Calculate the percentage distribution of HOCl in water at 20°C and pH 8. Compare this result with the graph in Fig. 12-3.

12-5. Residual chlorine is being determined by the starch-iodide method. Calculate the residual chlorine where 23 ml of 0.002N sodium thiosulfate are used with a 300-ml water sample.

12-6. The test in Prob. 12-5 depends upon the liberation of iodine from potassium iodide by free chlorine. Calculate the chlorine residual where 0.64 g of iodine are liberated in a 400-ml sample.

12-7. Well water (Table 12-4) containing 1,000 coliform organisms per milliliter is to be disinfected with ultraviolet light (wavelength 2,537 A) as it flows through a channel 4 ft wide and 10 ft long at a depth of 6 in. The ultraviolet lights are so arranged that the radiation intensity at the water surface over the channel is 600 μwatts/sq cm. At what rate can the water flow through the channel to attain a probable coliform density of 1 per liter?

12-8. Distilled water containing 10 coliform organisms per liter is disinfected by passing the water through a channel 3 ft wide, 8 ft long, and 4 in. deep. The water is flowing at the rate of 0.15 cfs and contains 1 coliform organism per 100 liters. What intensity of ultraviolet light at the water surface of 2,537 A wavelength will give this probable coliform density?

12-9. If the water in Prob. 12-8 is from Lake Erie, what light intensity would be necessary to give this probable coliform count?

12-10. A water plant is using ozone at the rate of 1 mg/l for the treatment of 25 mgpd. If electrical energy costs 0.4 cent per kwh and the other costs (capital recovery and operating) are equal to the electrical cost, what is the yearly cost for treating this water with ozone?

12-11. There are 10^3 *E. coli*/ml in a water and it is desired to reduce this number to 1 *E. coli*/100 l. Determine the gamma radiation in rads necessary to bring about this probable coliform reduction where L is equal to 150 krad.

12-12. When 310 krad of gamma radiation is applied to a water it is found that the resulting coliform count is 1 *E. coli*/100 l. What was the probable *E. coli* density in the untreated water if $L = 90$ krad?

12-13. Well water containing 1,000 coliform organisms per milliliter is to be irradiated with gamma radiation. What must be the radiation dose to attain a 1,000-to-1 degree of assurance that all coliform organisms have been destroyed? Assume $L = 100$ krad.

12-14. A sample volume of 125 ml was diluted to 700 ml in a threshold odor determination. What is the threshold odor number?

12-15. The threshold odor number is calculated to be 25 and the diluted volume is 500 ml. What was the original volume of sample?

chapter 13

Individual Water-Supply and Waste-Disposal Systems

Individual water and waste systems are usually small and often primitive, but the overall problem presented by these systems is a large and challenging one. The term "individual" is used here to describe those situations in which the services of water supply and waste disposal are privately owned, developed, and are normally kept within the property lines of the owner. Most of the water-supply and waste-disposal facilities for farms, ranches, and residences in fringe areas of cities are of the individual nature. The sanitary and economic implications of these systems must be gauged not only by the size of the population that is directly served by them, but also by the numbers of people that visit, vacation, or purchase food and drink in areas where such systems exist.

INDIVIDUAL WATER SUPPLY

13-1. COLLECTION AND STORAGE

Most of the water made available for individual systems is derived from wells, springs, or cisterns. However, in some areas it has become necessary to develop surface water sources. Theoretically, these small water systems should be developed in a manner similar to that for water supply for public use. Individual water systems are all too often improperly constructed or located, with the result that the water may be contaminated. Under such conditions, all water used for drinking or food purposes should first be adequately disinfected. Disinfection is discussed in Chap. 12.

Wells. State and local health authorities have developed regulations concerning the distance from a source of contamination that normally can be considered safe in specific areas. Since determination of a safe distance between a groundwater source and a point of contamination is dependent on many factors, it is impractical to establish arbitrary distances for all conditions. The minimum distance is normally 100 ft or more to a pit privy, septic tank, sewer, sewage-disposal field, or barnyard. This distance may be inadequate when unfavorable conditions prevail, however. Creviced earth formations, very permeable soils, and some forms of surface drainage may require an additional factor of safety.

When a properly located well shows the presence of waste pollution it is usually due to one or more of the following causes: (1) failure to properly disinfect the well following construction, (2) failure to seal topsoil from draining into the well, (3) failure to provide a satisfactory seal at the point where the pump lines pass through the casing, or (4) polluted groundwater. Figure 13-1 is a schematic diagram of a dug well which illustrates some safety measures that have been taken to protect the well against local pollution. Dug wells have a relatively large diameter and therefore exhibit considerable storage capacity. In some areas, properly developed dug wells provide an adequate and satisfactory water supply.

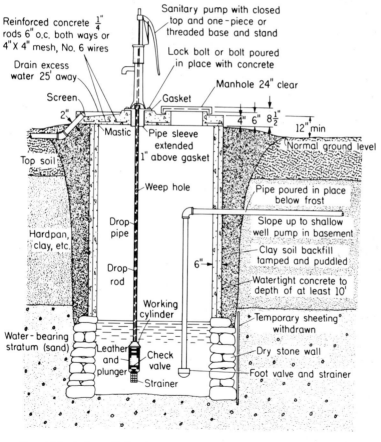

FIG. 13-1. A dug well showing construction details to safeguard against local pollution.

Drilled wells, in general, are superior to dug wells. They are less likely to become contaminated and usually provide a more dependable source of water because of their greater depth. Most drilled wells pass through an impervious layer, such as rock or clay which seals off surface water. A casing that forms the outer lining of the well is normally driven until it reaches the impervious stratum. A watertight connection is provided at the surface and the pump is generally submerged. A storage tank with water under pressure may be installed in the system. The pump is turned on and off by means of a pressure switch. This maintains a predetermined volume of water in the tank, assuring a steady flow in the distribution system. A booster pump may be required on large installations to pump the water from the storage tank to assure greater volumes of water at relatively high pressure. Figure 13-2 illustrates a drilled well with a manually operated pump.

Cisterns. A cistern is a watertight tank in which rainwater collected from building roofs is stored. A cistern may be acceptable for the development of a limited water supply or as a source of soft water. Rainwater is soft and is excellent for laundry and other purposes. On the other hand, runoff from roofs will contain dust, bird droppings, leaves, and other material. As a result, cistern water should normally be filtered as it is collected. A typical installation with a sand filter is shown in Fig. 13-3. If tastes and odors prevail, charcoal may be added to the top of the filter. A bypass is normally provided so that the first runoff, which contains much of the foreign material, may be discharged to waste.

The capacity of a cistern is determined by the size of the roof catchment area, volume of water needed, average rainfall, and length of dry periods. Cistern filters must operate over a wide range of hydraulic rates and are normally not very effective in removal of bacterial contamination. It is recommended that the cistern be treated with a disinfectant such as chlorine after every rainfall or before the water is used for drinking. This may be accomplished by adding approximately 1 oz of calcium hypochlorite for each 1,000 gal of water in the cistern.

Surface Water. Surface waters are generally not satisfactory for domestic use without continuous disinfection. Spring supplies may be safe, provided they are developed in such a way that surface pollution is avoided. Before any spring can be considered as a source of drinking water without disinfection, the ground in the vicinity should be examined to locate any possible source of pollution. Particular attention should be given to areas of higher elevation which might drain into the spring during periods of rainfall.

13-2. DEMAND FOR WATER

The quantities of water to be developed from individual supplies and resulting amounts of waste water vary in magnitude from the values com-

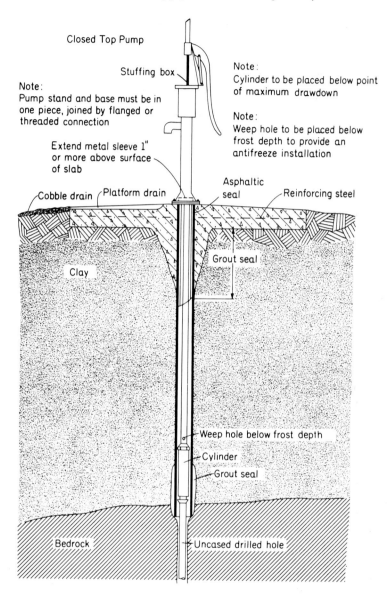

FIG. 13-2. A drilled well with a manually operated pump.

mon to urban areas as described in Chap. 3 to much smaller amounts. The quantity of water used for domestic purposes will, in general, vary directly with the availability of water, the number and type of plumbing fixtures, water pressure, air temperature, and other factors. Special adjustments must be made for industrial and other uses. Table 13-1 gives estimates of water consumption for various uses and conditions.

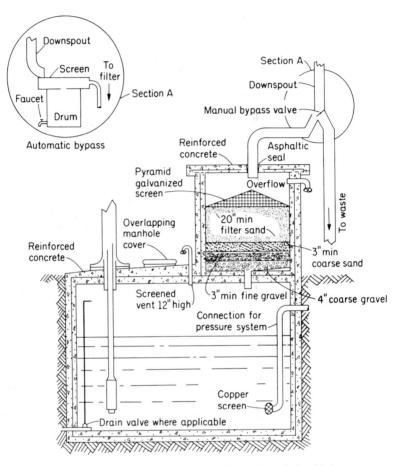

FIG. 13-3. Cistern with sand filter. The filter sand should have an effective size of 0.3 mm. Size of the coarse sand should be approximately ⅛ in. and the fine gravel, ⅛ to ⅜ in. The coarse gravel should be ¾ to 1¼ in. The automatic bypass may be used to replace the manual bypass.

Wherever possible, water consumption under similar circumstances should be used for design purposes. If provision is made for fire fighting, this will be in addition to the normal requirements. The approximate division of flow for water in a private dwelling is shown in Table 13-2.

Sizing of a water-supply system for a large building can be complex and confusing. Many "rule of thumb" procedures have been developed but most are hardly better than a "good guess." A building water supply system should be capable of conveying water at the maximum rate required during periods of maximum probable simultaneous use while

TABLE 13-1
MISCELLANEOUS WATER USAGE ESTIMATES

Domestic Use

With hand pump	10 gpcd
With pressure faucet in kitchen	15 gpcd
With hot and cold running water	50 gpcd

Camps and Schools

With hot and cold running water	45 gpcd
Without running water	5 gpcd

Livestock, per Animal

Horse, mule, or steer	12 gpd
Dairy cow	15 gpd
Dairy cow and stable	35 gpd
Hog	4 gpd
Sheep	2 gpd
Chickens (100)	4 gpd
Turkeys (100)	7 gpd

Types of Establishment

Motels, per unit without kitchen	100–150 gpd
Restaurant (per person served)	
Regular dinners	7–10 gpd
Short order, including toilet	4 gpd
Hospitals (per bed)	150–250 gpd
Service stations (per vehicle serviced)	10 gpd
Airport (per passenger)	2–3 gpd

NOTE: These figures are offered as a guide; they should not be used indiscriminately.

maintaining the minimum pressure required for operation of equipment. The rate of flow and required pressure for various plumbing fixtures is shown in Table 13-3.

A lavatory faucet has been used as a standard called a "fixture unit," all other outlets are then rated in terms of "fixture units." Table 13-4 shows some demand weights of fixtures by fixture units. The fixture units are totaled and volume rate of flow is obtained from a graph of flow versus fixture units. The graph is based on the probability of simultaneous use. Figure 13-4 is a graph of flow vs. fixture units based upon a report of the coordinating Committee for a National Plumbing Code.

TABLE 13-2
APPROXIMATE DIVISION OF FLOW PER
PERSON PER DAY IN PRIVATE DWELLINGS [1]

Use	Percent of Flow
Kitchen	20
Toilet	25
Shower	25
Washbasin	10
Laundry	20

TABLE 13-3
RATE OF FLOW AND REQUIRED PRESSURE
DURING FLOW AT ENTRANCE OF FIXTURE [2]

Fixture	Pressure at Entrance to Fixture, psi	Flow Rate, gpm
Ordinary basin faucet	8	3.0
Self-closing basin faucet	12	2.5
Sink faucet, $\frac{3}{8}$ in.	10	4.5
Sink faucet, $\frac{1}{2}$ in.	5	4.5
Bathtub faucet	5	6.0
Laundry tub, $\frac{1}{2}$ in.	5	5.0
Shower	12	5.0
Ball cock for closet	15	3.0
Flush valve for closet	10–20	15–40
Flush valve for urinal	15	15
Garden hose, 50 ft., and sill cock	30	5

TABLE 13-4
DEMAND WEIGHTS OF FIXTURES BY FIXTURE UNITS [2]

Fixtures	Supply Control	Fixture Units Private	Fixture Units Public
Water closet	Flush valve	6	10
Water closet	Flush tank	3	5
Urinal, pedestal, stall or wall		....	
	Flush valve	....	5
	Flush tank	....	3
Lavatory	Faucet	1	2
Bathtub	Faucet	2	4
Shower	Mixing valve	2	4
Service sink	Faucet	2	4
Kitchen sink (restaurant)	Faucet	....	4
Kitchen sink (residence)	Faucet	2	....
Bathroom group	Flush valve f/closet	8	....
Bathroom group	Flush tank f/closet	6	....
Laundry trays (1–3)	Faucet	3	4
Combination fixture	Faucet	3	....
Hose connection	....	3	5
House trailer	....	5	5
Bedpan washer	....	....	10
Bidet	....	2	4
Dental unit or cuspidor	....	....	1
Dental lavatory	....	1	2
Drinking fountain	....	1	2
Wash sink, circular or multiple (each set of faucets)	....	....	2

EXAMPLE 13-1. Determine the maximum probable rate of flow in gallons per minute for a new 25-bed nursing home where the following fixtures are to be installed:

Fixture	Number of Fixtures
Water closet (flush tank)	20
Lavatory	25
Bathtub	3
Shower (mixing valve)	2
Bidet	2
Laundry trays	2
Drinking fountain	3
Kitchen sink (restaurant type)	1
Bedpan washer	1
Service sink (slop sink)	1
Flush sink	1
Hose connection	4

Solution:

1. Fixture units are taken from Table 13-4.

Fixture	Number of Fixtures	Fixture Units per Fixture	Fixture Units
Water closet (flush tank)	20	3	60*
Lavatory	25	1	25*
Bathtub	3	4	12†
Shower (mixing valve)	2	4	8†
Bidet	2	4	8†
Laundry trays	2	4	8†
Drinking fountain	3	2	6†
Kitchen sink (restaurant type)	1	4	4
Bedpan washer	1	10	10
Service sink (slop sink)	1	4	4†
Flush sink	1	10	10‡
Hose connection	4	5	20†
Total			175

*Fixtures that are furnished for each bedroom are classed as private.
†Fixtures that are not furnished for each bedroom are classed as public.
‡Same as a water closet.

2. From the curve in Fig. 13-4, using 175 fixture units, the rate of flow is found to be 60 gpm.

The service-entrance, meter, and main-building pipe size must be selected so that 60 gpm is available at minimum pressure in the water main and satisfactory pressure at all fixtures.

In comparison with municipal sewage, water-carried wastes from individual systems are likely to be smaller and more variable in volume.

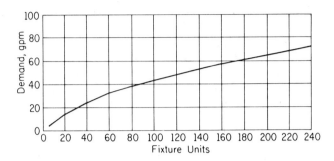

FIG. 13-4. Estimated curves for demand load based on fixture units for a water-supply system with predominately flush-tank closets.

The waste tends to be more concentrated and the discharge is largely confined to about 16 hr of the day with virtually no flow at night.

INDIVIDUAL WASTE DISPOSAL

A major factor influencing the health of individuals where public sewers are not available is the disposal of excreta. Diseases such as typhoid fever, dysentery, and various types of diarrhea are transmitted from one person to another by fecal contamination. This is largely due to the improper disposal of human wastes. These wastes must be disposed of so that:

1. They will not contaminate any drinking water supply.

2. They will not be accessible to insects, rodents, or other possible carriers.

3. They will not be accessible to children.

4. They will not pollute waters used for shellfish or for recreational purposes.

5. They will not produce an odor or unsightly appearance.

These criteria can best be met by the discharge of domestic wastes to a central collection system. Where the installation of an individual system is necessary, a properly constructed septic tank can be expected to give satisfactory service. Under certain conditions, privies or chemical closets may be used.

13-3. DISPOSAL OF EXCRETA WITHOUT WATER CARRIAGE

In the absence of waste plumbing, soapy and greasy waters from the kitchen and from washing are emptied on to the ground or into soakage pits and excreta are normally deposited in privies.

A privy, when safely located and properly built and maintained, is satisfactory for its purpose on the farm or in other rural installations.

Privies are so-called because they provide privacy during defecation. They should be located in excess of 50 ft from the house, preferably on the downwind side and at least 50 ft from a well. Tight construction with screened ventilators keeps insects and birds from entering, prevents rapid deterioration of the building, and provides comfort for the user. Other features, such as a paved walkway protected from the wind are, desirable, while not essential to sanitation.

The earth-pit privy is simple to build and widely used. It is not recommended where underground rock has crevices or where the pit extends to within 2 ft of the groundwater table. Figure 13-5 illustrates one type of pit-privy construction. The use of impervious material for risers and floors facilitates cleanliness. The main part of the structure is normally made of treated wood, which reduces the problem of moisture condensation and permits easy removal to a new location.

The annual per capita production of fecal solids is about 1.5 cu ft for adults and about half this amount for children. The annual production of urine is about twelve times this volume, but the urine leaches into the soil and evaporates. A pit with a capacity of 50 cu ft will usually serve a family of five people over a period of five to ten years. The privy should be moved when the pit is filled to within 1½ ft of the top.

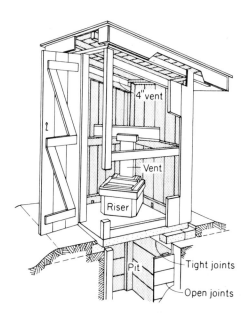

FIG. 13-5. Pit-privy construction. Detailed plans and bill of materials are available from the U.S. Public Health Service, Washington, D.C.

Privies require periodic attention. Fly and mosquito breeding in the pit is best controlled by good construction, screening of vents, and tight covers on the seats. Odors from privies can be reduced with commercial deodorants, crankcase oil, ashes, or sawdust spread over the surface. If a person in the family has typhoid fever or is a carrier of that disease or has dysentery, it is advisable to disinfect the excreta. Best results are obtained if the infected material is treated prior to depositing in the privy. Further advice may be obtained from the local health department.

Chemical closets are frequently used at construction sites and sometimes in the home where elderly or infirm people are unable to get outdoors. The principal advantage of a chemical closet is that it may be used within or adjoining the house and used without regard to soil or groundwater conditions. Caustic chemicals in the basin of the closet disinfect and deodorize the contents. Chemical closets are expensive and require careful and constant maintenance. A charge of 25 lb of caustic soda dissolved in 10 to 15 gal of water is generally placed in a tank of 125-gal capacity. Spent chemical and accumulating liquids and solids must be removed as the tank fills.

The tank or pail in a chemical closet may be removable. These tanks are small and require regular scavenger service. Dry-type chemicals are frequently used for this service. Tanks from chemical toilets may be flushed to the sewer through a manhole or other station. In the absence of a sewerage system, the contents may be buried at a suitable site.

13-4. SEPTIC TANKS

Where plumbing systems are installed, waste waters from rural dwellings and other buildings are usually disposed of in the ground. If soil and site conditions are favorable, the septic-tank system can be expected to give satisfactory service.

The first step in the design of a septic-tank system is to determine whether the soil is suitable for taking up the effluent water and, if so, at what rate. The soil must have a satisfactory absorption rate without interference from groundwater or impervious strata. The minimum depth to groundwater should be greater than 4 ft and impervious strata should be at a depth greater than 4 ft below the bottom of the tile trench or seepage pit. If these conditions cannot be met, the site is generally unsuitable for a septic-tank installation.

Percolation Tests. In the absence of groundwater or subsoil information, subsurface explorations are necessary. This investigation may be carried out with a posthole auger or soil auger with an extension handle. In some cases the examination of road cuts or foundation excavations will give useful information. If subsurface investigation appear suitable, percolation tests should be made at typical points where the disposal field is to be located.

Percolation tests determine the acceptability of the site and serve as the basis of design for the liquid absorption. The following procedure for percolation tests was developed at the Robert A. Taft Sanitary Engineering Center.[3]

1. Six or more tests shall be made in separate test holes uniformly spaced over the proposed absorption field site.

2. Dig or bore a hole with horizontal dimensions of from 4 to 12 in. and vertical sides to the depth of the proposed trench (Fig. 13-6).

3. Carefully scratch the bottom and sides of the excavation with a

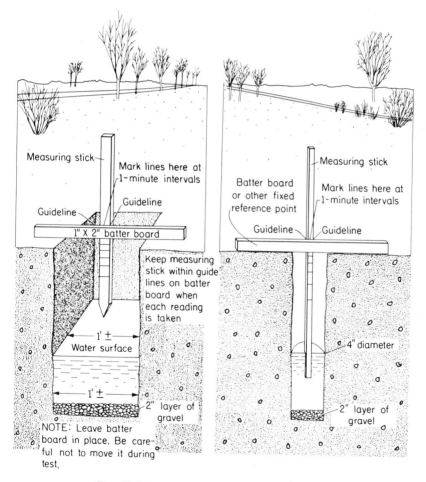

Fig. 13-6. Methods of making percolation tests.

knife blade or sharp-pointed instrument, in order to remove any smeared soil surfaces and to provide a natural soil interface into which water may percolate. Add 2 in. of coarse sand or fine gravel to the bottom of the hole.

4. Carefully fill the hole with clear water to a minimum depth of 12 in. above the gravel or sand. Keep water in the hole at least 4 hr and preferably overnight. In most soils it will be necessary to augment the water as time progresses. Determine the percolation rate 24 hr after water was first added to the hole. In sandy soils containing little clay, this prefilling procedure is not essential, and the test may be made as described under item 5(c), after water from one filling of the hole has completely seeped away.

5. The precolation-rate measurement is determined by one of the following methods:

(a) If water remains in the test hole overnight, adjust the water depth to approximately 6 in. above the gravel. From a reference batter board as shown in Fig. 13-6, measure the drop in water level over a 30-min period. This drop is used to calculate the percolation rate.

(b) If no water remains in the hole the next day, add clean water to bring the depth to approximately 6 in. over the gravel. From the batter board, measure the drop in water level at approximately 30-min intervals for 4 hr, refilling to 6 in. over the gravel as necessary. The drop in water level that occurs during the final 30-min period is used to calculate the percolation rate.

(d) In sandy soils (or other soils in which the first 6 in. of water seeps away in less than 30 min, after the overnight period), the time interval between measurements shall be taken as 10 min and the test run for 1 hr. The drop in water level that occurs during the final 10 min is used to calculate the percolation rate.

Leaching System. If the percolation rate is slower than 1 in. in 30 min, the soil is unsuitable for seepage pits, and if the rate is less than 1 in. in 60 min, the area is unsuitable for any type of soil-absorption system. Selection of the leaching system will be dependent to some extent on the site under consideration. The two common absorption systems are trenches and seepage pits. A seepage pit is a covered excavation with an open-joint lining through which water from the septic tank may seep or leach into the surrounding soil. Trench systems utilize tiled porous drains imbedded in gravel which distribute the septic-tank waste liquid over a large area of soil.

Where percolation rates are satisfactory, the required absorption area is determined by Table 13-5 and Fig. 13-7. In general, all soil absorption systems should be kept 100 ft away from any water-supply well, 50

TABLE 13-5
ABSORPTION-AREA REQUIREMENTS FOR PRIVATE RESIDENCES [3]
(Provides for Garbage Grinders and Automatic-Sequence Washing Machines)

Percolation Rate (Time Required for Water to Fall 1 in., min)	Required Absorption Area, in Square Feet per Bedroom* Standard Trench† and Seepage Pits‡	Percolation Rate (Time Required for Water to Fall 1 in., min)	Required Absorption Area, in Square Feet per Bedroom* Standard Trench† and Seepage Pits‡
1 or less	70	10	165
2	85	15	190
3	100	30§	250
4	115	45§	300
5	125	60§,‖	330

* In every case, sufficient area should be provided for at least 2 bedrooms.
† Absorption area for standard trenches is figured as trench-bottom area.
‡ Absorption area for seepage pits is figured as effective side-wall area beneath the inlet.
§ Unsuitable for seepage pits if over 30.
‖ Unsuitable for leaching systems if over 60.

ft away from any stream or watercourse, and 10 ft away from dwellings or property lines.

A trench absorption field consists of 12-in. lengths of 4-in. agricultural drain tile, 2 or 3-ft lengths of vitrified clay sewer pipe, or perforated, nonmetallic pipe, laid in such a manner that water from the septic tank will be distributed uniformly over the soil. Individual laterals (straight sections of pipeline) should not be over 100 ft in length and should be laid on a grade of 2 to 4 in./100 ft. Use of several shorter laterals is

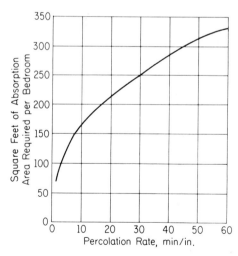

FIG. 13-7. Absorption-area requirements for private residences. [3]

preferred because if one should become clogged, most of the field will still be serviceable.

Several designs have been used in laying out the trench pattern. The choice may depend upon the shape of the available disposal area and the topography. Typical layouts are shown in Figs. 13-8 and 13-9. Details of sections of a trench are shown in Fig. 13-10. The minimum depth of trench should be 18 in. Additional depth may be necessary because of topography. The trench should be 18 to 24 in. in width and the tile laid on 6 in. of gravel. The absorption area is proportional to the width of trench up to 36 in. wide.

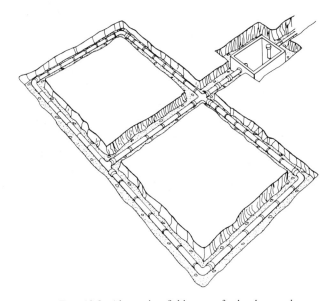

Fig. 13-8. Absorption-field system for level ground.

A distribution box is usually considered necessary for a trench absorption-field system. The purpose of the box is to insure equal distribution of effluent to all of the laterals. The box is particularly important on sloping ground. A typical distribution box is shown in Fig. 13-11.

A seepage pit is a covered pit with open-jointed lining through which septic-tank effluent may be absorbed into the surrounding soil. It is normally considered a less desirable method of liquid disposal than the trench method.

Sizing a Septic Tank. A septic tank allows solids to settle out of a waste and permits a clarified effluent to be discharged. The solids are broken down by anaerobic digestion. Remaining solids accumulate in the tank and must be pumped out periodically.

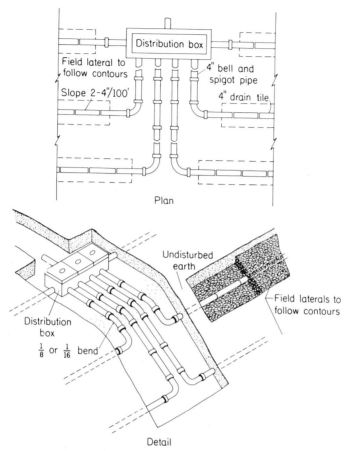

FIG. 13-9. Absorption field for sloping ground.[3]

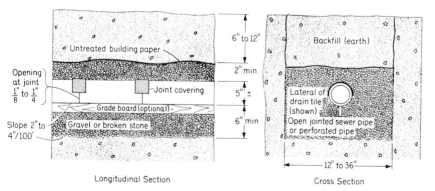

Note: Unevenness of ends of drain tile will usually provide the necessary openings between joints. Special collars may be used if desired.

FIG. 13-10. Absorption trench and lateral.[3]

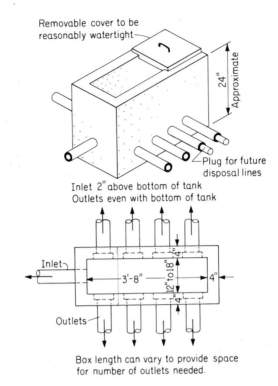

Inlet 2″ above bottom of tank
Outlets even with bottom of tank

Box length can vary to provide space
for number of outlets needed.

Fig. 13-11. Typical distribution box.

One of the most important considerations in septic-tank design is the liquid capacity. Table 13-6 lists the recommended capacities for private dwellings based upon the number of bedrooms. Table 13-6 includes capacity for the use of all normal household appliances, including garbage grinders.

Septic tanks should be of watertight construction and made of materials not subject to excessive corrosion or decay. Concrete, coated metal,

TABLE 13-6
LIQUID CAPACITY OF TANK
(Provides for Use of Garbage Grinders, Automatic
Washers, and Other Household Appliances)

Number of Bedrooms	Recommended Minimum Tank Capacity, gal	Equivalent Capacity per Bedroom, gal
Two or less	750	375
Three	900	300
Four*	1,000	250

*For each additional bedroom, add 250 gal.

vitrified clay, concrete block, or brick have been successfully used. The tank should be so constructed as to provide adequate access to each compartment of the tank, as well as the inlet and outlet. A 20-in. manhole is considered the minimum size for access. A typical domestic septic tank is shown in Fig. 13-12.

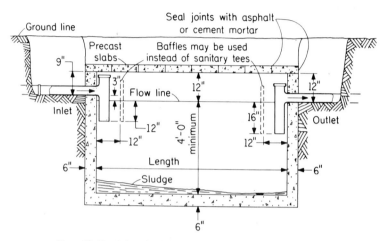

FIG. 13-12. A longitudinal section of a concrete septic tank.

13-5. COMMERCIAL SEPTIC-TANK SYSTEMS

Septic tanks are used in providing waste treatment and disposal for many types of establishments, such as schools, motels, rural hotels, trailer parks, housing projects, camps, and others. While many effluents from commercial septic tanks are disposed of by soil absorption, others are discharged to available watercourses after suitable treatment. Where soil absorption is contemplated, it is essential, as described in Sec. 13-4, to determine the characteristics of the soil as the first step in design.

Next, it is necessary to obtain information on the volume of waste to be treated. In the absence of definite information, the volume of sewage may be estimated from Table 13-7. Values listed in this table are averages and should be modified where additional information is available.

With information from percolation tests, the rate at which sewage may be applied to a trench field may be taken from Table 13-8 or Fig. 13-13.

Table 13-8 and Fig. 13-13 do not allow for wastes from garbage grinders and automatic washing machines. If wastes from these appliances are to be handled, the absorption field should be increased by 20 percent for garbage grinders, 40 percent for automatic washers, and 60 percent if both are to be used.

TABLE 13-7
QUANTITIES OF WASTE FLOW[3]

Type of Establishment	Gallons per Person per Day
Small dwellings and cottages with seasonal occupancy	50
Single-family dwellings..	75
Multiple-family dwellings (apartments)	60
Rooming houses	40
Boarding houses..	50
Additional kitchen wastes for nonresident boarders	10
Hotels without private baths...	50
Hotels with private baths (2 persons per room)	60
Restaurants (toilet and kitchen wastes per patron)...................	7 to 10
Restaurants (kitchen wastes per meal served)	2½ to 3
Additional for bars and cocktail lounges	2
Tourist camps or trailer parks with central bathhouse	35
Tourist courts or mobile home parks with individual bath units......	50
Resort camps (night and day) with limited plumbing	50
Luxury camps	100 to 150
Work or construction camps (semipermanent)........................	50
Day camps (no meals served)	15
Day schools without cafeterias, gymnasiums, or showers	15
Day schools with cafeterias, but no gymnasiums or showers	20
Day schools with cafeterias, gyms, and showers	25
Boarding schools	75 to 100
Day workers at schools and offices (per shift)	15
Hospitals	150 to 250+
Institutions other than hospitals	75 to 125
Factories (gallons per person per shift, exclusive of industrial wastes)	15 to 35
Picnic parks with bathhouses, showers, and flush toilets.............	10
Picnic parks (toilet wastes only), (gallons per picnicker)..............	5
Swimming pools and bathhouses	10
Luxury residences and estates..	100 to 150
Country clubs (per resident member).................................	100
Country clubs (per nonresident member present)	25
Motels (per bed space)	40
Motels with bath, toilet, and kitchen wastes.........................	50
Drive-in theaters (per car space)	5
Movie theaters (per auditorium seat)	5
Airports (per passenger)	3 to 5
Self-service laundries (gallons per wash, i.e., per customer)...........	50
Stores (per toilet room)	400
Service stations (per vehicle served)	10

Single compartment septic tanks as shown in Fig. 13-12 are acceptable for private household installations; tanks with two compartments are normally provided for large institutional systems. The first compartment serves as the primary settling basin and should be two to three times the capacity of the second compartment. The relative absence of

TABLE 13-8
ALLOWABLE RATE OF SEWAGE APPLICATION
TO A SOIL-ABSORPTION SYSTEM

Percolation Rate (Time in Minutes for Water To Fall 1 in.)	Maximum Rate of Sewage Application (Gallons per Square foot per Day)* for Standard Trenches† Seepage Pits‡	Percolation Rate (Time in Minutes for Water To Fall 1 in.)	Maximum Rate of Sewage Application (Gallons per Square Foot per Day)* for Standard Trenches† and Seepage Pits‡
1 or less	5.0	10	1.6
2	3.5	15	1.3
3	2.9	30§	0.9
4	2.5	45§	0.8
5	2.2	60§, ‖	0.6

*Not including effluents from septic tanks that receive wastes from garbage grinders and automatic washing machines.

†Absorption area for standard trench is figured as trench-bottom area.

‡Absorption area for seepage pits is effective sidewall area.

§Over 30 unsuitable for seepage pits.

‖ Over 60 unsuitable for leaching systems.

solid material in the second tank indicates that the system is functioning properly.

For flows between 500 and 1,500 gal per day, the capacity of the tank below the flowline should be equal to at least 1½ times the day's waste flow. With flows greater than 1,500 gal per day, the tank capacity below the waterline should equal 1,125 gal plus 75 percent of the daily sewage flow.

$$V = 1125 + 0.75Q \qquad (13\text{-}1)$$

where V = volume of tank below waterline, gallons

Q = daily waste flow, gallons

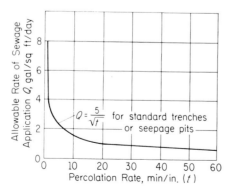

FIG. 13-13. Graph showing the relation between percolation rate and allowable rate of sewage applicable.[3]

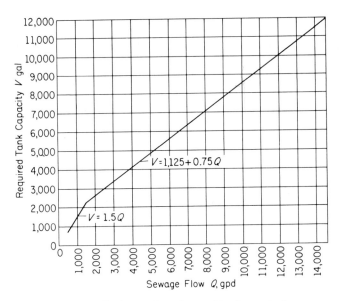

Fig. 13-14. Effective septic-tank capacities for waste flows
up to 14,500 gpd.

Figure 13-14 gives the required tank capacity below the flowline for flow from 500 to 14,500 gal/day. When the volume of waste exceeds the amount that can be absorbed in 500 lineal feet of trench, a dosing tank should be used. The dosing tank should be equipped with an automatic siphon which discharges the dosing chamber every 3 or 4 hr. The tank should have a capacity equal to about 70 percent of the interior volume of the tile to be dosed at one time. Figure 13-15 shows an arrangement of a two-compartment septic tank with dosing chamber. Additional in-

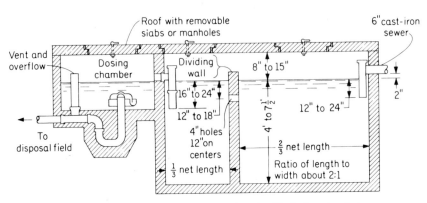

Fig. 13-15. Two-compartment septic tank with dosing chamber.

formation on the design of septic tanks and absorption fields will be found in *Manual of Septic-Tank Practice,* Public Health Service Publication No. 526.

EXAMPLE 13-2. Determine the volume of a septic tank and the length of absorption trench for a hotel without private baths to handle 100 persons. Results of a percolation test gave a rate of 1 in. in 5 min.

Solution:

1. The waste flow for a hotel without private bath is taken from Table 13-7 and is found to be 50 gal/day/person.

$$\text{Total waste flow} = 50 \times 100 = 5,000 \text{ gpd}$$

2. Volume of the septic tank below the waterline is obtained from Fig. 13-14 and is found to be 4,850 gal.

3. Allowable rate of sewage application to the absorption field is obtained from Fig. 13-13. The dosage rate is found to be 2.2 gpd/sq ft of trench.

4. The trench is assumed to be 2 ft wide.

$$\text{Absorption area} = 5,000 \text{ gpd}/2.2 \text{ g/sq ft}$$
$$= 2,270 \text{ sq ft}$$
$$\text{Length of trench} = 2,270/2$$
$$= 1,135 \text{ ft}$$

5. Volume of the dosing chamber is calculated to be 70 percent of the volume of 1,135 ft of 4-in. tile.

$$\text{Volume} = 1,135 \text{ ft} \times \frac{\pi}{36} \times 7.48 \times 0.70$$

$$\text{Volume of dosing chamber} = 518 \text{ gal}$$

REFERENCES

1. Joseph A. Salvato, Jr., *Environmental Sanitation* (New York: John Wiley and Sons, Inc., 1958), p. 67.

2. "Nursing Homes Environmental Health Factors," U.S. Public Health Service (Washington, D.C.: U.S. Government Printing Office, 1963), Publ. No. 1009-6.

3. "Manual of Septic-Tank Practice," U.S. Public Health Service (Washington, D.C.: U.S. Government Printing Office, 1957), Publ. No. 526.

PROBLEMS

13-1. Prepare a set of outline specifications for a private-well water supply in your state, city, or county.

13-2. Prepare a set of outline specifications for an individual public-well water-supply system in your state, city, or county.

13-3. Determine the maximum probable rate of flow in gallons per minute for a new 50-unit motel where the following fixtures are to be installed:

Fixtures	Number of Fixtures
Lavatory	6
Bathroom group (flush tank)	54
Laundry trays	4
Drinking fountain	2
Kitchen sink (restaurant type)	1
Flush sink	1
Hose connection	7

13-4. Determine the maximum probable rate of flow in gallons per minute for a subdivision consisting of 93 house units on medium-sized lots where there are 2 bathroom groups, 3 hose connections, 1 kitchen sink, and 1 laundry tray at each unit.

13-5. Prepare a set of outline specifications for an individual septic tank disposal system in your state, city, or country.

13-6. Abstract the ordinances or laws governing the sanitary requirements for construction crews in your state, city, or county.

13-7. Determine the volume of a septic tank and the length of absorption trench for a private 5-bedroom residence where the results of a percolation test gave a rate of 1 in. in 9 min.

13-8. Determine the volume of a septic tank and the length of absorption trench for a 60-unit motel with private baths. The results of a percolation test gave a rate of 1-in. in 25 min.

13-9. Design a distribution box for the absorption trench in Prob. 13-8.

13-10. Determine the volume and sketch the cross section of a two compartment septic tank for a waste flow of 9,000 gpd.

13-11. Design a septic tank for a waste flow of 5,000 gpd. Compute a bill of materials and make a cost estimate based upon local prices for labor and materials.

13-12. Design an absorption field for the septic tank in Prob. 13-11 where a percolation test gave a rate of 1 in. in 19 min. Compute a bill of materials and make a cost estimate based upon local prices for labor and materials.

chapter 14

The Reuse of Water

The increasing demands placed on the water resources of this country dictate that every avenue of supplementing this priceless natural resource must be explored.[29] As waste treatment processes are improved and the procurement and development of natural water supplies becomes increasingly expensive and difficult, water reuse becomes a significant consideration. In fact, there is no doubt but that various forms of water reuse will be implemented in an increasing manner as time goes on and the demand for useable water supplies is magnified.

Municipal and industrial waste waters constitute a vast potential source for supplementing current and future supplies. The mechanics of reusing these waters presents a significant challenge to the engineering profession. Recent technological advances have shown that it is not only practical but economically feasible to treat and use a spectrum of waste waters for many purposes. Such uses would preclude the waste of billions of gallons of water daily to the oceans. For example, it has been estimated that in 1963 about 580,000 acre-ft of water were discharged to the Pacific Ocean by the sewerage systems of the Los Angeles coastal plain area.[4] Over 55 percent of this wasted water was of a satisfactory quality to have been put to other uses. Obviously, a comprehensive program of water reclamation could have significantly increased the available water supply for that region.

Although water reclamation does not solve all the aspects of "water shortage" problems, it can serve as an important supplement through the recharge of groundwater basins or by meeting irrigation or industrial needs directly. Under most circumstances direct reuse of waste waters without any type of conditioning cannot be practiced because of the potential health hazard. By employing various degrees of treatment, however, reclaimed waters may be beneficially used for irrigating parks, golf courses, pastures, and certain crops; for recreational lakes; for industrial cooling and boiler feed; and after these waters have been diluted by natural waters or percolated through native soils to existing groundwater zones, they may also become part of a potable water supply.

Generally speaking, water reuse may be divided into two categories. The first classification is associated with reclamation which results indirectly from inland-water pollution-control measures. The second category is that of deliberate reclamation of waste waters for specific uses. An example of the first classification would be a river used as a source of supply and then a vehicle of disposal by various municipalities and industries along its course. The treated waste of community "A" would be diluted by the river and then extracted for treatment and use at some point "B." This continual reuse downstream has long been practiced although the waste-treatment facilities have usually been built primarily to control pollution in the stream rather than to develop the waste for downstream reuse. The second category of water reuse utilizes the waste streams of municipalities and industries directly as the raw product for producing a water which will adequately serve to supplement existing supplies in some prescribed manner.

A great deal is to be gained by water reclamation. In the Los Angeles area, for example, Parkhurst has indicated that a comprehensive reclamation program could increase the available water supply for basin recharge and direct industrial use by about 25 percent.[4] This amounts to approximately 300,000 acre-ft of water per year, a very significant supplement. Nevertheless, any program intended to develop waste flows for reuse must be carefully thought out if it is to be successful and economically sound. The construction of separate facilities for water reclamation should be encouraged only if the following criteria are met: (1) the water quality must be satisfactory for reuse, (2) the quantity available must be adequate to permit economical production, (3) the location at which the reclaimed water is to be used must be sufficiently close to preclude large transportation costs, and (4) the project must yield a benefit which will assure purchase of the water at a price adequate to cover all or a reasonable part of the cost of production.

THE NATURAL OR INDIRECT REUSE OF WATER

It has already been pointed out that surface bodies of water (streams, rivers, lakes) are often used by numerous municipalities, industries, and agricultural organizations for both water supply and waste-water disposal. In this manner the water in any surface source is generally reused many times before it finally flows to the sea.

Even though municipal and industrial waste-treatment processes effectively reduce the quantities of pollutants entering the receiving waters, varying quantities of polluting materials still pass through these units and tend to degrade the quality of the water to which they are returned. Fortunately, the forces of natural purification which are continually at work in natural waters result in further purification of these wastes. The degree of natural purification accomplished in a given river reach is dependent, however, upon numerous factors which include the degree of dilution, the character of the waste, the time involved, and other elements. Nevertheless the net result of discharging wastes into natural waters is normally an increase in the waste-water quality.

Before the diluted waste flows from upstream sources can be reused for potable water supplies, still further treatment is required. The type of purification process employed will depend primarily on the degree of pollution of the source waters. The methodology for attacking this particular problem has been presented in Chaps. 8 through 12. Some of the major treatment operations utilized in this respect are storage, coagulation, sedimentation, filtration, and disinfection.

While industry and municipalities are accelerating programs to cope with waste-abatement problems, the nature and dimension of these problems is also rapidly expanding. MacKichan in 1957 indicated that industrial water use increased 43 percent from 77 billion to 110 billion gpd from 1950 to 1953. Total waste volumes discharged by the chemical industry very likely rose even more strikingly during this period. New products such as synthetic detergents, insecticides (DDT), herbicides, (2,4D), and numerous others, are contaminating surface and groundwaters with the wastes associated with their manufacture. Some of these contaminants are exceedingly difficult to remove from waste waters and many technical problems concerning them are yet to be solved. Thus, although pollution-control practices have improved and their application has spread, industrial vitality has produced a whole new spectrum of waste disposal needs. An additional problem results from the fact that even when abatement methods are available, it is not always easy to institute them. As stated by McKee (1962), "There is no great technical or engineering block to building more waste-treatment plants. The trouble is getting people to vote bonds. Water issues pass, but sewerage bonds are tough, particularly when it takes a two-thirds vote."[6] Nevertheless, higher degrees of waste treatment are going to be required in the future as the number and variety of contaminants discharged into our surface and groundwaters increases and as the need for reusing these waters becomes more pressing.

The use of oxidation ponds, microstrainers, improved biological and chemical-treatment sequences, and coagulation and filtration are likely to find wider future use in the waste-treatment field to produce higher-quality effluents.

14-1. INDIRECT MUNICIPAL REUSE

The use of surface bodies of water that have been heavily polluted is often the only feasible alternative for municipalities located near such sources. To produce usable waters from these polluted supplies generally requires considerable pretreatment. One method of improving the quality of such waters prior to the utilization of normal treatment devices is to have the water withdrawn from wells constructed along the stream bank. In this manner the natural filtration capacity of the sand and gravel deposits can be utilized. Where geological construction permits this form of development, the approach should be given careful consideration.

Polluted waters can be effectively transformed into potable supplies by the utilization of various sequences of the unit processes previously discussed. A good example of the adequacy of conventional processes in treating heavily polluted waters is the case history of a situation which occurred in Chanute, Kansas, in 1956 and 1957.[3,10] During the critical drought the primary source of water supply (the Neosho River) was all but eliminated. In an attempt to alleviate this serious problem it was decided to take the sewage effluent from the biofiltration plant, dilute it with the available river water, and treat this mixture for municipal uses. For several months the sewage flows of the community constituted a considerable portion of the municipal water supply. There were no reports of ill effects on the population. The water was of a poor chemical quality however. After the water had been purified it was found that the enteric viruses evident in the treated sewage had been eliminated.

The primary difficulties associated with the indirect reuse of waste flows for municipal purposes are related to the bacteriological and chemical qualities of these wastes. Significant reductions in the quantity of enteric organisms can be effected through modern sewage treatment processes. Well-designed water-purification operations can then produce a supply which meets current bacteriological standards. Where complex or toxic chemicals are involved, special treatment operations must often be employed.

14-2. INDIRECT INDUSTRIAL AND AGRICULTURAL REUSE

Industry and agriculture also indirectly reuse water which has previously served various purposes. The reuse problems are similar to those outlined for municipal uses. In industrial operations, chemical quality is often the controlling criteria while bacteriological quality for example might not warrant consideration. Various forms of water supplies are suitable for industrial use.

Agricultural water should not contain chemicals which are toxic to plants or which would be toxic to persons utilizing the crops for food. In addition, these waters should not contain bacteria that would affect animals or persons using the plants, nor should they contain chemicals which develop unsatisfactory moisture characteristics upon reaction with the soil. Excessive quantities of the salts of calcium, magnesium, sodium, and potassium may be injurious to crops as they affect the ability of the plant to absorb nutrients from the soil and also affect the metabolism of these plants. Many other elements may also be toxic to plants or animals. Boron is particularly injurious in larger than trace amounts, and a concentration exceeding 4 mg/l is considered unsafe for even the most tolerant crops. Since boron is a constituent of many soaps, it may affect the use of sewage effluent for irrigation purposes. Tables of suggested water-quality tolerances for industrial uses and quality classifications of water for irrigation may be found in Ref. 7.

14-3. POLLUTION-CONTROL METHODS

There is no present general solution available for handling water-pollution problems. The scope and nature of these problems are so varied that individual practices must usually be designed to meet the needs of a specific case. There are those, however, who propose that uniform standards of water-quality control be established. The thinking behind this is that it is easier to enforce a uniform regulation where everyone involved is required to provide similar treatment than to permit variable treatment depending on the local benefits to be gained.

In recent years the Federal government has begun to assume a more prominent role in the abatement of water pollution. The first Water Pollution Control Act (Public Law 845, 80th Cong.) was passed in 1948. This was enacted as temporary legislation and was extended in 1953 for three more years to 1956. The first permanent comprehensive Federal Water Pollution Control Act (the Blatnik Act) was enacted in 1956. It represented a significant improvement of the 1948 Act. During the first five years of the 1956 Act the Federal program assisted more than 2,700 cities build sewage-treatment plants, accomplished the improvement of over 4,000 miles of streams through the application of Federal enforcement authority, and developed a vigorous research program.[8] It was recognized however, that the authority was not substantial enough to cope with all the aspects of the increasing water pollution problem.

In response to President Kennedy's request for more effective pollution-control measures, Congress in 1961 passed Public Law 87-88, which amended the 1956 act. This important legislation accomplished the following:

1. It provided for increased Federal support for constructing municipal waste-treatment facilities.

2. It increased the scope of and strengthened the enforcement power of the Federal government.

3. It emphasized a strong research program geared to search for more effective methods of pollution control.

4. It authorized increased support of state and interstate water-pollution-control programs by the Federal government.

5. It incorporated the consideration of maintaining satisfactory water quality during periods of low flow through storage in planning and constructing Federal reservoirs.

The role of the Federal government in water-pollution control is nevertheless intended to be largely a supporting one with primary responsibility resting with the states. In fact in the 1961 law the statement exists that "nothing in this act shall be construed as impairing or in any manner affecting any right or jurisdiction of the States with respect to the waters (including boundary waters) of such States."

14-4. INTERSTATE AGENCIES FOR POLLUTION CONTROL

The maintenance of water quality in the United States is often undertaken by the various states individually. Under certain circumstances however, this approach leads to a disregard of the requirements of adjacent states. In many instances the water-pollution problems are regional in nature and a joint effort by several states is a necessity if effective control is to be practiced. Interstate compacts have been drawn up in some instances to provide standards for the treatment of polluted waters which will preclude the degradation of interstate or regional water resources.

One example of interstate cooperation is the Interstate Sanitation Commission created by the states of New York, New Jersey, and Connecticut. This compact was established for pollution abatement in the waters of the metropolitan area of New York. All of the waters under the jurisdiction of the commission are tidal and thus numerous problems are encountered which do not exist in nontidal pollution abatement work.[11] Another example of this nature is the seven-state compact between Connecticut, Rhode Island, Massachusetts, Vermont, New York, New Hampshire, and Maine. This compact was formed between 1947 and 1955 to provide proper coordination for a comprehensive river pollution-control program. The commission undertakes detailed studies of various river basins and makes recommendations for the improvement of these waterways. Water-quality standards are then established which conform to the use to which the river is to be put. The individual states through their regulatory agencies then undertake to regulate the river use so that the proposed standards are met. Many other examples of interstate cooperation may be found in the literature.[3,12,13] A discussion of pollution-control methods of some other countries is given in Ref. 3.

14-5. ENFORCEMENT OF WATER-POLLUTION ABATEMENT

The law enacted in 1961 extended the jurisdiction of the Federal government to all interstate or navigable waters, including coastal waters. The Act further provides for enforcement procedures by which government action can be taken to abate water pollution. Three steps are involved in instituting enforcement procedures: (1) A conference is arranged so that the problem can be discussed. (2) If satisfactory action to alleviate the problem is not taken, a public hearing before a special board is held. (3) If after an allotted time following the board meeting the pollution is not abated, the Secretary of Health, Education, and Welfare can ask the Attorney General to bring suit to obtain abatement in interstate situations.

Between 1956 and 1962, eighteen enforcement actions involving 24 states and the District of Columbia were instituted. These actions were concerned with over 250 municipalities and approximately the same number of industries. The enforcement actions have covered water bodies in large metropolitan areas such as New York, Washington, D.C., St. Louis, and Kansas City.[9] Some of the country's largest corporations have been involved.

The result of these enforcement actions has been the planning, construction, and operation of numerous waste collection and treatment facilities. With future actions that will develop it is considered that there will be a substantial increase in the construction of new waste-treatment facilities and the modification of existing ones.

DIRECT REUSE OF WASTE WATERS

It has been pointed out that water demands are rapidly increasing. Many areas are finding that they are imposing overdrafts on existing supplies. New supplies must often be developed at considerable distances from their expected point of use, with the result that transportation costs often become prohibitive. Such factors as these are instrumental in focusing greater attention on the modification of past practices of waste-water treatment and disposal. Considerable interest is now being brought to bear on the practicality of direct utilization of treated waste effluents.

Treated sewage effluents are not presently used directly as sources of municipal water supply. At the same time, however, a definite trend in the industrial use of such flows is in evidence. In the field of agriculture both treated and untreated waste effluents are used. Treated sewage effluent is also finding use in the development of artificial lakes for recreational purposes.

14-6. PUBLIC HEALTH CONSIDERATIONS

The two considerations of primary significance in planning waste-water reuse projects are public health and economics. If the results of a project are expected to prove hazardous to the public health, changes should be made or the project dropped.

Normally the risks associated with the use of sewage effluent increase with the directness of the reuse.[15] The primary hazard stems from the fact that sewage may be infectious due to the inclusion of pathogens in the form of bacteria, viruses, intestinal worms, or protozoa.[16] Industrial wastes, on the other hand, may contain toxic materials. Great care must be taken in planning reclamation projects to insure that proper treatment and handling are provided to combat the risks associated with waste-water reuse.

The elements of a modern sewage-treatment plant are usually designed so that the effluent produced will be assimilated by the receiving body of water. It is not intended that the quality of water produced be of a caliber satisfactory for municipal water supply. On the other hand, the modern water-treatment plant is expected to process turbid waters of moderate contamination so that they will be safe for drinking purposes. The elements of these treatment plants are usually not designed to cope with raw waters of the nature of sewage-plant effluent. It is generally true, therefore, that a combination of the commonly used water and sewage-treatment unit processes cannot be considered adequate to transform sewage effluent to safe drinking water. A more thorough understanding of the microbial and chemical changes which occur will be essential before direct conversion of sewage effluent becomes a reality.[16] Considerable research on new and improved methods of advanced waste treatment is a necessity.

14-7. THE CONCEPT OF ADVANCED WASTE TREATMENT

In order to meet the coming challenge of water reuse, additional treatment operations will have to be combined with the conventional processes of today to produce waters of satisfactory quality for a whole spectrum of purposes. Modern conventional waste-treatment processes achieve a reduction in BOD and suspended solids of about 90 percent.[18] They also are effective in reducing microbial contaminants. New and improved processes will be required to go beyond these limits of treatment. In addition, many non-BOD organics and inorganics which are not removed by current treatment operations will have to be removed in the future. The reason for this can be illustrated by considering that about 300 mg/l of inorganics and approximately 100 mg/l of organic material are added to a water which has been used only one time for municipal purposes.[17] If the water is reused many times additional amounts of contaminants are added and ultimately dilution is not enough to satisfactorily reduce the concentrations of these materials and removal is the only solution.

The water-quality problem is further complicated by the fact that many new materials are being disposed of in our watercourses. A number of these are classified as "refractory," which implies that they are not readily removed by conventional treatment processes. Most soluble inorganic salts are not removed in sewage-treatment operations. Many organic compounds are also highly resistant to natural purification and waste treatment. McCallum reports that a particular benzene derivative was found to persist in the Mississippi River for about 1,000 miles.[17] This waste was not affected or removed to any degree by passage through ordinary water-treatment processes.

The addition of refractory contaminants to a watercourse eventually degrades the source quality. Often this is a slow process which continually builds up until some significant event such as a large-scale fish kill occurs. Various kinds of damages to water quality can be attributed to refractory contaminants. The effects produced may be aesthetic, economic, or physiological. It is important to realize that while the ingestion of waters containing retractory materials may not produce any immediate harmful effects, it is possible that over a period of years an undesirable cumulative effect might be produced. Considering this, it is becoming more important that the various contaminants in our waters be identified and their effects determined. Only through such an approach as this can we prevent harmful materials from reaching critical concentrations.

To produce waters of a quality to satisfactorily meet the needs of future reuse operations, advanced waste-treatment methods will be required. The removal of many inorganic materials will be necessary. In addition, many synthetic organic chemical products which resist or are unaffected by biochemical treatment must be dealt with. Complete dependence on biodegradibility can no longer be the rule and therefore the application of physical-chemical principles will have to be extended. Such processes as adsorption, evaporation, extraction, electrodialysis, foaming, ion exchange, freezing, and oxidation may constitute an important part of future water-renovation plants. Considerable research on advanced waste-treatment techniques is essential.

For advanced waste treatment to be feasible, it will be necessary to efficiently separate contaminants from the water source and then to permanently dispose of the removed impurities.[17] The degree of purification and thus the type treatment required will depend entirely on the use to which the renovated water is to be put. Irrigation waters for example might require very little inorganic removal. The organic materials in this case might be treated primarily through disinfection. Industrial waters might require a high degree of removal of corrosive and scale-forming components. If the water is to be used for recreational purposes, disinfection, removal of suspended solids and color- and odor-producing agents might be essential. For municipal purposes an extremely high-quality water would be required. Both organic and inorganic impurities would have to be reduced and the water would have to be free of pathogenic organisms.

Technically, a water of any desired quality can be produced from a given waste-water source. The primary challenge in preparing water for reuse on a large scale is that of accomplishing the renovation at an acceptable cost. Considerable emphasis must be placed on the development of minimum cost operations.

14-8. DOMESTIC USES

Municipal sewage effluents or other waste waters are not used directly for drinking purposes without dilution and additional treatment. Some studies have been conducted relative to the reuse of sewage effluent for toilet flushing in individual residences, but much research remains to be done to determine the feasibility of such practice.[14]

14-9. INDUSTRIAL USES

Present direct reuse of treated municipal waste waters by industry is relatively small but the increasing number of examples where this is carried out attests to the enormous potential that exists. Sewage-treatment plant effluent can be used successfully for general plant application, for cooling water, and also for boiler feedwater if properly treated. Since about 50 percent of all industrial water use falls within the latter two categories, it can easily be seen that the value of reclaimed waste waters to industry is significant. Sewage effluents are used industrially in those areas of the United States where economic conditions make this a favorable choice.

Veatch, Keating, and Calise have listed some factors which must be considered in deciding on the practicality of the reuse of sewage-plant effluent by industry.[20,22] These factors are:

1. A local industry must exhibit the need for a process water which does not involve the public health.

2. The sewage-treatment plant must be of an adequate size to meet the required flows.

3. Processing costs, which include transportation and pumping, must not exceed those of an alternate supply.

4. The quality of the sewage-plant effluent should be consistent enough to allow its reuse by the particular industry.

The outstanding example of industrial use of sewage-plant effluent is the Bethlehem Steel Company's Sparrows Point plant in Maryland. In 1942 the steel mill first contracted to take 20 mgpd of water from the Baltimore sewage-treatment plant. This proved to be a better supply than the saline Chesapeake Bay water or the available groundwater supplies which were increasing in salinity due to overdraft. By 1960 the plant was using 110 mgpd of treated effluent and by 1965 it is expected that 150 mgpd will be utilized. This amounts to about 22 percent of the total plant requirement for cooling water. Costs anticipated in 1965 range from 3 to 4 cents per 1,000 gals.

Another example of industrial reuse is that of the Cosden Oil and Chemical Company at Big Spring, Texas. In 1943, Cosden was experiencing serious problems because of inadequate supplies of water which were, at best, poor quality. As a result, full rights for water from the Big Spring contact aeration plant were contracted for. About 15 mg/month are taken from the municipal sewage-treatment plant. The cost of this treated effluent is about 25 cents per 1,000 gals. The water is used as boiler feed and is of better quality than that of the existing wells. In the next five to ten years it is expected that further needs will arise and that reclaimed sewage effluent will be used for cooling purposes as well as for boiler feed. To anticipate this need, Cosden has recently expanded its own facilities for treating sewage.

Since 1955 a dependable and satisfactory source of boiler makeup and cooling water has been provided the Texas Company's Amarillo Refinery by the water reclamation and sewage treatment plant of the city of Amarillo, Texas.[21] Many factors prompted the use of this reclaimed waste by the refinery. In 1954 the company and municipality signed a contract which provided for the construction of a new sewage-treatment plant by the city, the provision of additional water-treatment facilities by the industry, and the delivery of an effluent by the sewage plant which would meet certain specifications.

Municipal waste effluents are often used more than once particularly in arid regions. At the copper plants at Hurley and Santa Rita, New Mexico for example, municipal wastes are used for process makeup water and copper recovery. Septic-tank effluent is used as process water at Santa Rita and is then reclaimed and used again at the copper-precipitating plant.

One approach to the reduction of costs in water renovation projects is to build the reclamation plant at a suitable location along the sewer upstream of the principal sewage-treatment works. In this way the solids can be transported from the reclamation site to the central sewage-treatment plant with the resultant elimination of sludge processing and handling operations at the renovation works. Information available on reuse practices at Azusa and Pomona, California indicates that savings of from 50 to 70 percent were derived through such practice for these locations.[3]

The requirements for water used in industry are highly variable. Because of this, and also because of the variability in quality of sewage effluents, the necessary degree of treatment can be determined only on an individual basis. The cost of renovating the water for industrial use is therefore also variable with the particular circumstances. Some comparisons between costs of renovated waters and fresh water supplies are given in Table 14-1.

TABLE 14-1*,**
COST COMPARISON OF REUSED WATER VS. ALTERNATE
WATER IN INDUSTRY

Location	Type of Use	Quantity Used per Year, mg	Cost of Reused Water, $/mg	Cost of Alternate Water, $/mg	Note[†]
Grand Canyon, Ariz.	Power plant	65	$370	$2,000	([‡])
Los Angeles, Calif.	Sewage plant	3,900	12	122	([§])
Baltimore, Md.	Steel plant	40,000	35	135	([‖])
Amarillo, Tex.	Oil refinery	520	43	138	([#])
Big Springs, Tex.	Oil refinery	720	49	175	

    * From Table 8, Cost Data for Reclaimed Water Use, Publication No. 12, "A Survey of Direct Utilization of Waste Waters," State Water Pollution Control Board, Sacramento, Calif.
    [†] 1955 cost data.
    [‡] Effluent also used for irrigation.
    [§] Only cost is pumping.
    [‖] 1959 cost data. Includes all operating costs and amortization of $5 million investment.
    [#] Does not include amortization. If added, would equal minimum city costs.
    ** Reprinted from E. F. Gloyna, J. B. Wolff, J. C. Geyer, and Abel Wolman, "A Report Upon Present and Prospective Means for Improved Reuse of Water."[3]

14-10. AGRICULTURAL USES

Irrigation of lands with sewage has been practiced for centuries. In some cases the object is simply to dispose of the sewage, whereas in other cases the primary purpose is production of crops and raising of animals. In the United States, the practice of irrigating with municipal sewage effluents is confined largely to the arid or semiarid regions.

The primary consideration to be made regarding the use of reclaimed domestic sewage for agricultural purposes is whether or not a public health hazard will result. The risks associated with sewage farming are dependent to a great extent on the type of crops being irrigated and on the degree of treatment of the effluent used. In general it is believed that disease can be transmitted by the ingestion of uncooked vegetables which have been irrigated with sewage.

Practice in the United States is to prohibit the use of sewage effluent for the irrigation of crops which are usually eaten raw. This holds true regardless of the amount of treatment provided. It is also considered good procedure to suspend sewage irrigation about 20 to 45 days before the harvest for products which are to be cooked.[3] Evidence of sewage-borne organisms has been found on fruits and vegetables after marketing where sewage effluents were used for irrigation. As a result of such findings, the health standards of this country do not permit the irrigation of truck crops with raw sewage. An example of the regulations governing the use of sewage for irrigation by the California State Board of Public Health (Sections 7897-7901 of the California Administrative Code, Title 17) will be of some interest here. A part of these regulations reads as follows:

Effluents of septic tanks, Imhoff tanks, or of other settling tanks, or partially disinfected effluent of sprinkling filters, or activated sludge plants or similar sewages, shall not be used to water any growing vegetables, garden truck, berries, or low-growing fruits, such that the fruit is in contact with the ground, or to water vineyards or orchard crops during seasons in which the windfalls or fruit lie on the ground. Nursery stock, cotton, and such field crops as hay, grain, rice, alfalfa, sugar beets, fodder corn, cow beets, and fodder carrots may be watered with such settled or undisinfected or partially disinfected sewage effluents, provided that no milch cows are pastured on the land while it is moist with sewage.

The foregoing restrictions do not apply against the use of well oxidized, non-putrescible, and reliably disinfected or filtered effluents which always meet the following bacterial standard: in any twenty consecutive samples from which five 10-ml portions each are examined, not over 10 portions shall be positive for members of the coliform group and in no single sample shall over one-half the 0.1-ml portions of the same sample be positive for coliform.

Treated sewage effluent is considered to be safe for use on cotton, sugar beets, flax, nursery stock, or vegetables grown for seed production; for animal feed and pasture crops; for woodlands; and for a variety of other crops where sewage irrigation will not affect the public health. There are also some decided advantages associated with the use of sewage effluent. In arid or semiarid lands, the fresh-water supply may be signifiicantly supplemented, sewage effluent has a fertilizer value, and stream pollution may be controlled or eliminated through a well-devised irrigation program.

Application of sewage effluent to farmlands is usually accomplished through the use of one of the following methods: flooding, spraying or sprinkling, ridge and furrow, or subsurface irrigation. Some agricultural uses of sewage effluent are described in Table 14-2.

In semiarid and arid regions water is often difficult to obtain and in very dry years a sizable supplementary water supply can often be derived from waste flows. One of the difficulties is that the large centers of population and therefore collection points for municipal and industrial wastes are often located at considerable distances from farmlands. Under these circumstances transportation costs might make it uneconomical to use the water for agricultural purposes. On the other hand, where isolated com-

TABLE 14-2

SOME EXAMPLES OF THE USE OF SEWAGE EFFLUENT FOR
AGRICULTURAL PURPOSES

Location	Use
Tucson, Ariz.	Cotton, grain, and pastures
Bakersfield, Calif.	Alfalfa, cattle, cotton, and grasses
Pomona, Calif.	Alfalfa, cattle, citrus, grain, and grasses
San Francisco, Calif.	Pastures and park lawns
Abilene, Tex.	Cattle, grain, grasses, and maize
Lubbock, Tex.	Barley, cotton, sorghum, and wheat
Ephrata, Wash.	Corn and hay

munities are situated near good farmlands, the practice might prove to be
highly economical. Table 14-3 compares the cost of reclaimed water with
alternate waters for agricultural purposes in several areas.

TABLE 14-3*,§§

COST COMPARISON OF REUSED WATER VS.
ALTERNATE WATER IN AGRICULTURE[†]

Location	Type of Use	Quantity Used, acre-ft	Cost of Reused Water acre-ft	Cost of Alternate Water acre-ft	Note
Pomona, Calif.	Irrigation	2,200	$6 to $7.50	$20	(†)
San Bernardino, Calif.	Irrigation	5,000	0.31	10	(§)
San Francisco, Calif.	Park, lakes	700	23	70	
Taft, Calif.	Irrigation	250	6		(‖)
Talbert, Calif.	Irrigation	2,800	6		(#)
Abilene, Tex.	Irrigation	5,500	No cost	80	(**)
Kingsville, Tex.	Irrigation	1,100	No cost	65	(**), (††)
San Antonio, Tex.	Irrigation	2,600	No cost	22	(**,‡‡)

*From Table 8, Cost Data for Reclaimed Water Use, Publication No. 12, "A Survey of Direct
Utilization of Waste Waters," State Water Pollution Board, Sacramento, Calif.
  †1955 Cost data. Costs are shown as dollars per acre foot.
  ‡Effluent is sold to two water users.
  §Effluent is sold to a water company.
  ‖No alternate water available.
  #Alternate water unsatisfactory.
  **Cost shown is municipal water cost.
  ††Effluent free in return for furnishing plant site.
  ‡‡Effluent free in return for granting city easement on 700 acres.
  §§Reprinted from E. F. Gloyna, J. B. Wolff, J. C. Geyer, and Abel Wolman, "A Report Upon
Present and Prospective Means for Improved Re-Use of Water."[3]

14-11. RECREATIONAL USES

A striking demonstration of the reuse of waste waters for recreational purposes is the project at Santee, California.[5,18,23]

The Santee County Water District in San Diego County, California, has undertaken a reclamation project which has provided for the development of a series of artificial lakes fed by the effluent of a standard activated-sludge sewage-treatment plant. The effluent from this plant is held in a 16-acre lagoon for 30 days (Lake 1). It is then chlorinated and spread onto a percolation area of sand and gravel through which it travels for about ½ mile. The percolated water is collected in an interceptor trench and then flows into Lake 4 (11 acres), then into Lake 3 (7.5 acres), and ultimately to Lake 2 (6.8 acres) after which the overflow passes on to Sycamore Canyon Creek. Lakes 3 and 4 are used for fishing and boating. Playgrounds and picnic areas line the shores. In 1965, Lake 5 is to be opened and will be approved for swimming by the California Department of Public Health. This approval follows three years of study by an Epidemiology Advisory Committee of the California Department of Public Health. The state health director indicated that biological, hydrological, bacteriological, and virological information supported approval by the committee.[23] This community recreational area is provided through the utilization of waste waters and permits an aquatic environment in an area which affords little attraction of this type. The public acceptance of these facilities has been exceptional. Considering the important emphasis being placed on the recreational use of our water resources, there is little doubt but that expanded development of facilities of this type will be forthcoming in the very near future.

Reclaimed waste waters are also being used successfully for the irrigation of golf courses in many areas of the southwest.[19] Some locations where this is being practiced are the El Toro Marine Air Base near Santa Ana, California; Camp Pendleton Marine Base near San Diego; the Naval Ordnance Test Station near China Lake in California; Eagle Pass, Texas; Prescott, Arizona; Santa Fe, New Mexico; and Los Alamos, New Mexico.

14-12. LEGAL CONSIDERATIONS

Some legal questions arise concerning the utilization of waste waters for specific purposes. For example, how can legal rights to reclaim waste water be obtained? Which agencies shall be permitted to conduct reclamation operations? Where will the liability rest for damages which may result from reuse practices?[15,24]

Water rights may be either riparian or appropriative. In either case the user may reclaim waste waters for reuse. The riparian user must ultimately return the flow to the stream from which it was derived however. No such restriction is placed on the appropriation user.

Reclaimed waters may contain harmful chemicals or pathogenic organisms if not properly treated. Therefore, any injury resulting from the use of such waters may become the liability of the waste-water supplier. Contracts stipulating that the purchaser of the reclaimed water does so at his own risk might eliminate this liability.

THE USE OF WASTE WATERS TO RECHARGE GROUNDWATER STORAGE

The replenishment of groundwater supplies through artificial recharge has been given considerable attention in recent years. Impetus to this movement has been derived through a realization that in many areas of this country groundwater levels have been rapidly falling and are not being recovered through natural means. Waters which are suitable for artificial recharge may be classified generally as flood waters, industrial wastes, and municipal sewage. Such wastes may be introduced into the ground by surface spreading or by pumping underground.

There are many advantages to be gained by groundwater recharge. Some of these are:[25]

1. Supplementation of natural recharge where man's activities have reduced or eliminated this opportunity.

2. Reduction of aquifer overdrafts.

3. Provision for concurrent development of surface and groundwater supplies.

4. Control of saline water intrusion.

5. Salt-balance control.

6. Control of or aid in combating land-subsidence problems.

14-13. THE NEED FOR RECHARGE

A considerable number of municipalities, industries and agricultural users rely heavily on groundwater supplies to satisfy their needs. Unfortunately, overdrafts on these supplies have been imposed for many years in numerous locations. As a result of this, water tables have dropped to critical levels in some regions and the continued use of many of these groundwater supplies is becoming uneconomical.

The mounting evidence that many aquifers are being mined has led to the conclusion that control of our groundwater resources is vital. Recharge operations are one means of rectifying many aspects of the groundwater problem. Many communities and industries in recognition of this are undertaking projects to recharge groundwater supplies. In addition, states such as Arkansas, California, Illinois, New Mexico, New York, Texas, Utah, Washington, and Wisconsin have become involved in regional projects. In 1957, a total of 42 recharge projects designed specifically for municipal, industrial, irrigational and regional supplies were under way.[26] As ground water quantity and quality problems become more pressing, it is certain that large-scale recharge operations will become more common.

14-14. RECHARGE WITH SEWAGE EFFLUENT

Waste flows from sewage-treatment plants constitute a potentially valuable and significant source of supply for groundwater recharge. Millions of gallons of municipal sewage effluent are being wasted daily and could easily be used to replenish overdrawn aquifers. Indirect recharge with sewage effluent is actually being accomplished where septic tanks are used or sewage farming is the practice.

Early studies (1930) in Los Angeles indicated that a well-treated sewage could be used for. groundwater recharge by spreading. The operation was considered to be completely safe. In 1949 studies indicated that groundwater recharge with treated sewage or industrial wastes was practical and economical.[27] Spreading basins of an experimental nature were set up by the Los Angeles County Flood Control District at Azusa and Whittier. In both cases the sewage received secondary treatment before spreading. No significant bacterial contamination below a depth of 7 to 10 ft was reported. There was no significant contamination of the groundwater. In addition, it was proven that a substantial organic mat was formed at the soil surface. This mat exhibited an increasing ability to remove bacteria from the effluent being filtered, thereby significantly reducing the number of bacteria passing into the soils.

In 1955 the University of California completed a three-year project whose objective was the determination of the practicality and public-health aspects of injecting treated sewage effluent into aquifers directly.[3] The sewage was injected into a 5-ft-thick confined aquifer through a recharge well. Findings were that bacterial pollutants moved a maximum of 100 ft in the direction of normal groundwater movement. Additional findings of the study were that the injection was one-half that of the safe yield. Periodic chlorine injection and redevelopment of the well were found to be a requirement in order to assure continued operation. The important conclusion of the study was that groundwater recharge by direct injection was safe and hydraulically feasible.

Experience at the Hyperion Sewage Treatment Plant in Los Angeles and in the other areas indicates that an economical solution to the problem of groundwater replenishment can be obtained by the surface spreading of sewage effluents. One advantage of this procedure is that less treatment is required than if the effluent is injected or directly discharged to a receiving body of water. Actually, the spreading basin functions as an additional treatment operation in which oxidation is provided for sewage stabilization.

An outstanding example of the potential of water reclamation and groundwater recharge using sewage effluent is the Whittier Narrows water-reclamation project in Los Angeles County, California.[4] The objective of this project is to conserve and assist in restoring the water resources of the agricultural area of Southern California. Since the initiation of plant operation in 1962 the project has reclaimed about 12,000 acre-ft of sewage annually. The treated sewage is distributed over spreading grounds in the San Gabriel and Rio Hondo River Basins. Once spread, the reclaimed waters percolate through the ground to the groundwater table and are then pumped for use in the irrigation of agricultural lands.

The plant itself has an initial design capacity of 10 mgpd. It is basically an activated-sludge plant and is superimposed on the existing sewerage system. The trunk sewer providing the inflows to the reclamation plant carries about 50 mgpd of waste water which is primarily derived from domestic sources. This large supply source makes possible uniform operation of the plant and also permits variation to meet mechanical and biological treatment requirements. There are no solids processing units in the plant. All solids are returned to the main trunk sewer after separation from the feed. This precludes the considerable expense of processing and disposing of the solid wastes at the reclamation plant site. Operation of the Whittier Narrows plant is being closely watched by various agencies interested in public health, education, pollution control, and industry.

Sewage effluent contains higher concentrations of suspended matter and bacteria than fresh water and thus its spreading rates are lower. For sewage farms, typical rates are about 0.01 to 0.09 ft/day. For final sewage effluents results have indicated a range in rates of from about 0.2 to 1.2 ft/day for various field and lysimeter tests.[7] In general, it is recommended that alternate wetting and drying periods of from 7 to 14 days be used.

Groundwater recharge by spreading is highly practical where sufficient low cost land is available. Where land is expensive, injection is the preferable practice. Unless highly treated effluents are used, however, injection wells will frequently clog and operating and maintenance costs will be high (see Sec. 4-32).

As in the case of reusing waste flows directly, the buildup of chlorides and other salts through continual recycling must be considered in recharge operations. Very little information is currently available on the effects of recycling waste flows to the ground. To provide the needed information, water-quality studies of aquifers will have to be conducted over long periods of time. A great deal of additional information on chemical and bacterial pollution of groundwaters is also needed. Some important work in this area has been done by Butler, Orlob, and McGauhey.[28] Considerable future research and evaluation of field results is a prerequisite to the maximum development of groundwater recharge as a method of waste-water reuse.

14-15. COSTS OF GROUNDWATER RECHARGE

As might be expected, costs for artificial recharge projects are highly variable. Richter and Chun have indicated a number of factors which affect cost.[2] These are:

1. Purpose of recharge
2. Manner in which effluent is spread
3. Quality, quantity, and flow regimen of the water
4. Surface and subsurface soil and geologic conditions
5. Location of the project site
6. Regulations and standards of controlling agencies

From a study of all of these items it can be easily understood that little significance can be attached to the comparison of individual project costs. In the long run, the important consideration is whether or not the cost of the water supply developed through recharge is less than the cost of an alternate source or whether the benefits resulting from the recharge operation exceed the cost of the project.

A limited study of the costs of groundwater recharge compared with the cost of an alternate source (Colorado River) for the Southern California area indicated that the cost of recharge per acre-foot might vary from $2 to $30 depending on whether a surface water or a treated sewage was used for recharge and whether spreading or injection was the procedure. The cost of the alternate water[3] was estimated to be $40 to $42 per acre-ft.

The results of current research and development should produce marked improvements in methodology and equipment which will ease the economic burden of water reclamation and facilitate its adoption for various purposes. Reclaimed water can be used for cooling, boiler feed, plant processes, fire-protection standby, irrigation, leaching of alkali soils, recreational purposes, and groundwater recharge. As experimentation continues, the number of uses is sure to increase. The degree of treatment required for many of our wastes is continually being expanded and with this trend the terms *water reclamation* and *sewage treatment* are becoming closely allied. There is no doubt that waste-water reuse practices will someday be adopted on a large scale.

REFERENCES

1. David K. Todd, "Ground Water Has to be Replenished," *Chem. Eng. Progr.*, vol. 59, no. 11 (November 1963).

2. R. C. Richter and R. Y. O. Chun, "Artificial Recharge of Ground Water Reservoirs in California," *Proc. Am. Soc. Civil Engrs., J. Irrigation Drainage Div.*, vol. 85, no. IR 4 (December 1959).

3. E. F. Gloyna, J. B. Wolff, J. C. Geyer, and Abel Wolman, "A Report Upon Present and Prospective Means for Improved Reuse of Water," The Johns

Hopkins University, Dept. of Sanitary Engineering, Baltimore, Md., January 1960.

4. J. D. Parkhurst, "Progress in Waste Water Re-Use in Southern California," Paper presented at American Society of Civil Engineers Environmental Engineering Conference, Salt Lake City, Utah, May 1964.

5. A. M. Caldwell, "Stretching the Life of a Natural Resource," *Navy Civil Engr.* (March 1964).

6. J. M. McKee, "We Need Researchers," *Eng. News-Record* (October 1962).

7. David K. Todd, *Ground Water Hydrology* (New York: John Wiley and Sons, Inc., 1959).

8. "Protecting Our Water Resources—The Federal Water Pollution Control Program," *U.S. Dept. of Health, Education and Welfare* (Washington, D.C.: U.S. Government Printing Office, 1962).

9. Murray Stein, "Legal Aspects Stimulate Pollution Control Program," *Civil Eng.* (July 1962).

10. D. F. Metzler et al., "Emergency Use of Reclaimed Water for Potable Supply at Chanute, Kansas," *J. Am. Water Works Assoc.* (August 1958).

11. T. R. Glenn, "Water Pollution Control Based on Facts," *Public Works* (October 1961).

12. E. B. Ransom, "Progress and Cost Data in Ohio's Program for Water Pollution Control," *Public Works* (November 1958).

13. "First Annual Water Resources Program," Delaware River Basin Commission, Trenton, N.J., October 1963.

14. "Report on Individual Household Aerobic Sewage Treated Systems," National Research Council Publication No. 586 (February 1958).

15. H. J. Ongerth and J. A. Harmon, "Sanitary Engineering Appraisal of Waste Water Re-Use," *J. Am. Water Works Assoc.* (May 1959).

16. B. B. Berger, "Public Health Aspects of Water Re-Use for Potable Supply," *J. Am. Water Works Assoc.* (May 1960).

17. G. E. McCallum, "Advanced Waste Treatment and Water Re-Use," *J. Water Pollution Control Federation* (January 1963).

18. F. M. Middleton, "Advanced Treatment of Wastewaters for Re-Use," *Water Sewage Works* (September 1964).

19. R. C. Merz, "Wastewater Reclamation for Golf Course Irrigation," *J. Sanit. Eng. Div., Am. Soc. Civil Engrs.,* no. SA6 (Nov. 1959).

20. R. J. Keating and V. J. Calise, "Treatment of Sewage Plant Effluent for Industrial Re-Use," *Sewage Ind. Wastes* (July 1955).

21. C. H. Scherer, "Wastewater Transformation at Amarillo," *Sewage Ind. Wastes* (September 1959).

22. N. T. Veatch, "Industrial Uses of Reclaimed Sewage Effluents," *Sewage Works J.,* vol. 20 (January 1948).

23. Water Pollution Control Federation Highlights, vol. 1, no. 10 (October 1964).

24. Adolphus Moskovitz, "Some Legal Aspects of Wastewater Reclamation," *Proc. Conf. on Water Reclamation,* University of California, Berkeley, Calif., March 1956.

25. R. C. Richter and Y. D. Chun, "Artificial Recharge of Ground Water Reservoirs in California," *J. Irrigation Drainage Div., Am. Soc. Civil Engrs.,* no. IR 4 (December 1959).

26. Task Group Report, "Developments in Artificial Ground Water Recharge," *J. Am. Water Works Assoc.* (July 1958).

27. "Studies in Water Reclamation," Sanitary Engineering Research Laboratory, University of California, Berkeley, Calif., Tech. Bull. 13, July 1955.

28. R. G. Butler, G. T. Orlob, and P. H. McGauhey, "Underground Movement of Bacterial and Chemical Pollutants," *J. Am. Water Works Assoc.,* vol. 46 (1954).

29. W. Viessman, Jr., "Developments in Waste Water Reuse," *Public Works,* vol. 96, no. 4 (April 1965).

PROBLEMS

14-1. Make a list of some of the exotic materials which may have a pronounced effect on the quality of surface or groundwaters.

14-2. For the area in which you live, cite some examples of the indirect reuse of waste waters. For what purposes are these waters reused?

14-3. Comment on some water-pollution problems in your locality. How might these be corrected?

14-4. By consulting the literature, discuss at least one case history of direct waste-water reuse. Indicate the quantity of water involved, treatment required, type of use, and cost of developing the waste flow.

14-5. Write a brief discussion related to the application of the various advanced waste-treatment techniques presented in Sec. 14-7.

14-6. For the area in which you reside, obtain information on the character and quantity of waste flows. Make a study of the feasibility of directly reusing these waters for any purpose or purposes. Estimate the type of treatment required and indicate whether the reuse of the waste flows would be economic.

14-7. By consulting the literature, write a paper on some current ground-water recharge project which utilizes waste flows.

chapter 15

Water-Resources Engineering

Water-resources engineering is an extremely broad field which encompasses numerous disciplines such as planning, economics, sociology, government, and law, in addition to the purely engineering aspects. Because of this, it is impossible in a single chapter to deal with more than a few of the many and varied problems that the water-resources engineer is likely to encounter. It is the intent of this chapter to acquaint the student briefly with a variety of topics with the hope that this will stimulate him to further work in this important and fascinating field.

COMPREHENSIVE PLANNING FOR WATER-RESOURCES PROJECTS

The first and often most critical phase of any water-resources project is that of planning the project for optimum economy and efficiency.

15-1. COMPREHENSIVE PLANNING AND PROGRAMMING

Planning may be defined as an attempt to foresee future requirements and to arrange for the provision of these requirements in an economical manner. Programming, as used here, means the scheduling of actions to be taken to accomplish certain prescribed objectives. Comprehensive planning as related to water-resources problems means all-inclusive planning. For example, the planning might be for all anticipated uses of water in a river basin or region and as such it is concerned with water, land, social patterns, political structure, and economic objectives.[1] It involves a consideration of both present and future water requirements.

Comprehensive planning must include the following: (1) a study of all possible sources of water, (2) a determination of the needs for the water and the uses to which it is to be put, (3) an evaluation of the effects of the anticipated uses on the water quality, and (4) a study of the way in which the preceding elements interact with one another. In addition, the interests of various political subdivisions and institutions in the area must be considered. Legal and social patterns, economic resources, aesthetic preferences, and community values must also be carefully integrated into the planning function.

Comprehensive programs must be designed to cover entire river basins or regions, they must be capable of caring for present and future needs, and they must encompass numerous concepts, processes, facilities, and organizational arrangements if realistic objectives are to be met.

15-2. OBJECTIVES OF RIVER-BASIN DEVELOPMENT PROJECTS

Only a small proportion of the total volume of the world's river systems is presently being harnessed and used for human welfare. In general, no stream has been fully regulated or used to its maximum potential. An exception to this might be a few minor drainage basins in arid regions. The degree to which the physical limit of regulation is approached is a function of technological, political, economic, sociological, and ethical factors.

By making application of the concept of comprehensive river-basin development, each major drainage system may be looked upon as the potential foundation for an integrated system of multipurpose projects which will promote regional growth.

An objective shared by most water-development projects is to meet expected requirements for water by varying the quantity, and quality of delivered supplies and by modifying the time and place of use of these supplies as conditions permit.[2] Normally, available supplies are allocated among potential uses on the basis of value, but this approach may be affected to a considerable extent by legal, political, or other considerations. In formulating the project, all possible uses of water should be studied, otherwise a truly comprehensive development plan will not be produced. For example, municipal, industrial, and agricultural supply, hydroelectric power, flood control, navigation, pollution control, recreation, and esthetic considerations may all be motivating factors in the development of river-basin projects.

In order to select the optimum combination of alternative, competitive, and complementary water uses while capitalizing on the economy and resource allocations permitted by multipurpose project development, a coordinated exercising of engineering, economic, ecological, and social principles is a requirement. An efficient balance of purposes should be determined on the basis of the nature and extent of the resources available, relative requirements for various uses, legal restrictions, local and regional policies, and public interest.[2]

15-3. PRINCIPAL STEPS IN RIVER-BASIN PLANNING

In general, river-basin planning can be divided into three basic steps. (1) the determination of current and future needs, (2) the appraisal of all possible means to meet these needs, and (3) the selection of the most economic approaches for satisfying the anticipated requirements. While straightforward in concept, the planning process may be exceedingly complex in practice. Numerous detailed investigations and studies are usually required. Examples of the most important of these are as follows.[1]

1. Population, economic land use, and other associated planning studies which are essential for the prediction of the water quality and quantity requirements for the various anticipated uses for the duration of the planning period chosen.

2. Hydrologic investigations to provide estimates of the quantities of fresh surface and groundwaters entering the basin and of the temporal distribution of these supplies. It is often the case that sufficient data on the meteorologic and hydrologic characteristics of the basin are not available. Additional field measurements and statistical analyses must frequently be relied upon, therefore, to yield the required information.

3. Comprehensive field investigations to evaluate the physical, chemical, radiological, and biological characteristics of the surface waters of the basin. The information determined will indicate: (a) the degree of treatment the water will have to be subjected to for various purposes, (b) the ability of the watercourse to assimilate waste discharges while continuing to sustain fish and wild life, and (c) the recreational and aesthetic values of the waters.

4. Studies of the storage capacities and uses of existing and proposed reservoirs in the basin. In some cases it will also be necessary to make detailed studies of the topography and geology of the basin with the object of determining additional reservoir sites of a satisfactory nature. Storage estimates for these potential storage locations would also be required.

5. Investigations to determine the location and extent of groundwater storage, aquifer characteristics, and the quality of the underground water supplies.

6. Studies to provide information on existing and anticipated sources of wastes which will be introduced into surface or groundwater bodies. A knowledge of the characteristics and volumes of these wastes will be necessary. Information on the optimum treatment that these wastes could be economically expected to undergo will also be required.

7. Estimates of water requirements to be used to augment low flows for quality and quantity control of surface water bodies. Low-flow augmentation can play an important role in fish and wildlife preservation and in combating pollution.

8. Evaluation of benefits which will result from the proposed water resources program. In arriving at conclusions regarding these benefits, it is important that the optimum economic or socially desirable development of the basinwide water resources be based on studies of all practical combinations and alternatives of objectives.

In making plans for the future development and allocation of water resources it should be emphasized that economic, social, and technological advances have an impact on water demand. An attempt should therefore be made to include these effects, insofar as possible, in any rational planning for future water needs. To counteract the effects of unforeseen modifying factors on water requirements or type of allocation, maximum flexibility should be built into the project plan. Programming events for stage construction is one way of providing the desired flexibility.

15-4. COORDINATION BETWEEN ECONOMIC AND TECHNOLOGIC CONCEPTS

Water-resource systems designs must be based on a coordination of economic and technologic considerations if they are to be practical and efficient. The engineer must be able to indicate feasible solutions to the proposed problem and determine the cost of these solutions. The economist, on the other hand, must establish the value of the project and decide whether or not it is worth doing.

With the exception of a few very small local water-resource projects, numerous alternative solutions are usually feasible. The choice of the solution to be used should be based firmly on economic principles.

By utilizing the high-speed computer and improved analytical approaches it is now possible to evaluate the relative costs and benefits of a whole spectrum of alternatives.[7] The optimum solution can then be obtained in a semiautomatic manner although the computer is powerless to compare any but those systems presented to it by the engineer. The role of the engineer is to formulate a number of feasible systems and to provide the criteria which will serve as a basis for making selections. Mathematical techniques are employed which permit an optimization analysis of the proposed engineering systems. In general, these techniques are employed to evaluate the maximum or minimum of a particular function which is subjected to certain restrictions or constraints. An elementary problem will serve to better illustrate this point. For a more comprehensive treatment of this subject the reader is referred to Ref. 7 and 8.

EXAMPLE 15-1. Consider that a small community is to be supplied with water from a nearby stream and pumping station. It will be assumed that the cost of supplying water is given by the general equation,

$$C = A + BQ + DQ^2$$

where C = cost, dollars per day
$\quad Q$ = rate of delivery, mgpd
A, B, D = constants

The fixed costs which are not dependent on flow rate are represented by A. These costs are primarily amortization and maintenance. Pumping costs and other costs dependent on flow rate are represented by BQ. The term DQ^2 is introduced to account for pumping costs associated with frictional resistance in the line. The equation represents a reasonable approximation of costs for the particular system being studied. For the case at hand it will be considered that the cost equation is

$$C = 28 + 12Q + Q^2$$

Obviously this equation is valid only for $Q \geq 0$ in a real sense even though the mathematical function is defined for both positive and negative values of Q. Next, consider that the maximum practical capacity of the pumping station is 6 mgpd and that the minimum flow permissible for community needs is 1 mgpd. The following statements may then be written:

$$Q \geq 0 \qquad Q \leq 6 \qquad Q \geq 1$$

These are called *constraints* on the variable Q. Thus the cost of operation will be restricted to the region of the function defined by the various constraints. The problem is to find the minimum cost of operation.

The solution to this problem may be obtained in a relatively simple manner as indicated on Fig. 15-1. It should be noted that the minimum value of the function obtained by differentiation is not a valid solution because it does not fall within the feasible region defined by the constraints.

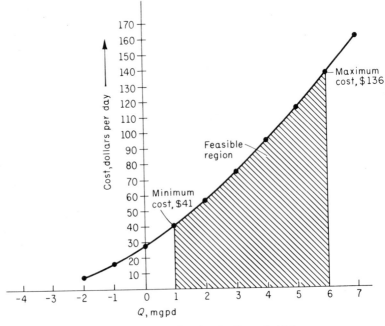

FIG. 15-1. Cost function for Example 15-1.

Another solution to this problem may be had by using the method of Lagrange multipliers.[7] This approach is more tedious for the simple problem at hand but in more complex problems involving numerous independent variables it will yield the required solutions.

The method of Lagrange multipliers can be used to maximize or minimize a given function of n variables.[7]

$$f(x_1, x_2, \ldots, x_n) \tag{15-1}$$

which is subject to k constraints of equality

$$q_j(x_1, x_2, \ldots, x_n) = a_j \qquad (j = 1, 2, \ldots, k) \tag{15-2}$$

Application of the procedure requires the formation of a function of $n + k$ variables

$$F(x_1, x_2, \ldots, x_n, \lambda_1, \lambda_2, \ldots, \lambda_k) = f(x_1, x_2, \ldots, x_n)$$
$$- \sum_{j=1}^{k} \lambda_j [q_j(x_1, \ldots, x_n) - a_j] \tag{15-3}$$

and then setting the partial derivatives of F with respect to the $n + k$ arguments equal to zero. As a result, $n + k$ equations are obtained. Solution of these equations for the variables $x_1, x_2, \ldots, x_n, \lambda_1, \lambda_2, \ldots, \lambda_k$ will yield values of $x_1, x_2, \ldots, x_n$ which produce the maximum and minimum values of f. The procedure will be illustrated by applying it to the problem at hand.

First, since we are dealing with inequalities as constraints we must transform these to equalities by the introduction of a set of new variables s. These will be called *slack variables* and they represent the difference between the actual value of Q and the imposed limitations on Q. In this problem they can be represented as follows (for $Q \geqq 0$, the difference between Q and 0 will be called s_1^2):

$$s_1^2 = Q$$

In like manner, for the other two inequalities, we can write

$$s_2^2 = 6 - Q \qquad \text{and} \qquad s_3^2 = Q - 1$$

The use of squared terms for the slack variables assures us that the inequalities are satisfied. Next, the equalities are substituted in Eq. 15-3 with the resulting expression

$$F(Q, s_1, s_2, s_3, \lambda_1, \lambda_2, \lambda_3) = 28 + 12Q + Q^2$$
$$- \lambda_1(Q - s_1^2) - \lambda_2(6 - Q - s_2^2) - \lambda_3(Q - 1 - s_3^2)$$

The partial derivatives of this equation are then taken with respect to Q, $s_1, s_2, s_3, \lambda_1, \lambda_2,$ and λ_3 and set equal to zero. Seven equations in seven unknowns result:

(1) $\qquad 12 + 2Q - \lambda_1 + \lambda_2 - \lambda_3 = 0$
(2) $\qquad\qquad\qquad\qquad\quad 2s_1\lambda_1 = 0$
(3) $\qquad\qquad\qquad\qquad\quad 2s_2\lambda_2 = 0$

(4) $$2s_3\lambda_3 = 0$$
(5) $$s_1^2 - Q = 0$$
(6) $$s_2^2 - 6 + Q = 0$$
(7) $$s_3^2 - Q + 1 = 0$$

Two solutions will be obtained for these equations. One will yield the maximum, the other the minimum.

From Eq. (2), either $s_1 = 0$ or $\lambda_1 = 0$. Let $s_1 = 0$. Then from Eq. (5),

$$Q = 0$$

Equation (7) then yields

$$s_3^2 = -1$$

which is impossible. Therefore,

$$s_1 \neq 0 \qquad \text{and} \qquad \lambda_1 = 0$$

Now either $s_2 = 0$ or $\lambda_2 = 0$. If $s_2 = 0$, Eq. (6) yields

$$Q = 6$$

and Eq. (5) yields

$$s_1^2 = 6$$

So far then,

$$\lambda_1 = 0 \qquad s_1^2 = 6 \qquad Q = 6 \qquad s_2 = 0$$

From Eq. (7),

$$s_3^2 = 5$$

Therefore,

$$\lambda_3 = 0$$

From Eq. (1),

$$12 + 12 - 0 + \lambda_2 - 0 = 0 \qquad \text{and} \qquad \lambda_2 = -24$$

These values and the second solution are shown in Table 15-1.

TABLE 15-1
SOLUTIONS OF THE SET OF SEVEN EQUATIONS

	Q	s_1^2	s_2^2	s_3^2	λ_1	λ_2	λ_3	Cost
Maximum cost solution	6	6	0	5	0	−24	0	136
Minimum cost solution	1	1	5	0	0	0	14	41

It will be noted that the minimum cost of $41 per day and the maximum cost of $136 per day agree with the values found in the graphical solution earlier. A more comprehensive treatment of the use of Lagrange multipliers can be found elsewhere.[7,8]

15-5. FORMULATION OF THE PROJECT

After the necessary data such as were indicated in Sec. 15-3 have been collected, the formulative stage of the project can get underway. The first undertaking should be the establishment of a set of alternative objectives. In doing this every attempt should be made to include all possible uses and combinations of uses which are considered to be feasible. Competition for water supplies should not be overlooked nor should possibilities of converting from one type of water use to another.

In general, project formulation may be divided into three primary steps: (1) the delineation of boundary conditions which will impose certain limitations on the project, (2) the establishment of alternative land use plans for the region under consideration, and (3) the listing of all possible types of units such as dams, channels, etc. which might be employed at a specific site to accomplish a given objective.[3]

Imposed boundary conditions may have the effect of eliminating certain proposals from consideration and maximizing the practicality of others. For example, the geology and topography at a particular location may be of such a nature as to preclude the consideration of a damsite for that location. The constraints imposed in Example 15-1 also indicate the restrictive nature of boundary conditions. Some additional examples of possible restraints are as follows.

1. The physical limitations of the area may restrict the use of the regional water resources in numerous ways. The example just given is an illustration.

2. Some aspects of the overall water-resources problem may be confined to particular locations. For example, pollution-control works for a specific municipal area would be restricted to the general vicinity of the city.

3. The usable quantity of available water occurring naturally in a region may be limited due to hydrologic, geologic, or topographic conditions. The volume of water that can be diverted into the region from other areas may also be limited due to economic, technological, political, legal, and other considerations.

4. Existing land-use patterns affect the type and location of water requirements.

5. The number and size of good storage sites will be affected by the topographic and geologic features of the region. They may also be affected by political, economic, sociological, legal, and other factors.

In imposing any boundary condition, great care should be exercised to insure that the restraint actually exists, will exist in the future, or is realistic.

Since land-use patterns may affect both the allocation and quality of regional water resources, an attempt should be made to investigate several alternate patterns which are considered feasible for the area under study. Changing land use from agricultural to industrial might significantly alter water quality and quantity requirements for that area for example. The utilization of the land for parks, game preserves, etc. would have a decided effect on water-use patterns for those areas. It is important therefore that the various possibilities of land use that would likely have a serious impact on water use should be explored.

The listing of all possible types of units which could be used at a given site to accomplish a desired objective is a necessity if the most economic solution to a particular problem is to be had. The cost of each proposed unit should be estimated so that the costs of alternatives can be compared. The discussion of the selection of the most economical aqueduct in Sec. 5-6 illustrates this point.

15-6. ANALYSIS OF THE PROJECT

The objective of a water-resources system design is to select that combination of variables which will maximize the net benefits resulting from the system design in accordance with the imposed design criterion.[4,9] Areawide objectives and alternatives chosen by the population, their elected representatives, their consultants, or some combination of these will define the design criterion.

If a model system is used to simulate the various project designs for multiunit, multipurpose river-basin systems, two general techniques can be applied to effect the desired solution:

1. The system behavior is simulated on a high-speed digital computer. In this manner the response of the system to various combinations of project units, and degrees and purposes of development, can be forecast over long periods of time. The optimum combination of factors is then indicated by the computer.

2. The best solution for relatively simple problems can sometimes be obtained by the application of mathematical methods which will automatically proceed to this solution. The method of Lagrange multipliers illustrated in Sec. 15-4 is an example.

In general, a simplified river-basin system model should include the following properties:[4]

1. It should be comprehensive enough to represent proposed operating conditions but not so complex as to preclude easy experimentation.

2. Adequate information must be available on system costs and benefits so that a complete analysis of various combinations of project units and system inputs and outputs can be made.

3. All forms of water-resources inputs and outputs that exist or are contemplated should be included. Hydrologic inputs, imported water, diverted water, withdrawal uses, nonwithdrawal uses, and holding uses must all be considered.

4. Hydrologic inputs and outputs must conform to the local climatic and physical conditions.

5. The model must be amenable to analysis by available computational procedures. Normally the use of a digital computer will be required.

The complexity of the system analysis depends essentially on the complexity of the system.[3] For a single-purpose project unit which is not dependent economically or physically on any other project unit, the optimum solution can be obtained in a relatively simple and straightforward manner. In this case a plot of benefits minus costs can be used to indicate the degree of project development which will produce the largest net benefit. Figure 15-2 illustrates this point. For independent multiple purpose projects a net-benefit surface must be defined. If two uses are dominant, the response surface will be of the form indicated in Fig. 15-3.

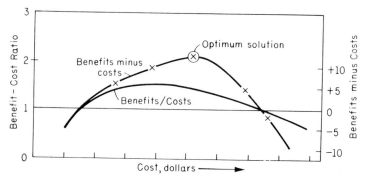

FIG. 15-2. Typical benefit-cost-ratio-vs.-cost curve.

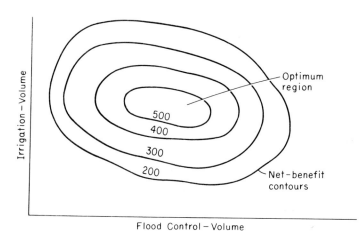

FIG. 15-3. A net-benefit-response surface for an independent multipurpose project.

For *n* important uses an $(n + 1)$-dimensional space is required. In many cases however, two uses will emerge as the most significant and the optimum solution can be approximated by a three-dimensional surface with other uses held at a constant level. For the multiple-unit system a complex response surface will result, and detailed operation studies for each proposed system must be conducted. A more comprehensive discussion of the techniques of analysis may be had elsewhere.[3,8,9]

15-7. MULTIPURPOSE PROJECTS

The Hoover Dam, constructed on the Colorado River, is an outstanding example of the use of a single project unit to impound water for multiple purposes. The dam is built of concrete and is of the gravity type. Its height is 726 ft. This structure intercepts the flow of the Colorado River in Black Canyon and provides ample storage and control so that the flow can be utilized downstream for four major purposes. The impounded waters are used for irrigation, residential supplies, and commercial and industrial needs in Southern California. Hydroelectric power is generated and sold in Arizona and California. Approximately 9,500,000 acre-ft of storage volume is reserved for flood-control purposes. In addition to the four primary objectives of irrigation, municipal water supply, hydroelectric power, and flood control, the dam was also designed to aid in maintaining flows in the downstream channel for navigational purposes.[5]

All multipurpose projects do not involve the storage of water, however. For example, the construction of cutoffs, deepened channels, or training works may be carried out to improve navigation conditions and at the same time provide a measure of flood control.

Essentially, any project can be classified as multipurpose if it is specifically designed to serve at least two different purposes. The primary purposes for which projects are constructed include irrigation, power, navigation, water supply, pollution control, recreation, flood control, and fish and wildlife conservation. Because it is so important that our water resources be utilized to their fullest extent, the consideration of multipurpose projects is mandatory. Many of the choice reservoir sites have already been put to use and thus economic justification of new storage works can often be had only when multiple uses are proposed.

In the design and operation of multipurpose projects it is important that the engineer realize that some form of compromise between uses is essential.[3,6,9] This is because different uses are not completely compatible with one another and are in a sense competing. For example, maintaining an available volume to impound flood waters for short periods during which they are slowly released does not satisfy the objective of obtaining the maximum storage of water. The operating rules for the project must thus be devised to permit relatively efficient operation for the various purposes while recognizing that maximum efficiency might not be obtained for even one purpose.

The requirements imposed by the major water uses must be carefully evaluated if an efficient multipurpose unit is to be designed. A brief summary of the nature of some of these uses follows, with the intent that it will indicate possibilities for coordinating them.

1. *Municipal Water Requirements.* As indicated in Chap. 3, municipal water requirements may be quite variable from region to region. For a specific location however, a representative average per capita use rate can be determined. From the point of view of development of supplies for municipal uses it is important to know something about the seasonal variation of these uses and of the seasonal and annual fluctuations in supply. In general, the maximum daily municipal use will be about 180 percent of the annual average, with summer averages higher and winter averages lower. In planning projects to furnish municipal water a curve of demand vs. time is important. In addition, storage must often be provided and maintained to carry the community through long periods of drought. The storage of water for drinking purposes may restrict the scope of recreational activities at the reservoir site. The storage and use of a specific volume of water for municipal purposes may also be in direct competition with the storage of water for other uses such as agriculture.

2. *Irrigation.* The water requirements for irrigation are in general seasonal. The quantities of water required for irrigation purposes vary with the climate of the region and the type of crops that are to be raised in that area. For purposes of estimation it is sometimes assumed that the growing season lasts for about three months during the summer and that the irrigation draft is uniform during that period. The growing period for all crops is not coincident, however, so that the overall irrigation season in any region is variable. In humid regions the water requirements for irrigation may not be uniform and may range from about 10 percent in May to 30 percent in September. For arid and semiarid regions the rate of withdrawal will be more nearly uniform. In general, as much reserve storage as possible should be provided to insure against critical shortages during protracted dry periods. Storage and use for irrigation needs may conflict with many other uses. For example, during the winter months irrigators want to store as much water as possible and minimize releases while power demands are often largest, with the result that maximum releases are desirable to generate power.

3. *Hydroelectric Power.* The requirements for hydroelectric power are usually seasonal, with the winter months often the critical period. Available hydroelectric capacity should be used on the system load so that the energy derived is employed in the most effective manner. This re-

quires that water be taken from storage during periods of peak demand and that storage be replenished during periods of light load. The principal causes of conflict between water use for power vs. other uses result from different seasonal requirements. For example, heavy summer releases for navigation on the Missouri River can conflict with needs for considerable hydropower generation during the winter months. In many cases power production is compatible with other uses. Water passed through the turbines during the summer months can also be used downstream to meet irrigation, navigational, flow-augmentation, or other needs.

4. *Navigation.* As in the case of many other water uses, navigational requirements are highly seasonal. The largest releases are generally required during the driest months of the year. Navigation requirements are usually competitive with irrigation demands, hydropower demands, and recreational needs at the reservoir site.

5. *Recreation.* Water requirements for recreational purposes are usually greatest in the summer months. The sportsman and vacationer desire to have the maximum storage during this period. This permits optimum conditions for fishing, boating and other water sports. Obviously, this condition is not compatible with many other summer water requirements.

6. *Flood Control.* The utilization of storage works for flood control requires that ample volume be available to impound flood waters and that means be available to release this volume as rapidly as possible to prepare for the next flood. Of all the potential uses, flood control is the least compatible.

ENGINEERING ASPECTS OF RIVER-BASIN DEVELOPMENT

River-basin development projects include a variety of aspects, the design of which requires the exercise of various types of engineering skills. In fact, almost all phases of engineering must be brought to bear on these problems. The spectrum of areas includes hydrology, hydraulics, meteorology, machinery, electricity, structures, soils, foundations, and materials.

The engineer must concern himself with the collection of data pertaining to the river basin under consideration. These data must describe the hydrology of the basin and the allocation of the water resources. They must also describe the physical, political, and sociological characteristics of the area and the type and degree of development of the region. Using these data and a knowledge of the anticipated needs of the basin, the engineer must then plan, design, construct, and operate river-project units for the betterment of society.[6]

15-8. NATURAL CONTROL OF RIVERS

Before undertaking the design of river-control works the engineer must recognize that the river basin in reality acts as a controlling mechanism on hydrologic events within the basin. For example, large, wide, gently sloping valleys will store large quantities of water during floods. In essence, then, these areas serve as natural flood-control works for downstream locations. With a little reflection the student should be able to think of numerous other natural controls. In general, drainage-basin shape, drainage density, storm patterns and tracks, and numerous physical features of the area are the primary elements of natural forms of control. The engineer should maximize the use of these features in the design and operation of artificial control works. In this way engineering control can be made to supplement natural control in the most efficient manner.

15-9. ENGINEERING CONTROL METHODS

Engineering control methods can be considered generally as falling into two categories: (1) man-made control structures and (2) specially devised operational procedures or land-use practices.[6] Typical of the first category are dams, levees, drainage works, water-transportation systems, and treatment works. The second classification of controls includes irrigation practices, soil-conservation methods, certain errosion-control techniques, and waste-disposal practices.

Among all the man-made control works, major dams are usually the most costly and impressive. As stated previously, these structures may be designed for any one or a combination of purposes. An impoundment which is filled to the spillway height will have only a minor effect on streamflow but will afford maximum head for power production and maximum potential for meeting irrigation needs. However, impounded waters can be put to use for irrigation, water supply, and other purposes only if the water is withdrawn. The maximum potential for flood control is realized only when the reservoir is empty. The operating rules for the reservoir formed by the dam thus play an important role in controlling a variety of complementary and conflicting demands.

Levees form an important part of major flood-control works. Their purpose is to confine the river flows at high stages so that adjacent lowlands will not be flooded. By imposing restrictions on the channel width, the levee system may actually create greater depths of flow which will benefit navigation. On the other hand, levees constructed in one river reach may adversely affect conditions upstream. For this reason, great care must be taken to evaluate the impact of these control works on the entire stream system.

Land-management practices such as contour plowing, strip cropping, and the use of special water-holding crops may produce significant benefits from the point of view of retaining water on the land and suppressing erosion. Some degree of flood control might be provided as well.

Engineering controls are required for the effective regulation of waters for a wide variety of purposes. A brief discussion of several of the most important areas requiring artificial or supplementary control will be found in the sections that follow.

15-10. MUNICIPAL WATER SUPPLIES

Because municipal water requirements are vital to life, business, and industry, careful regulation of both water quality and quantity for these purposes is essential. Detailed information on the regulation of these supplies by storage, treatment, transportation and distribution works, and system-operation techniques has already been presented in earlier chapters. The student should now be in a position to visualize and categorize all of these forms of engineering control.

15-11. STREAM POLLUTION

If our waters are to be effectively and economically used on a semi-continuous basis within a region, pollution-control techniques must play a primary role. Indirect reuse practices, fish and wildlife conservation, and recreation are all affected by the quality of our surface and ground-water supplies. Principal control methods include various forms of physical, chemical, and biological treatment and dilution. Major control works are composed of process units and storage works. Where large impoundments are constructed along watercourses, it is conceivable that during dry periods no flow would appear downstream of the dam. Thus any wastes entering the stream below the reservoir would be undiluted and could possibly destroy many desirable forms of aquatic and wild life. To preclude this type of circumstance it is often the policy to augment the downstream flows by releasing water from storage. In this way a minimum flow having an acceptable DO content can be maintained with the result that downstream pollution problems are alleviated. The low-flow operating policy of the reservoir then becomes a primary form of engineering control.

15-12. NAVIGATION

If rivers and streams are to be used for navigation it is essential that adequate depths in specified channel areas be established. Depth requirements can generally be met in two ways—either by dredging out the channel bottom or by raising the water level by the use of dams or flow releases. During periods of low flow many rivers are actually composed of a series of steps navigationwise and ships must travel through locks to pass from one slack-water pool to the next.

The control of navigation by a series of low dams generally has little effect on other water uses within the river basin. This is because the purpose of these structures is to maintain a river level close to the minimum required for navigation. Flood flows are not appreciably affected by this form of control, nor are flow rates of the river. Some important advantages may be derived from the maintenance of minimum depths however. For example, benefits to fish and wildlife, recreation, pollution control, and aesthetic enhancement may directly result.

In some cases the use of a number of small dams will create excessive time delays in the movement of barge tows and thus raise transportation costs. To combat this, current design practice is usually to build fewer navigation dams of greater height so that a smaller number of locks will be required.

The depth of water in a river reach can also be controlled by confining the channel between levees. This approach can produce flood-control benefits at the same time and also serve to provide more usable land along the water course.

Multipurpose reservoirs may have as part of their function the release of flows to maintain minimum navigational depths downstream. Storage volumes required for this purpose can be estimated by considering low-flow sequences, and the seasonal nature of the navigational requirements. In operating the reservoir to release the required flows it is necessary that the time required for the flow to reach an eventual location be determined. Adequate forecasts of downstream river stages are thus essential in scheduling releases to augment natural flows.

15-13. FLOOD CONTROL

Floods may be defined as abnormally high flows or flows in excess of some base value for a particular stream. In general, any flow which overlaps the normally confining channel can be classified as a flood.

The problems resulting from flood flows are generally associated with the attempt by man to occupy the flood plains of rivers and streams for various purposes. Although these regions may be dry for years at a time, they are in reality a part of the river or stream channel during periods of peak flows. Each year an economic toll is exacted from man by nature for occupancy of these areas. The magnitude of this charge is variable and may range from a simple delay in time to the loss of human life. In dollars, the average annual charge for the United States likely exceeds $95 million in property losses alone, and very few regions in this country are free of the flood hazard. The charge can be avoided or reduced by not using flood-plain areas, by the controlled use of these areas, or by the development of protective works.

Floods may affect a particular community in several ways. First, they may cause the loss of human life. Second, they may damage physical properties such as crops, soil, structures, utilities, household goods, and automobiles. Third, they may interrupt the production of goods and services. For example, industrial operations may be halted, transportation delayed, communications disrupted, and commercial transactions brought to a standstill. Finally, the inhabitants of the area may be forced to remove properties from the area for varying periods of time and then return them at the conclusion of the flood.

To alleviate the problems caused by flooding, various methods for controlling floods or minimizing their influence have been employed. Principal among these are dams, levees, channel improvements, diversion works or floodways, zoning laws, land-management practices, flood-proofing, and evacuation.

In order for flood-control benefits to accrue, floods must be prevented or minimized. To evaluate the potential benefits, it is necessary that the frequency of floods of various magnitudes be known and the damage that they would cause if uncontrolled be calculated. The benefits resulting from control measures can then be determined and compared with the cost of the proposed control works.

In evaluating the potential damages to an area from various floods it is common to first develop a flood-frequency curve for the area. From this information a stage-frequency curve can be derived. Then an estimate can be made of the area which would be flooded by each flood stage and the damages associated with this flooding computed. A stage-damage curve results. By combining the stage-frequency and stage damage curves, a damage-frequency curve can be produced.

Benefits are usually computed for an entire program on a river basin. The major flood-control benefit is the aversion of flood losses. Both direct and indirect losses must be considered. The evaluation of these losses is exceedingly complex, especially for the indirect losses. Costs of flood-control activities are based on project costs, which include total investment and operation and maintenance. Once the benefits and costs have been determined, a benefit-cost ratio can be calculated.[3,11]

A traditional form of engineering flood-control work has been the levee. It is essentially an earth dike which is constructed to hold the floodwaters back from a designated area. One problem associated with the use of levees is that of handling the drainage which develops behind them. In many cases, pumping plants are required at intervals to provide for this. Generally, a well-developed levee system extending along a river will produce the following hydraulic results: (1) for a specified flood, the river stage is raised; and (2) the flood volume at any time is increased because of the elimination of natural storage areas along the river. The degree of protection to any area afforded by the levee system depends on the extent of the system, height of the levees, and magnitude of the flood. Despite many disadvantages, levees often provide the most economical means of protecting local areas. They are especially applicable for the protection of individual cities.

Although major Federal flood-control projects have centered around levee construction, channel improvements have been applied extensively to improve the hydraulic capacity of the channel. These improvements include: (1) modifying channel cross sections by widening and deepening, (2) lining the channel, (3) straightening the channel, and (4) clearing vegetation and debris.

Auxiliary floodways or secondary channels which parallel the main river are often constructed to carry part of the main channel flow during major floods. These channels are usually closed off by gates or by fuseplug levees which are overtopped and wash out when a particular river stage is exceeded. Lands within these floodways can be used for agricultural purposes during most years, but crop losses must be expected whenever the floodway must be put to use.

Reservoirs can be used effectively to control floods where physical conditions permit. In general, two types of reservoirs are used for this purpose in the United States. Detention reservoirs are constructed which have the single objective of slowing up excess waters and sediment flows. Storage reservoirs serve to impound floodwaters and slowly release them downstream while at the same time serving other purposes. Reservoir storage effectively reduces flood peaks in the river reach immediately below the dam, but this effect diminishes rapidly with distance downstream. In addition, for a given amount of reservoir storage, the percentage reduction in peak flow is greater for rapidly rising and falling floods than for those of longer duration. On major rivers, reservoirs are generally used to supplement the control provided by other protective works such as levees. This can be illustrated by the fact that about 3,000 miles of levees are required along the lower Mississippi even though a total of 171 reservoirs with a combined capacity exceeding 180 million acre-ft is ultimately proposed for this system.

Various forms of "upstream engineering" can also be used to provide a certain degree of flood control. Such measures as reforestation, improvement of vegetal cover, the use of soil-conservation practices, construction of farm ponds, construction of erosion-control works, and improved farming practices all have utility.

15-14. POWER DEVELOPMENT

Whenever it is found to be economical, power is generated in hydroelectric plants. The engineering control of water for power-development purposes must therefore be carefully considered by the water-resources engineer.

There are three categories of hydroelectric plants—run-of-the-river, storage, or pumped-storage. Run-of-the-river plants are characterized by very limited storage capacities. They take water from the river essentially as it comes. Storage plants contain adequate reservoir capacity to impound wet-season flows for use during low-flow periods. They are able to develop a firm flow which is considerably greater than the minimum river flows. Pumped-storage plants are used to produce power during peak-load periods. Releases from the turbines are retained in a tailwater pool and pumped back to the headwater pool for reuse during periods of load.

Power available from a river is directly proportional to the quantity of water which passes through the turbines and the head available for operation of the turbines. When expressed as horsepower the following relation is obtained:

$$\text{hp} = \frac{Q \gamma h}{550} \tag{15-4}$$

where Q = discharge, cfs
  γ = specific weight of water, lb/cu ft
  h = head, ft

Adjustments must be made in values obtained by Eq. 15-4 to account for efficiency.

The student should understand that the prime feature of water control for power development is the production and maintenance of the maximum possible head at the power plant. Any flow releases from the reservoir will reduce the pool level and thereby affect the power potential. For example, if the water level is reduced by 50 percent, the power output of the plant will also be cut by 50 percent for the same rate of flow. Where the storage of water is intended to satisfy other uses besides power production, an optimum program of operation must be designed to provide for maximum efficiency of power production under the circumstances.

15-15. IRRIGATION

Surface waters used for irrigation may be diverted to canals which afford gravity flows to the irrigation project. Various means of controlling the rates of delivery are employed (gates, flumes, weirs, etc.). Where the irrigated lands lie above the river valley, pumping may be required.

In some cases, water requirements might be less than the safe yield of a neighboring stream and flows can be taken directly with no thought of storage. For large-scale irrigation projects, particularly in the arid or semiarid regions, storage reservoirs must be constructed to provide the necessary quantities of water at the right season. The primary engineering works are reservoirs, canals, ditches, pumping plants, and measuring stations.

15-16. LAND MANAGEMENT

Various forms of land-management practices can be effective in modifying the effects of the waters in a region. These practices tend to reduce flood damage by improving soil structure, increasing infiltration rates, and reducing erosion losses. The principal engineering works associated with these practices are erosion-control dams and terraces.

Erosion-control dams are built across streams to decrease the gradient of the stream and thus reduce its ability to erode the channel. They may vary widely in size, method of construction, and in number along a particular reach of stream. Considerable information on these structures is available from the Soil Conservation Service.

Terraces are constructed to break long erodible slopes into a series of short steps. Sheet erosion is reduced in this manner and the step areas can be put to use for various purposes such as the raising of crops. By retaining surface waters for longer periods of time, these relatively flat steps have a tendency to increase infiltration.

ECONOMIC ASPECTS OF WATER-RESOURCES PLANNING

As has been indicated previously, the design of water-resources systems requires the selection of some optimum combination of components. In general, the final selection should be based soundly on economic considerations.

In Chap. 5 the student was acquainted with the problem of designing a water-transportation system which could consist of various means of conveyance. The final design was based on the selection of the most economic combination of pumping units, pipelines, canals, tunnels, etc. This example serves to point out that a rational design must include a comprehensive study of the relative economics of a set of feasible engineering alternatives.

15-17. ENGINEERING ECONOMY

The ultimate objective of engineering design is to deal with the materials and physical forces of nature in such manner that human desires are satisfied. This involves consideration of both a method and a need. To illustrate this, consider the questions: (1) is there a need for a bridge at this location and (2) how shall the bridge be constructed? Obviously, questions of this type involve both engineering and economic decision-making.

Engineering economy has been defined by Thuesen and Fabrycky as "a body of knowledge, techniques, and practices of analysis and synthesis involving an attitude toward human factors useful in evaluating the worth of physical products and services in relation to their cost."[10] In general, it may be said that the definition conveys the concept of providing the optimum service per unit cost through the application of engineering practices.

The principal objective of engineering-economy studies is the quantitative evaluation of alternate engineering designs in terms of benefits and costs before construction is undertaken. These studies involve both the collection and mathematical analysis of all relevant data.

15-18. ECONOMIC DECISION-MAKING

All of us are faced with economic decision-making practically every day of our lives. Each dollar we consider spending or saving serves as the basis for this.

The decision to spend $80,000 for new pumping equipment is certainly an economic decision. Nonetheless, it cannot be considered competent unless: (1) all practical alternatives have been studied, (2) all cost and income-producing elements have been included, and (3) the principles and methods used in evaluation are valid.[11] For example, considering the case at hand, the correct decision might be to repair the old pumps for $30,000, to buy new equipment costing $100,000, to replace part of the existing equipment and keep the remainder, to spend the $80,000 as proposed, or to elect some other alternative.

Simply stated, economic decision-making is a process involving both the generation and evaluation of alternatives. The final objective is the selection of some alternative and thus there can be no real economic decision unless a group of alternatives has been proposed.

An engineering-economy study often includes the following requirements.[3] (1) All feasible engineering alternatives should be set forth. (2) These alternatives should be expressed in terms of money in such a manner that they are comparable. (3) One of the alternatives must be decided upon or recommended. The selection will be based on economic comparisons but may be influenced by other factors which cannot be expressed in money terms.

15-19. AN ECONOMIC MODEL FOR WATER USE

An economic model may be defined as a device relating the desires of the consumer to resources which can be used to satisfy these desires.[12] The model includes demand functions for goods, services, and productive resources, production functions for goods and services, and supply functions of resources. The market place provides a means of transformation for various resources into goods and services and permits the delivery of products to the consumer. Desires of the consumer are also transmitted through the system, and these in turn influence the outcome. All of these features constitute a part of the economic model for water use. The salient features of the model will be discussed in the following sections.

15-20. PRODUCT DEMAND FUNCTIONS

In the most elementary form, the demand function for goods and services may usually be represented graphically by a price-quantity relationship which slopes downward to the right. This is illustrated in Fig. 15-4. A study of the figure will indicate that, in general, the lower the cost the larger will be the quantity taken by the consumer. To qualify this statement, however, it should be understood that these consumers have specified incomes, tastes, and preferences and that other competing goods and services are available. Shifts in the demand function for any particular product may result from variations in any or all of these factors.

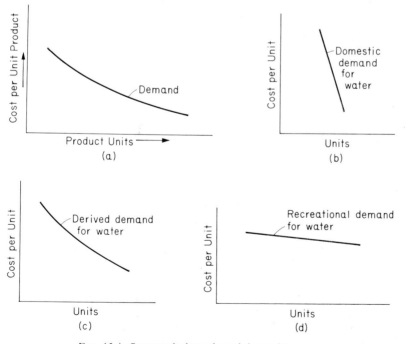

FIG. 15-4. Some typical supply-and-demand curves.

Water is in demand for many purposes as has already been discussed. Some of these are (1) domestic uses, (2) recreational uses, and (3) uses made of water in the production of other products. It is expected that consumers will be willing to pay a fairly high price for water rather than go without it. In addition, to meet basic domestic needs, the demand will be relatively constant regardless of price. In other words, we are going to use a certain amount of water for cooking, washing, and maintaining health standards even if water is expensive. At the same time, we are not going to use much more water than we really need no matter how cheap the water is. Thus the price-quantity relationship for domestic use is very steep and approaches the vertical (Fig. 15-4*b*). The demand for products derived from water may not be so steep, particularly if the products are luxury items or if the products can be substituted for (Fig. 15-4*c*). Evidence indicates that the price-quantity relationship for recreational water use may have a relatively flat slope.[12] This can be explained in part by the fact that if water recreation costs become too high, other forms of recreation will be substituted.

It is quite likely that the actual demand functions the engineer would encounter are more complex than the simple cases outlined here. This is because of variations in such factors as income, personal preferences, and the relationships of other products and their prices. In the more complex sense, the demand function for water is represented by an *n*-dimensional demand surface which takes into consideration many variables.

15-21. PRODUCTION FUNCTION

In general, the development of useful products depends on the combination of various resources through the utilization of certain production techniques. For example, the development of a specified head for power production may require the construction of a dam and other engineering works, all of which represent a resource input to obtain a product output. A modern concept of the agricultural production function includes water, technology, land, labor, capital, and other items among the factors of production.

There is no question but that water is an independent and productive resource which has economic utility in both industry and agriculture. Thus it can be employed at a greater than zero price.[12] It is also well established that production techniques are subject to change which implies that additional products can be obtained using the same inputs. The difficulty is that it is usually not possible to predict accurately what the future will bring in the field of technological improvement. Nevertheless, it can be stated that products of the past can be employed in developing new techniques through the channels of research. Thus the proper management of resources can lead to capital creation, which in turn will produce useful products and new techniques.

A study of the production processes which include water as an input will serve as the basis for allocating the water resource among alternative uses. To illustrate this, consider that a specific allocation of irrigation water can be used to produce a wide variety of crops. On a given land area and with a defined growing season, the farmer cannot hope to raise every type of crop that could possibly be raised on his land. He must make an economic decision based on the net payment he can expect to receive from the final produce. In other words, he should choose some combination of crops so that he will obtain the maximum return from his available resources. Product prices are obtained from demand functions such as were discussed in Sec. 15-20.

The farmer establishes demand functions for the resources (including water) he must use to produce his crops. These demand functions are based on the alternatives of production he can choose between and the consumer's alternative demand functions. The demand function for water or any other resource is also a price-quantity relationship. For agricultural water use this is generally a curve which slopes downward to the right. Figure 15-4c is somewhat representative.[13,14] In general, the farmer will take larger quantities of water as the price is lowered but the amount he can use may be limited by the number of acres he can farm or other restrictions.

If the farmer desires to maximize his profits, he will commit water to his production process until the cost of the final unit of water added is equal to the value of the product which is produced by this last unit of water. Mathematically this may be stated as[12]

$$\frac{\partial(PF)}{\partial R}(P_p) = P_R \tag{15-5}$$

where PF = production function
R = resource
P_p = price of the product
P_R = price of the resource

By equating these values for all of the products the farmer produces, he can make an allocation of water among the several alternatives indicated as profitable by consumer-demand information. Thus, production methods and consumer demands play an important role in influencing the allocation or use of resources such as water.

It will take but little imagination for the student to see that the relative value of water resources for use in various ways is strikingly affected by consumer desires.

15-22. RESOURCE-SUPPLY FUNCTIONS

The resource-supply function may be defined as the quantity of resource made available per unit time as a function of the price per unit of

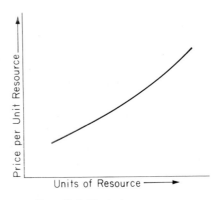

FIG. 15-5. Typical resource-supply function.

resource. Figure 15-5 illustrates a typical price-quantity relationship for resource supply. In general this relationship indicates that if the price for a given resource is high, the resource supplier will be willing to deliver a large quantity.

In the case of water resources, additional quantities can be made available through storage, development of well fields, diversions, etc. if the price is right. Of course, other factors (political, social, health) may also influence the resource supply. Whenever money must be spent to develop water resources, the development costs must be carefully considered in the economic decision-making process regarding the degree, mode of development, and allocation of the water resource.

For the rational allocation of our water resources among the numerous alternatives, complete information on product demands, production functions, and resource supply functions must be had. Unfortunately, information of this type is often not available and in many instances it cannot be accurately determined.[15] If water supplies are plentiful in relation to demands, the cost of water may be low. On the other hand, in regions of short supply, high prices might be paid to satisfy the various water requirements. For a given supply, as demands increase, water users such as industries which can afford to pay more per unit volume of water than agriculture, for example, may transfer additional increments of the available supply to themselves while agricultural production declines. Theoretically, under the ordinary market-price system, water can be readily transferred from low-value uses to high-value uses. Again, political pressures or legal restrictions may significantly influence the process.

15-23. BENEFIT-COST ANALYSES

As has been pointed out earlier in this chapter, benefit-cost analyses find widespread use in engineering economy studies which are related to water-resources projects. For example, a particular flood-retention dam may be proposed to minimize or eliminate flood damage in some locality. The benefits resulting from this construction can then be compared to the costs required to produce them. Generally, the government interpretation of benefits means economic benefits. In the water-resources field, this is founded on the Flood Control Act of 1936, which indicated that water-oriented projects should be evaluated so that "the benefits to whomsoever they may accrue are in excess of the estimated costs." At a benefit-cost ratio of one, benefits exactly equal costs at an interest equal to the cost of capital. This establishes the minimum economic justification for an expenditure, barring the consideration of other factors that might on occasion be unavoidable.

In determining benefits, the engineer must realize that "benefits" mean all of the advantages of the project minus the disadvantages to the user. For example, a good project might actually have some disadvantage associated with it. This must be considered as a negative benefit and subtracted from the overall benefits. On the other hand, costs mean all disbursements, less any savings, that are derived through the project construction. If the project actually produces some savings in costs, these should be deducted from the overall project cost and not added to the benefits. If a proper accounting is not made, the benefit-cost ratio may be considerably in error.[11]

An example will serve to illustrate the application of benefit-cost data in analyzing a water resources project. A more detailed treatment may be found elsewhere.[3,9,11]

EXAMPLE 15-2. A particular flood-control district can construct a number of alternative control works to alleviate the flood problem in that area. These alternatives include the construction of dam A, dam B, and a system of levees C. Each of these works can be built to function alone or together with any other or all other projects. Thus we have a possibility of the following combinations: ABC, A, B, C, AB, AC, BC. The life of each dam is considered to be 80 years and the life of the levee system is expected to be 60 years. The cost of capital is 4 percent. Information on total investment, operating and maintenance costs, and average annual flood damages is given in Table 15-2. What form of flood control would be the most economic?

Solution:

1. Compute the average annual investment charges for each project by using the capital recovery factors of Table 15-3 with the appropriate structure life and interest rate.

For dam A = 6,000,000 × 0.04181 = $251,000/yr
For dam B = 5,000,000 × 0.04181 = $209,000/yr
For levees C = 6,000,000 × 0.04420 = $265,000/yr
For AB = $460,000/yr
For AC = $516,000/yr

TABLE 15-2
FLOOD CONTROL PROJECT DATA

Project	Total Investment, dollars	Annual Operation and Maintenance, dollars	Average Annual Flood Damages, dollars
Reservoir *A*	$ 6,000,000	$ 90,000	$1,100,000
Reservoir *B*	5,000,000	80,000	1,300,000
Levees *C*	6,000,000	100,000	700,000
Combination *AB*	11,000,000	170,000	900,000
Combination *AC*	10,000,000	190,000	400,000
Combination *BC*	9,000,000	180,000	500,000
Combination *ABC*	15,000,000	270,000	250,000
No control at all	0	0	2,000,000

TABLE 15-3
CAPITAL RECOVERY FACTORS (CRF) FOR VARIOUS
LIVES AND INTEREST RATES

Years of Life	Interest Rate, percent							
	0	2	3	4	5	6	8	10
5	0.20000	0.21216	0.21835	0.22463	0.23097	0.23740	0.25046	0.26380
10	0.10000	0.11133	0.11723	0.12329	0.12950	0.13587	0.14903	0.16275
15	0.06667	0.07783	0.08377	0.08994	0.09634	0.10296	0.11683	0.13147
20	0.05000	0.06116	0.06722	0.07354	0.08024	0.08718	0.10185	0.11746
25	0.04000	0.05122	0.05743	0.06401	0.07095	0.07823	0.09368	0.11017
30	0.03333	0.04465	0.05102	0.05783	0.06505	0.07265	0.08883	0.10608
35	0.02857	0.04000	0.04654	0.05358	0 06107	0.06897	0.08580	0.10369
40	0.02500	0.03656	0.04326	0.05052	0.05828	0.06646	0.08386	0.10226
50	0.02000	0.03182	0.03887	0.04655	0.05478	0.06344	0.08174	0.10086
60	0.01667	0.02877	0.03613	0.04420	0.05283	0.06188	0.08080	0.10033
80	0.01250	0.02516	0.03311	0.04181	0.05103	0.06057	0.08017	0.10005
100	0.01000	0.02320	0.03165	0.04081	0.05038	0.06018	0.08004	0.10001

For *BC* = $474,000/yr

For *ABC* = $725,000/yr

2. To these values add annual operating and maintenance costs to yield total annual costs.

A = $341,000/yr

B = $289,000/yr

C = $365,000/yr

AB = $630,000/yr

AC = $706,000/yr

BC = $654,000/yr

ABC = $995,000/yr

3. Find the annual benefits for each type project by subtracting average annual flood damages (Table 15-2) from $2,000,000.

4. Tabulate the information in (2) and (3) in the form shown in Table 15-4 and compute benefit-cost ratios and benefits minus costs for each type project.

TABLE 15-4
BENEFIT-COST ANALYSIS FOR EXAMPLE 15-2

Project	Annual Benefits, Dollars	Annual Costs, Dollars	Benefit-Cost Ratio	Benefits Minus Costs
A	$ 900,000	$341,000	2.64	$559,000
B	700,000	289,000	2.42	411,000
C	1,300,000	365,000	3.56	935,000*
AB	1,100,000	630,000	1.75	470,000
AC	1,600,000	706,000	2.27	894,000
BC	1,500,000	654,000	2.29	846,000
ABC	1,750,000	995,000	1.76	755,000

*Optimum design.

The most economical design is selected from Table 15-4 as the one in which the greatest excess of benefits over costs is displayed. In this case the system of levees alone would be selected for construction.

REFERENCES

1. Melvin E. Scheidt, "Planning for Comprehensive Water Quality Management Programs," Presented at Water Resources Workshop of Division of Water Supply and Pollution Control, U.S. Public Health Service, at Sanitary Engineering Center, Cincinnati, November 1961.

2. Kenneth C. Nobe, "Another Look at River Basin Planning," *J. Soil Water Conserv.*, vol. 16, no. 5 (September–October 1961).

3. R. K. Linsley and J. B. Franzini, *Water Resources Engineering* (New York: McGraw-Hill Book Co., Inc., 1964).

4. John F. Osborn, "Water Resources Development," University of Wisconsin, Dept. Civil Engineering, May 1963, mimeographed.

5. Gilbert F. White, "A Perspective of River Basin Development," *Law and Comtemporary Problems*, vol. 22, no. 2 (Spring 1957).

6. Arno T. Lenz, "Some Engineering Aspects of River Basin Development," *Law and Contemporary Problems*, vol. 22, no. 2 (Spring 1957).

7. H. D. Block and W. R. Lynn, "Systems Analysis Applications," Cornell University Water Resources Center, Department of Sanitary Engineering, Ithaca, New York, 1963.

8. Harvard Water Resources Group, "Operations Research in Water Quality Management," Division of Water Supply and Pollution Control, 1963.

9. A. Maas *et al.*, *Design of Water Resources Systems* (Cambridge, Mass.: Harvard University Press, 1962).

10. H. G. Thuesen and W. J. Fabrycky, *Engineering Economy*, 3d ed. (Englewood Cliffs, N.J.: Prentice-Hall, Inc., 1964).

11. G. A. Taylor, *Managerial and Engineering Economy.* (Princeton, N.J.: D. Van Nostrand Co., Inc., 1964.)

12. H. W. Grubb, "Water Resource Use and Water Resource Problems of the Southern High Plains of Texas," Participants Paper, New Mexico State University NSF Water Resources Conference, June 1964, mimeographed.

13. Nathaniel Wollman, Ralph Edgel, Marshall Farris, H. R. Stucky, and Alvin J. Thompson, *The Value of Water in Alternative Uses.... With Special Application to Water Use in the San Juan and Rio Grande Basins of New Mexico.* (University Park, N.M.: University of New Mexico Press, 1962), p. 39.

14. H. R. Stucky, "Uses of Water for Agricultural Purposes in New Mexico," Water and Its Use, *Proc. 7th Annual Conference*, New Mexico Municipal League, Santa Fe, N.M., 1964.

15. Nathaniel Wollman, "The National Water Situation as Developed by the Select Committee on Water Resources," *Proc. 6th Annual New Mexico Conf.*, New Mexico State University, University Park, N.M., November 1961.

PROBLEMS

15-1. Select some river basin or subbasin of interest to you and list the water-resources problems that exist. What information would you need to prepare a comprehensive plan for this area?

15-2. How would you obtain the type of information indicated in Sec. 15-3?

15-3. Why is it important to coordinate economic and technologic concepts?

15-4. A small community is supplied water by a well and pumping station. Assume the cost function in dollars per day is

$$C = 30 + 11Q + Q^2$$

The maximum capacity of the well and pump is 4.5 mgpd and the minimum permissible flow is 1 mgpd. Find the minimum cost by a graphical analysis.

15-5. Solve Prob. 15-4 by using the method of Lagrange multipliers.

15-6. Write a brief paper on one of the engineering aspects of river-basin development presented in the chapter.

15-7. Refer to Example 15-2 in Sec. 15-23. Solve the problem for a capital cost of 5 percent.

15-8. Refer to Example 15-2 in Sec. 15-23. Solve the problem for a capital cost of 6 percent.

15-9. A flood-control district can construct a number of alternative control works to alleviate the flood problem in that area. These alternatives include dam *A*, dam *B*, and a levee system *C*. The levee system can be built alone or in combination with dams *A* or *B*. Both dams cannot be built together but either one can function alone. The life of each dam is 80 years and the life of the levee system is 60 years. The cost of capital is 3 percent. Information on total investment, operating and maintenance costs, and average annual flood damages is given below. What form of flood control would be most economic?

Project	Total Investment, Dollars	Annual Operation and Maintenance, Dollars	Average Annual Flood Damages, Dollars
No control at all	0	0	$2,150,000
Dam *A*	$6,200,000	$ 93,000	1,100,000
Dam *B*	5,300,000	89,000	1,400,000
Levees *C*	6,700,000	110,000	800,000

15-10. Solve Prob. 15-9 if the cost of capital is 4.5 percent.

15-11. Eight-hundred gallons per minute of water are to be pumped from a reservoir at elevation 100 to a second reservoir at elevation 180 through 3,000 ft of cast-iron pipe. Electricity costs 1.5 cents per kwh. The pump operates 24 hr a day and has an efficienciency of 83 percent. Consider the minimum attractive return to be 7 percent and a project life of 25 years. Find the most economical pipe size.

Pipe Size, in.	Cost per Foot Installed
6	$2.75
8	3.60
10	4.05
12	4.20
14	4.70

15-12. Indicate how a taxpayer may benefit from a flood-control project which does not directly protect the area in which he resides.

15-13. A flood-control district can build a series of dams to provide flood relief. The life of each dam is 80 years. Any one dam or some combination of dams can be constructed. If more than one dam is built, the total savings are considered to be the sum of the savings of each dam separately. Capital cost is 4 percent. What installation would be most economic?

Dam	Construction Cost, dollars	Annual Maintenance and Operation, dollars	Annual Cost of Damage, dollars
None	0	0	$2,500,000
A	$11,100,000	$260,000	1,300,000
B	8,300,000	205,000	1,600,000
C	6,950,000	190,000	2,100,000

Index